Task Panel Reports Submitted to The President's Commission on Mental Health

1978

Volume II
Appendix

For sale by the Superintendent of Documents, U.S. Government Printing Office
Washington, D.C. 20402
Stock No. 040-000-00391-6

VOLUME II

A P P E N D I X

TASK PANEL REPORTS

Submitted to

THE PRESIDENT'S COMMISSION ON MENTAL HEALTH

The Report to the President from the President's Commission on Mental Health consists of four volumes:

Volume I contains the Commission's Report and Recommendations to the President.

Volumes II, III, and IV are Appendices to the Report. These contain the reports of task panels comprised of approximately 450 individuals from throughout the country who volunteered their expertise, perceptions, and assessments of the Nation's mental health needs and resources in specific categories.

Although the Commission has adopted certain of the options proposed by the task panels, the opinions and recommendations contained in the panel reports should be viewed as those of the panel members; they do not necessarily reflect the views of the Commission. Rather, their publication is intended to share with the public the valuable information these individuals so generously contributed to the Commission.

THE PRESIDENT'S COMMISSION ON MENTAL HEALTH

Rosalynn Carter, Honorary Chairperson

Thomas E. Bryant, Chairperson
Ruth B. Love, Vice-Chairperson
Priscilla Allen
Allan Beigel
Jose A. Cabranes
John J. Conger
Thomas Conlan
Virginia Dayton
LaDonna Harris
Beverly Long

Florence Mahoney
Martha L. Mitchell
Mildred Mitchell-Bateman
Harold Richman
Julius B. Richmond, Ex-Officio
Reymundo Rodriguez
George Tarjan
Franklin E. Vilas, Jr.
Glenn E. Watts
Charles V. Willie

THE PRESIDENT'S COMMISSION ON MENTAL HEALTH

The Commission was established by Executive Order No. 11973, signed by President Carter February, 17, 1977, to review the mental health needs of the Nation and to make recommendations to the President as to how the Nation might best meet these needs.

The Commission held public hearings across the country, and received the assistance of hundreds of individuals who comprised special fact-finding task panels.

These task panels, made up of the Nation's foremost mental health authorities and other volunteers interested in mental health, produced and submitted to the Commission the reports which are published here.

ACKNOWLEDGEMENTS

The task panels of the President's Commission on Mental Health wish to acknowledge the dedicated assistance of the Commission's excellent support staff, without which the contributions of the panel members from all parts of the country would not have been possible. In addition to the staff liaison persons cited in the individual task panel reports, we owe our thanks and deep appreciation to the following staff assistants: Mary Kay Buckley, Maxine Costanzo, Patricia Jarrett, Benedict Latteri, Vyvyanne Lee, Esther Prince, Caroline Simms, Estelle Thompson, Sue Vogelsinger, and Marilynn Wilkins.

In addition, we are grateful for the assistance of other individuals who served with the Commission during the course of the year: Francine Barber, Christopher Bates, Mary Camp, Lewis Dalton, Veneda Deitrick, Lorrayne Jackson, Shelbia Lengel, Doris Sanborn, and Marcia Vastine.

We wish to acknowledge also the contributions to our work of staff volunteers: Luisa Costanzo, Beverly Dodd, Lucy Doody, Katherine Klein, Judy Lansing, David Lyon, Karen McCall, Ruth Ann McQuade, Ann Reinert, Anne Robbins, Barbara Shaw, Rita Thompson, Margaret Treadwell, Valerie Verra, Ruth Wiener, and Nancy Zanes.

In publication of these reports, we appreciate the highly competent professional assistance of William Bowman, Kathleen Dubois, Bernardine Moore, Margaret Rutherford, and Helen Scoredos.

VOLUME II APPENDIX
TABLE OF CONTENTS

TASK PANEL REPORTS:	Page
Mental Health -- Nature and Scope of the Problems	1
Community Support Systems	139
Mental Health Service Delivery
Planning and Review	236
Organization and Structure	275
Community Mental Health Centers Assessment	312
Access and Barriers to Care	340
Deinstitutionalization, Rehabilitation and Long-Term Care	356
Alternative Services -- A Special Study	376
Mental Health Personnel	411
Cost and Financing	497

To order copies of Commission Report and Appendices, see information at the end of this Volume.

Report of the Task Panel

on

THE NATURE AND SCOPE OF THE PROBLEMS

Submitted to

THE PRESIDENT'S COMMISSION ON MENTAL HEALTH

February 15, 1978

Task Panel: The Nature and Scope of the Problems

MEMBERS

David Mechanic, Ph.D., Coordinator
John Bascom Professor of Sociology
University of Wisconsin
Madison, Wisconsin

Donald Cohen, M.D.
Associate Professor, Pediatrics,
 Psychology and Psychiatry
Yale University
New Haven, Connecticut

Ruth Diggs, Ed.D.
Professor, Department of
 Special Education
Norfolk State College
Norfolk, Virginia

Barbara S. Dohrenwend, Ph.D.
Professor
City College of The City University
 of New York
New York, New York

Bruce Dohrenwend, Ph.D.
Social Psychiatry Research Unit
Columbia University
New York, New York

Barry Gurland, M.D.
Chief of the Department of
 Geriatrics Research
New York State Psychiatric
 Institute
New York, New York

Morton Kramer, Sc.D.
Professor, Mental Hygiene
Johns Hopkins School of Hygiene
 and Public Health
Baltimore, Maryland

Gloria Powell, M.D.
Director, Child Psychiatry
Outpatient Department
University of California at
 Los Angeles
Los Angeles, California

Lee Robins, Ph.D.
Professor of Sociology
Department of Psychiatry
Washington University
St. Louis, Missouri

Robin Room, M.A.
Social Research Group
Berkeley, California

Lisbeth Schorr, B.A.
Consultant
Children's Defense Fund
Washington, D.C.

Robert Spitzer, M.D.
Chief of the Department of
 Biometrics Research
New York State Psychiatric
 Institute
New York, New York

John Strauss, M.D.
Professor of Psychiatry
Yale University
New Haven, Connecticut

Myrna Weissman, Ph.D.
Associate Professor of Psychiatry
 and Epidemiology
Depression Research Unit
Yale University
New Haven, Connecticut

Helen Wright
National Association of
 Mental Health
Washington, D.C.

SCOPE 2

TABLE OF CONTENTS

		Page
Task Panel Members		2
Executive Summary		4
Recommendation		10
I	Introduction	11
II	The Burden of Mental Disorders	13
III	Schizophrenia	18
IV	Affective Disorders: Depression and Mood Disorders	21
V	Emotional Distress, Mental Disorders, and Community Care	27
VI	Drug Use Problems	29
VII	Alcohol-Related Disorders	33
VIII	Mental Disorders in Childhood	37
IX	Mental Disorders of the Elderly	47
X	Location of Patients	51
	Appendix	92
	Acknowledgements	121
	Bibliography	122

EXECUTIVE SUMMARY

The past decade has seen substantial progress in the development of methods appropriate to detecting, through epidemiological research, the nature and scope of mental disorders.

Our approach has been to rely on the best data available, searching for trends, making extrapolations, and cross-checking our inferences as much as possible by comparing findings obtained by different methods.

The burden of mental illness in the United States is very large and probably constitutes our primary public health issue. For the past few years, the most commonly used estimate is that at any one time, 10 percent of the population needs some form of mental health care. This estimate has been used primarily for planning purposes in developing projections for manpower/personnel needs, Federal, State and local budgets, and for comparisons with similar data describing other health and social problems. There is new evidence that this figure may be closer to 15 percent of the population.

According to the National Institute of Mental Health, Division of Biometry and Epidemiology, the current cost of mental illness is $17 billion a year and is escalating. This represents about 11 percent of all health care expenditures nationally.

In this report, we first briefly describe the results of epidemiological studies on the prevalence and incidence of psychological and emotional disorders, including some background on the methods used to obtain such information. Data are then presented on specific syndromes such as schizophrenia and depression with some description of the current status of these areas. There is also a discussion of alcohol and drug use in relation to mental health. Attention is also given to the occurrence of illness by life stages, such as childhood, adult life, and old age. Finally, we describe contexts where patients are identified, treated and maintain their residence.

Schizophrenia

Schizophrenia continues to be one of the major mental health problems in the country. Despite the relatively low incidence of the disorder, schizophrenia has a disproportionately high prevalence rate due to the early age of onset and the lengthy nature of the disorder. Although there can be a range of outcomes, the course is usually chronic. As a result, it can be anticipated that there will be repeated episodes of severe disability and a lifetime of varying degrees of impairment and emotional stress for both the patient, the family or the significant others. Therefore, the total burden of this illness to society is considerable.

Over recent years research has also suggested the importance of a variety of treatment approaches, including vocational and social skills training where necessary, partial hospitalization and other incremental programs for re-entry into the community, on-going psychotherapeutic work with the family and patient, and, of course, the use of anti-psychotic medications.

These practices appear to have made a major contribution to the considerable drop in the number of schizophrenics residing in hospitals and to reducing the frequency of deterioration and chronicity commonly believed in the past to have been the hallmark of the disorder.

Depression (Affective Disorders)

Comprehensive surveys of clinical depressive symptoms in the community, which include both treated and untreated cases, show remarkable consistency. The rates are highest in women, non-whites, the separated and divorced, the poor, and the less educated. Persons with these symptoms tend to seek general medical but not psychiatric help and usually receive psychotropic drugs for relief. These findings point out the importance of the nonpsychiatric physician and of primary care facilities in the recognition and treatment of depressive symptoms since it is a very common mental disorder.

The severe clinical depressive syndrome is also discussed. It is generally agreed that when treated actively, an acute severe depressive episode carries a good prognosis, that the chance of recovery is excellent, and that social functioning between episodes will be unimpaired. Recovered depressed patients can resume their work, childcare, and social life. However, data on the long term course of depression suggest that depressions are less benign than commonly believed. While most acute symptoms resolve rapidly, especially with modern treatment, there is a tendency for episodes to recur. These findings document the intermittent and chronic nature, and potential mortality, of depressive disorders. They also indicate the need for further research on these disorders, spurred by the advances of the past two decades.

Mental disorders such as depression, which have a high morbidity and a potential mortality by suicide, share many features of nonpsychiatric chronic diseases and also require comprehensive lifetime planning. A flexibility of treatment resources is needed so that patients can have crisis intervention for acute episodes, and continuing periodic care as appropriate.

Emotional Distress Syndrome

The findings of community epidemiological studies show a large number of persons suffering from mild-to-moderate depression, anxiety, psychophysiological discomforts, insomnia, loneliness, and other indicators of emotional disorders.

Although many nonpsychiatric physicians feel inadequately prepared to deal with such problems, these patients constitute a significant part of primary care practice in the United States. Planning to ensure that patients with distress syndromes receive appropriate assistance from the general medical sector deserves policy attention. This aspect of mental health care can be enhanced by improving the capacity of primary care practitioners to recognize such common problems as depression, alcoholism, and anxiety, and by increasing their ability to deal with such patients. Primary care physicians can improve their pharmacological knowledge of psychoactive drugs and the relation of drug use to counseling and emotional support. More effort can also be given to developing consultant roles for mental health professionals in primary care settings.

Drug Use Problems

There are broad and extremely complex issues of human behavior related to patterns of drug use. Much more epidemiological information about the incidence, prevalence, ecological settings, and lifetime drug use history of the various sectors of the population is needed. The magnitude, the underlying nature, and adverse individual and societal consequences of drug abuse vary greatly not only with the substances used but are greatly influenced by the personal characteristics of the involved individuals and their families, and social settings. The mental health field has a special responsibility to explore these aspects of the problem.

This report summarizes briefly current information on misuse of various drugs. There is a separate Panel of the President's Commission on Mental Health on drug issues.

Alcohol-Related Disorders

The importance of alcohol abuse as a serious social, physicial and mental health problem in the United States has probably been underestimated. There is a plausible case to be made for considering alcoholism to be one of the most pressing public health problems that confronts the Nation. Survey data on persons reporting a significant recent alcohol-related problem of some sort produce estimates of the order of 10 million. Of the order of 20 million Americans report having experienced alcohol-related problems of some sort in the course of their lifetimes.

Although the alcohol treatment services and mental health systems are currently quite separate, and will probably remain so, there is an urgent need to coordinate them more closely, particularly in such areas as policy, research, and training.

At State and local levels, regular liaison should be a formal part of the duties of alcohol and mental health program personnel. Alcohol treatment personnel need to be sensitized to the possibility of concurrent mental health problems, and mental health treatment personnel to alcohol problems, and routine systems for cross-referral need to be established.

The past decade has been a time of rapid change in the patterns of drug use among adolescents. There has been an overall increase in drinking among youth. The most disturbing trend has been the increasing trend toward initiation into regular alcohol use at early adolescence, children as young as 10-11 years of age. In a 1974 nationwide survey of junior and senior high school students, 27.8 percent were found to be problem drinkers. Finding ways to prevent alcohol abuse among our children is an issue of highest priority.

There is a separate panel of the President's Commission on Mental Health that has looked at mental health aspects of alcoholism.

Mental Disorders in Childhood

New developments have made it possible for the first time to carry out epidemiological studies to compare the frequency, course, and social correlates to children's mental health problems.

Childhood disorders vary in frequency according to age, sex, and social circumstances. Mental health problems are more common in boys than in girls, are somewhat more frequent in adolescence than in earlier childhood, and more frequent among children living in inner-city areas than in small towns and rural areas. Although precise estimates cannot be made, mental health problems in childhood are clearly sufficiently common to constitute a major concern in the planning of health services and to make it impractical for them to be dealt with exclusively by child psychiatrists.

Three groups of problems particularly contribute to the overall prevalence rates of emotional problems in children: emotional and conduct disorders, impairments or delays in the development of normal functions, and learning disability. Childhood psychosis and autism, although low in prevalence, are serious problems.

Emotional and mental disorders of childhood are not only a source of considerable suffering to the child and his family, but they are also associated with serious social problems and may be forerunners of serious difficulties in adult life.

Most emotional disorders in young children have a relatively good prognosis. Disorders with onset in adolescence, however, frequently continue as anxiety or depressive conditions in adult life. Therapies for conduct disorders and childhood autism are not reliably effective and constitute important areas for research.

In many areas there has been progress in early detection and useful remediation. Many more of the disorders of childhood will be increasingly amenable to preventive intervention as research progresses in years to come. When properly implemented, a good deal of current knowledge of infancy, childhood, and adolescence can help prevent mental disorders of adult years.

Mental Disorders of the Elderly

Currently there are 23 million people over 65 in the United States. This represents 11 percent of the total population.

By the year 2000, according to our best projections of trends, there will be 30 million people over 65, nearly 15 percent of the population of this country. The major mental disorder of old age is senile dementia. It is a severely disabling condition and it affects millions of our elderly citizens, although there are no exact figures.

Until recently there has been very little research in this area. Multifaceted research into the biology of the aging brain, the role of the personality and psychological variables of the afflicted individual, and studies of the social conditions of the elderly will begin to yield answers to some of the pressing questions. This is an area of research that has heretofore been neglected but deserves the highest priority, and the allocation of research resources should match the importance of the problem. Senile dementia is most prevalent in the isolated elderly in the community or the institutionalized population. Diagnosis of this condition is sometimes overlooked. Effective medication regimens have not been clearly established. The psychopharmacology of the aging brain is not well understood.

Until recently, the role of affiliative and supportive structures to help ease the pain of depression, loneliness, and helplessness has been minimal. There are models for personal and community supports for the elderly that should be disseminated. The need for integration of health and social services is no where so clear or so urgent as in the care of the elderly. New institutions, new models of service, and creative new ways of mobilizing youth in the service of their elders can contribute to meeting the needs of the elderly, probably at less expense, and certainly with more respect for their own preferences and their dignity.

Location of Patients

During the year 1975, an estimated 15 percent of the population of the United States was in need of mental health services. Of this number, 15 percent were under care of the specialty mental health sector; 3.4 percent were under care of the general hospital and nursing home sector; and 54.1 percent were under care of the primary care medical sector. Six percent were under care both in the primary care medical sector and the specialty mental health sector. Another 21 percent of these persons were either receiving some assistance or services from the other human services sectors or not receiving services at all.

Unfortunately, data are not available to differentiate between the number of persons with mental disorders who receive no treatment in the health and mental health systems, and those who may be in correctional institutions, and those who are served by family service agencies, religious counselors and other social welfare agencies outside the usually defined health arena. This is a critical area for research.

It must be emphasized that there are considerable differences between the diagnostic characteristics of the groups of patients seen in these different settings: for example, patients who come to nonpsychiatric physicians are more likely to present problems associated with anxiety and depression, personality disorders, and psychophysiologic problems. Persons with more severe disorders, such as schizophrenia, major affective disorders, organic brain syndromes, and other severe mental disorders requiring intensive specialized therapies are more likely to come under care of inpatient services in the mental health sector. Persons under care of outpatient services in the mental health sector present a broader spectrum of the mental disorders, with variations depending upon the admission policies of the clinic, its relationship to the mental hospitals serving the community, and referral practices of physicians, local public health and social agencies.

Shift in Locus of Care

In 1955, 1.7 million episodes of care were provided by the totality of facilities that report to the National Institute of Mental Health. Of these, 49 percent were accounted for by State and county mental hospitals, 23 percent outpatient psychiatric services, 16 percent general hospital inpatient psychiatric units, and 12 percent for all other facilities. By 1975, the number of episodes of care provided by all facilities increased to 6.4 million. Of these, only 9 percent were accounted for by State and county mental hospitals, 47 percent by outpatient psychiatric services, 29 percent by community mental health centers, 9 percent by general hospital inpatient psychiatric units, and 6 percent by other reporting facilities.

These changes have had a marked effect on the composition of the institutional population. In 1950, 1.6 million persons (1 percent of the population of the United States) were in institutions. The largest portion were in mental institutions (39 percent); the second largest portion in homes for the aged and dependent (19 percent); and the third largest portion in correctional institutions (17 percent). By 1970, the number of persons in institutions increased to 2.1 million persons, about 1 percent of the total population. The largest portion were in homes for the aged and dependent (44 percent); the next largest in mental institutions (20 percent); and the third largest in correctional institutions (15 percent).

As can be seen, despite the fact that 20 years later the overall percentage of institutionalized patients was still at the level of 1 percent of the population, the pattern of distribution among facilities was quite different. The most notable change has been the increase of the elderly in nursing homes, the sharp shift of mentally disabled patients from mental institutions to care in the community, and the rise of the treatment of alcohol-related disorders in mental institutions.

This report presents detailed descriptions of the institutionalization rates (i.e., numbers of persons in specific types of institutions per 100,000 population) specific for age, sex, and race. The report also speculates on the effect of projected changes in the age distribution of the population of the United States between 1970 and 1985 on the expected numbers of persons that will be under care of mental health facilities; the numbers of schizophrenic persons in the population; the numbers of persons in correctional institutions and in homes for the aged and dependent by 1985. Of particular importance is the fact that large increases are expected in numbers of persons in high risk age groups for the use of mental health facilities and correctional institutions, homes for the aged and dependent, and other institutions that constitute the institutional population. The changes in the numbers of persons in specific types of institutions have been the resultant of a variety of factors: social legislation; new discoveries for treatment of disorders; demographic changes; increasing costs of general hospital and domiciliary care for persons with chronic illnesses; social conditions and problems; racist and other discriminatory practices; inadequate community programs; and inappropriate living arrangements for persons who are aged, disabled, or mentally ill. The implications of these changes for manpower, research, and services are considered.

The task panel urges the Commission to review the above data in relation to their implications for developing policy related to such issues: (1) socioeconomic, attitudinal, and geographical factors that account for differential patterns of use of specific types of facilities within and among various subgroups of our population; (2) the effectiveness and efficiency of services rendered in different types of facilities; (3) methods of payment for services; (4) manpower needs; (5) gaps in services; and (6) relationships of psychiatric facilities to each other, as well as to other human service agencies.

The data and trends reviewed in this report emphasize the need for more basic and applied research in the biological, psychological, and social and political phenomena that are responsible for producing the problems that eventually require people to be institutionalized. Only through such knowledge can primary prevention be achieved. Additional research is also needed in the development of more effective treatment and rehabilitation programs; i.e., secondary and tertiary prevention techniques. The deinstitutionalization of large numbers of persons from mental hospitals with brain syndromes, schizophrenia, affective disorders, and other disorders continues to emphasize the need for more knowledge about biological, social, and psychological factors that affect the course and outcome of these disorders in persons from various age, sex, socioeconomic and cultural groups. This, in turn, will require more epidemiologic, statistical and demographic research. Among the high priority problems that need solution are the development of generally applicable procedures for case finding, improved diagnostic procedures, more precise measures of need for specific types of mental health services, followup studies, classifications of psychosocial factors, and social indicators.

Of particular importance for epidemiologic research is the establishment of several field research units with adequate staffing and stable, long term financing to design and implement research for determining the extent to which community health programs are affecting the level of disability from mental disorders. Such units can document quantitatively our ongoing needs, opportunities, and paths of future progress.

RECOMMENDATION

> Support for research in the epidemiology of mental disorders should be increased substantially and maintained on a stable basis at a level commensurate with the importance of the field.
>
> Continuing sophisticated data collection on the incidence and prevalence of mental disorders, the impact of treatments and services on outcomes, and the tracking of the distribution of patients in existing facilities, is vital as a basis for framing health and mental health policies.

I. INTRODUCTION

A periodic reexamination of the nature and scope of mental health represents a necessary contribution to the ongoing process of effective planning for the needs of our Nation's people.

The burden of mental illness in the United States is very large and probably constitutes our primary public health issue. For the past few years, the most commonly used estimate is that at any one time, 10 percent of the population needs some form of mental health care. This estimate has been used primarily for planning purposes in developing projections for manpower/personnel needs, Federal, State and local budgets, and for comparisons with similar data describing other health and social problems. There is new evidence that this figure may be closer to 15 percent of the population.

According to the National Institute of Mental Health, Division of Biometry and Epidemiology, the current cost of mental illness if $17 billion a year and is escalating. This represents about 11 percent of all health care expenditures nationally.

Furthermore, the social stigma associated with mental illness is still so strong that the true incidence and prevalence of most types of mental illness and behavior disorders are probably underestimated. Stigma also has significant implications for the utilization of currently available services.

Serious mental and behavioral disorders may arise from a broad range of biological, psychological and socio-cultural factors. By now, it is clear that the causes of mental disorders are often multiple and a resulting illness can represent complex interactions among these factors.

In the broadest sense, the general health and mental health of the Nation also reflects the quality of life, the soundness of childhood socialization, and the effectiveness of the social integration of all subgroups in our population. From this perspective, mental health is a reflection of our society and its values.

Many policies of the Federal Government have indirect, but highly significant, impacts on the mental health of the Nation. Policies affecting income support and welfare practices, work and retirement, equity among age and sex groups, racial equality, the education of children, housing, and intactness and strength of family and kinship structures, all have mental health consequences. In addressing those issues that are applicable to the mental health services system, we do so with the expectation that Federal policy can be responsive and will reflect concern for the mental health of all our citizens as an essential priority when the issues are clarified.

While it is important to be comprehensive in understanding the wide range of issues and possible concerns in the mental health field, selectivity will be required in the allocation of scarce national resources. Beyond meeting the pressing needs of the mentally disabled, priorities must be set for choosing among the options available for concentrated effort in the coming years. There must be a commitment to meet the valid and neglected needs of underserved sectors of the population.

SCOPE 11

There are important decisions to be made concerning the best public and private arrangements for appropriately meeting the mental health field's responsibilities with or without the advent of national health insurance coverage. For these purposes, it is necessary to delineate the areas of responsibility of the health care system from that of other societal systems which also have as their purpose improving or otherwise changing human functioning, such as the educational, social services, or criminal justice systems.

A significant proportion of the population experiences serious suffering and disability as a result of mental and emotional states. It is imperative that the population of such persons be described as precisely as possible both for the purposes of investigation and to plan necessary services. While there has been vigorous debate among proponents of different models of psychiatric and behavioral disorders, the fact is, a classification system is essential to describe the incidence and prevalence of these disorders. It should also provide a rationale for decisions as to which conditions should be included or excluded from a mental disorder classification. In addition, the classification should attempt to provide guidelines for determining the boundaries of those disorders which are seemingly continuous with variations in "normal" functioning.

It is only relatively recently that there are data on which to base a more differentiated view of mental disorder. With appropriate data, the mental health needs and fates of all sectors of the population can be better understood and appropriate services delivered.

Epidemiological information is the source of reliable comparative data on the incidence, duration, and prevalence of mental disorders in the population; on the utilization patterns for available mental health services; on the evaluation of the outcomes of existing therapies; on the results of efforts to reduce the amount of residual handicap and distress in chronic cases; and on the effectiveness of preventive efforts in disorders that are known to be preventable. The same type of epidemiologic data can be of value in evaluating manpower requirements for service delivery and for decisionmaking regarding allocation of resources for a variety of research activities. Only very limited data exist to answer many of the complex questions raised above.

In the discussion that follows, we first briefly describe the results of epidemiological studies on the prevalence and incidence of psychological and emotional disorders, including some background on the methods used to obtain such information. Data are then presented on specific syndromes, such as schizophrenia and depression, with some description of the current status of these areas. There is also a discussion of alcohol and drug use in relation to mental health. Attention is also given to the occurrence of illness by life stages, such as childhood, adult life, and old age. Finally, we describe contexts where patients are identified, treated, and maintain their residence.

II. THE BURDEN OF MENTAL DISORDERS

In providing information to the Commission on the prevalence of mental disorder in the population, we must depend on the studies currently available. The need for further epidemiological studies is very much apparent. The studies cited have been based on existing systems of case finding and classifying mental disorders that will require further refinements in the future.

A classification system is a necessary tool for grouping symptom clusters that share certain characteristics and to differentiate them from other symptom clusters. These then may be studied as groups to examine their first occurrence, their progression, causative factors, prognosis, and possible treatment modalities. Through classification and reclassification, we refine our knowledge and gain new understanding. The adoption of a descriptive classification of mental disorders implies neither a specific theory of causation nor a definition of appropriate services to treat the disorders involved. It is primarily a convenience for organizing the task.

Epidemiology is that branch of research that investigates how disorders are distributed in the population. It is only in the past few decades that epidemiology has begun to develop the tools needed to generate the data base necessary to understand and address crucial problems in mental disorder. Before that time, most epidemiological research was confined to hospitalized patients, and guesses about causes were based on noting that relatively high proportions of some populations entered psychiatric hospitals. But soon it was observed that the closer people lived to the hospital, the more likely they were to enter it. Studies were then expanded to include psychiatric outpatients as well as hospitalized patients. This expansion culminated in the establishment of a limited number of countywide psychiatric registers which overcame these geographical biases.

It soon became clear that much of what appeared to be social correlates of psychiatric disorder were, in fact, largely the social correlates of coming to psychiatric care. Studies of general medical practice, of prison populations, and of school children showed that many persons with psychiatric disorders were cared for by general practitioners, internists, school counselors and remedial teachers, social workers, and the courts. These cases never appeared in even the most complete register of psychiatric facilities. There was such a confounding of factors affecting treatment with factors predicting the occurrence of psychiatric disorder that our findings were judged inconclusive.

To avoid this confounding, about 30 years ago epidemiologists started trying to determine rates of mental disorder in untreated populations. But here new problems arose. In untreated populations, there was difficulty in deciding who did and did not have a mental disorder and how best to characterize the mental disorder noted. In the earliest studies, epidemiologists talked to key informants in small towns and rural populations, people who knew the whole community personally and knew who had severe mental illness or very disturbing behavior.

A little later, epidemiologists began personal mental health diagnostic interviews with adult community members. Those interviews were confined to questions that were not likely to upset anyone. The researcher was able to assess depression and anxiety adequately, but questions about homosexuality, promiscuity, violence, drinking and drug problems, and arrests or other legal encounters were omitted. These omissions were justified by arguing that not only were such questions upsetting but that informants would be too ashamed to answer honestly in any case. Questions about deviant behavior first became part of some interviews given to general populations about 20 years ago. Only recently have they been in common use. Surprisingly, these questions turn out to be answered quite honestly when checked against record information, and they do not seem to be upsetting. These "embarrassing" symptoms when studied have been found to have their greatest frequency in young men. Their systematic omission from early epidemiological studies led to apparently erroneous findings in early studies that "psychiatric disorder" is more common in women than in men and that rates of disorder increase with age.

Until very recently, attempts to assess the incidence of mental retardation or organic brain syndrome in general populations were made only by interviewers speaking to key informants or to elderly people. Again, it was thought too embarrassing to ask most persons to perform simple arithmetical tasks or to test intactness of mental functions by their ability to remember dates. Unfortunately, this tactfulness was inefficient because assessments of brain dysfunction by mere observation are highly unreliable.

The ascertainment of mental disorder in children has been biased in a different direction. Since interviews have been with parents and teachers rather than with the children themselves, there has been less hesitancy about asking about socially disapproved behavior and learning problems. Reports of learning and conduct disorders were consistently higher for boys than girls. However, the frequency of syndromes of depression and anxiety in children is undoubtedly underestimated, since these symptoms may not be obvious to parents and teachers. Direct interviews with children are now being done to obtain depression ratings, but the methodology and conclusions are still being validated. On the basis of established data, it is believed that mental disorder is more common in boys than in girls.

A useful mental health assessment interview for epidemiological studies of a general population must ensure accurate diagnosis even when administered by a nonphysician. Until recently, whether a person was counted as a "case" or not depended on the global impression of psychiatrists as to whether or not they would be likely to find such a person in a treatment setting. When studies grew too large for psychiatrists themselves to see all of the subjects, they based their clinical judgments on the patterns of answers to questions elicited for the psychiatrist by nonphysicians.

Only in the last two or three years have we begun to develop instruments capable of making differential diagnoses on a standardized basis. These instruments will cover all the major diagnostic categories by evaluating both the presence and the severity of diagnostic symptoms. They can be administered by nonpsychiatrists, and diagnosis is made by computer in a systematic fashion rather than relying on the interviews or interpretations of a psychiatrist. These instruments are now being refined and tested for reliability and validity.

At last we are about ready to approach the task of estimating the frequency of specific mental disorders in the general adult population with tools worthy of the task.

The development of diagnostic interviews appropriate for children still has a long way to go. Recently it has been shown that diagnostic interviews with children do not upset them and are much more productive than might have been expected. Much work remains to be done in deciding how questions should vary with the child's developmental stage, in discovering how early in life such interviews become reliable and valid.

In addition to lacking proper diagnostic instruments, epidemiological research has lacked tools for measuring environmental factors at a sufficiently detailed level to suggest potential methods of prevention and intervention. Most early studies relied on the classic demographic variables of social class, race, sex, age, size of town or city, and marital status. Correlates with these factors are readily found but are difficult to translate into social action without an understanding of how these factors are mediated. In place of these global variables, we need to specify, for example, what it is about being poor, old, living in a large city, being unmarried, or being female that increases the risk for particular diagnoses. Only when we can identify specific environmental causes such as diet, or lack of emotional support, higher rates of specific traumatic life events, or higher rates of specific physical illnesses, do we begin to have a handle on something that we might try to modify. The development of instruments capable of describing the total environment in meaningful detail is just beginning. There have been great advances in describing critical life events, but these systematic questionnaires have not yet been combined with questions assessing aspects of the environment.

Because each mental disorder has its own age range of high risk, a general population survey in which rates are sought for all disorders at the same time, works out poorly. The elderly have forgotten the disorders of their childhood and youth, and the young should not figure in our estimates of the incidence of disorders that first appear late in life. Instead studies should be limited to those disorders which share a common age of risk, and subjects of the appropriate ages chosen accordingly. In the last 10 years, the development of designs for multicohort longitudinal studies has solved most of these problems.

Thus, the past decade has seen substantial progress in the development of methods appropriate to detecting, through epidemiologic research, the nature and scope of mental disorders.

Despite methodological shortcomings we have tried to ascertain the rate of occurrence and distribution of mental health problems in the population of the United States. Ideally, we would like to know the true prevelance of psychiatric disorders; that is, the rate of cases of such disorders in existence at a particular point in time or during a given interval of time, such as a year, regardless of time of onset. We would also like to know the true incidence as indicated by the rate of new cases that arise within, say, the period of a year. To gain even a portion of such knowledge, we would have to learn the number of persons in the population who have a psychiatric disorder but who have never been formally treated, as well as those who have had and/or are receiving treatment. How do we come to terms with the fact that such data do not yet exist?

Our approach has been to rely on the best data available, searching for trends, making extrapolations, and cross-checking our inferences as much as possible by comparing findings obtained by different methods. These analyses have focused for the most part on several bodies of epidemiological studies of true prevalence conducted mainly in specific communities located in the United States, Canada and Europe (Dohrenwend et al. 1978). One substantial body of information consists of 25 investigations of functional psychiatric disorders published since 1950 and covering 27 communities in North America and Europe. Another is comprised of studies in 13 United States communities in which psychiatric screening scales have been used.

We present the results of our analyses of these studies not as firm conclusions but rather as the best hypotheses that we could formulate on the basis of the existing evidence. The term "prevalence" in these hypotheses refers to a brief period somewhere between a point in time and the period of a year.

At least 8 United States and 20 European and Canadian studies, reporting rates for functional psychiatric disorders in the general population, have been published since 1950. The average overall rate for functional disorders is around 20 percent, regardless of whether the estimate is based on the U.S. or the non-U.S. investigations. As for major subtypes of disorder, the best estimates (Dohrenwend et al. 1978) that can be made from these and related studies are:

```
Schizophrenia...........................................0.5 to 3.0 percent
Manic-Depressive Psychosis..........................0.3 percent
Neurosis (also including the other
    depressive disorders)............................8.0 to 13.0 percent
Personality Disorder................................7.0 percent
```

Whether the lower or higher figure is accepted for schizophrenia depends on whether a relatively narrow, more typically European, or relatively broad, typically U.S. definition of this disorder is used. Similarly, the low figure for neurosis comes from European and the higher figure from U.S. studies. European and U.S. studies are in relatively close agreement on the rates of manic-depressive psychosis and personality disorder.

Despite its importance, surprisingly little research has been done on the relation of untreated to treated rates of psychiatric disorder in the general population. The overall median proportion of true cases in treatment for 11 studies providing the necessary information is 26.7 percent. This means that only about one-fourth of those suffering from a clinically significant disorder have been in treatment. The median proportion of true cases ever in treatment among those suffering from all psychotic disorders is 59.7 percent based on evidence from seven studies, and the corresponding rate for schizophrenia alone is 81.1 percent, based on six studies. If these figures are accurate they mean that two out of every five persons with psychosis and one out of every five with schizophrenia have never received treatment. This is important information.

In order to provide adequate help, the Nation needs the most accurate available information on the magnitude of the burden of illness posed by various kinds of mental disorder; the relative severity of various kinds of mental disorders and mental handicaps, in terms of numbers and degree of suffering (by the afflicted individual, his/her family, and other affected members of the society); and the direct and indirect costs of caring for these illnesses and their consequences. What follows is a concise summary of such information insofar as present knowledge permits for major mental health issues. This account does not attempt to be exhaustive, since this would not be of practical value in the present context. Instead, this account centers on several major components of the burden of mental disorders in order to clarify their nature and delineate their scope.

III. SCHIZOPHRENIA

Schizophrenia continues to be one of the major mental health problems in the country. Despite the relatively low incidence of the disorder, schizophrenia has a disproportionately high prevalence rate due to the early age of onset and the lengthy nature of the disorder. Although there can be a range of outcomes, the course is usually chronic. As a result it can be anticipated that there will be repeated episodes of severe disability and a lifetime of varying degrees of impairment and emotional stress for both the patient, and the family or significant others. Therefore, the total burden of this illness to society is considerable.

Symptoms

The symptoms of schizophrenia include altered motor behavior, ranging from total immobilization to frenetic and purposeless activity, sometimes accompanied by peculiar mannerisms. Perceptual distortions, often including auditory hallucinations, also occur. There are disturbances in thought processes that can lead to distorted concept formation, bizarre speech, and illogical thinking. This last may be expressed in paranoid delusions ranging from pervasive suspiciousness to fully developed beliefs in complex but improbable plots against the patient. Expression of emotion are either completely absent or inappropriate to the speech and actions of the individual.

Diagnosis

Although there continue to be major disagreements about which criteria are best, the development of standardized patient evaluation procedures over the past 15 years has made it possible to test the reliability of various diagnostic systems, and permits empirical research to test which diagnostic system proves most valuable in terms of reliability regarding prognosis, effective treatment, and etiology (Gottesman and Shields 1972; Kety et al. 1968; Strauss and Carpenter 1974). For example, one study using standardized evaluation methods has noted that antipsychotic medications may be helpful for certain diagnostic types of schizophrenia, but not for others (Evans et al. 1972). The advances in methodology, as simple as they seem in retrospect, have provided powerful tools for testing the various diagnostic approaches to schizophrenia. Research in this area is ongoing.

Etiology

The nature of schizophrenia is currently being actively investigated and findings have done much to dispel old myths. For example, following the results of several studies, it now seems that schizophrenia may be only one of several related outcomes of a particular genetic constitution. Which of these outcomes occurs may depend on the specific challenges of the environmental situations with which the individual must cope (Rosenthal 1970). It is also now generally agreed that the occurrence of schizophrenic symptoms is not necessarily associated with progressive deterioration of the patient's ability to function but includes the possibility of a wide range of outcomes (Strauss and Carpenter 1977).

Epidemiology

Community surveys, the only approach to the accurate assessment of the prevalence of such a disorder, suggest that currently about 2 million persons in the United States would be diagnosed as schizophrenic. About 100,000 new cases of schizophrenia occur in the United States each year. The overall prevalence rate in the United States is 0.7 to 1.0 percent of the population.

Treatment

As shown recently in a study from the Continuous Case Register of Monroe County, New York, treatment rates may vary considerably depending on the accessibility of care, especially for persons in lower socio-economic groups. In general, the number of patients diagnosed schizophrenic receiving active treatment in any one year in the United States is about 600,000. For at least 62 percent (372,000) of these, hospitalization is required at some point in the illness (Strauss 1977). Extrapolations from incidence and prevalence data and from information about utilization of available treatment facilities suggest that over 80 percent of the diagnosed schizophrenics are in treatment. This unusually high treatment rate may be due to the fact that the disorder is so prominent and disabling that most schizophrenics cannot be ignored.

The older practice of exclusively institutionalized care of patients far from their families and communities is no longer seen as the desirable model for the treatment of people with schizophrenia. In a small number of instances long term care in residential facilities may be required, but we now have the knowledge to design care for these patients that is much more therapeutic.

Over recent years research has also suggested the importance of a variety of treatment approaches, including vocational and social skills training where necessary, partial hospitalizations and other incremental programs for reentry into the community, ongoing psychotherapeutic work with the family and patient, and, of course, the use of anti-psychotic medications. These practices appear to have made a major contribution to the considerable drop in the number of schizophrenics residing in hospitals and to reducing the frequency of deterioration and chronicity commonly believed in the past to have been the hallmark of the disorder.

Although there is every indication that current treatment approaches to schizophrenia are superior to those used previously, still no definitive cure has been identified, and further research in this area is needed to determine which specific treatments are most effective with various kinds of patients, and to develop still more effective methods of care. However, it is also clear that treatments already known to be valuable are not available to many patients who need them. There is a scarcity of transitional treatment facilities, such as halfway houses, partial hospitalization programs, and day treatment centers. Community living, social and financial support programs required to provide comprehensive care for reintegrating patients into the community are often inadequate.

It is still the rule rather than the exception that most treatment plans for schizophrenics are focused almost entirely on the patient. Either because of treatment philosophy or limited resources, family members are often dealt with only minimally. Clearly, even now, there is enough information to show that there are many reasons to attend to the needs of the families of schizophrenic patients, including providing them with social and community supports to help ease their burdens in caring for their impaired family member.

Policy Implications

At present, there are increasing questions being raised about the preparedness of communities to deal with deinstitutionalized schizophrenic and other disabled mental patients, and there is concern over possible negative impacts on the individuals themselves and their families or significant others. There are special concerns that arise for the isolated schizophrenic patients in the community who have no families or network of significant others and supportive persons. Arrangements for the care of chronic patients with various types of mental disorder within the community are in need of scrutiny from the perspectives of both the public and private sectors.

IV. AFFECTIVE DISORDERS: DEPRESSION AND OTHER MOOD DISORDERS

Affective disorders refer to a group of psychiatric conditions in which disturbances of mood predominate. This group of disorders is frequently differentiated from disorders of thinking, which conventionally include schizophrenia and paranoid states. It is generally agreed that psychotic depression, excessive elation ("mania"), and manic-depression (bi-polar) are the major affective disorders.

Diagnosis

The term depression covers a broad spectrum of moods and behavior which range from the sadness of normal life through severe psychiatric disorder and the suicidal acts of melancholy. It can usefully be divided into three categories:

1. <u>Mood</u>--This is normal and transient and appears in relation to personal loss, disappointments of life, or stresses that are beyond current coping skills. It is a universal phenomenon.

2. <u>Symptom</u>--Depression as a symptom, or abnormal mood, is also common. In this case, there is an indistinct line between what is normal and what is pathological. A moderate to severe depression of mood that is unduly persistent, pervasive, or inappropriate to circumstances is generally considered pathological. The symptoms of depression are also commonly experienced by many physically ill patients and by most psychiatric patients, regardless of their other symptoms. They tend to seek general medical help.

3. <u>Syndrome</u>--This is a severe disorder with a specific cluster of symptoms that produces notable disability and occurs in the absence of other symptoms. This is the clinical condition of deep concern to mental health professionals involved in treatment.

To understand the scope of the problem, it is important to make the distinction between depressive symptoms on the one hand, and the clinical condition or syndrome on the other. Although sharing some features, they are distinct. The prevalence rates of cases derived from symptoms are considerably higher than the rates derived from the syndrome.

Depressive Symptoms

Depressive symptoms are usually detected by interview. In recent years a number of rating scales have been developed to detect depressive symptoms (Beck et al. 1961; Zung 1965; Weissman et al. 1976). These scales include a set of questions about the presence or absence of symptoms. This approach is quantitative and uses certain cut-off points on a rating scale. The number of symtoms and their severity are added up and a quantitative estimate of the symptoms is obtained. It has been estimated that only about one-third of the subjects who score high on depressive symptom scales actually have the clinical syndrome of depression (Weissman et al. 1976). The remaining subjects scoring high on these scales may have other emotional or psychophysiological disorders as their clinical picture.

Comprehensive surveys of depressive symptoms in the community, which include both treated and untreated cases, show remarkable consistency. The overall point prevalence rates of depressive symptoms generally range between 16 and 20 percent. The rates are highest in women, non-whites, the separated and divorced, the poor, and the less educated. Persons with these symptoms tend to seek general medical but not psychiatric help and usually receive psychotropic drugs for relief. In one longitudinal study conducted in New Haven, Connecticut, (Weissman et al. 1977) in 1967, 1969, and 1975, only a small percent (18 percent) suffering with depressive symptoms saw a mental health professional, 10 percent saw a psychiatrist, and 4 percent were hospitalized. These findings point out the importance of the nonpsychiatric physician and of primary care facilities in the recognition and treatment of depressive symptoms since it is the most common mental disorder.

Depressive Syndrome--The Clinical Condition

The clinical depressive syndrome is characterized by a specific set of symptoms, of certain severity and persistence, which produce impairment or disability and which occur in the absence of other symptoms. Recent advances in specifying and operationalizing these criteria, and in defining subtypes, have greatly improved the reliability of their detection and the agreement between clinicians as to their presence (Spitzer et al. 1977; Endicott and Spitzer 1977). These new techniques have been applied to community samples so that data are now available on both treated and untreated cases for a variety of subtypes of the depressive syndrome.

Whereas depressive symptoms have a current point prevalence rate of 16 to 20 percent, the current rates for the clinical depressive syndrome are considerably lower. Based on new diagnostic techniques the current overall point prevalence rate for the clinical depressive syndrome was found to be 6.9 percent (Spitzer et al. 1977; Endicott and Spitzer 1977). This syndrome was found to be more common in women and in persons in the lower social classes. However, when lifetime rates of the disorder were examined, the relationship with social class was not found, suggesting that lower and upper social class persons have the same rates of occurrence but that lower social class persons have a longer duration of illness. This may be a reflection of receiving inadequate treatment. Only about 35 percent of persons currently suffering from a major depression were receiving any general medical treatment and only 30 percent received psychiatric or mental health treatment in the year before the disabling episode; only 8 percent of those with minor depression received general medical or psychiatric treatment in the previous year. Psychiatric hospitalization for these conditions was rare.

Depressive Personality (Intermittent or Chronic Depression)

A substantial number of persons (4.7 percent) have chronic or intermittent dysphoric mood which appears to be lifelong and recurring. This syndrome appears with equal frequency in men and women, all social classes, but currently is higher in young persons (under age 45). About one-third of the persons with this disorder seek psychiatric help in a 1-year period.

Bipolar Disorder (Depression and Elation or Mania)

Bipolar disorder, i.e., a disorder which includes both periods of depression and elation (or mania), is the most serious and socially disruptive form of affective disorders and one which carries a significant risk of death by suicide. Fortunately, its prevalence is low (0.3 percent to 1.2 percent). The ratios for this disorder among men and women are about equal and it appears to be more common in the upper social classes.

Over 80 percent of the persons with this disorder receive some treatment, usually psychiatric, in a 1-year period.

In summary, it should be repeated that this grouping of affective disorders does not imply common etiology or treatment; rather, the similarities in clinical symptomatology probably represent common manifestations of multiple processes and influences.

Etiology

The understanding of causation in depressive disorders is the subject of intense investigation. Evidently, multiple factors interact to produce depression. These include stressful life events, genetic predisposition, vulnerability to stress based on personality characteristics, and biological abnormalities which can be either inherited or acquired. This is a prime area for biomedical and behavioral research. The new behavioral biology is especially significant for ultimate prevention of severe depression, as well as the manic disorders, and for schizophrenia.

Treatment

Early detection is facilitated by knowledge of risk factors. There is considerable evidence that certain life periods or situations carry a higher risk for being associated with the development of a depressive disorder. Also there are vulnerable persons. These are persons who have a higher than average risk of a depressive response to life events that would not ordinarily be expected to elicit that reaction.

High Risk Periods

High risk periods include times of transition in which there are personal losses involving disruptions of attachment bonds and disruptions in life patterns that require new adaptations (Klerman 1974). These include periods of serious ill health, death of a loved one with consequent bereavement, divorce, separation, or moving to a new neighborhood. The postpartum period, particularly the first three months after delivery, is an especially vulnerable time (Weissman and Klerman 1977). An excess of admissions for depressive disorders has been observed during this period and it has been noted that mild symptoms of depression which never receive treatment are quite common in the postpartum period.

High Risk Persons

Persons who are at high risk for developing depressive disorders include those who have suffered parental deprivation either by early childhood separation from parents, by having psychiatrically ill parents, or by being reared in a family that was abusive and rejecting. Risk is also increased in persons with a strong history of affective disorders or suicide. Anyone who has had a past episode of clinical depression or elation becomes at higher risk for a subsequent episode. Women, non-whites, the poor, and single parents are also at higher than average risk.

Methods of Detection

Early detection can often be done by a nonpsychiatric physician or other professional if properly trained. There are many clues to help in the detection of depression. The patient who seems apathetic, listless, has multiple complaints, or is extremely irritable may be harboring depressive symptoms. Answers to direct inquiries such as, "Have you felt sad, moody?" "Have you had difficulty in sleeping?" "How has your appetite been?" "Have you felt life is worth living?" are all useful in diagnosis of previously undetected depression. (The rating scales described earlier give a more precise assessment.)

Treatment of the Acute Episode

A promising advance in the treatment of the affective disorders has been the development of a rnage of effective antidepressant medications. Such medications are widely available, relatively safe if properly used and monitored, and can be administered by most physicians. These medications are particularly useful in reducing the acute symptoms of depression, improving mood and sleep, and restoring appetite and energy. Drug-induced remissions do not appear until 1 to 4 weeks after the start of medication. A resumption of social functioning follows symptom reduction, although often at a slow pace over the next 2 months.

The antidepressants have by no means replaced psychological treatments. Indeed, there is evidence that one important function of the antidepressant is to sufficiently alter the symptoms so that the patient can begin to engage in therapy aimed at improving social adaptation. In fact, some form of psychological intervention combined with antidepressants often yields the best treatment outcome. However, either treatment may be used independently

(Klerman et al. 1974). A wide range of psychological treatments may be used to provide emotional support, to bolster coping skills, to help in dealing with the family consequences of the disorder, and to provide an understanding of the maladaptive patterns or antecedents that may have predisposed the person to the depression.

Continuing Care

There is good evidence now that maintenance treatment by combined pharmacotherapy and psychotherapy over 6 to 8 months is valuable in preventing relapse after recovery from the acute symtoms of depression and to enhance social functioning (Klerman et al. 1974). There is also evidence that affective disorders tend to recur so that most patients benefit from continuing, readily available care even beyond the maintenance phase. Depending on the patient, the care required may be intensive for sustained durations, or periodic and not intensive. During the period following symptomatic recovery, there is opportunity for interventions that are focused on rehabilitation and achievement of maximal functioning.

Long Term Course

It is generally agreed that when treated actively, an acute depressive episode carries a good prognosis, that the chance of recovery is excellent, and that social functioning between episodes will be unimpaired. Formerly depressed patients can resume their work, child care and social life. However, data on the long term course of depression suggest that depressions are less benign than commonly believed (Weissman et al. 1976). While most acute symptoms resolve rapidly, especially with modern treatment, there is a tendency for them to recur. Followup studies have found that only 30 percent of women who had initially recovered from an acute depression remained completely asymptomatic over the following two years. Ten percent were chronically symptomatic and the majority, nearly 60 percent, had mild recurring symptoms including disturbances of mood, sleep, and appetite. These episodes of symptom recurrence were usually accompanied by difficulties in participating fully in occupational or caretaking roles. There is also evidence that about 10 to 15 percent of patients remain chronically symptomatic 2 to 5 years after a depressive episode. Moreover, there is evidence that persons suffering from bipolar (manic-depressive) disorders have an increased mortality by suicide. These findings document the intermittent and chronic nature, and potential mortality, of depressive disorders. They also indicate the need for further research on these disorders, spurred by the advances of the past two decades.

Impact on the Family

The prevalence of the affective disorders has important public health implications. Recent research has documented the serious impact of maternal depression on family relations and the fulfilling of roles in the community (Endicott and Spitzer 1977). When acutely depressed women were compared to their normal neighbors who had never had a depressive episode, it was found that the depressed women's impairments reached into all aspects of their lives--as wives, mothers, workers, and members of the community. Although depressed women often continued to go to work during an acute episode, their satisfaction with their work and their general level of performance was diminished. Communication was poor between husband and wife and hostility between patient and spouse was often overt. Relationships with children were markedly disturbed. During the height of the illness, the depressed women were only moderately involved in their children's lives, had difficulty communicating with the children, and expressed a loss of affection and considerable anger at the children. Conflicts with adolescent children were reported to be serious. At times the children became rebellious and demanding. A substantial percentage of these adolescents developed problems in school, with friends, or with the law.

Implications for Program Planning

Our understanding of depression and its impact has implications for program planning and health policy. In this country, general health policy is focused on chronic diseases with high mortality such as cancer and heart disease. Mental disorders such as depression, which have a high morbidity and a potential mortality by suicide, share many features of nonpsychiatric chronic diseases and also require comprehensive planning. A flexibility of treatment resources is needed so that patients can have crisis intervention for acute episodes, and continuing periodic care as appropriate. Because of the recurring nature of depression and its consequences for families, continuity and accessibility of care are essential to effective treatment, including attention to the children and family as well as to the adult depressive.

V. EMOTIONAL DISTRESS, MENTAL DISORDERS, AND COMMUNITY CARE

The findings of community epidemiological studies show a large number of persons suffering from mild-to-moderate depression, anxiety, psychophysiological discomforts, insomnia, loneliness, and other indicators of emotional disorders. The term "demoralization" has been coined by Frank (1973) to describe this syndrome but it has found only limited usage in the field. Although most of these problems do not constitute mental disorders as conventionally defined, many of these persons suffer intensely and feel a need for assistance from time to time. They may constitute as much as 25 percent of the population at any given time, although the extent and composition of the group varies over time. Indeed, acute episodes of highly stressful experience and associated emotional distress are ubiquitous. Mostly, individuals cope with these stresses with the aid of family, friends, or professionals outside the mental health system. Only a small minority of these patients are referred for care in mental health settings. When this occurs, it is because the emotional or behavioral symptoms tend to be quite prominent and severe. However, large numbers of such problems are brought to primary health care settings.

Although many nonpsychiatric physicians feel inadequately prepared to deal with such problems, these patients constitute a large part of primary care practice in the United States and in Europe. When the distress of these patients' problems brings them to medical attention, they may, at times, be recipients of intensive medical and even surgical care that is of marginal value. Personal, psychotherapeutically-oriented counseling and relief of suffering through pharmacological intervention are usually more helpful to them. Psychoactive drugs are used extensively in medical practice, especially mild tranquilizers. Indeed, they are the most frequently used drugs in ordinary medical practice. Tranquilizers are the most prescribed of all drugs. Ninety-seven million prescriptions are written annually in the United States and the trend of use is rising,[1] along with medications intended to improve sleep patterns. This large volume of prescriptions is one indication of the important responsibilities of the general health care system for this set of mental/emotional problems.

It is believed that as many as 70 percent of patients who commit suicide had sought out a physician shortly before the act or had been under the recent care of a physician. Over two-thirds of the patients had histories of suicide threats or attempts, but these suicide gestures were known to only two-fifths of the physicians who provided care for them. There is evidence that three-quarters of the patients were depressed, but this diagnosis was rarely made by nonpsychiatrists nor was the depression treated. More than half of those who died by drug overdose had had an unlimited prescription of the substance ingested or had received a prescription within a week or less before their deaths. Thus, a sustained effort is needed to enhance the knowledge and competence of nonpsychiatric physicians in treating depression and recognizing the signs of potential suicide.

---

[1] Drug Use Patterns, Consequences and the Federal Response. A Policy Review, Office of Drug Abuse Policy, 1978.

Policy Implications

Whatever mental health benefits are provided under national health insurance, it appears virtually inevitable that most services for common mental health problems will continue to be provided within the general medical sector by nonpsychiatrists. These problems are not only common and associated with physicial symptoms, but the patients tend to resist a psychological definition of their distress. Any effective system of primary medical care services must take account of such patients and be responsive to their needs.

From a public policy perspective, it would be neither productive nor economical to attempt to shift these patients to more specialized care. Such a shift would be difficult and improbable at best, and would take away scarce resources from patients with more profound psychological disabilities who need the available specialized services. Planning to ensure that patients with distress syndromes receive appropriate assistance from the general medical sector deserves policy attention. This aspect of mental health care can be enhanced by improving the capacity of primary care practitioners to recognize such common problems as depression, alcoholism, and anxiety, and by increasing their ability to deal with such patients. Primary care physicians can improve their pharmacological knowledge of psychoactive drugs and the relation of drug use to counseling and emotional support. More effort can also be given to developing consultant roles for mental health professionals in primary care settings. As medical care comes increasingly to be given in organized settings, such as group practices, it will become possible to integrate nonphysician mental health personnel into primary care to provide counseling, supportive care, behavior therapy, and to assist in organizing self-help and group-help efforts.

Efforts must be made to integrate more mental health care within the mainstream of medical care. At the same time, however, sustained categorical efforts will be required to provide effective services to patients with chronic mental disorders that involve considerable handicap. In doing so, emphasis should be given to interventions that have the highest probability of minimizing disability and reducing suffering, as indicated by careful and systematic research. Priority should be given to patients with the greatest distress and impairment. Interventions should be measured by the degree to which they not only reduce distress but enhance personal effectiveness and ability to function in society. This is an important area for research in health services.

VI. DRUG USE PROBLEMS

Problems of drug use continue to pose extremely serious social and health concerns in our society. For the average person, it is also an issue that causes anxiety and a sense of confusion about the trends, the nature, and the scope of the problem.

One of the central lessons that professionals have learned is that drug abuse is a chronic, recalcitrant problem which can be resolved only through sustained, committed effort, greater ingenuity, and multifaceted research. In the past, expectations of immediate success based on intensive short-term, large-scale efforts have gone largely unfulfilled. These experiences have led us to suspect that total elimination of drug use in the country is an unrealistic goal. However, given our knowledge of the spread of drug use, we can have an impact on the extent of use through implementation of an epidemiological monitoring system and the development of an effective intervention policy. These, together with controls of supply and adequate resources for prevention, treatment, and rehabilitation, are essential first steps in controlling the problem of drug abuse.

While a direct count of drug-abusing populations is difficult, if not impossible, a reasonable estimate can be made on the basis of surveys of drug use. In addition, analysis of drug indicator trends illuminates relative levels of current drug use. It should be emphasized that the drug problem is a multifaceted phenomenon. In describing drug abuse, it is useful to differentiate between the various categories of drugs since the magnitude, underlying nature and adverse individual and societal consequences vary as a function of the substance abused.

Although no agreement has been reached about a standard terminology, it may be useful to give the definitions to be used in this discussion.[1]

Definitions

<u>Drug abuse</u> is defined as the nontherapeutic use of any psychoactive substance in such a manner as to adversely affect some important aspect of the user's life. The use pattern may be occasional or habitual. Drugs used may be licit (legal) or illicit (illegal).

<u>Drug misuse</u> refers to the inappropriate use of drugs in therapeutically-intended contexts. It includes inadvertent errors in judgment or knowledge by the consumer or the prescribing physician:

- lack of knowledge on part of physician;
- use by patient not in accordance with prescription.

---

[1] This glossary is taken from the just published report of the Office of Drug Abuse Policy, <u>Drug Use Patterns, Consequences and the Federal Response: A Policy Review</u>. 1978.

It should be noted that there can be considerable overlap in the health and social consequences whether the drug problem results from abuse or misuse.

There is no attempt to be exhaustive in the brief discussion that follows. There is a separate task panel of this Commission that treats the problems of drug abuse more fully.

However, even in this brief summary, it must be noted that there are broad and extremely complex issues of human behavior related to patterns of drug use. Much more epidemiological information about the incidence, prevalence, ecological settings, and lifetime drug use history of the various sectors of the population is needed. The magnitude, the underlying nature, and adverse individual and societal consequences of drug abuse vary greatly not only with the substances used but are greatly influenced by the personal characteristics of the involved individuals and their families and social settings.

The mental health field has a special responsibility to explore these aspects of the problem. For example, most women abusing drugs are of childbearing age. There are significant implications for the vicissitudes of the mother-child interactions.

Parenting by drug-abusing mothers is inconsistent at best and often involves severe neglect, rejection, and sometimes child abuse. From what we know of the long term effects of these kinds of adverse childhood experiences, it places the child at high risk for repeating the pattern of the mother.

It is also the case that a great deal of drug misuse, especially the over-prescription of tranquilizers, occurs in women of child-bearing age. Single parents and mothers of many small children are especially likely to seek and receive these prescriptions for their symptoms of emotional distress and depression which are undiagnosed and not treated with psychotherapy or perhaps needed emotional supports.

There clearly are challenges and opportunities in the mental health field to identify the target populations which are both misusing and abusing drugs and to apply existing knowledge to help these persons. With continued research, better understanding, more effective treatments can be offered and ultimately, preventive measures taken.

Heroin

The National Institute on Drug Abuse estimates that more than one-half million individuals are chronic, daily heroin users not now receiving treatment, and the Federal Strategy of 1976 indicates that as many as 2 to 4 million may have used heroin at some point in their lives. Current indicators of heroin trends suggest that the number of heroin users may have leveled off or is declining, but the problem is still very serious. Some major cities are cautiously reporting declines in the heroin problem, and the Office of Drug Abuse Policy is reporting that average retail heroin purity, an indicator thought to reflect heroin availability, is at the lowest point since data collection was initiated in 1973. Nevertheless, government officials well informed on urban matters are deeply concerned about endemic opiate use as an obstacle to an effective urban revitalization.

Cocaine

Cocaine, a stimulant with effects similar to the amphetamines, continues to receive unusual media attention. However, it presents unique problems of assessment since, typically, severe adverse medical consequences rarely emerge. The Federal Strategy of 1976 indicated that close to 7 million people reported ever having used cocaine and between 3 to 4 million reported having used cocaine during the previous year. While overall use of cocaine may be increasing, the high cost suggests that large amounts are not being used by most individual cocaine users.

Hallucinogens

While hallucinogens as a general category have lost some of the popularity they had in the late 1960's, one particular hallucinogen, PCP (Phencyclidine), appears to be emerging as an increasingly popular drug of abuse. PCP, a drug which is legitimately available as an animal tranquilizer, was developed in the late 1950's. Recreationally, PCP use first became apparent in San Francisco in the late 1960's. Today PCP is available in most parts of the United States and indicators of use show that its popularity has been increasing steadily during the past several years. PCP is often sold on the streets as THC or tetrahydrocannabinol which makes it a particularly dangerous drug since the purchaser is not prepared for the erratic and unpleasant effects which are often experienced. The use of this drug is especially unfortunate since it sometimes causes severe toxicity ranging from psychosis to death. Because PCP is easily synthesized and is available at low cost across the Nation, it poses a special current problem.

Age Related Drug Abuse

In terms of lifetime prevalence and current use, consideration of particular age groups is an important factor in drug abuse. Analysis of drug use surveys and drug indicator data show that the greatest concentration of nonmedical drug use occurs among young adults between the ages of 18 and 25. These young adults report levels of use for all categories of drugs which far exceed any other age group. In addition, drug-related deaths rank as one of the leading causes of death among individuals in this age category.

These findings indicate the clear need for priority attention in understanding and intervening in the drug use practices of youth. Increasingly, introduction to nonmedical, street use of drugs is occurring in the 10 to 15 age group. This problem deserves special attention in research, services, and education.

Abuse and Misuse of Licit Drugs

Tranquilizers are the most prescribed of all drugs. Ninety-seven million prescriptions are written annually and the trend of use is rising. Although there is some current scientific discussion as to the appropriateness or inappropriateness of this usage level by the American people, it clearly reflects a response to some form of psychological and emotional need.

The chronic non-medical use of barbiturates has been recently identified as a problem with partiuclarly serious adverse consequences. Although barbiturate death rates have been declining for the past several years, these drugs remain second only to heroin as a cause of drug-related deaths in the United States. Barbiturate addiction is also a sizable problem. For these reasons, President Carter, in his message to Congress, recommended that increased attention be paid to these drugs and directed the Secretary of Health, Education, and Welfare to undertake a study of barbiturates and the conditions under which they could be most safely used. At the same time, he directed the Attorney General to begin a concerted drive to identify and prosecute physicians who misprescribe barbiturates.

It has been estimated that 7 million people used prescribed medication without medical supervision during 1976 and that, overall, almost 19 million had used prescribed medication without medical supervision some time in their lives. Current indicators suggest that these estimates have not changed substantially in the last year.

The elderly is a population at high risk for drug misuse because their consumption of drugs is substantially higher than for other age groups. This sector of the population is increasing in size, living longer, becoming more medicated, and more isolated. For all of these reasons, the problems of drug misuse in this group are highly significant and likely to increase in the coming years.

Physicians are not always aware of the altered, usually lower, tolerance to drugs that characterize the elderly. They may inadvertently over-medicate them and can induce toxic reactions at times.

Problems of drug use are formidable and will require a sustained, commited, and collaborative national effort. The mental health field has a major contribution to make in this effort.

VII. ALCOHOL-RELATED DISORDERS

The importance of alcohol abuse as a serious social, physical, and mental health problem in the United States has probably been underestimated. Alcohol consumption has been such an integral and long-standing feature of our culture that there are powerful social factors to encourage the drinking of alcohol and to support a high public tolerance of intoxication that is less than extreme. In a sense, familiarity has bred a misleading complacency about the gravity of the ongoing and the long term effects of alcohol abuse. There is, on the contrary, a plausible case to be made for considering alcoholism to be one of the most pressing public health problems that confronts the Nation. The President's Commission on Mental Health has established a task panel to examine the mental health implications of alcohol abuse.

There are multiple severe consequences of heavy alcohol use over long periods of time. There is physical damage to the brain, the liver, and other vital organs. Heavy drinking plays a role in causing some forms of cancer. It is a major factor in automobile accidents and fire-setting. There are significant psychological effects on the abuser such as despair, sense of hopelessness and failure, and proneness to suicide. There is extensive emotional pain and suffering caused to families. Violence in the family is highly correlated with alcohol abuse. The social consequences and costs are enormous in destruction of families, unemployment, medical and welfare costs. Recently, a specific hazard has been highlighted. This is the fetal alcohol syndrome (FAS).

While the exact extent and pattern of drinking by pregnant mothers that leads to the fetal alcohol syndrome has not been made explicit, it clearly can result from even mild to moderate alcohol intake during pregnancy. Alcoholic pregnant women are clearly at maximum risk.

FAS babies are born with a typical small head and facial deformities. The perinatal mortality for these babies is 17 percent compared to about 2 percent for the general population. At birth the FAS babies are irritable and have a tremulousness that may persist for months or years. Mental retardation has been reported in 44 percent of FAS babies as compared to 9 percent of comparison babies in a study cited in the report of the Institute of Medicine, <u>Perspectives on Health Promotion and Disease Prevention in the United States, 1978</u>. It is also pointed out in that discussion that aside from the mental and physical development that is stunted in intrauterine life, an FAS infant is born to a mother who, if alcoholic, is poorly equipped to care for herself, much less for a child with a chronic disability.

Some alcohol-related problems are commonly viewed as mental disorders in their own right. Various conditions labeled as "Alcoholic psychosis" have long been a major category in classifications of mental hospital patients. These alcoholic psychoses include Wernicke's and Korsakoff's syndromes. Both of these psychotic disorders now appear to be due more specifically to the Vitamin B deficiency that results from the dietary deficiency so often linked with chronic alcohol abuse. Alcohol hallucinosis is a well-known syndrome in which very vivid, usually highly frightening and disturbing perceptions are a prominent feature. Delirium tremens is also a well-known psychotic state.

It is associated with a chronic history of alcoholism and is rarely seem in individuals under 30 years of age. It is a medically dangerous condition as well as an acutely psychotic state. Although it is typically associated with alcohol withdrawal, it may also be triggered by injury or infection.

It should also be noted that mental disorder may lead to alcoholism. For example, there is evidence that depressive symptoms may underlie much of the alcoholism seen in poverty class, nonwhite women.

Etiology

In recent decades, a social movement has promoted acceptance of the disease concept of alcoholism. The illness is characterized by a loss of control over responsible drinking behavior. Other terms, such as "alcohol dependence" and "drug dependence--alcohol type," have also been used for essentially the same concept. While a physiological predisposition has been assumed as a basis for the disease, psychological dependence, a mental condition has been seen as a factor for some patients. A recent World Health Organization (WHO) group of investigators, proposed the term "alcohol dependence syndrome" for this particular concept. They recognized that it was, however, only one among many "alcohol-related disabilities." Following this view, therefore, some but not all alcohol-related problems may be seen as mental illness or symptoms or consequences of mental illness.

Prevalence

Conceptual confusion has meant that most estimates of the prevalence of alcohol-related problems have been in terms of a global and ill-defined category of "alcoholism" or "problem drinking." If "alcoholism" is defined by the number of persons receiving treatment or assistance under that rubric, the United States prevalence is under 1 million persons. Traditional indirect estimating techniques using questionable assumptions produce estimates of a few million. Survey data on persons reporting a significant recent alcohol-related problem of some sort produce estimates of the order of 10 million. Of the order of 20 million Americans report having experienced alcohol-related problems of some sort in the course of their lifetime.

Epidemiology

Those in treatment as "alcoholics" typically differ considerably from those reporting drinking problems in general population samples. The 1 percent population of "alcoholics" under care is typically aged 35 to 55, while general population alcohol problems are concentrated among males 18 to 24. Treatment populations include large proportions who are disaffiliated--not in a family and without jobs--and typically have a lengthy history of drinking problems of many types. If "alcoholism" was defined as those who, whether or not in treatment, match the social position and the history and extent of those who are in treatment for alcoholism, the prevalence might not be very much larger than the population in treatment. Some particular ethnicities show especially high rates of alcohol problems, including Native Americans,

SCOPE 34

Blacks, and persons of Irish, Mexican, Puerto Rican, and Scandinavian heritage.

Treatment

Patients with alcohol-related diagnoses have traditionally formed a very large part of mental hospital caseloads. This trend seems to be rising. Some community mental health centers provide treatment and services for alcoholism. Nevertheless, in recent years outpatient treatment for alcoholism has become increasingly divorced from the mental illness treatment network. Alcoholism agencies at State and Federal levels, reflecting the views of their constituencies, seem to have become disenchanted with the level of attention and services provided alcoholics under mental health auspices.

The alcohol field has the important asset of the alcoholism movement, with its enormous reservoir of lay concern and volunteer effort. There are some signs that this movement may expand beyond its traditional concerns with treatment to become involved in community organization around the prevention of alcohol problems.

Although the alcohol treatment services and mental health systems are currently quite separate, and will probably remain so, there is an urgent need to coordinate them more closely, particularly in such areas as policy, research, and training. Despite their formal coordination under the Alcohol, Drug Abuse, and Mental Health Administration (ADAMHA), there has historically been very little day-to-day coordination between the National Institute of Alcohol Abuse and Alcoholism (NIAAA) and the National Institute of Mental Health (NIMH) staffs. Grant and contract programs could be designed to encourage rather than discourage research and training which relate the two areas. At State and local levels, regular liaison should be a formal part of the duties of alcohol and mental health program personnel. Alcohol treatment personnel need to be sensitized to the possibility of concurrent mental health problems, and mental health treatment personnel to alcohol problems, and routine systems for cross-referral need to be established. Rational procedures for helping the client who has concurrent alcohol and mental illness problems need to be established and evaluated.

For both alcohol and mental health problems, any conceivable treatment system staffed by highly paid professionals cannot hope to cope with the full magnitude of the problems. For the foreseeable future, there will remain a need for formal professional treatment services where informal efforts have failed, and for places of refuge for cases who can no longer be maintained in the community. But, as in the past, most potential alcohol and mental health problem cases will be "treated" informally and by nonprofessionals. There are a wide variety of such nonprofessional community resources. Much of the control and prevention of mental illness and alcohol problems happen among intimates--in the family, among friends, workmates, or associates. But there are also many other community resources that are not formally mental health or alcoholism agencies: established churches and new religious movements, traditional community health and welfare services, and the newer "alternative" services--volunteer and service groups, self-awareness and self-actualization groups. Very little is known about how these informal and nonprofessional efforts impinge on mental illness and alcohol problems. The processes involved need close study, and the two fields need to develop new kinds of expertise, including abilities in community organization and facilitation, to help improve and focus such community responses to potential alcohol and mental illness problems.

Prevention

New and renewed directions of thought in the field point to fresh governmental and organizational initiatives in the prevention of alcohol problems.

Linkage of health professionals to community efforts focusing on early treatment or prevention of alcohol abuse deserves further development. Especially in adolescence and young adulthood, promising opportunities for primary and secondary prevention deserve exploration.

The past decade has been a time of rapid change in the patterns of drug use among adolescents. There has been an overall increase in drinking among youth. Most disturbing has been the increasing trend toward initiation into regular alcohol use at early adolescence, children as young as 10 to 12 years of age. In the 1974 nationwide survey of junior and senior high school students, 27.8 percent were found to be problem drinkers (Institute of Medicine 1978). Finding ways to prevent alcohol abuse among our children is an issue of highest priority.

Alcohol-related problems are a major part of the national burden of illness--not only in the mental health system but far beyond it. Yet, research activity in this field has historically been at a low level. This is a prime area for upgrading of research spanning biological, psychological, and community approaches.

VIII. MENTAL DISORDERS IN CHILDHOOD

Assessment, Diagnosis, and Classification

In the past, one of the barriers to assessing the prevalence of childhood mental disorders has been the lack of agreed methods for evaluating and differentiating between the varieties of mental health problems. This has made it difficult to compare findings from different studies and to exchange potentially useful information and experience. However, in recent years considerable advances are being achieved in the development of assessment and classification tools for children.

New developments have made it possible for the first time to carry out epidemiological studies to compare the frequency, course, and social correlates to children's mental health problems. Screening questionnaires of demonstrated reliability and validity for parents have been developed to identify children needing further evaluation. Standardized personal interviews for use with children are being developed. Interviews which can be reliably given by well-trained nonprofessional interviewers are also an important new tool.

In the field of classification, a multiaxial scheme for children has been developed. In this system, children are assessed with respect to five axes: clinical psychiatric syndrome, intellectual level, specific delays in development, underlying or associated medical conditions, and distrubed psychosocial environment (Rutter et al. 1975). This system of diagnosis appears in the ninth revision of the World Health Organization (WHO) International Classification of Diseases, and is similar to that planned for DSM III of the American Psychiatric Association. There is a glossary included in the WHO ninth revision providing definitions of classification categories and also instructions for the use of codings.

All of these recent developments should contribute to greater precision and comparability of information on childhood mental disorders.

However, in spite of these achievements, further work is necessary to improve assessment tools for children of various ages and various social backgrounds. It is necessary to develop simple and reliable assessment tools that can be used by nonspecialist workers in a wide range of services (educational, social, forensic, pediatric, etc.) and to develop techniques for evaluating family functioning and children's psychosocial environment in different sociocultural settings. The best studies so far have been carried out in Britain. We need to apply the most effective of these currently available tools to American populations. It is not known how comparable American data would be. The British data make it clear that different answers are obtained when different screening methods are used.

Methodology

Assessments of the frequency and duration of mental disorders of children are necessary for planning services. However, in moving from population frequencies to service implications, a number of cautions must be kept in mind:

1. Prevalence levels of disorders in which there is a continuum between normal and abnormal behavior depends on arbitrary decisions about where the cut-off lies between "normal" and "abnormal." Often we use definitions that simply decide <u>a priori</u> to consider a certain percentage of the population as "abnormal." To designate that certain percentage as abnormal, we typically construct a scale along which a particular characteristic varies, fix the scale's midpoint at the population mean, and call "pathological" those cases which fall more than two standard deviations above or below that midpoint. In other words, we create a standardized scale. The national reading evaluation test is an example of a standardized scale, designed so that a fixed proportion will be defined as backward readers. The lowest group is then offered remedial efforts. Thus, Rutter's finding that 6.5 percent of ten-year-olds on the Isle of Wight are backward in reading is useful only as a baseline against which children from specially disadvantaged or advantaged backgrounds can be contrasted.

2. Although estimates for most types of childhood psychiatric disturbance do not have such a predetermined distribution of scores in the general population, in part because no standardized measuring devices like reading tests exist, estimates of impairment rates are very dependent on the criteria applied and the assessor's estimate of whether help is available. For example, Rutter found an incidence of 8 percent for disturbed 14-year olds when he based his estimate on teacher and record data, but after obtaining questionnaire responses from the children themselves, his estimate rose to 21 percent. When teachers are asked to nominate children in need of treatment, they may feel obligated to name at least one. If they have classes of 30, this guarantees a minimum rate of at least 3 percent. In Davie's (1972) report on the National Child Development Study, when first grade teachers were asked to identify children who would hardly ever sit still, they named 11 percent of the boys and 5 percent of the girls. When asked to assess children on the Bristol Social Adjustment Guide, they placed 14 percent in the "maladjusted" range. In a sample of 136 children followed from birth to adolescence, Thomas and Chess (1976) identified one-third with serious enough emotional problems at some time in their childhoods that help was sought. This rate, two to three times that of other studies, does not mean that New York-born middle class children are especially disturbed. Rather, it means that their parents were especially predisposed to seek psychological counseling for them. The parents had been self-selected to participate in the study in part by the offer of free professional help to the child should they ever need it.

3. The determination that there is a given level of disorder among children does not necessarily imply that exclusively psychiatric manpower to treat all these cases is required. Followup studies of children have shown that some improve spontaneously without treatment, and for those who do not, appropriate treatment may be delivered through nonpsychiatric sources such as remedial education programs, school counseling, and family social agencies. Further, there is little evidence that the most common serious childhood disorder, conduct disorder, responds well to the treatments currently available.

Thus, needs are both for improving methods of detecting children in need of help and in developing and evaluating more adequate treatment methods. For some disorders, parents have been taught to be effective therapists. Discovering ways of improving the capacity of those routinely in contact with the child--parents, older siblings, teachers, and pediatricians--in identifying and coping with mental disorders is a high priority need.

There is some concern that the identification of mental disorders in children might be disadvantageous to them because of stigma and negative discrimination resulting from labeling. This does sometimes arise when labels are misused as mechanical guides to administrative action or when diagnoses are misused as permanent labels that continue in existence after the disorders have remitted. On the other hand, some forms of categorization are essential for initiating appropriate treatment and can serve as a guide to needed preventive services. It is the responsibility of those who use diagnostic terms to ensure that they are understood and acted upon in ways that benefit individual children. Identifying children's special needs can and should result in advantage, not disadvantage, when the information is used with discretion and concern, and appropriate treatment or needed care is given.

Prevalence of Mental Health Problems in Children

Surveys of general populations show that the overall prevalence of persistent and socially handicapping mental health problems among children aged 3 to 15 years is about 5 to 15 percent (Robins 1978). There cannot be an exact prevalence for mental disorders in childhood, because prevalence figures will necessarily be affected, as pointed out above, by the threshold or cut-off point used in making a diagnosis and methods of ascertainment. Disorders vary in frequency according to age, sex, and social circumstances. Thus, mental health problems are more common in boys than in girls, are somewhat more frequent in adolescence than in earlier childhood, and more frequent among children living in inner-city areas than in small towns and rural areas. Although precise estimates cannot be made, mental health problems in childhood are clearly sufficiently common to constitute a major concern in the planning of health services and to make it impractical for them to be dealt with mainly by child psychiatrists.

Three groups of problems particularly contribute to the overall prevalence rates of defined mental disorders in children: <u>emotional disorders</u>, <u>conduct disorders</u>, and impairments or <u>delays in the development of normal functions</u>. Emotional disorders (e.g., fears, anxiety, depression, obsessions, hypochondriasis) occur with the same frequency in boys and girls, while conduct disorders (in which poor peer relationships, aggressiveness, theft, and destructiveness constitute the main features) are significantly more common in boys. A large proportion of juvenile delinquents have conduct disorders. Delinquency peaks in males 14 to 15 years of age, particularly those in large cities. There is an overrepresentation of minority youth living in poverty and who are deficient in educational skills. Delinquency rates are influenced by official and unofficial policy with respect to diversion from appearance in juvenile court and local law with respect to the ages subject to the juvenile code. Paradoxically where efforts at diversion are pursued actively, the labeling of predelinquency and delinquency is markedly increased. Where the age cut-off is 18, as many as one-third of boys in large cities may become identified as delinquents.

Drug-Related Disorders

Related disorders are dependency on drugs (including alcohol and nicotine as well as illicit drugs). While most children dependent on drugs do not have conduct disorders, children with conduct disorders have especially high rates of drug involvement. Onset is typically in adolescence, rather than early childhood, as for conduct disorders. High drug involvement is similar to conduct disorders in being associated with urban residence, being male, and (for illicit drugs) minority group membership. Although drug use in early and later adolescence is the norm rather than the exception, use with sufficient frequency to lead to problems is exceptional, involving probably no more than 2 or 3 percent of adolescents, as reported in the Drug Use Patterns, Consequences and Federal Response: A Policy Review, 1978.

Mental Disorders of School-Age Children

Particularly in younger children, a subgroup can be identified in which overactivity is associated with a serious impairment in attention (hyperkinetic syndrome). Both hyperkinesis and impairments or delays in development are markedly more common in boys than in girls, and may affect up to 10 percent of boys 7 to 10. Developmental disorders of speech and language occur in some 1 to 5 percent of children (rates vary according to the severity levels used); regular bedwetting is present in about 3 percent of children at the age of 10; and reading retardation is found to be present in about 3 to 10 percent of children of normal intelligence.

Mental Disorders of Pre-School Children

Relatively little is known about the prevalence of mental health problems in children under 3 years of age, but emotional disorders and developmental delays do occur in very young children. In many cases the problems in this age group concern parent-child interaction rather than the behavior of the child alone. The most severe example of this is "child battering" (or "nonaccidental injury"). Available figures indicate that, up to the age of 4 years, approximately one child per thousand suffers serious injury initiated by parents each year, and about one in ten of the injuries proves fatal. No reliable figures are available for less serious disorders of parent-child interaction.

Psychotic Disorders of Childhood

Psychotic disorders are far less prevalent in childhood than they are later in life. Autism occurs in about 3 or 4 children out of every 10,000, and functional psychoses such as schizophrenia or manic-depressive disorder are quite rare before adolescence.

Mental Retardation

Severe mental retardation affects about 4 children per 1,000 and mild retardation some 30 per 1,000. While extensive study of mental retardation

SCOPE 40

is not included in the present report, it is important to the area of childhood mental disorders because of the striking association between retardation and mental health problems. These linkages are discussed in the Report of the Liaison Panel on Mental Retardation of the President's Commission on Mental Health.

In discussing the frequency of mental health problems in children, it is important to mention the <u>role of physical problems</u> including epilepsy, organic brain syndromes, sensory impairments, communicable diseases, and systemic physical disorders. Not only are they important problems in their own right but they also tend to occur in association with mental health problems in children and aggravate their course and consequences. Their public health importance is particularly great since, in addition to being widely prevalent, they are amenable to primary prevention through better obstetric care, immunization, and accident prevention.

Course of Mental Disorders in Children

Emotional and mental disorders of childhood are not only a source of considerable suffering to the child and his family, but they are also associated with serious social problems and may be forerunners of serious difficulties in adult life.

Most emotional disorders in young children have a relatively good prognosis. Disorders with onset in adolescence, however, frequently continue as anxiety or depressive conditions in adult life. Conduct disorders tend to run a chronic course and in many cases become personality disorders in adulthood. Followup studies (Robins 1966) show that children with such disorders are liable to have serious difficulties in their social functioning as adults, and often have persisting mental disorder, as well as high rates of crime and alcoholism. Children with the hyperkinetic syndrome also have relatively poor educational attainment and a somewhat increased rate of delinquency, although most cease to be grossly overactive after adolescence. While the number of children actively addicted to drugs and alcohol is small, adult addicts come almost exclusively from the ranks of those who began frequent use of drugs in early adolescence.

Autism is usually associated with handicaps that persist in some form throughout life. However, the prognosis is greatly influenced by whether or not there is associated mental retardation. About one-half the autistic children of normal nonverbal intelligence will eventually be able to hold regular jobs as adults. In contrast, virtually all severely retarded autistic children remain dependent and in need of continuous supervision; many are placed in long term hospital care. Inability to acquire some language by age 5 years is usually associated with poor prognosis for autistic children and lifetime disability.

The great majority of otherwise normal children with specific delays in speed or language usually talk normally by middle or later childhood. However, many of these children go on to have serious difficulties in reading and spelling. In some cases these are associated with emotional or conduct disorders which appear to be a response to the stresses of the learning failure and its concomitants.

Short term followup studies of children who have suffered physical abuse by parents suggest that a higher proportion have learning and behavior problems at school.

Factors Influencing Psychosocial Development

There is extensive literature on causes and correlates of mental disorder in childhood and on factors thought to influence psychosocial development. In summarizing and interpreting this literature it is important to note that the factors responsible for the occurrence of mental health problems of children must be distinguished from those that influence their persistence. For example, the circumstances that predispose children to start taking drugs are probably not the same as those that determine which drug experimenters will develop drug dependence and become habitual abusers.

Biological Factors

Individual differences among children are observed from birth onwards. Children differ in temperamental characteristics and rate of development. Of course, temperament is greatly influenced by the child's experiences and opportunities, but biological factors are also important. Whereas few mental disorders in childhood are inherited as such, genetic factors do play a role through their influence on personality and on vulnerability to environmental stress.

Brain damage or dysfunction (such as indicated by cerebral palsy or epilepsy) has been found greatly to increase the risk of mental health problems. There is good evidence that brain dysfunction is important in its own right as a cause of mental illness, quite apart from the effects of psychosocial stress or disadvantage with which it may be associated, and the intellectual impairment or specific cognitive deficits that may follow it. Chronic physical handicaps are also associated with an increased rate of mental health problems, although the effect is much less than in the case of brain damage. This increased likelihood probably results from some combination of the lack of sensory stimulation, lowered self-esteem, restrictions on physical activities, social ostracism, and stresses associated with recurrent hospital admissions.

Cognitive Factors

Emotional and conduct problems have been found to be relatively common in both mentally retarded children and children with specific disorders of learning or language development. It is probable that several different causal processes are involved in these associations. First, the mental disorders may stem from the same basic factors that led to the cognitive impairment--i.e., the brain damage or the psychosocial deprivation. Second, the risk of poor mental health may stem in part from the experience of school failure. This is suggested both by the fact that the association between cognitive impairment and mental disorder tends to be more marked in relation to children's behavior at school than at home. Thus, alterations in the school environment to aid both the social acceptance and educational functioning of the low-achieving child might bring benefits.

Geographic Distribution and Social Status

Mental health problems in children are more common among those living in inner cities than among those in town or rural areas. It appears that this is due in large part to the higher rates of multiproblem families in inner-city areas. It is not known whether specific features of city life may additionally have adverse effects of family functioning. It is clearly not urbanization per se that is disadvantageous because many medium-sized towns have rates of disorder comparable to those in rural areas; now is it primarily a function of population density or of industrialization, because some industrial areas have relatively low rates of psychosocial disorder. There is an urgent need to identify specific features of city life that may hamper family functioning and predispose to mental disorder. Knowledge on this matter carries the possibility of instituting effective preventive measures. One interesting effort in this direction associates housing design with the ability of parents to supervise school-aged children's activities, and consequently to prevent delinquency.

Other data on mental health aspects of housing are complex and difficult to interpret. While good housing is obviously desirable, epidemiological studies indicate that neither the type of housing nor the extent of household amenities (e.g., bathrooms, kitchen) has a clear association with rates of mental disorders. While there is some association of mental health problems with multiple occupancy dwellings and serious overcrowding, the transfer of families to housing with better physical facilities has shown no consistent benefit for children's mental health.

The association between poverty or low socioeconomic status and the occurrence of mental health problems in children is complex. Since poverty is often the background for a whole cluster of psychosocial phenomena (e.g., unemployment, broken homes, difficult family situations, educational disadvantage, increase rates of delinquency and crime, illegitimate births), it is likely that its effects on child mental health are mediated through those factors rather than through income levels only. If the relief of poverty facilitates family functioning, the mental health benefits of such measures may be substantial. On the other hand, raising the level of income alone does not automatically have this beneficial effect, and there is ample evidence that increased affluence in the higher socioeconomic classes does not necessarily reduce mental health problems of children in those homes.

Patterns of Upbringing

It has been well demonstrated that children's emotional problems are strongly associated with qualities of parent-child interaction. In particular, it is known that when children are reared in homes where there is a lack of conversation exchange, where parents do not interact positively with their children, and where there is a lack of play opportunities, the development of language, intelligence, and scholastic skills is likely to be impaired. This pattern of inadequate parent-child interaction is sometimes discussed in terms of "lack of stimulation" but it is more probably the quality rather than the amount of stimulation that matters. Parents need to be helped to understand that it is not enough to do things to their children; they must do things with them. There is good evidence from numerous studies that there is a very substantially increased rate of mental health problems in children who are unwanted or who experience rejection, hostility, or serious family discord.

At one time it was thought that even temporary separation of a child from his parents inevitably created a serious psychosocial hazard. It is now clear that these arguments were oversimplified. Children do need continuous relationships and secure attachments with a small number of consistent parent figures, but brief separations need not necessarily disrupt these relationships. Good quality day care and a working mother are both compatible with secure parent-child relationships.

Continuity of relationships to parent figures is especially important in the first few years of life. It has been found that the children most at risk are those who experience multiple substitutions of parent figures, such as repeated foster home placement, or those who are reared in institutions where attendants are not given special responsibility for relating consistently to individual children. Thus, there are dangers in delaying the adoption of children abandoned by their parents, in taking children in and out of institutional or foster care, and in an impersonal institutional upbringing where inconsistency of interactional patterns results from a multiplicity of changing caretakers.

Studies of the effects of parental deviance have shown that children brought up by persistent legal offenders or mentally disordered parents show an increased rate of mental health problems. While genetic factors may play some part in this association, it is also clear that the hazards are in considerable part a function of the disturbed patterns of childrearing that often accompany parental mental disorder.

In the past, great attention has been paid to patterns of child care, such as timing of weaning and toilet training and the like. It is now clear that these concerns were largely misplaced. Within quite broad limits, the timing and mechanics of these aspects of child care have little effect on emotional health. On the other hand, the quality of care (in terms of sensitivity and responsiveness to the child's needs), the relationship between the child and those who look after him, and the consistency and efficiency of childrearing methods are of considerable importance. Markedly inconsistent patterns of punishment, repressive or brutal handling, and a lack of concern all increase the risk of mental health problems.

Children reared by very young mothers, and those brought up in nuclear families with very many children are also more likely to show problems. The mechanisms underlying these associations are not well understood. That such families are often poor, that the children are often unwanted, and that there are greater difficulties in childrearing when parents have to divide their time and resources among many children may be pertinent factors.

Very young children frequently experience distress and disturbances as a result of hospital admission. However, it has been shown that the mental health risks can be markedly reduced by encouraging parents to spend time with the child in the hospital and by allowing a parent to be admitted with very young children and stay in the hospital through the course of illness.

Policy Implications

For health service planning it would be helpful to have information not only on the course of psychosocial problems but also on the extent to which psychosocial difficulties are likely to recur in the next and succeeding generations. Studies have shown important links between childhood experiences and behavior as parents in later life. Individuals who suffer rejection and discord during their childhood are more likely when adult to have both marital problems and difficulties in bringing up their own children. A background of seriously abnormal upbringing is often seen in the case of parents who deliberately injure or grossly neglect their offspring. Another group in whom intergenerational continuities are evident is individuals with conduct and personality disorders. Children with conduct disorder who eventually become parents are more likely to have children with similar disorders than are children without such a history.

Although these data show that childhood disorders increase the risk that the individual will have adult disorders and will have disturbed children, it is crucial to note that discontinuities are far more frequent than continuities. Many children with conduct disorders become healthy adults and have healthy children. Contrary to popular belief, most individuals from unhappy homes subsequently have stable marriages. These discontinuities suggest that bad outcomes and transmission of problems from one generation to the next are not inevitable. Research to discover ways of successfully treating these disorders in childhood should get highest priority.

Potential for *prevention* is generally greatest in the early developmental stages of a disorder. Effectiveness is correlated with early detection, early intervention, and the availability of reliable measures that are feasible for implementation.

The concept of developmental review needs to be sharply differentiated from mass screening. Developmental review refers to a process, repeated at meaningful intervals, that is relevant to the individual, comprehensive in approach, and places greatest emphasis on remediation and followthrough. Further, there is emphasis on coordinated delivery of service using family and community supports as well as the traditional services in the health, education, and welfare systems.

A periodic, comprehensive, developmental review should be available to all children with consent of parents and with maximal parental involvement in all stages of the processes. Children not presently eligible under publicly financed programs, should be able to purchase these services.

The existing national program for screening of poverty children, Early and Periodic Screening, Diagnosis and Treatment Program (EPSDT), and its proposed successor, Child Health Assessment Program (CHAP), can benefit from explicit attention to maximizing their potentiality as vehicles of comprehensive assessment and mental health service delivery. The current state of knowledge indicates that a very large number of persons with mental disorder have environmentally linked problems. Much can be done now, and this environmental component should be increasingly amenable to preventive intervention as research progresses in years to come. When properly implemented, a good deal of current knowledge of infancy, childhood, and adolescence can help prevent mental disorders of adult years.

Finally, health service planning depends on as firm a knowledge base as possible of the epidemiology of disorders in children and the assessment of outcomes of treatments and services that are in use.

IX. MENTAL DISORDERS OF THE ELDERLY

Currently there are 23 million people over 65 in the United States. This represents 11 percent of the total population. Every day the ranks of the over 65 have a net increase of 1,000. Most of us have an excellent chance of surviving to well past 65. By the year 2000, according to our best projections of trends, there will be 30 million people over 65, nearly 15 percent of the population of this country.

Most of us can, therefore, expect to experience old age in America. Many elderly persons are capable of living alone and outside institutions. When they have not survived all of their relatives, they could be contributing members of a household. Contrary to popular beliefs, research has shown that old age does not necessarily limit intellectual capacity, sexual activity, or the potential for meaningful work.

There are, however, stresses affecting mental health in old age. These stresses are not unique but they tend to be multiple and pervasive. The elderly are faced with social role changes, personal losses that lead to bereavements, retirement from jobs, drop in income, economic worries, isolation, fear of crime, and concerns about health prospects. They are not unaffected by their plight. The elderly account for 25 percent of all reported suicides although they constitute only 11 percent of the population.

Because of our stereotype of the frail, dependent, incompetent elderly, it is contrary to most expectations to find that 75 percent of the elderly are living in homes. The remaining 25 percent includes 5 percent in nursing homes and 20 percent in other community based care. Individuals residing in nursing homes tend to be largely women and 80 years or over.

Over $30 billion was spent on health care of the elderly in fiscal year 1975, accounting for 30 percent of all national health care expenditures. Per capita, this averaged $1,360, of which almost 70 percent went for hospital and nursing home care.

It is not generally the choice of elderly persons to be institutionalized for years in nursing homes. It is not the best use of our national resources to expend such a high proportion of our health dollars for this kind of care. Practicalities of financing may be compelling a reexamination of policies, both public and private, that have given incentives to continue to keep elderly persons in institutions. In the following section on location of patients, the shift of the elderly from mental institutions to nursing homes will be discussed.

The major mental disorder of old age is senile dementia. This clinical syndrome is characterized by a severe loss of intellectual function and markedly decreased ability to adapt to changes in routine or new experiences. Varying degrees of irrational, bizarre, or paranoid thinking may appear. Severe memory loss is a prominent feature.

This is a diagnosis that is made by exclusion. Geriatrics is not a well-developed specialty in this country and knowledge of geriatric medicine is meager among general practitioners, internists, and other physicians. It is likely, therefore, that "senility" may be misdiagnosed at times and patients are needlessly relegated to institutions or situations in which incompetence is expected and reinforced into a permanent pattern.

The President's Commission on Mental Health has a task panel on the elderly. Their report discusses, at length, the reversible, treatable conditions that can be mistakenly diagnosed as senile dementia. These conditions include depressive symptoms, normal pressure hydrocephalus, infections, pernicious anemia, thyroid changes, nutritional deficiencies, and misuse of drugs.

Despite the possibility of misdiagnosis, it is nevertheless the case that senile dementia is an increasingly common condition as our population of aged persons increases. The population of late stage senile dementia is being further swelled by the medical advances that prevent intercurrent infection and prolong the lives of these patients. It is a very real and very large mental health problem. Senile dementia is a severely disabling condition and it affects millions of our citizens, although there are no exact figures. It is an important problem both in terms of severity of disorder and magnitude of the population affected.

Until recently there has been very little research in this area. Multifaceted research into the biology of the aging brain, the role of the personality and psychological variables of the afflicted individual, and studies of the social conditions of the elderly will begin to yield answers to some of the pressing questions. This is an area of research that has heretofore been neglected but deserves the highest priority and the allocation of research resources should match the importance of the problem.

The elderly are at high risk for misuse of drugs. They use 25 percent of all medications prescribed. Many physicians are unaware of the difference in tolerance to drugs, usually lower, that characterizes the elderly. For this reason, many elderly patients are inadvertently given dosages of medication that can have toxic or side effects including alterations in mental status. There are other hazards for the elderly as well. They may be the recipients of a number of medications from the same or different physicians. There are possible adverse effects from the interactions of these multiple drugs. Finally, when patients are elderly they are often placed on long term medication and the physicians may fail to monitor to be sure that the drug use is decreased or terminated if the condition remits. Many elderly patients are also medicating themselves in similarly adverse ways with over-the-counter medications. Their functioning and mental status may be quite severely affected by drug misuse. This is an area for further medical and epidemiological research.

As was indicated earlier, depression is an important problem for the elderly. It is most prevalent in the isolated elderly in the community or the institutionalized population. Diagnosis of this condition is sometimes overlooked. Effective medication regimens have not been clearly established. The psychopharmacology of the aging brain is not well understood. Until recently, the role of affiliative and supportive structures to help ease the pain of loneliness and helplessness has been minimal. There are models for personal and community supports for the elderly that should be disseminated.

Policy Implications

More research is needed into the causes of brain disorders of the elderly so that preventive measures and less costly treatments can be found. Such research has been meager in relation to the magnitude and severity of the clinical problems.

The proportion of aged persons with chronic mental disorders has been rising for the past 40 years. This trend will continue. Persons with senile and arteriosclerotic dementia who formerly would have died of influenza and pneumonia now live longer because these complications can now be cured.

The number of aged in need of service is the size of the base population at high risk and the proportion that develops the condition requiring service. In view of the demographic estimates, we can expect a heavy burden of senile dementia in the future.

Our society has only begun to face the scope of these problems in the 20th century.

A recent report of the Institute of Medicine opens with this statement (1977):

> Functional dependency among the elderly is emerging as a critical challenge to our society. The functionally dependent elderly are those individuals over 65 whose illnesses, impairments, or social problems have become disabling, reducing their ability to carry out independently the customary activities of daily life.

The report goes on as follows:

> There are valid economic as well as humanitarian reasons for public concern with the functionally dependent elderly. It is in the interest of society as well as the elderly individual to prevent the development of unnecessary dependency or minimize its impact once functional capacity has declined. Meeting the challenge of dependency requires a concentration of society's efforts on those who are at high risk of becoming dependent, such as the recently widowed, in addition to individuals who already are dependent on others for care.
>
> Functional dependency is not exclusively a mental health problem. But the difficulties often involve factors such as isoalation from family, loss of old friends, and lack of access to community support systems that can lead to emotional distress, depression, and, at times, hasten the onset of senile dementia.
>
> The need for integration of health and social services is no where so clear or so urgent as in the care of the elderly. New institutions, new

models of service, and creative new ways of mobilizing youth in the service of their elders can contribute to meeting the needs of the elderly, probably at less expense, and certainly with more respect for their own preferences and their dignity in planning for the future. The mental health system must pay attention to this great social problem in its allocations for research, services, and training efforts.

X. LOCATION OF PATIENTS

Introduction

During the year 1975, an estimated 15 percent of the population of the United States was in need of mental health services (Regier et al. 1976, in press). Of this number, 15 percent were under care of the specialty mental health sector; 3.4 percent were under care of the general hospital and nursing home sector; 54.1 percent were under care of the primary care medical sector; and 6 percent were under care in both the primary care medical sector and the specialty mental health sector. Another 21.5 percent of these persons were either receiving some assistance or services from the other human services sector or not receiving services at all.

Unfortunately, data are not available to differentiate between the number of persons with mental disorders who receive no health or mental health treatment, and those who may be in correctional institutions, and those who are served by family service agencies, religious counselors and other social welfare agencies outside the usually defined health arena. This is a critical area for research. The above data are presented in the appendix table 1* and figure 1.

Rank ordered, the number of persons seen in each type of setting emphasizes the large numbers of persons served by nonpsychiatric physicians and in other types of nonpsychiatric settings:

Type of Setting	Total No. of Persons
1. Office based primary care physicians[1]	10,710,000
2. General hospital outpatient and emergency rooms	6,391,000
3. Other office based nonprimary care physicians	2,337,000
4. Free-standing psychiatric outpatient and multiservice clinics	1,763,000
5. Community mental health centers	1,627,000
6. Health department clinics	941,000
7. Non-Federal general hospitals with psychiatric units	927,000
8. Office based private practice psychiatrists	854,000
9. Non-Federal general hospitals without separate psychiatric units	812,000
10. State and county mental hospitals	789,000
11. Private practice psychologists	425,000
12. VA - psychiatric units of general and neuropsychiatric hospitals	351,000
13. Community (Neighborhood) Health Centers	314,000
Industrial Health Units	314,000

*All tables are to be found in the appendix and all figures in the text.

[1] This is generally taken to include family practitioners, general practitioners, internists, pediatricians, and obstetricians/gynecologists.

SCOPE 51

Type of Setting	Total No. of Persons
14. Private mental hospitals and residential treatment centers	233,000
15. Nursing homes	207,000
16. College campus mental health clinics	131,000
17. Federal general hospitals (excludes psychiatric units of VA hospitals)	59,000
18. Nonpsychiatric specialty hospitals	22,000
19. Halfway houses for the mentally ill	7,000

It must be emphasized that there are considerable differences between the diagnostic characteristics of the groups of patients seen in these different settings: For example, patients who come to nonpsychiatric physicians are more likely to present problems associated with anxiety and depression, personality disorders, and psychophysiologic problems. Persons with more severe disorders, such as schizophrenia, major affective disorders, organic brain syndromes, and other severe mental disorders requiring intensive specialized therapies are more likely to come under care of inpatient services in the mental health sector. Persons under care of outpatient services in the mental health sector present a broader spectrum of the mental disorders, with variations depending upon the admission policies of the clinic, its relationship to the mental hospitals serving the community, and referral practices of physicians, local public health and social agencies.

Appendix table 1 underscores the fact that the largest number of persons under care in the specialty mental health sector in 1975 occurs in the freestanding outpatient clinics and community mental health centers. This represents a significant shift in the locus of care of patients in this sector over the past 20 years. In 1955, the year in which the resident patient population of the State and county mental hospitals was at its maximum, 77 percent of services were provided in inpatient settings and only 23 percent in outpatient settings (appendix table 2 and figure 2). In 1975, this situation was reversed, with 76 percent of the services being provided in outpatient settings and only 24 percent in inpatient settings. In this latter instance, the most significant reduction occurred in the inpatient services of State mental hospitals which provided 49 percent of all services in 1955 and only 9 percent in 1975.

Trends and Patterns of Use of Mental Health Services

Detailed data on the characteristics of patients under care of all of the facilities described in table 1 are not available. However, a considerable amount of systematic data have been collected by NIMH over the years on the patterns of use of the major mental health facilities. These data will be used to present a quantitative description of trends that have occurred. But first, a review of events that have played a major role in bringing about changes in the delivery of mental health services will be given.

FIGURE 1

ESTIMATED PERCENT DISTRIBUTION OF PERSONS WITH MENTAL DISORDER, BY TREATMENT SETTING, UNITED STATES, 1975

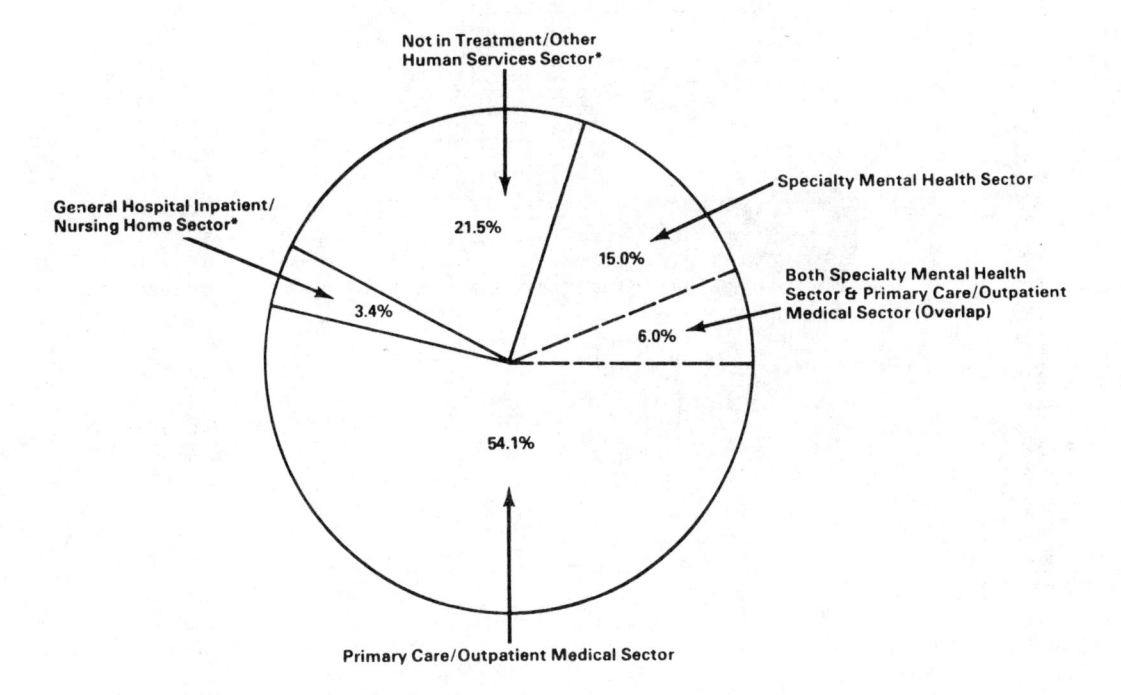

- Not in Treatment/Other Human Services Sector* — 21.5%
- Specialty Mental Health Sector — 15.0%
- Both Specialty Mental Health Sector & Primary Care/Outpatient Medical Sector (Overlap) — 6.0%
- General Hospital Inpatient/Nursing Home Sector* — 3.4%
- Primary Care/Outpatient Medical Sector — 54.1%

Note: Data relating to sectors other than the specialty mental health sector reflect the number of patients with mental disorder seen in those sectors without regard to the amount or adequacy of treatment provided.

* Excludes overlap of an unknown percent of persons also seen in other sectors.

FIGURE 2
PERCENT DISTRIBUTION OF INPATIENT AND OUTPATIENT CARE EPISODES
IN MENTAL HEALTH FACILITIES, BY TYPE OF FACILITY: UNITED STATES
1955 AND 1975[2]

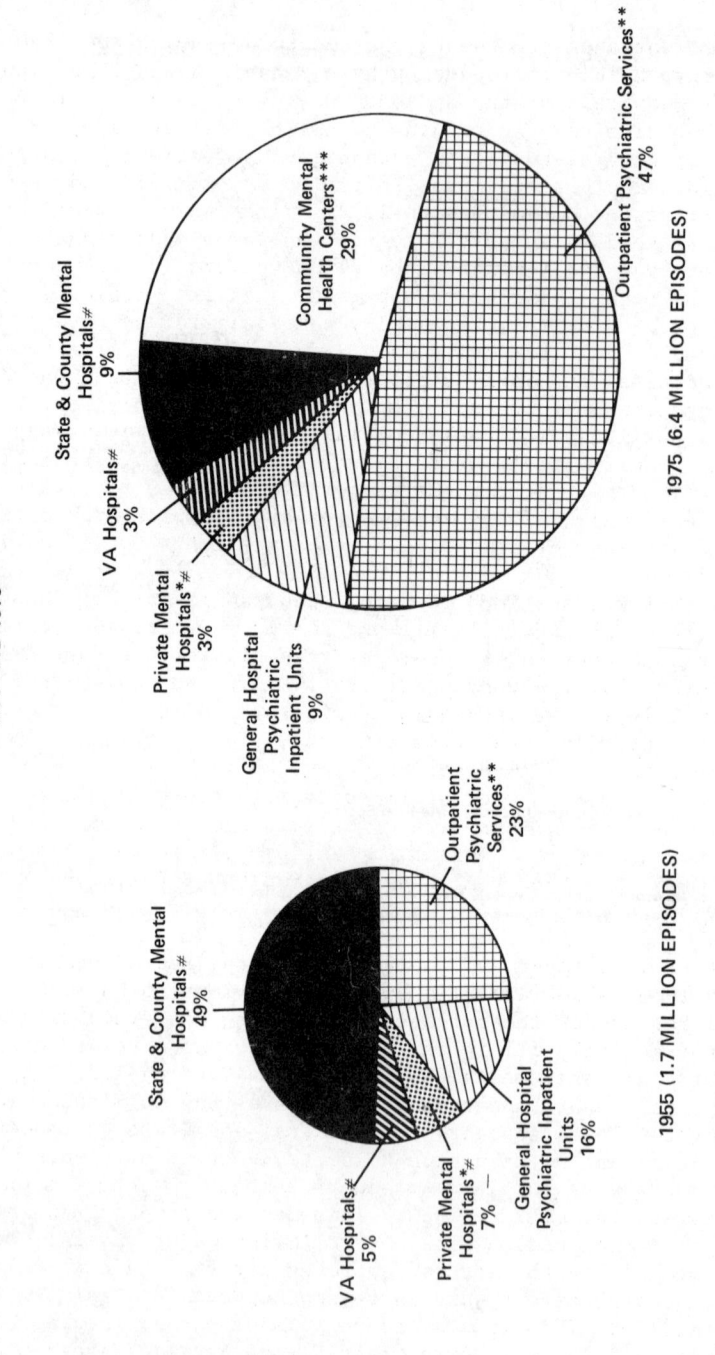

1975 (6.4 MILLION EPISODES)

- Outpatient Psychiatric Services** 47%
- Community Mental Health Centers*** 29%
- State & County Mental Hospitals# 9%
- VA Hospitals# 3%
- Private Mental Hospitals*# 3%
- General Hospital Psychiatric Inpatient Units 9%

1955 (1.7 MILLION EPISODES)

- Outpatient Psychiatric Services** 23%
- State & County Mental Hospitals# 49%
- VA Hospitals# 5%
- Private Mental Hospitals*# 7%
- General Hospital Psychiatric Inpatient Units 16%

* Includes residential treatment centers for emotionally disturbed children
\# Inpatient services only
** Includes free-standing outpatient services as well as those affiliated with psychiatric and general hospitals
*** Includes inpatient and outpatient services of federally funded CMHC's

SCOPE 54

Background

Of particular importance are events that occurred during the 1950's and 1960's which were responsible for reducing by a sizable amount the population of the State mental hospitals of the Nation. During these years, increasing numbers of outpatient clinics were opened (Bahn 1961; Kramer 1966, 1967) and increasing numbers of general hospitals established outpatient units for psychiatric patients (Glasscote and Kannon 1965; Giesler, Hurley, and Person 1966; National Institute of Mental Health 1972). Increasing numbers of nursing homes were established which served to relieve the pressure on the State mental hospitals for beds for the aged. Many innovations in treatment and rehabilitation of the mentally ill also appeared, such as: intensive activity programing, "total push," for the chronically hospitalized and intensive treatment of the acutely ill (Galioni, Adams, and Tallman 1953); group psychotherapy, the open hospital and various programs for counteracting the dehumanizing effect of long term institutionalization in the impersonal environment of the large mental hospitals (Milbank Memorial Fund 1958). There had also been exposes of the shameful state of affairs in many of the large State institutions (Deutsch 1948). All of these happenings did much to develop an attitude among professionals, lawmakers, and the public which seemed to demand that society change its ways of providing care of its mentally ill citizens.

A major event that was destined to bring about still further changes in programs for the care of the mentally ill and the locus where such care would be provided was the introduction of the major tranquilizers in the early 1950's (Cole and Gerard 1959; Efron et al. 1968; Klein and Davis 1969; Gallant and Simpson 1976). The increasingly widespread use of psychoactive drugs since 1955, in inpatient and outpatient care of the mentally ill and, indeed, in all aspects of medical practice, provided much of the impetus for accelerating the pace of development of improved methods for the care, treatment, and rehabilitation of persons with mental disorders and in the development of community mental health programs for the prevention and control of these disorders (American Public Health Association 1962; Felix 1967; Mechanic 1969; Lieberman 1975).

Another event of importance was the passage of the Mental Health Study Act by Congress in 1955, which established the Joint Commission on Mental Illness and Mental Health for the purpose of analyzing and evaluating needs and resources of the mentally ill in the United States as a basis for making recommendations for a national mental healh program (P.L. 84-182,1955). Consideration of the final report and recommendations of the Commission (Joint Commission 1961) by top level groups within Federal and State governments and by various professional and citizen groups led to a series of events which culminated in the message of the late President Kennedy to Congress on Mental Illness and Retardation in Feburary 1963. This message proposed an intensified national program for mental health with the following major facets: comprehensive community mental health centers, improved care in State mental institutions, expanded research effort, and increased support for training manpower for research and service. This led to the next major event, the passage by Congress, in October 1963, of the Mental Retardation Facilities and Community Mental Health Centers Construction Act (P.L. 88-164, 1963). This law and similar ones enacted by various States (Alcohol, Drug Abuse, Mental Health Administration 1976) stimulated the development of programs that accelerated the shift in the primary locus of care of the mentally ill from State hospitals to facilities located in the community. In effect, these programs have discouraged the use of State hospitals for the treatment and rehabilitation of persons with mental disorders by encouraging the creation and use of community mental health centers and other community based services for these purposes (Hersch 1972; Arnhoff 1975; Greenblatt and Glazier 1975; Becker and Schulberg 1976). These programs have also discouraged the use of mental hospitals for aged patients with chronic brain syndromes associated with cerebral arteriosclerosis and senile brain disease by encouraging the use of nursing homes and other facilities for such patients (Kramer, Taube, and Starr 1968; Kramer, Taube, and Redick 1973; National Center for Health Statistics 1974).

Changes in the Population of State Mental Hospitals

The dramatic drop in the resident patient population of the State mental hospitals is shown in appendix table 3 and figure 3. The number of residents at the end of 1975 (191,391) was 34 percent of the number at the end of 1955 (558,922), the year in which the mental hospital population was at its highest level.

Appendix table 4 shows the changes in the age specific resident patient rates between 1965-1975. Decreases have occurred in all age groups, with that in the older age groups being more pronounced. An important change has taken place in the rates for the age group under 15 years. In the years prior to 1972, these rates were increasing steadily. Since that time they have tended to decrease.

Appendix table 5 shows the extraordinary change that has taken place in the role of mental hospitals--State and county, V.A. and private--in providing services to the aged mentally ill. The nursing home has steadily replaced these facilities as the primary locus for the care of these persons. In 1969, 56 percent of persons 65 years and over with a mental disorder--resident in either a mental hospital or nursing home--were in mental hospitals, and 44 percent in nursing homes. By 1973, the corresponding proportions were 29 percent and 71 percent, respectively.

Figure 5 and appendix table 6 show the changes in the age specific first admission rates to State and county mental hospitals for the years 1946, 1955, and 1962 to 1975. Between 1962 and 1969, the rates of the age groups under 65 years of age tended to increase. Between 1969 and 1975, these rates declined except for those in the age group under 15 years, which tended to increase. In contrast, the rates for the age group 65 years and over declined sharply over the entire period from 163.7 per 100,000 in 1962 to 36.7 per 100,000 in 1975, a decrease of 78 percent.

Appendix table 7 shows the changes in diagnostic composition of first admissions to State and county mental hospitals between the years 1946 and 1972. Decreases have occurred in organic brain syndromes (excluding alcohol and drug abuse), from 44 percent to 10 percent; schizophrenia, from 19 percent to 14 percent; and other psychoses (essentially all affective disorders), from 14 percent to 3 percent. The increase in alcoholic admissions is very

SCOPE 56

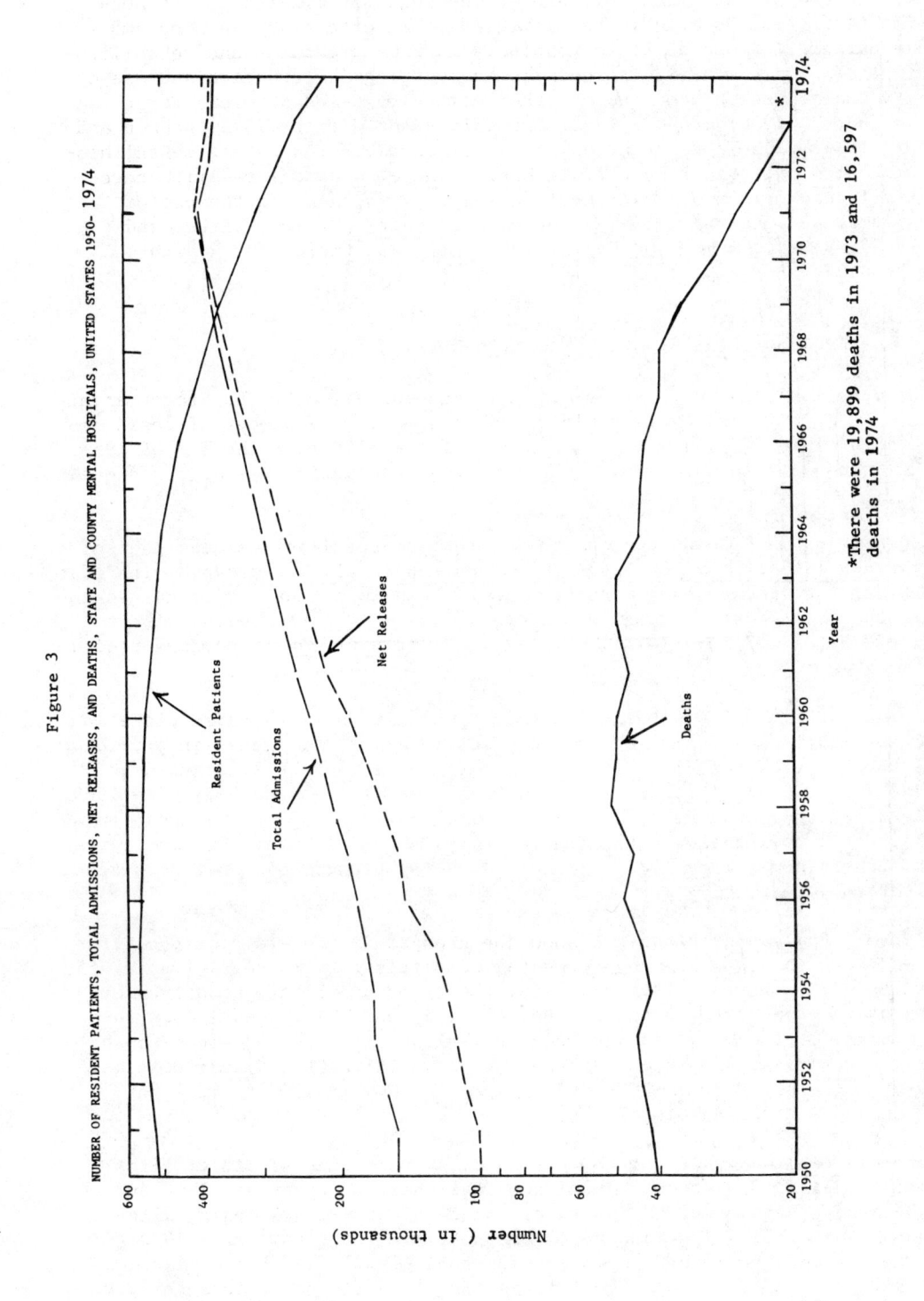

Figure 3

NUMBER OF RESIDENT PATIENTS, TOTAL ADMISSIONS, NET RELEASES, AND DEATHS, STATE AND COUNTY MENTAL HOSPITALS, UNITED STATES 1950-1974

*There were 19,899 deaths in 1973 and 16,597 deaths in 1974

SCOPE 57

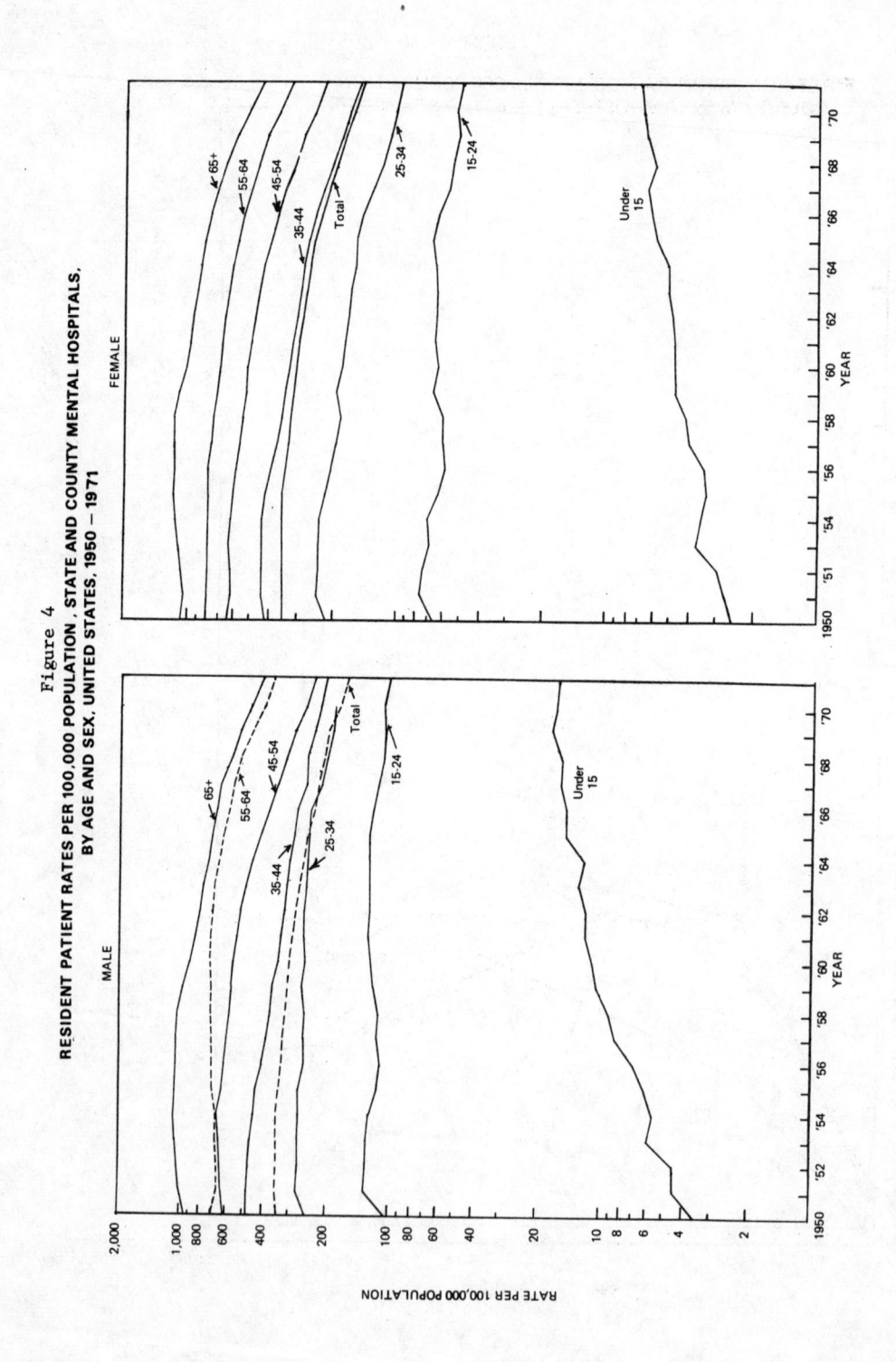

Figure 4
RESIDENT PATIENT RATES PER 100,000 POPULATION, STATE AND COUNTY MENTAL HOSPITALS, BY AGE AND SEX, UNITED STATES, 1950 – 1971

FIGURE 5

FIRST ADMISSION RATIOS PER 100,000 POPULATION BY AGE, STATE AND COUNTY MENTAL HOSPITALS, UNITED STATES, 1946, 1955 AND 1972

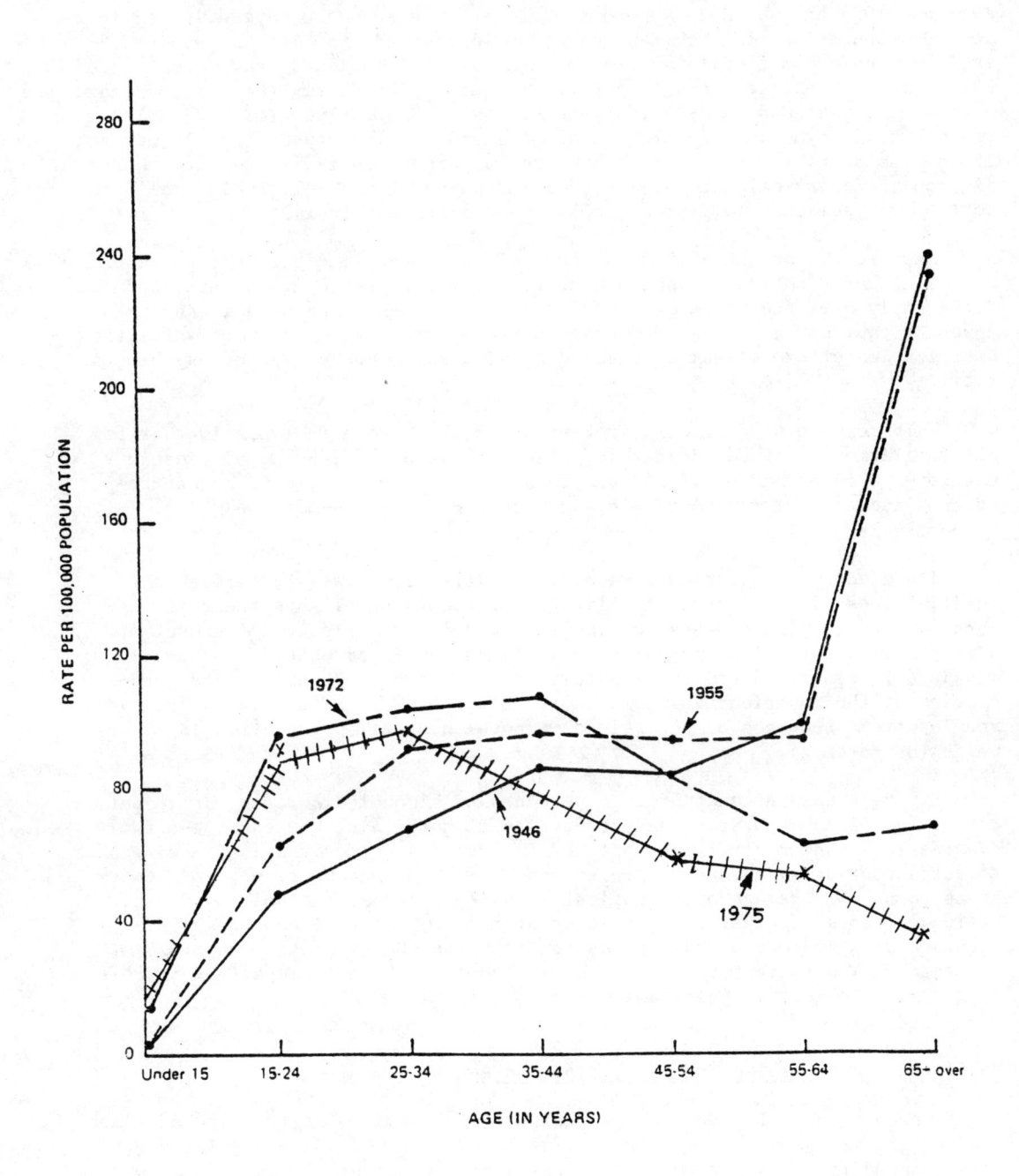

pronounced, 9 percent to 26 percent; as are the increases in psychoneuroses, 4 percent to 12 percent; personality disorders, 2 percent to 11 percent; and drug abuse, 1 percent to 7 percent.

Changes in the diagnostic composition of the resident patients between 1955 and 1973 are shown in appendix table 8. The resident patient rates (per 100,000 population) for schizophrenia have decreased from 165 in 1955 to 59 in 1973, and organic brain syndromes (excluding alcohol and drug) from 85 to 23. Nevertheless, schizophrenia still accounted for nearly the same percent of resident patients in 1973 (49 percent) as it did in 1955 (48 percent). Organic brain syndromes (excluding alcohol and drug) accounted for 19 percent of the residents in 1973, as compared to 25 percent in 1955. Depsite their high admission rates, alcohol disorders accounted for a relatively small proportion of residents (6 percent in 1973 and 3 percent in 1955).

As a result of the shifts in locus of care described earlier, patients with different demographic and diagnostic characteristics are distributed differently over the range of psychiatric facilities. The details shown in appendix tables 9 and 10, and figures 6 and 7 demonstrate, respectively, the distribution of admissions by age and by diagnosis and by type of psychiatric facility.

With respect to diagnosis, for example, it is seen in table 10 that for all facilities combined, depressive disorders were the leading diagnostic category, accounting for 18 percent of all admissions, followed by schizophrenia and alcohol disorders, 16 and 9 percent of all admissions, respectively.

The diagnostic distributions differed markedly, however, between the various types of psychiatric facilities. Figure 7 highlights these differences. For example, depressive disorders accounted for only 13 percent of admissions to outpatient psychiatric services and 12 percent of total admissions in State and county hospitals, but for a considerably higher proportion of the inpatient episodes in private mental hospitals (43 percent) and inpatient services of non-Federal general hospital psychiatric inpatient units (38 percent).

Schizophrenia accounts for 34 percent and alcohol disorders for 28 percent of admissions to State and county mental hospitals, whereas these two disorders accounted for 11 percent and 4 percent, respectively, of admissions to outpatient services and 24 percent and 7 percent, respectively, of admissions to non-Federal general hospital inpatient psychiatric units. Organic brain syndromes (exclusive of brain syndromes with alcohol and drugs) accounted for 5 percent of admissions to State and county mental hospitals, 2 percent to outpatient clinics, and 4 percent of those to inpatient psychiatric units in general hospitals.

Variations in Admissions Rates by Race and Age

Appendix table 11 shows the distribution of admissions to selected mental health facilities by race and age during 1975. For the white population the rates ranged from 936 per 100,000 in the age group under 18 years to a maximum

FIGURE 6
PERCENT DISTRIBUTION OF ADMISSIONS BY AGE BY SELECTED
TYPE OF MENTAL HEALTH FACILITY, UNITED STATES, 1975

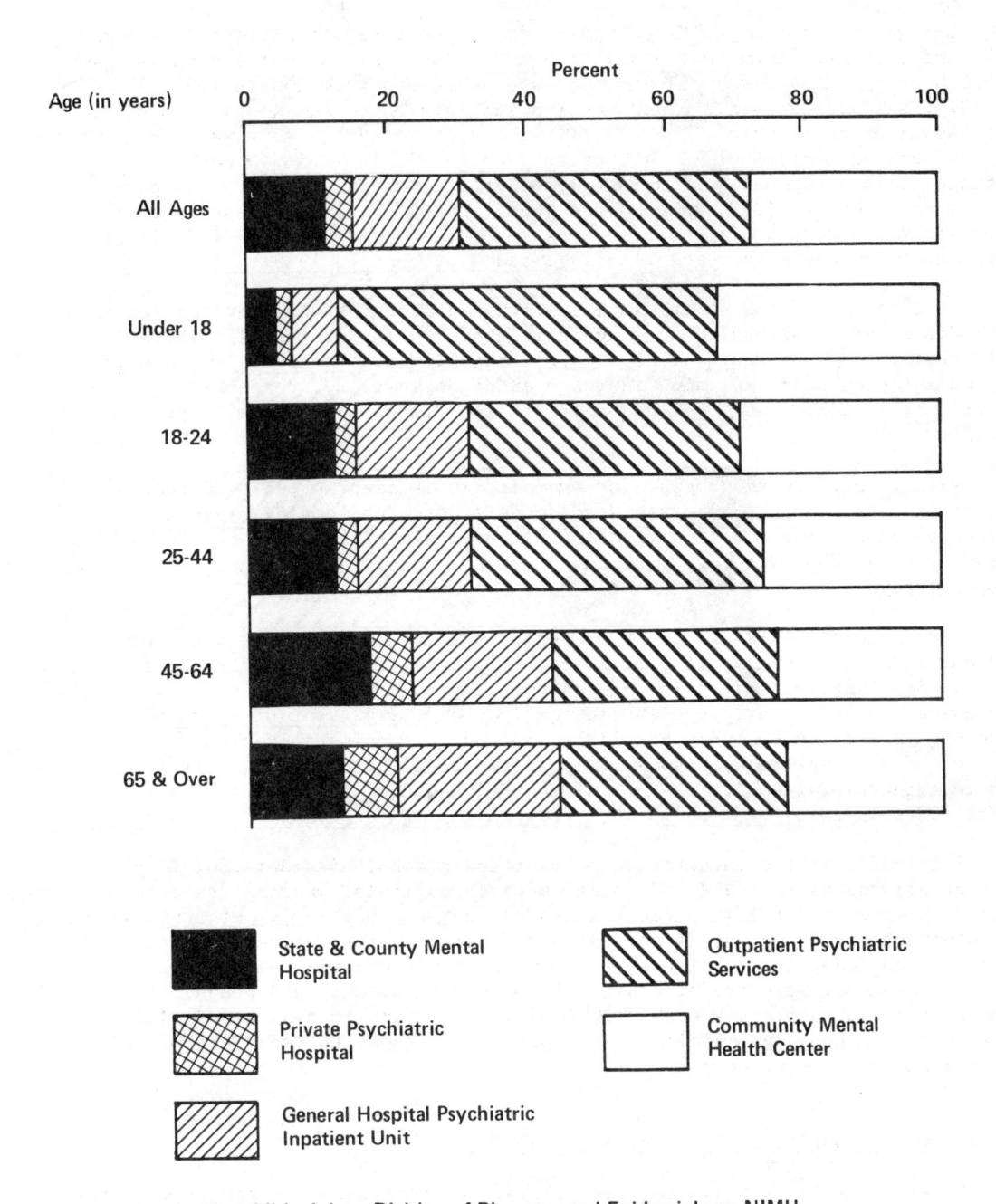

Legend:
- State & County Mental Hospital
- Private Psychiatric Hospital
- General Hospital Psychiatric Inpatient Unit
- Outpatient Psychiatric Services
- Community Mental Health Center

Source: Unpublished data, Division of Biometry and Epidemiology, NIMH

SCOPE 61

FIGURE 7
PERCENT DISTRIBUTION OF ADMISSIONS BY MENTAL DISORDER BY SELECTED TYPE OF MENTAL HEALTH FACILITIES. UNITED STATES, 1975

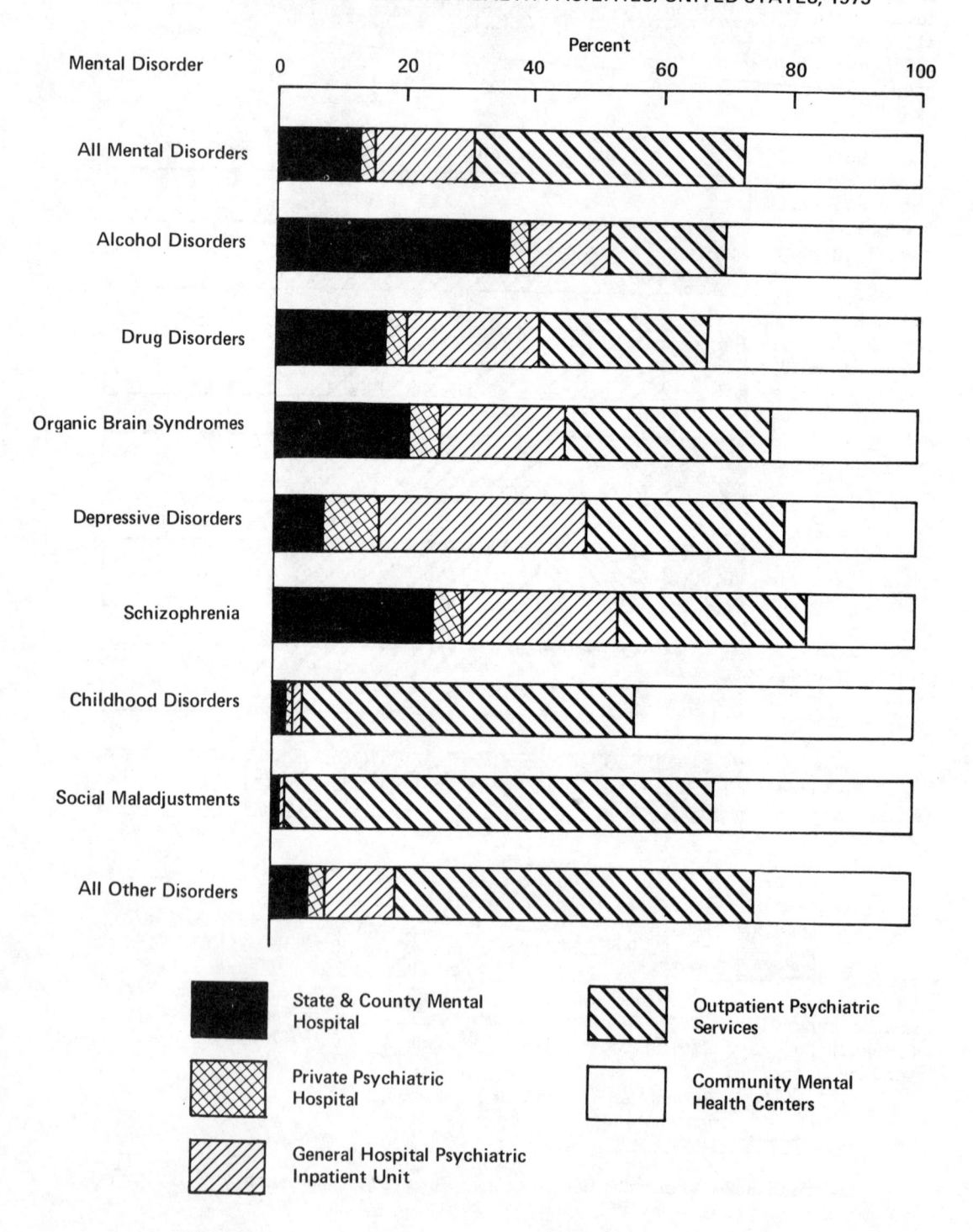

Source: Unpublished data, Division of Biometry and Epidemiology, NIMH

of 2,436 per 100,000 in the age group 25-44, and then decreased to their lowest value per 100,000 in the age group 65 years and over. The rates for all other races follow a similar pattern but at a higher level, ranging from 1,258 per 100,000 in the age group under 18 to a maximum of 3,494 in the age group 25-44, and to their lowest value of 978 in the age group 65 years and over.

The total rate for all other races (2,010 per 100,000) is 1.3 times, or 30 percent higher than that for whites (1,523 per 100,000), and is consistently higher than the white rate in every age group, varying from 1.2 times the white rate in the 18-24 years age group to 1.4 times the white rate in the age groups 25-44 and 65 years and over.

Appendix table 12 presents the age adjusted admission rates to specific types of mental health facilities specific for race and sex. Males of all other races have considerably higher admission rates than white males to all types of facilities, with two exceptions: private mental hospitals and non-public, non-Federal general hospitals to which the rate for white males (57 and 142 per 100,000 respectively) is higher than that for males of other races (40 and 111 per 100,000, respectively). The admission rate to State and county mental hospitals for males of all other races (477 per 100,000) is 2.2 times higher than that for white males (213 per 100,000).

A similar pattern holds for the females of all other races. The admission rates to the State and county mental hospitals for females of all other races (226 per 100,000) is 2.1 times higher than that of white females (110 per 100,000).

Within racial groups, the admission rate for white males to State and county mental hospitals is 1.9 times that of the white females and to non-Federal general public hospitals 1.1 times that of white females. The admission rates to all other services are higher for females.

Among persons of all other races, males have the higher admission rate to State and county hospitals (2.1 times that of the females), and community mental health centers (1.1 times the female rates). For private mental hospitals there is no difference in male and female rates (1.03 vs. .80).

The task panel urges the Commission to review the above data in relation to their implications for developing policy related to such issues: (1) socioeconomic, attitudinal, and geographical factors that account for differential patterns of use of specific types of facilities within and among various subgroups of our population; (2) the effectiveness and efficiency of services rendered in different types of facilities; (3) methods of payment for services; (4) manpower needs; (5) gaps in services; and (6) relationships of psychiatric facilities to each other, as well as to other human service agencies.

The Total Institutional Population

The task panel recommends that the Commission consider the implications of the effect changes in the locus of mental health services have had on the populations of other institutions which collectively constitute the institutional population of the Nation (as defined by the Bureau of the Census). These institutions are:

1. correctional institutions (prisons, reformatories, local jails, and work houses)

2. mental institutions (mental hospitals and residential treatment centers for emotionally disturbed children)

3. tuberculosis hospitals

4. chronic disease hospitals

5. homes for aged and dependent (includes homes with and without nursing care)

6. homes and schools for mentally handicapped

7. homes and schools for physically handicapped

8. homes for dependent and neglected children

9. homes for unwed mothers

10. training schools for juvenile delinquents

11. detention homes

The series of figures and tables for this section show the change and, in some instances, lack of change, that has taken place between 1950 and 1970 in the numbers and proportion of the population in different types of institutions specific for age, race, and sex. Unfortunately, data for 1970 are the most recent available on persons in institutions by type of institution, age, race, sex, and other sociodemographic factors. Such data are published in conjunction with each decennial census and will not become available again until the 1980 census.

Changes in the institutional population, 1950 to 1970, figure 8 and appendix table 13, show the resident rates, i.e., the number of persons per 100,000 population in different types of institutions in 1950 and 1970.[2]

Overall, there was a slight increase in the rate for all institutions combined (from 1,035 to 1,047 per 100,000). Sizable decreases occurred in resident rates for two classes of institutions--a 47 percent decrease for mental institutions (from 405 to 214 per 100,000), and an 84 percent decrease

---

[2] The actual census populations as enumerated in 1950, 1960, and 1970 have been used in the computation of these rates. Adjustment of the rates presented in this paper for underenumeration of the population would reduce the differences by age-sex-race noted in this paper, but would not account for the major differences observed.

FIGURE 8

DISTRIBUTION OF PERSONS IN INSTITUTIONS PER 100,000 POPULATION BY TYPE OF INSTITUTION, BOTH SEXES, UNITED STATES, 1950 AND 1970

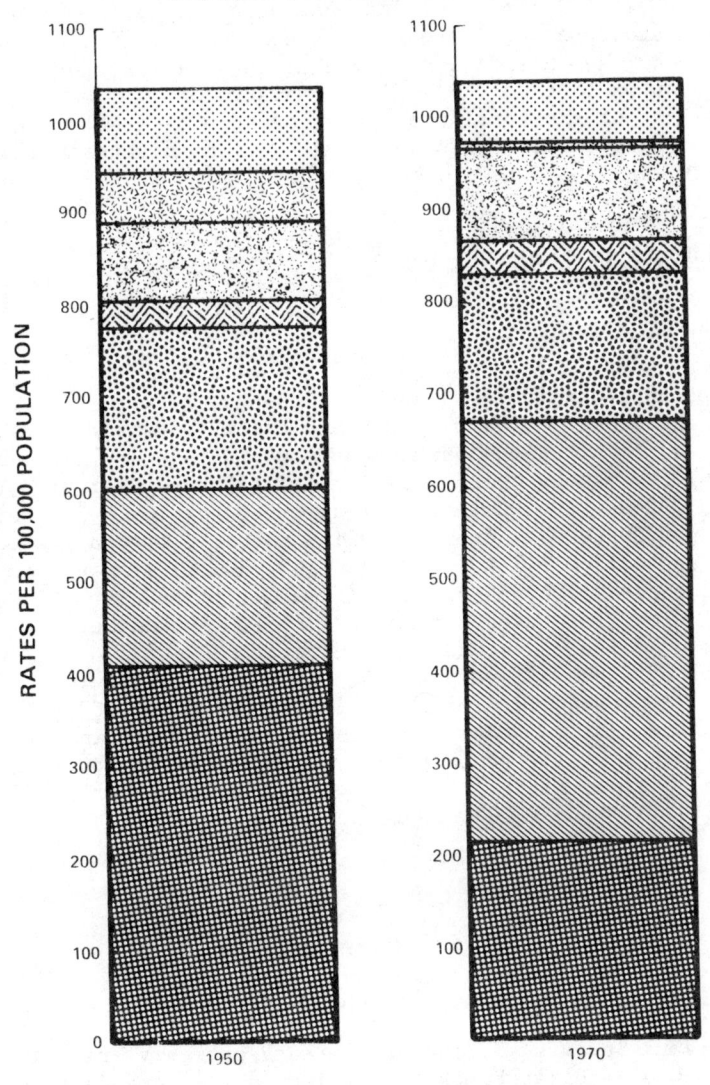

BOTH SEXES, TOTAL

- MENTAL INSTITUTIONS
- HOME FOR THE AGED & DEPENDENT
- CORRECTIONAL INSTITUTIONS
- TRAINING SCHOOLS FOR JUVENILE DELINQUENTS
- HOMES & SCHOOLS FOR MENTALLY HANDICAPPED
- T.B. HOSPITALS
- ALL OTHER

SOURCE: U.S. BUREAU OF THE CENSUS, PERSONS IN INSTITUTIONS, 1950 & 1970

SCOPE 65

in hospitals for the tuberculous (from 50 to 8 per 100,000). There was an 8 percent decrease in the rate for correctional institutions (from 175 to 161 per 100,000). A 38 percent increase occurred in the resident rate of training schools for juvenile delinquents (from 24 to 33 per 100,000), and an 11 percent increase in homes and schools for the mentally handicapped (from 89 to 99 per 100,000). A 133 percent increase occurred in the population of homes for the aged and dependent (from 196 to 456 per 100,000).[3] The trends in the composition of the institutional population varied markedly by race and sex. This is shown in figure 9, which demonstrates the changes that occurred in the percent of the total population of each race-sex group in institutions by type of institution.[4] These trends will be discussed in detail in the following sections.

Changes Specific for Age, Sex, and Color

Persons Under 20 Years of Age

Figure 10 and appendix table 14 show the changes between 1950 and 1970 in rates for persons under 20 years by sex and color. Striking changes occurred in the rates of white and nonwhite persons in this age group for all institutions combined. Among white males, the total rate decreased by 21 percent (from 545 to 432 per 100,000), and among white females by 39 percent (from 390 to 239 per 100,000). Among nonwhite males, the total rates increased by 56 percent (from 641 to 1,003 per 100,000), and among nonwhite females the rates increased by 14 percent (from 301 to 342 per 100,000). The differences in level of rates between the races is considerable. Thus, the 1970 rate for nonwhite males under 20 years (1,003 per 100,000) was 2.3 times that for white males (432 per 100,000), and that for nonwhite females (342 per 100,000) 1.4 times that for white females (239 per 100,000). The 1970 rates for nonwhite males under 20 years in correctional institutions (285 per 100,000) and training schools for juvenile delinquents (333 per 100,000) are 5 and 4 times higher, respectively, than the corresponding rates for white males (52 and 81 per 100,000 respectively).

---

[3] The institutions included in the "all other" category are: detention homes, homes for unwed mothers, homes for neglected and dependent children, chronic disease hospitals, and homes and schools for the physically handicapped. The reader who is interested in the trends of specific institutions in this group is referred to appendix table 2, where age-sex-race specific rates for each type of institution are given, in Psychiatric Services and the Changing Institutional Scene, 1950-1985, DHEW Publication No. (ADM) 77-433, 1977.

[4] The detailed data by sex and color on which figure 9 is based are given in appendix table 14.

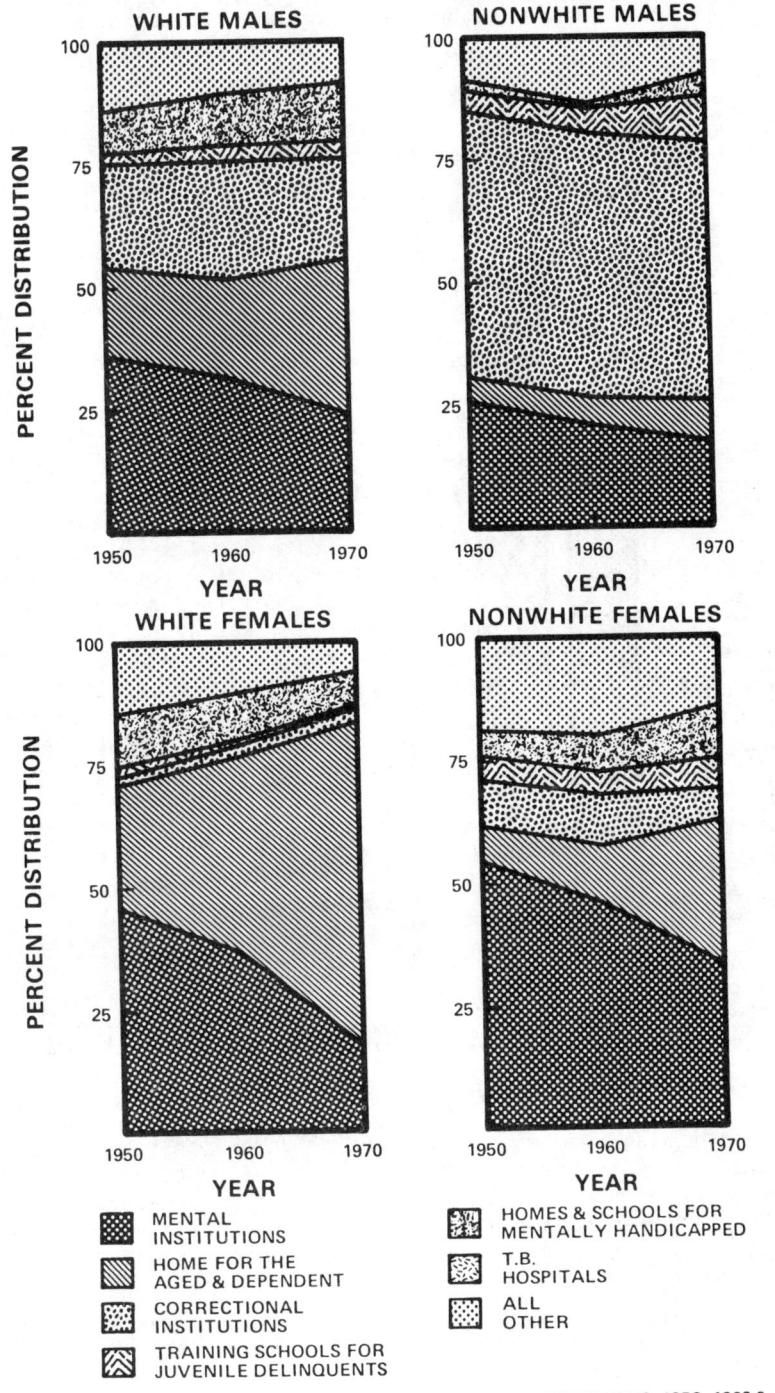

FIGURE 9
PERCENT DISTRIBUTION OF PERSONS IN INSTITUTIONS BY TYPE OF INSTITUTION, BY SEX AND COLOR, UNITED STATES, 1950, 1960, AND 1970

Legend:
- MENTAL INSTITUTIONS
- HOME FOR THE AGED & DEPENDENT
- CORRECTIONAL INSTITUTIONS
- TRAINING SCHOOLS FOR JUVENILE DELINQUENTS
- HOMES & SCHOOLS FOR MENTALLY HANDICAPPED
- T.B. HOSPITALS
- ALL OTHER

SOURCE: U.S. BUREAU OF THE CENSUS, PERSONS IN INSTITUTIONS, 1950, 1960 & 1970

SCOPE 67

FIGURE 10
DISTRIBUTION OF PERSONS IN INSTITUTIONS PER 100,000 POPULATION BY TYPE OF INSTITUTION, BY SEX AND COLOR, AGE UNDER 20 YEARS, UNITED STATES, 1950 AND 1970

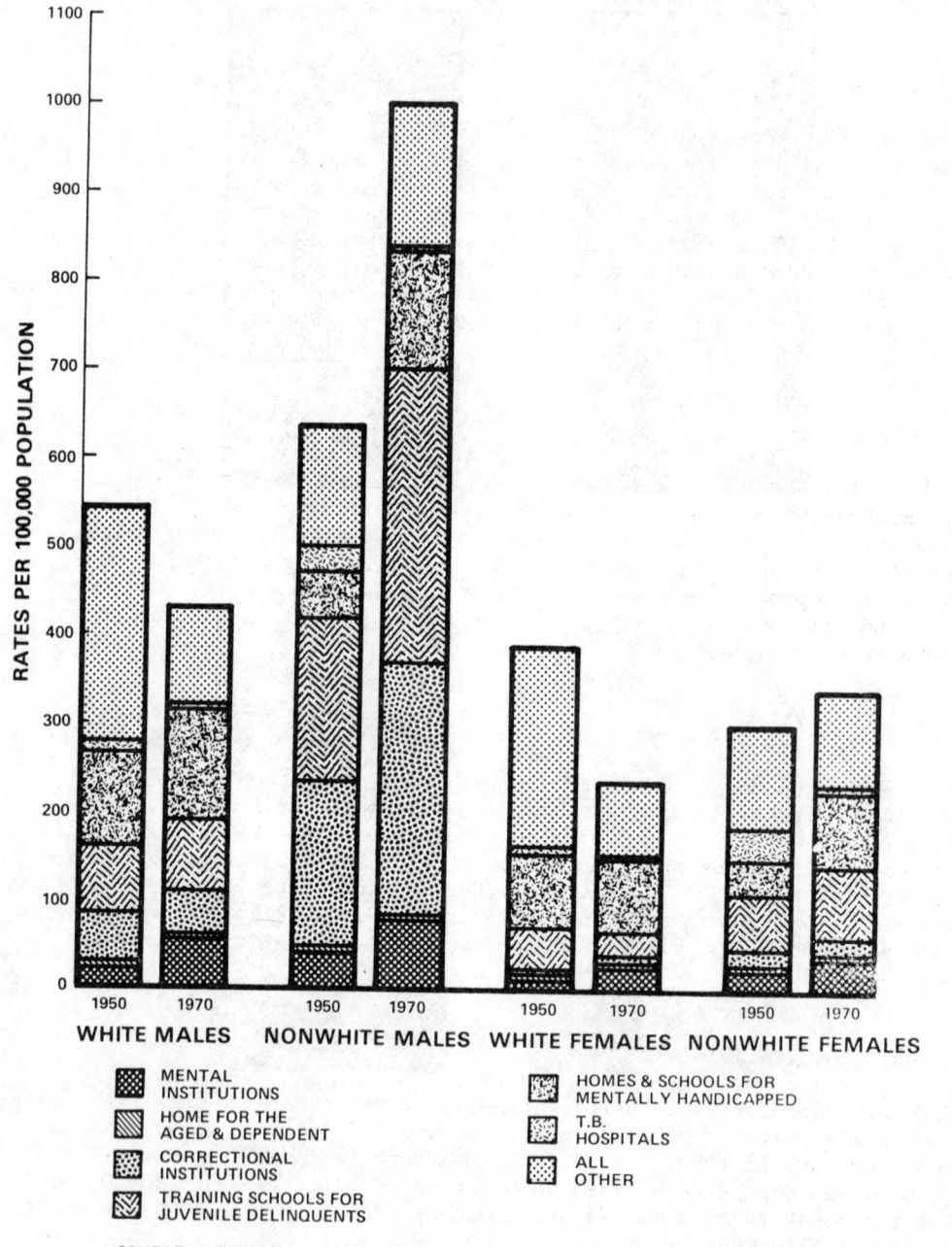

Legend:
- MENTAL INSTITUTIONS
- HOME FOR THE AGED & DEPENDENT
- CORRECTIONAL INSTITUTIONS
- TRAINING SCHOOLS FOR JUVENILE DELINQUENTS
- HOMES & SCHOOLS FOR MENTALLY HANDICAPPED
- T.B. HOSPITALS
- ALL OTHER

SOURCE: U.S. BUREAU OF THE CENSUS, PERSONS IN INSTITUTIONS, 1950 & 1970

SCOPE 68

Persons 20 Years of Age and Over

Figure 12 and appendix table 14 show the changes that occurred between 1950 and 1970 in rates for different institutions in persons 20 years and over, by sex and color. (Figure 11 has been deleted.)

All Institutions

Between 1950 and 1970, the total institutionalization rate for white males 20 years and over decreased by 9 percent (from 1,501 to 1,363 per 100,000), and that for nonwhite males increased by 5 percent (from 2,929 to 3,078 per 100,000). The rates for white females increased by 37 percent (from 1,034 to 1,419 per 100,000), and those for nonwhite females decreased 6 percent (950 to 897 per 100,000). The relative differences between the rates for white and nonwhite persons 20 years and over in 1970 were considerable: The rate for nonwhite males was 2.3 times that for white males, while the rate for the white females was 1.6 times that of nonwhite females.

Mental Institutions

Between 1950 and 1970, the rates declined for each of the sex-color groups. However, the relative decrease was greater for white males (46 percent) and white females (53 percent) than for nonwhite males and females (25 percent and 42 percent, respectively). As of 1970, the rate for nonwhite males (621 per 100,000) was 1.8 times that for white males (342 per 100,000), and for nonwhite females (355 per 100,000), 1.4 times that for white females (254 per 100,000).

Homes for the Aged and Dependent

The 1970 rates for each color-sex group were considerably higher than those in 1950. The 1970 rates for white and nonwhite females were, respectively, 3.26 and 4.43 times their corresponding rates in 1950. The rate for white males was 1.7 times and that for nonwhite males 2.23 times their corresponding rates for 1950. As of 1970, the rate for white males (525 per 100,000) was 1.56 times that for nonwhite males (336 per 100,000), and that for white females (1,013 per 100,000) about 3 times that for the nonwhite (337 per 100,000).

Correctional Institutions

The 1970 rate for white males was about 12 percent lower than their rate for 1950, while that for nonwhite males was about 8 percent higher than the corresponding rate in 1950. As of 1970, the rate for nonwhite males (1,845 per 100,000) was more than 6 times that for white males (303 per 100,000), and that for nonwhite females (75 per 100,000), about 7 times that for white females (11 per 100,000).

FIGURE 12

DISTRIBUTION OF PERSONS IN INSTITUTIONS PER 100,000 POPULATION, BY TYPE OF INSTITUTION, BY SEX AND COLOR, AGE 20 YEARS AND OVER, UNITED STATES, 1950 AND 1970

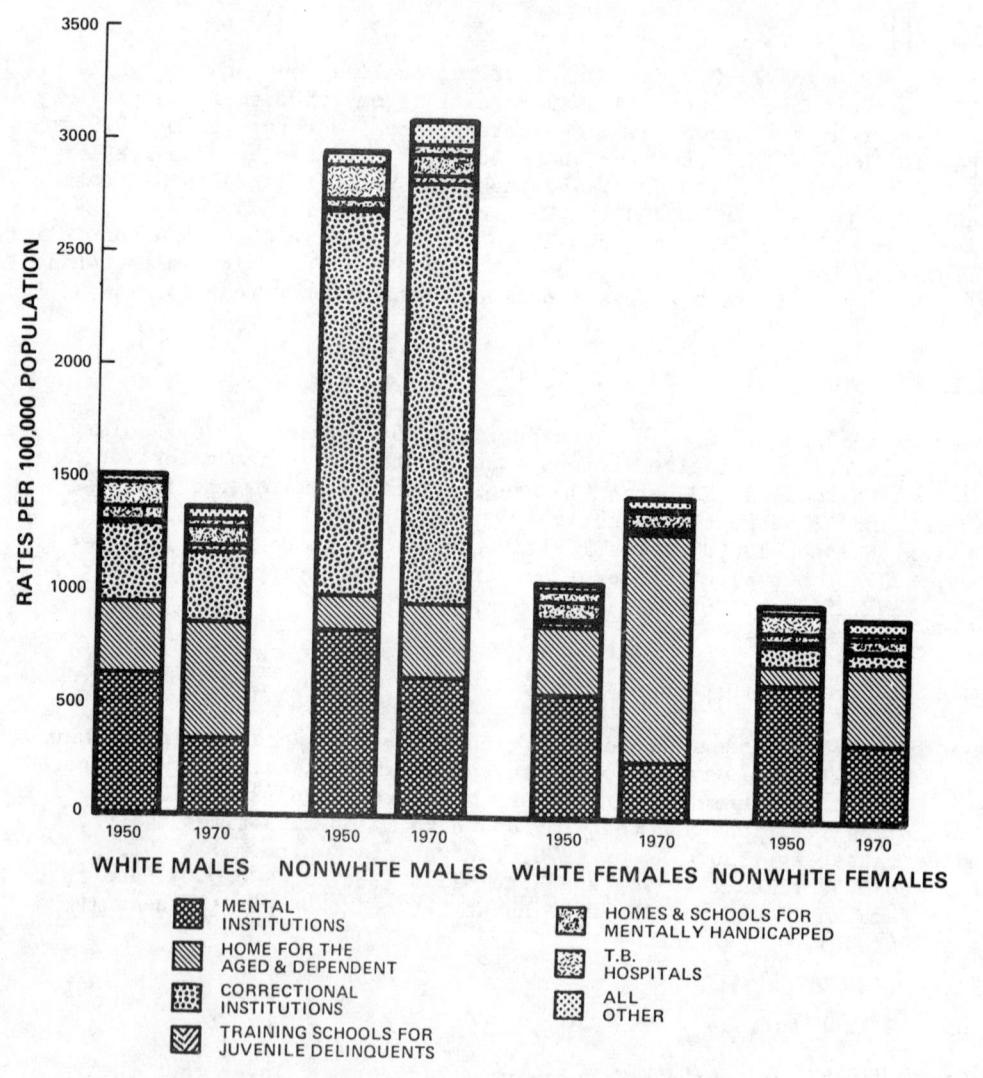

SOURCE: U.S. BUREAU OF THE CENSUS, PERSONS IN INSTITUTIONS, 1950 & 1970

Homes and Schools for the Mentally Handicapped

These rates increased for white and nonwhite males by about 22 percent and 108 percent, respectively, and for nonwhite females by about 40 percnet. They decreased by about 9 percent for white females. As of 1970, the rate for white males (110 per 100,000) was 1.31 times greater than that for the nonwhite (84 per 100,000), and the rate for white females (87 per 100,000) was 1.6 times that for the nonwhite (54 per 100,000).

Tuberculosis Hospitals

The rates decreased dramatically for each color-sex group, but the relative decline was greater for white males (83 percent) and white females (87 percent) than for nonwhite males (65 percent), and nonwhite females (80 percent). As of 1970, the rate for nonwhite males (53 per 100,000) was 3.5 times greater than that for the white (15 per 100,000), and for nonwhite females (19 per 100,000), 3.1 times greater than that for white females (6 per 100,000).

Detailed Age Groups: 20-24 Years and 65 Years and Over

Figures 13, 14, 15, and 16 demonstrate the trends in use of institutions by detailed age groups. Differences in the rates by sex and color as of 1970 will be illustrated for two age groups: persons 20-24 years; and persons 65 years and over. These two age groups were selected for a specific reason: They are contrasting ones in which the age specific institutionalization rates (i.e., the number of persons in a specific age-color-sex group in institutions per 100,000 population of the corresponding age-color-sex group of the general population) are at a maximum. Thus, the maximum rate for nonwhite males occurs in the age group 20-24 years, while that for white males, white females, and nonwhite females occurs in the age group 65 years and over.

Males, Age 20-24 Years

The 1970 institutionalization rate was at its maximum for nonwhite males in this age group (4,749 per 100,000) population (appendix table 15). The largest part of that rate was accounted for by persons in correctional institutions (3,865 per 100,000) and the second largest part by persons in mental institutions (422 per 100,000). These rates were considerably higher than the corresponding rates for white males (665 and 180 per 100,000, respectively). In terms of the persons aged 20-24 enumerated in institutions as of the 1970 census, 81 percent of such nonwhite males were in correctional institutions; 9 percent in mental institutions; 4 percent in institutions for mentally handicapped; and 6 percent in other institutions. The corresponding proportions for the white males were 60 percent; 16 percent; 17 percent; and 8 percent, respectively.

FIGURE 13
NUMBER OF PERSONS IN INSTITUTIONS PER 100,000 POPULATION BY TYPE OF INSTITUTION, BY AGE, WHITE MALES, UNITED STATES, 1950 AND 1970

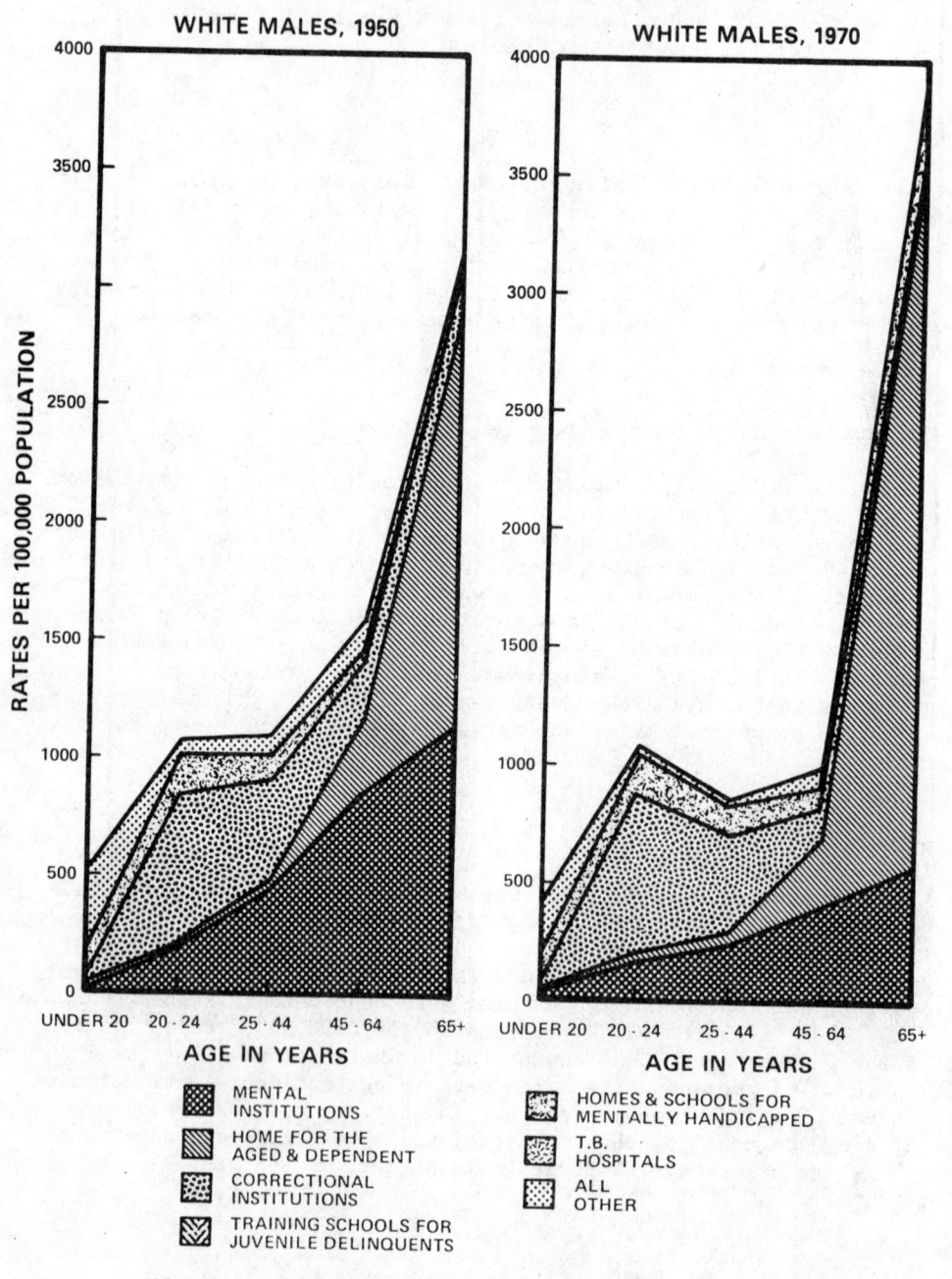

SOURCE: U.S. BUREAU OF THE CENSUS, PERSONS IN INSTITUTIONS, 1950 & 1970

FIGURE 14

NUMBER OF PERSONS IN INSTITUTIONS PER 100,000 POPULATION BY TYPE OF INSTITUTION, BY AGE, NONWHITE MALES, UNITED STATES, 1950 AND 1970

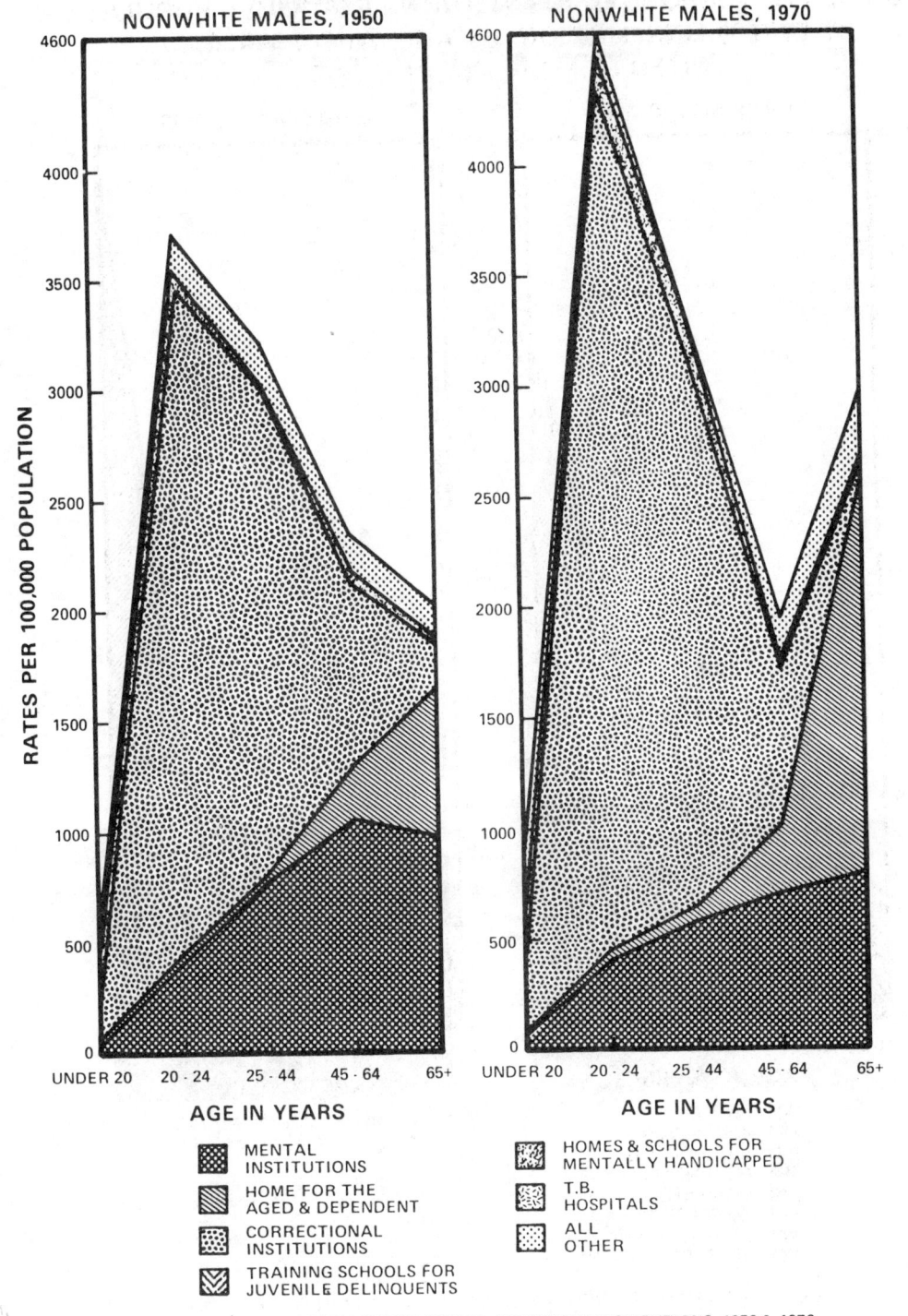

NONWHITE MALES, 1950

NONWHITE MALES, 1970

- MENTAL INSTITUTIONS
- HOME FOR THE AGED & DEPENDENT
- CORRECTIONAL INSTITUTIONS
- TRAINING SCHOOLS FOR JUVENILE DELINQUENTS
- HOMES & SCHOOLS FOR MENTALLY HANDICAPPED
- T.B. HOSPITALS
- ALL OTHER

SOURCE: U.S. BUREAU OF THE CENSUS, PERSONS IN INSTITUTIONS, 1950 & 1970

SCOPE 73

FIGURE 15
NUMBER OF PERSONS IN INSTITUTIONS PER 100,000 POPULATION BY TYPE OF INSTITUTION, BY AGE WHITE FEMALES, UNITED STATES, 1950 AND 1970

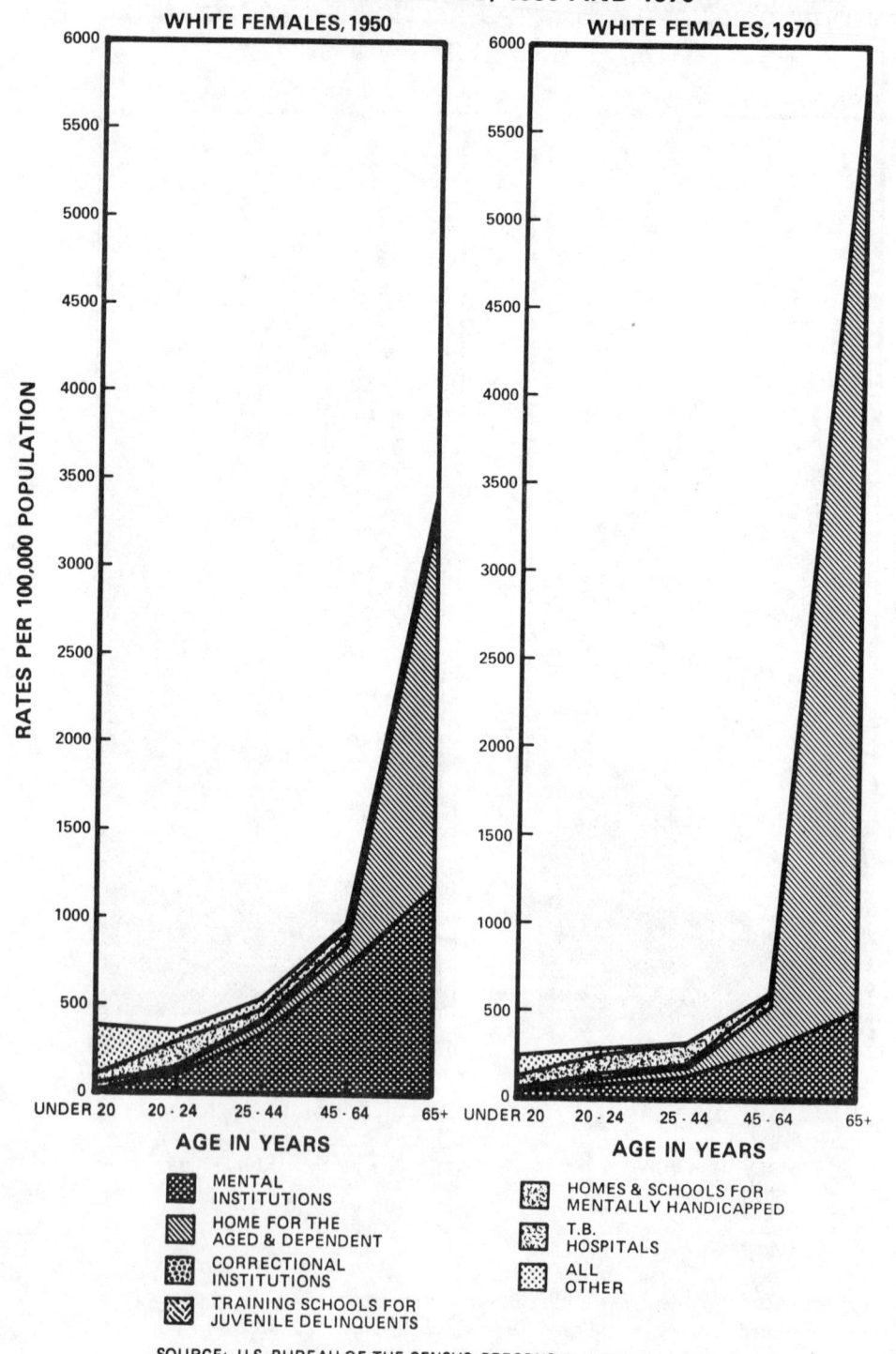

- MENTAL INSTITUTIONS
- HOME FOR THE AGED & DEPENDENT
- CORRECTIONAL INSTITUTIONS
- TRAINING SCHOOLS FOR JUVENILE DELINQUENTS
- HOMES & SCHOOLS FOR MENTALLY HANDICAPPED
- T.B. HOSPITALS
- ALL OTHER

SOURCE: U.S. BUREAU OF THE CENSUS, PERSONS IN INSTITUTIONS, 1950 & 1970

SCOPE 74

FIGURE 16

NUMBER OF PERSONS IN INSTITUTIONS PER 100,000 POPULATION BY TYPE OF INSTITUTION, BY AGE, NONWHITE FEMALES, UNITED STATES, 1950 AND 1970

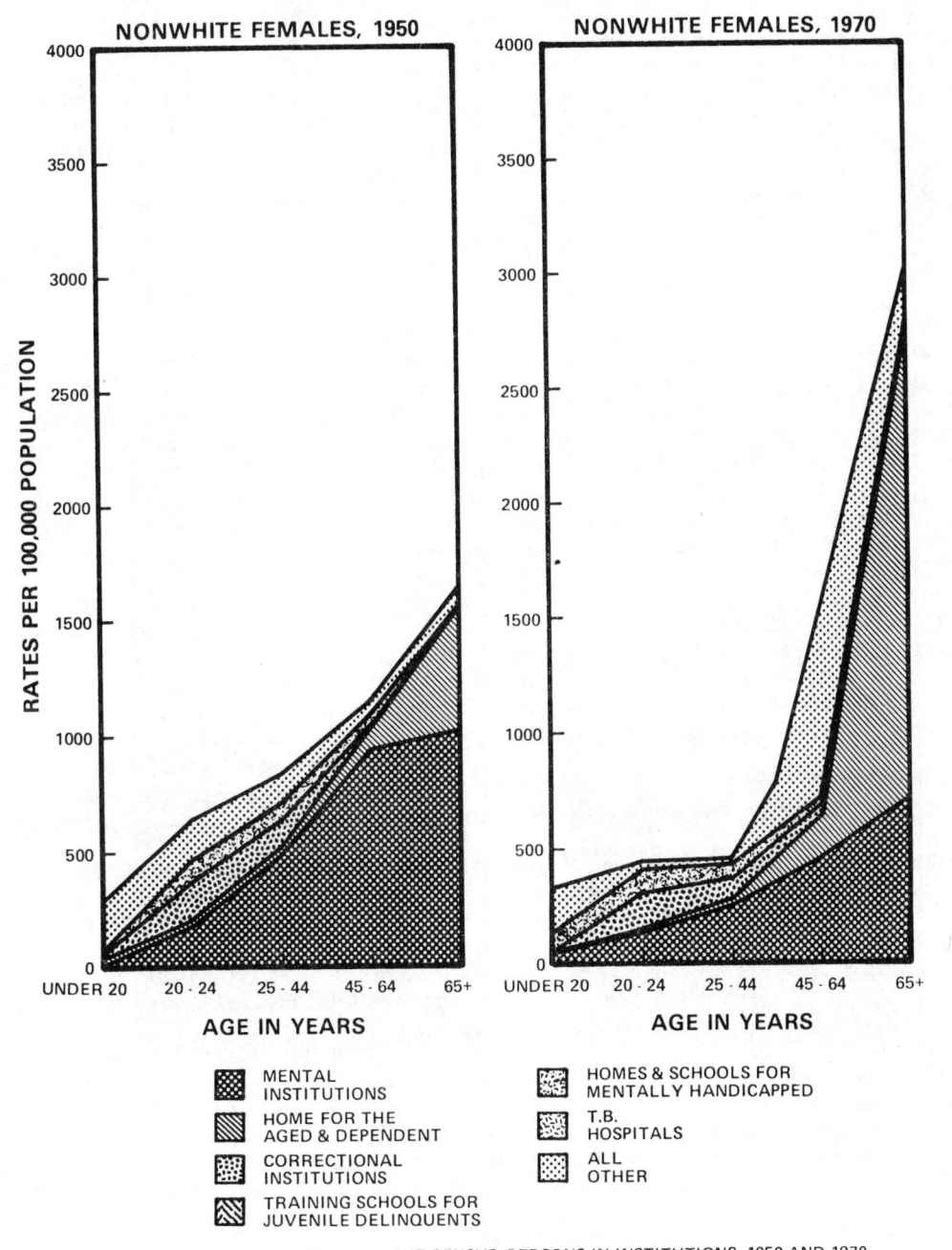

SOURCE: U.S. BUREAU OF THE CENSUS, PERSONS IN INSTITUTIONS, 1950 AND 1970

Males, Age 65 Years and Over

The maximum rate of institutionalization in 1970 for white males was in the age group 65 years and over (3,798 per 100,000) (table 16). This rate was 1.23 times that for nonwhite males in the same age group (3,039 per 100,000). Homes for the aged and dependent account for the largest part of the total for white males (2,889 per 100,000), followed by the rate for mental institutions (586 per 100,000). These rates are 1.7 and 0.7 times, respectively, the corresponding rates for nonwhite males (1,718 and 800 per 100,000, respectively). In terms of white males 65 years and over in institutions, 76 percent were in homes for the aged and dependent, 15 percent in mental institutions, and 9 percent in other institutions. The corresponding proportions for nonwhite males were 57 percent, 26 percent, and 17 percent, respectively.

Females, Age 20-24 Years

The total institutionalization rate for white females in 1970 in this age group was 274 per 100,000 (table 15). The largest part of that rate was accounted for by persons in institutions for the mentally handicapped (126 per 100,000), followed by mental institutions (81 per 100,000), and correctional institutions (25 per 100,000). For nonwhite females, the total rate was 458 per 100,000. The largest part of that rate was accounted for by persons in correctional institutions (171 per 100,000), followed by mental institutions (134 per 100,000) and institutions for the mentally handicapped (109 per 100,000).

In terms of percent of white females 20-24 years in institutions, 46 percent were in institutions for the mentally handicapped, 30 percent in mental institutions, 9 percent in correctional institutions, and 15 percent in other institutions. Of the nonwhite females, the corresponding proportions were 24 percent, 29 percent, 38 percent, and 9 percent, respectively.

Females, Age 65 Years and Over

The maximum rate of institutionalization for both white and nonwhite females was in the age group 65 years and over. As of 1970, the rate for white females (5,843 per 100,000) was 1.9 times that for the nonwhite (3,054 per 100,000) (appendix table 16). The rates for homes for the aged and dependent accounted for the largest part of this total rate for white females (5,072 per 100,000), followed by the rate for mental institutions (516 per 100,000), and for institutions for the mentally handicapped (58 per 100,000). Among nonwhite females, the rate for homes for the aged and dependent (2,048 per 100,000) also accounted for the largest part of the total rate, followed by the rates for mental institutions (723 per 100,000), tuberculosis hospitals (28 per 100,000), and institutions for the mentally handicapped (25 per 100,000). In terms of the female population 65 years and over in institutions, among the white females, 87 percent were in homes for the aged and dependent, 9 percent in mental institutions, 1 percent in institutions for the mentally handicapped, less than 1 percent in tuberculosis hospitals, and 2 percent in all other institutions. Among nonwhite females, the corresponding proportions were, respectively, 67 percent, 24 percent, 1 percent, 1 percent, and 7 percent.

Factors Responsible for Change in Composition of
Institutional Population

The factors that accounted for the changes that occurred in the population of specific institutions are many and complex. The underlying statistical model for explaining differences over time in the number of persons in an institution is similar to that used to explain variations in the prevalence of a disease (i.e., the number of cases of a disease in a population as of a given point in time). Prevalence of a disease on a given day is a function of the incidence of the disease (addition of cases of the disease to a population during a stated interval of time) and the average duration of the disease from onset to termination (Framer 1957, 1969; MacMahon, Pugh, and Ipsen 1960). A similar phenomenon determines the number of persons in an institution on a given day. This number is a function of two basic variables: number of admissions per year, and their durations of stay. To illustrate, annually some members of a population group (defined by such variables as age, sex, color, socioeconomic status) develop and manifest a condition or behave in a way that results in their admission to an institution (incidence). Sometimes the admission is a result of a legal procedure whereby the individual may be sentenced to a prison or committed to a mental institution. Of those admitted, sentenced, or committed, as the case may be, some stay for short periods, others for longer periods (duration). The number in the institution on any one day (prevalence) is a function of the numbers admitted and their duration of stay. Explanations of differences in numbers of admissions, durations of stay, and numbers of residents as of a specific date require answers to such questions as the following:

1. What causes the problem(s) that result(s) in a member of a defined group becoming a candidate for admission to a medical, social, or correctional institution?

2. What factors account for the proportion of such persons being admitted to a certain type of institution?

3. What factors account for long/short stays in institutions?

4. How do the factors that lead to institutionalization and those that account for length of stay vary within and among the different types of institutions in the various States of the Nation?

Thus, the size of the population of a specific institution and the characteristics of its inmates as of a given point in time represent the end result of the interaction of all factors that accounted for the numbers of persons admitted to a specific type of institution and their durations of stay.

The following discussion highlights various factors that have operated over the years, singly and in various combinations, to affect admissions to specific institutions, and their duration of stay:

Social Legislation

As indicated earlier, programs developed to implement the Community Mental Health Centers Legislation played an important role in reducing the population of the State mental institutions (Feldman and Goldstein 1971; Committee on Interstate and Foreign Commerce 1975). These programs placed a high priority on preventing admission to mental hospitals, returning to the community as rapidly as possible patients who were admitted to these hospitals, and placing long-term chronic patients in alternate facilities (Redick 1971). These actions facilitated the shift in locus of care of the mentally ill from the mental hospital to community based facilities. Still other actions resulted in the placement of large numbers of patients with mental disorders of the senium in nursing homes and residential facilities for the aged, rather than in the State mental hospitals. The Special Health Revenue Act of 1975 (Public Law 94-63) provided additional impetus to reducing admissions to State mental hospitals by requiring State Mental Health Authorities

> . . . to establish and carry out a plan which is designed to eliminate inappropriate placement in institutions of persons with mental health problems, to insure the availability of appropriate non-institutional services for such persons and to improve the quality of care for those with mental health problems for whom institutional care is provided. . . .

The Social Security Act of 1935 had a marked effect on the growth of proprietary boarding and nursing homes (Committee on Finance, U.S. Senate 1975). The growing number of elderly persons, changes in the patterns of illness resulting from advances in medical technology, and changes in family living arrangements have resulted in a growing demand for the provisions of limited medical and nursing care outside of hospitals. The 1965 amendments to the Social Security Act (Medicare) provided for the financing of up to 100 days of extended care services for persons 65 years and over in a certified facility during a single spell of illness that provides a level of care distinguished from the level of intensive care ordinarily furnished by a hospital. Title XIX of the Social Security Act in 1965 (Medicaid) also had a marked effect on the provision of nursing home care. Thus, States administering medical assistance programs under title XIX must offer skilled nursing services and home health services to individuals over 21 years of age who qualify for benefits under the program. Title XIX also recognizes another level of institutional care called "intermediate care." This is care in an intermediate care facility (i.e., one which provides health related care and services to those who do not need care in skilled nursing facilities, but require institutional care beyond room and board). As a result of all of the foregoing, the number of nursing care and related homes increased from about 1,200 with approximately 25,000 beds in 1939 to 22,000 nursing and related homes with 1,202,000 beds in 1971 (National Center for Health Statistics 1974).

The Omnibus Crime Control and Safe Streets Act of 1968 (Public Law 90-351, 1968) and the Crime Control Act of 1973 (Public Law 93-83, 1973) led to the establishment of programs that expedited improvements in the criminal justice system and law enforcement activities at the State and local levels to deal with the increasing crime rate in the United States. Even though the Safe Streets Act encouraged greater use of diversionary programs from the criminal justice system, as well as increased use of community based alternatives to incarceration, it seems likely that the increased law enforcement, prosecutorial, and judicial resources which were also developed led to increased arrests and imprisonment (U.S. Dept. of Justice 1974).

New Discoveries for Treatment of Diseases

The availability and use of new therapeutic agents reduced the numbers of persons requiring the services of institutions created to care for persons with a specific disease or disabling condition, such as pharmacotherapy for tuberculosis (American Thoracic Society 1974; Comstock 1975; Beneson 1970), schizophrenia, and affective disorders.

Demographic Changes

Several factors have operated to produce increased numbers of persons subject to risk of institutionalization. Thus, improved medical care, health and social services prolonged the lives of many persons and, by so doing, produced a large population of persons with chronic illnesses and disabling conditions that require long term care in nursing homes, homes for the aged and dependent, and chronic disease hospitals (Breslow 1965). The coming of age of children born during the post-World War II baby boom of the 1950's also had its impact. By 1975, these children had entered the age group 18-24 years, one in which the incidence of certain conditions that lead to institutionalization is high. Thus, it is a high risk age group for schizophrenia, a mental disorder that frequently requires admission to a mental hospital. It is also a high risk age group for arrests for crimes of violence, burglary, and other types of offenses that may lead to prison sentences.

Rapidly Increasing Costs of General Hospital and Domiciliary Care for Persons with Chronic Illnesses

The increases in such costs made it impossible for many families to finance long term care for themselves, parents, or relatives with chronic disabling conditions in general hospitals or to maintain such patients at home (U.S. DHEW 1976). This resulted in their using chronic disease hospitals and nursing homes.

Social Conditions and Problems

Problems associated with poverty, unemployment, and broken homes resulted in increases in crime and delinquency. In turn, these problems led to intensified law enforcement activities and increased arrests which resulted in more persons being sentenced to training schools for delinquents, detention homes, and correctional institutions (Sykes 1972).

Racist and Other Discriminatory Practices

Such practices resulted in persons of one racial or socioeconomic group who manifested certain behavioral problems being placed in a mental hospital or community treatment facility, while persons of another race with the same problems would end up in the correctional system. Other practices resulted in creating and/or perpetuating conditions which produce physical health, mental health, and social problems for members of minority groups which require institutional care (Kramer, Rosen, and Willis 1973).

Insufficient and Inadequate Community Programs

Many areas of the country lack community based programs to provide services which, on the one hand, could possibly prevent the occurrence of problems that result in persons being admitted to institutions and, on the other, could facilitate the early return of eligible residents to the community, provided appropriate resources were available.

Inapprropriate Living Arrangements for Persons Who Are Aged, Disabled, or Are Known to be Mentally Ill

There has been an increase in numbers of persons living in households the composition of which may be inappropriate to meet the many needs of members who are aged, infirm, bedridden, disabled, or disturbed (Kramer, Taube, and Redick 1973; U.S. Bureau of Census 1974). Examples are persons living in two-person husband-wife families in which both members are 65 and over; never married, divorced, separated, and widowed persons who are depressed and live alone; aged parents who have chronic illnesses, disabling conditions, and/or behavioral disorders associated with organic brain syndromes, living in homes or apartments of daughters and sons-in-law with young children; children who are living in households headed by an emotionally disturbed mother who is divorced or separated. The data in appendix table 17, which shows the distribution of persons 65 years and over by their marital status and the role they occupy in the household, demonstrates the situation for persons in this age group. A very high proportion of widowed persons in this age group live alone (about 46 percent for males and 53 percent for females). Another sizable proportion live with other relatives (24 percent for males and 22 percent for females).

Many other causes of institutionalization could be listed. However, those discussed above are sufficient to provide insight into the many complex factors that account for the rise and fall of the populations of our various health, social, and correctional institutions.

Implications of Expected Changes in the Composition of the Population for the Mental Health Services and the Institutional Population

The preceding data illustrates the striking changes that have occurred in the composition of the institutional population of the United States between 1950 and 1970. By relating these trends to expected changes in the composition of the population of the United States between 1970 and 1985, considerable insight can be gained into the significance of these changes for mental health and related human services.

Appendix table 18 and figure 17 show the expected changes in the composition of the population of the United States between 1970 and 1985 specific for age and color (U.S. Bureau of Census 1975). By 1985, the population of the United States will have increased to about 234.1 million people, about 15.2 percent greater than in 1970 (203.2 million). The increase will be 13 percent for whites (from 177.7 to 200.5 million), and 32 percent for nonwhites (from 25.5 to 33.5 million). Nonwhites are expected to constitute about 14 percent of the population in 1985, as compared to 13 percent in 1970. The relative increases expected in the size of each age group of the nonwhite population range from 87 percent increase in the age group 25-34 years to 7 percent in the age group under 15 years. These increases are considerably in excess of those in the white population which range from 56 percent in the age group 25-34, to 3 percent in the age group 45-64 years. The number of white children under 15 will decrease by 9 percent. Of particular importance is the fact that large increases will be occurring in age groups known from past experience to be characterized by consistently high admission rates to psychiatric facilities, correctional institutions, training schools for juvenile delinquents, homes for the aged and dependent, and homes and schools for the mentally handicapped.

The following examples will illustrate the possible effects of the above changes in the age and racial structure of the population on the numbers of persons who might be residents in specific types of institutions as of 1985. The expected number of residents in selected types of institutions were computed on the assumption that the proportions of the population that will be in such institutions in 1985 will be the same as those which existed in 1970. No attempt has been made to develop projections of institutionalization rates since their trends are determined essentially by political and administrative decisions rather than by the operation of a set of "natural" laws that would make it possible to predict reliably the rates of growth or decline of specific types of institutions. On the other hand, the population estimates for 1985, with the exception of the age group under 18 years, are quite dependable. Persons who will be 18 years and over in 1985 were born in 1967 or earlier. Their number will change by 1985 through death and immigration, components of change which can be forecast rather well. Since their number can be predicted sufficiently well, the Census Bureau has made only one forecast of persons 18 years of age and over. The population under 18 years is another matter.

The age group under 18 years in 1985 will contain a portion of individuals who were both between 1967 and 1976, plus another portion yet to be born. The number of children to be born between July 1, 1976, and July 1, 1985, can be projected only within a wide range. Accordingly, the estimate of the population under 18 years in 1985 used in this paper is the Census Bureau's Series II projection (U.S. Bureau of the Census 1975). That is, it is a projection based on the estimated July 1, 1974, population and assumes a slight reduction in mortality, an annual net immigration of 400,000 per year, and an ultimate fertility level (average number of lifetime births per

Figure 17

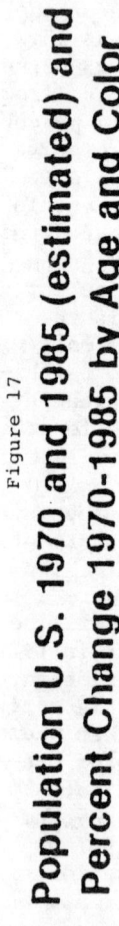

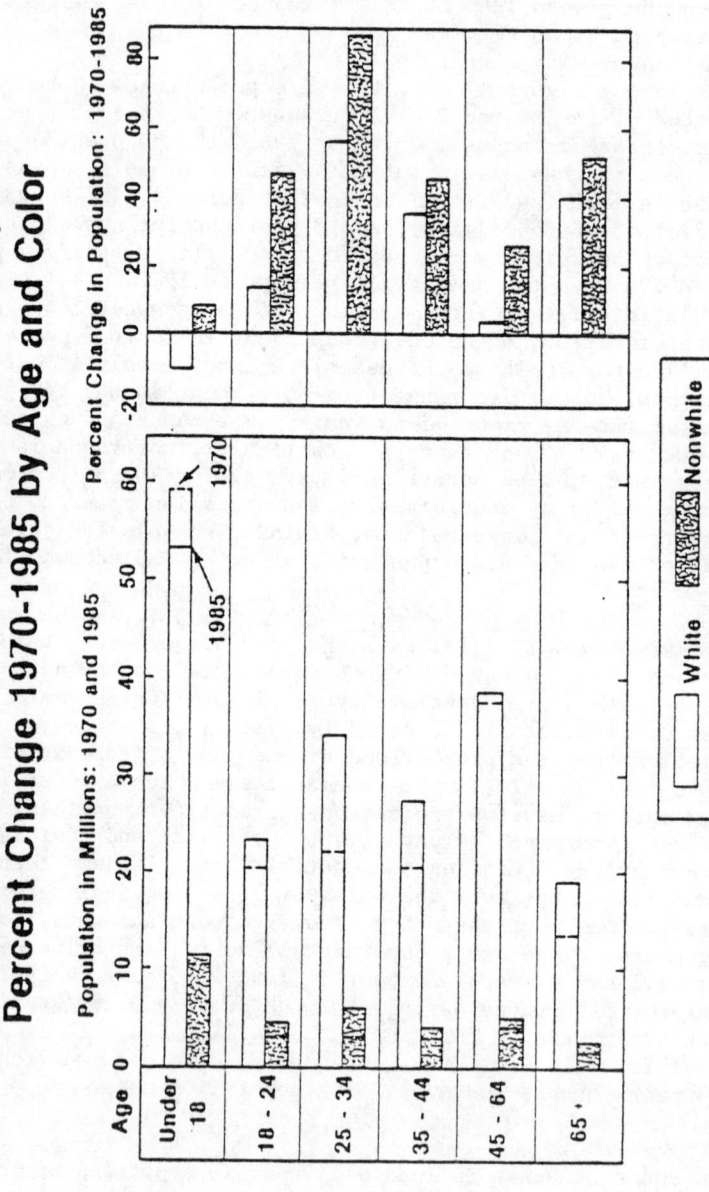

Population U.S. 1970 and 1985 (estimated) and Percent Change 1970-1985 by Age and Color

Source: 1970-U.S. Bureau of the Census, U.S. Census Population, 1970, General Population Characteristics, PC(1)-131, Table 52.

1985-U.S. Bureau of the Census, Current Population Reports, Series P-25, No. 601, Table 8 (Series II Projection which assumes an average of 2.1 lifetime births per woman).

SCOPE 82

woman) at the replacement level figure of 2.1. Thus, the population estimate used for 1985 is a conservative one.

Implications for the Mental Health Field

Planning of Mental Health Agencies

The following illustrates the implications of population changes for the planning of mental health services, particularly those provided by our State and county mental hospitals, private hospitals, general hospitals with psychiatric services, V.A. hospitals, outpatient psychiatric services, and community mental health centers. Assume that the 1971 admission rates to the universe of psychiatric services described in appendix table 19 applied to the population of the United States as of 1970. If only the same level of services (admissions per 100,000 population) is maintained until 1985, then the following increases in admissions would occur:

Year	Total	White	Nonwhite
1970	2,529,586	2,095,927	433,659
1985	3,134,753	2,506,087	628,666
Increase (1970-85)	605,167	410,160	195,007
Percent Increase	23.9	19.6	45.0

Appendix table 20 presents these changes specific for age and race. The percent changes in number of admissions in each age group would be the same as the corresponding percent changes in the numbers of persons in each age group. To illustrate, the percent increases in the high risk age group 25-44 years would be 46 percent for the white population and 67 percent for the nonwhite.

New Cases of Mental Disorders (Incidence): Schizophrenia as an Example

The expected population changes have implications for the number of new cases of mental disorders that will be occurring per year.

The following example demonstrates how these changes will apply to schizophrenia. Although there are no precise estimates of the incidence of schizophrenia for the Nation as a whole, community studies done in various areas of the United States have produced estimates of incidence rates specific for age and that may be used to illustrate the effect of population increases on the number of new cases of schizophrenia that might be expected to occur in the United States between 1970 and 1985. For the purposes of this illustration, the age-color specific annual treated incidence rates for 1970 for Monroe County, New York, provide a basis for speculating on what the situaton in the United States would have been if rates of the order of magnitude for Monroe County applied to the United States in 1970 (appendix table 21). The basic data for these rates were obtained from the Psychiatric Case Register for that county (Babigian 1975). Assume that these age-color specific rates applied to the corresponding age-color groups in the population of the United States in 1970. Then, there would have been 147,139 new cases of schizophrenia occurring in the United States that year--110,982 white and 36,157 nonwhite. Assuming no change in the age-color specific incidence rates between 1970 and 1985, we would expect to have 185,649 new cases occurring during 1985--133,998 white and 51,651 nonwhite (appendix table 22). The following table summarizes the expected changes:

Year	Total	White	Nonwhite
1970	147,139	110,982	36,157
1985	185,649	133,998	51,651
Increase (1970-85)	38,510	23,016	15,494
Percent Increase	26.2	20.7	42.9

The relative increases would vary in the different age groups and, in these computations, would be the same as the relative increases in the population of the United States in the specified age group. For example, in the age group 25-34, the number of new cases of schizophrenia in the white population would have increased by 56 percent (from 27,224 to 42,486) and for the nonwhite population, by 87 percent (from 8,164 to 15,287).

It is important to note that the overall percentage increase in numbers of new cases of schizophrenia exceeds the overall percentage increase expected in the general population. The reason is that the highest incidence rates for schizophrenia occur in those age groups where the expected relative increases in population are also the highest: 15-24 years; 25-34 years; and 35-44 years (see appendix table 18). Thus, although the expected relative increase in the total population for whites is 13 percent and for nonwhites 32 percent, the corresponding increases in new cases of schizophrenia are 21 percent and 43 percent, respectively.

Indeed, it cannot be emphasized too strongly that the number of new cases of schizophrenia will continue to increase until research produces the knowledge needed to prevent its occurrence. At this time, it is very difficult to predict the date by which sufficient knowledge about the causes of this disorder and, equally important, the methods needed to apply this knowledge, will be developed. It is even more difficult to predict when it will be possible to achieve significant reductions in the rate at which new cases of this disorder are being added to our population. Even though a major research breakthrough might occur, the likelihood of achiving significant reductions in new cases quickly would seem to be small in view of the large increases expected in the size of the population groups in which the risk of acquiring this disorder is known to be high. Very effective and efficient methods of prevention would be required to counterbalance the increases in numbers of new cases that can be expected to occur as a result of population increases shown in appendix table 18 and figure 17. However, current research advances suggest directions in which such progress can reasonably be sought.

The above example concerned schizophrenia, but the same reasoning applies to the occurrence of new cases of affective (mood) disorders and organic brain syndromes.

Prevalence of Mental Disorders

The immediately preceding discussion considered factors related to the incidence of mental disorders, i.e., the number of new cases of these disorders occurring in a defined interval of time. A consideration of factors that affect the prevalence of mental disorders (i.e., the numbers of cases present in the population as of a given moment in time) indicate that prevalence will increase.

As indicated earlier, prevalence is dependent not only on the incidence, but also the duration of these disorders; i.e., the interval between date of occurrence and date of their termination, variously defined as the date of remission, the date of "cure," date of death, depending on the question under study.

The following table illustrates the changes to be expected in prevalence merely as a result of shifts in the size and age distribution of the population of the United States between 1970 and 1985. Again, let us draw on the age-color specific treated prevalence rates of Monroe County as a basis for speculation (appendix table 23). Assume these rates applied to the corresponding age-color groups of the population of the United States in 1985, as well as in 1970. Then the changes in prevalence of schizophrenia would be as follows:

Year	Total	White	Nonwhite
1970	974,972	809,668	165,304
1985	1,247,806	1,008,622	239,184
Increase (1970-85)	272,834	198,954	73,880
Percentage Increase	28.0	24.6	44.7

Here, again, the relative increases in the various age groups would be the same as in the general population (appendix table 24). In the age group 25-34 years, for example, the number of cases in the white population would increase from 194,704 in 1970 to 303,862 in 1985 (56 percent), and in the nonwhite from 34,971 to 65,481 (87 percent).

Note, again, that the relative increases in total number of cases of schizophrenia exceeds the corresponding increase in the general population of the United States. As with incidence, the highest prevalence rates occur in those age groups in which the relative increases in population are also the highest (e.g., 15-24, 25-34, 35-44 years).

Mortality and Mental Disorders

In considering factors that determine the size of the population of persons with mental disorders in a country, it is essential to take into account those factors that can affect mortality rates both of the persons who have a mental disorder and those who do not have such disorders. Stated differently, factors that operate to increase the longevity of the mentally ill and the not-mentally ill will tend to increase the prevalence of mental disorders.

Let us first consider the mortality of the mentally ill. A variety of studies have demonstrated that the age-specific mortality rates among the mentally ill--the hospitalized, as well as those under care of outpatient clinics, private psychiatrists, and psychiatric units of general hospitals--are considerably in excess of those in the corresponding age groups of the general population (Yolles and Kramer 1969; Babagian and Odoroff 1969; Keehn, Goldberg, and Beebe 1974). The excess mortality is the resultant of a vareity of factors. These include: (a) the high fatality rates for many of the conditions (infective diseases, metabolic disorders, neoplasms, cerebrovascular diseases, skull fractures, intracranial injuries, poisonings, etc.) that cause or are associated with organic brain syndromes; (b) patterns of behavior and attitudes of persons with mental disorders which, in turn, affect their lifestyle, living arrangements, general health status, and the extent to which they seek and obtain psychiatric and medical care and related human services; (c) the extent to which psychiatrists are able to predict suicidal and violent behavior in patients and are successful in preventing such acts; (d) possible effects of somatic, pharmacologic and other treatment procedures for mental disorders on essential life processes; (e) problems specific to the hospital, nursing home, or other facility in which the patient receives treatment (e.g., lack of adherence to sanitary, safety, and other standards for hospitals, clinics, etc.; inadequate and substandard psychiatric, medical care and related health maintenance services; inadequate staff, etc.); (f) problems associated with long term institutionalization that affect the physical and mental health and the social well being of patients; and (g) possibly unique factors associated with the etiology of a specific mental disorder which may, in some way as yet unknown, subject individuals with such a disorder to an increased risk of mortality.

Thus, activities that tend to reduce mortality rates of the mentally ill associated with any of the above factors will tend to increase the number of persons in our population with a history of mental disorders. The number who will be "active" or "inactive" or "cured" cases will depend on the state of our knowledge concerning the treatment of specific disorders and how effectively such knowledge is being applied. The application of advance in public health practice that result in better levels of environmental sanitation, control of tuberculosis, syphilis, and other infectious diseases, improved diet, and improved general medical care, led to reductions in the mortality rates of the institutionalized mentally ill. Advances in clinical medicine have also prolonged the lives of the large population of aged persons who suffer from brain syndromes with cerebral arteriosclerosis and senile brain disease. Although studies on the subject are lacking, it is to be hoped that the new treatment methods for schizophrenia and affective (mood) disorders will also increase the longevity of persons with these disorders. It is also to be hoped that the large number of persons now under care of community based psychiatric programs will have access to medical care services so that their general physical health status may be improved and to human services agencies for assistance in dealing effectively with psychosocial problems that affect not only their mental health, but their physical health and social well-being.

These factors tend to increase the survival rate of persons with mental disorders. Still other factors are operating that should increase the number of persons with such disorders. The application of advances in clinical medicine has increased the duration of life of many persons with conditions that were once associated with high fatality rates (e.g., premature births, brain damage, cancer, heart disease, cardiovascular disorders, etc.). Thus, lifesaving and lifeprolonging proceudres have produced a sizable population of persons with chronic illnesses and disabling conditions. Many of these persons are known to have associated mental disorders. Others who have survived and have not yet developed psychiatric disorders remain candidates for the development of schizophrenia, affective disorders, psychoneuroses, brain syndromes, mental retardation, and other types of mental and emotional problems.

The net effect of all these factors is to push upward the number of mentally ill persons in our Nation. This trend can only be offset by advances in research and education which are translated into improved therapeutic and preventive services, and by general improvement in the quality of life.

Implications of Population Changes for Other Segments of the Institutional Population

The expected increases in population have implications for the other segments of the institutional population.

Correctional Institutions

Appendix table 25 provides a detailed distribution of the inmates of the correctional institutions of the United States by age, sex, and color as of 1970. If the age specific number of inmates per 100,000 population were the same in 1985 as in 1970, then the following changes in number of inmates would occur, merely as a result of the expected changes in the age distribution of the population:

Year	Total	White	Nonwhite
1970	328,020	187,199	140,281
1985	464,925	244,070	220,855
Increase (1970-85)	136,905	56,871	80,034
Percent Increase	41.7	30.4	56.8

The highest correctional institutional rates occur in the age groups 18-24, 25-34, and 35-44 years--three age groups that will experience the largest relative increases in population. This means that the white correctional institutional would increase, respectively, by 16 percent, 58 percent, and 36 percent on these three age groups and the corresponding increases for the nonwhites would be 51 percent, 88 percent, and 44 percent. To illustrate, in the age group 25-34, the number of white inmates would increase from 57,455 to 90,954 (57 percent), and the number of nonwhite from 44,678 to 84,084 (88 percent) (appendix table 26).

Sykes (1972) has commented on the increasing pressures on the penal system as follows:

The increasing burden on our existing penal system is due, first and most obviously, to an unquestioned increase in the number of crimes committed in our society each year. This, in turn, is due, in part, to the general growth of the population of the U.S.--and more particularly--to the disproportionate growth of those segments of the population that have relatively high crime rates, such as the younger age groups and those living in metropolitan areas. In addition, there is the fact that the crime rate itself, in various parts of the social structure, seems to be increasing.

The growing pressure on the system, it should be pointed out, does not flow from the fact that the police are catching a greater proportion of criminals. The percentage of known offenses that lead to arrest has actually been falling since 1962 and now stands in the neighborhood of 19 percent; for every 100 offenses known to the police, only about 5 percent result in a conviction (U.S. Department of Justice 1971: 30-33). Nor is the growing pressure due simply to an increase in the amount of crime that gets reported, although that is a factor.

The argument here, however, is that the amount of crime in the U.S., whether reported or not and regardless of population growth or changes in the demographic structure, has in fact increased greatly, will continue to increase, and is in the process of inundating a penal system that is growing at a much slower rate. The increase in crime is, then, one important variable in the situation; the other is the reluctance of our society to provide a correctional system for the steadily rising number of lawbreakers.

The overcrowding in penal institutions has become a national problem. Prison officials throughout the country are seeking ways to reform the penal system in an effort to relieve a situation that has reached crisis proportions in Federal and State prisons (Glaser 1973, 1975; King 1975, 1976; Jenkins 1976; Oppenheimer 1976).

Homes for the Aged and Dependent

With respect to homes for the aged and dependent, assuming no increase in the 1970 age specific resident rates, the number of persons 25 years and over in these institutions by 1985 would be as follows:

Year	Total	White	Nonwhite
1970	921,136	874,886	46,249
1985	1,201,169	1,134,240	66,929
Increase (1970-85)	280,034	259,354	20,680
Percent Increase	30.4	29.6	44.7

The increases that would occur in each age group are shown in appendix table 27. For the age group 65 years and over, in which the rate is the highest, the number of persons would increase by 33 percent for the white population (from 762,805 to 1,011,650) and by 49 percent for the nonwhite (from 33,002 to 49,229). Indeed, unless more knowledge is gained about how to prevent those conditions that lead to use of these and other institutions and techniques are developed for applying such knowledge effectively, the demands for facilities, personnel, and funds for their operation will increase enormously.

Discussion

The data and trends reviewed in this report emphasize the need for more basic and applied research on the biological, psychological, social, and political phenomena that are responsible for producing the problems that eventually require people to be institutionalized. Only through such knowledge can primary prevention be achieved. Additional research is also needed on the development of more effective treatment and rehabilitation programs; i.e., secondary and tertiary prevention techniques. The deinstitutionalization of large numbers of persons from mental hospitals with brain syndromes, schizophrenia, affective disorders, and other disorders continues to emphasize the need for more knowledge about biological, social, and psychological factors that affect the course and outcome of these disorders in persons from various age, sex, socioeconomic, and cultural groups. This, in turn, will require more epidemiologic, statistical, and demographic research. Indeed, this knowledge (taken together with laboratory and clinical data) is basic to the development of more effective community programs for prevention and control of mental disorders and promotion of mental health.

The data presented in this report indicate the dimensions of some of the problems that have to be solved. It should be borne in mind that the projections of numbers of residents of different types of institutions have taken into account only the effect of expected changes in the numbers of persons in the various age, sex, race groups of the population of the United States. If increases also occur in the rates of use of mental health facilities, the projections presented would be increased over and above those described. Similarly, increases in the incidence and prevalence rates of schizophrenia would add to the number of persons with this disorder in the population, and increases in the rate of imprisonment and duration of prison sentences would add to the numbers of persons in correctional institutions.

Indeed, the expected increase in the size of the problems presents a major challenge to the researchers in all of the sciences that are involved in clarifying the causes of mental disorders and related social problems, and developing improved methods to treat affected individuals. The challenge is particularly great to those responsible for the development of the statistical and epidemiological services essential to meet the requirements of the Community Mental Health Centers legislation.

Despite the progress made in epidemiologic and biostatistical research on the mental disorders, there is still a considerable agenda of unfinished business (Kramer 1975). The accomplishments of the past 30 years also highlight shortcomings of our knowledge concerning the distribution of mental disorders, the patterns of use of mental health and related human services, and their effectiveness. Among the high priority problems that need solution are the development of generally applicable procedures for case findings, improved diagnostic procedures, more precise measures of need for specific types of mental health services, followup studies, classifications of psychosocial factors, and social indicators.

Of particular importance for epidemiologic research is the establishment of several field research units with adequate staffing and stable, long term financing to design and implement research for determining the extent to which community health programs are affecting the level of disability from mental disorders. Such units can document quantitatively our ongoing needs, opportunities, and paths of future progress.

Summary

We have here reviewed the trends in patterns of use of psychiatric facilities in the United States from 1946 to 1975 and the impact such changes have had on the composition of the institutional population.

As a result of the development of community based programs for the diagnosis, treatment, and rehabilitation of persons with mental disorders, the locus of care of persons with such disorders has shifted from the large State mental hospitals to community based facilities, particularly to outpatient services and community mental health centers. To illustrate, in 1955, 1.7 million episodes of care were provided by the universe of facilities that report to the National Institute of Mental Health. Of these, 49 percent were accounted for by State and county mental hospitals, 23 percent outpatient psychiatric services, 16 percent general hospital inpatient psychiatric units, and 12 percent for all other facilities. By 1975, the number of episodes of care provided by all facilities increased to 6.4 million. Of these, only 9 percent were accounted for by State and county mental hospitals, 47 percent by outpatient psychiatric services, 29 percent by community mental health centers, 9 percent by general hospital inpatient psychiatric units, and 6 percent by other reporting facilities (figure 2).

These changes have had a marked effect on the composition of the institutional population. In 1950, 1.6 million persons (1 percent of the population of the United States) were in institutions. The largest portion was in mental institutions (39 percent); the second largest portion in homes for the aged and dependent (19 percent); and the third largest portion in correctional institutions (17 percent). By 1970, the number of persons in institutions increased to 2.1 million persons, about 1 percent of the total population. The largest portion was in homes for the aged and dependent (44 percent); the next largest in mental institutions (20 percent); and the third largest in correctional institutions (15 percent) (appendix table 13).

This report presented detailed descriptions of the institutionalization rates (i.e., numbers of persons in specific types of institutions per 100,000 population) specific for age, sex, and race and speculated on the effect of projected changes in the age distribution of the population of the United States between 1970 and 1985 on the expected numbers of persons that will be under care of mental health facilities; the numbers of schizophrenic persons in the population; the numbers of persons in correctional institutions and in homes for the aged and dependent by 1985. Of particular importance is the fact that large increases are expected in numbers of persons in high risk age groups for the use of mental health facilities and correctional institutions, homes for the aged and dependent, and other institutions that constitute the institutional population.

The changes in the numbers of persons in specific types of institutions have been the result of a variety of factors such as social legislation, new discoveries for treatment of disorders, demographic changes, increasing costs of general hospital and domiciliary care for persons with chronic illnesses, social conditions and problems, racist and other discriminatory practice; and inadequate community programs and inappropriate living arrangements for persons who are aged, disabled, or mentally ill. The implications of these changes for manpower, research, and services have been considered.

Appendix Table 1

ESTIMATED NUMBER AND PERCENT DISTRIBUTION OF PERSONS WITH MENTAL DISORDER, AND PERCENT OF TOTAL POPULATION, BY TYPE OF TREATMENT SETTING, UNITED STATES, 1975

Treatment Sector and Setting	Estimate of Persons with Mental Disorder[1/] Number	Percent of total	Percent of Total U.S. Population
Total [2/]	31,955,000	100	15
Specialty Mental Health Sector			
State and county mental hospitals [3/]	789,000		
V.A. - psychiatric units of general and neuro-psychiatric hospitals [3/]	351,000		
Private mental hospitals and residential treatment centers [3/]	233,000		
Non-federal general hospitals with psychiatric units [3/]	927,000		
Community mental health centers [3/]	1,627,000		
Freestanding outpatient and multiservice clinics [3/]	1,763,000		
Halfway houses for the mentally ill [4/]	7,000		
College campus mental health clinics [5/]	131,000		
Office-based private practice psychiatrists [6/]	854,000		
Private practice psychologists [7/]	425,000		
Subtotal	7,107,000		
Unduplicated sector total [8/]	6,698,000	21.0	3.1
General Hospital Inpatient/Nursing Home Sector			
General hospital inpatient facilities			
Non-federal general hospitals without separate psychiatric units [9/]	812,000		
Federal general hospitals (excludes psychiatric units of V.A. hospitals [9/]	59,000		
Nursing homes [10/]	207,000		
Non-psychiatric specialty hospitals [11/]	22,000		
Unduplicated sector total	1,100,000	3.4	0.5
Primary Care/Outpatient Medical Sector			
Office-based primary care physicians [12/]	10,710,000		
Other office-based non-primary care physicians [12/]	2,337,000		
Community (Neighborhood Health centers [13/]	314,000		
Industrial health facilities [14/]	314,000		
Health department clinics [15/]	941,000		
General hospital outpatient and emergency rooms [16/]	6,391,000		
Subtotal	21,007,000		
Unduplicated sector total [17/]	19,218,000	60.1	9.0
Unduplicated subtotal across specialty mental health and general medical sectors [18/]	25,094,000	78.5	11.8
Not in Treatment/Other Human Services Sector			
Unduplicated Sector total [19/]	6,861,000	21.5	3.2

SCOPE 92

Appendix Table 2

Number and percent distribution and rate per 100,000 population of inpatient and outpatient care episodes[1], in selected mental health facilities, by type of facility: United States, 1955, 1965, 1971 and 1975 (Provisional)

Year	Total all facilities[1]	Inpatient services of:						Outpatient psychiatric services of:		
		All inpatient services	State & county mental hospitals	Private mental hospitals[2]	Gen.hosp. psychiatric service (non-VA)	VA psychiatric inpatient services	Federally assisted comm.men. health cen.	All outpatient services	Federally assisted comm.men. health cen.	Other

Number of patient care episodes

1975	6,409,447	1,791,171	598,993	165,327	565,696	214,264	246,891	4,618,276	1,584,968	3,033,308
1971	4,038,143	1,721,389	745,259	126,600	542,642	176.800	130,088	2,316.754	622,906	1,693,848
1965	2,636,525	1,565,525	804,926	125,428	519,328	115,843	-	1,071,000	-	1,071,000
1955	1,675,352	1,296,352	818,832	123,231	265,934	88,355	-	379,000	-	379,000

Percent distribution

1975	100.0	27.9	9.3	2.6	8.8	3.3	3.9	72.1	24.7	47.4
1971	100.0	42.6	18.5	3.1	13.4	4.4	3.2	57.4	15.4	42.0
1965	100.0	59.4	30.5	4.8	19.7	4.4	-	40.6	-	40.6
1955	100.0	77.4	48.9	7.3	15.9	5.3	-	22.6	-	22.6

Rate per 100,000 population

1975	3033	847	283	78	268	101	117	2185	750	1435
1971	1977	843	365	62	266	87	64	1134	305	829
1965	1376	817	420	65	271	60	--	555	--	559
1955	1028	795	502	76	163	54	--	233	--	233

[1] In order to present trends on the same set of facilities over this interval, it has been necessary to exclude from this table the following: private psychiatric office practice; psychiatric service modes of all types in hospitals or outpatient clinics of Federal agencies other than the VA (e.g., Public Health Service, Indian Health Service, Department of Defense Bureau of Prisons, etc.); inpatient service modes of multiservice facilities not shown in this table; all partial care episodes, and outpatient episodes of VA hospitals.

[2] Includes estimates of episodes of care in residential treatment centers for emotionally disturbed children

Source (All years except 1975): The National Institute of Mental Health, Utilization of Mental Health Facilities, 1971, Series B, No.5 January 1974, Table 22

Source (1975): Unpublished provisional data from the National Institute of Mental Health

Appendix Table 3

Number of resident patients, total admissions, net releases, and deaths, State and county mental hospitals, United States, 1950-1973

Year	Number of Hospitals	Resident Patients at End of Year	Admissions	Net Releases	Deaths
1950	322	512,501	152,286	99,659	41,280
1951	322	520,326	152,079	101,802	42,107
1952	329	531,981	162,908	107,647	44,303
1953	332	545,045	170,621	113,959	45,087
1954	352	553,979	171,682	118,775	42,652
1955	275	558,922	178,003	126,498	44,384
1956	278	551,390	185,597	145,313	48,236
1957	277	548,626	194,497	150,413	46,848
1958	278	545,182	209,823	161,884	51,383
1959	279	541,883	222,791	176,411	49,647
1960	280	535,540	234,791	192,818	49,748
1961	285	527,456	252,742	215,595	46,880
1962	285	515,640	269,854	230,158	49,563
1963	284	504,604	283,591	245,745	49,052
1964	289	490,449	299,561	268,616	44,824
1965	290	475,202	316,664	288,397	43,964
1966	298	452,089	328,564	310,370	42,753
1967	307	426,309	345,673	332,549	39,608
1968	312	399,152	367,461	354,996	39,677
1969	314	369,969	374,771	367,992	35,962
1970	315	337,619	384,511	386,937	30,804
1971	321	308,983	402,472	405,681	26,835
1972	327	274,837	390,455	405,348	23,282
1973	334	248,518	377,020	387,107	19,899
1974	323	215,573	374,554	389,179	16,597

Note: For all years net releases were obtained by summing the resident patients at beginning of year and admissions and subtracting from this deaths and resident patients at end of year.

Sources of data for resident patients, admissions and deaths are as follows:

1) 1950-1955 and 1960-1964-NIMH, Patients in Mental Institutions;

2) 1956-1959-Mental Health Statistics, Current Reports. Provisional Movement and Administrative Data - Public Mental Hospitals 1961 and 1962. Table A;

3) Resident Patients End of Year 1965-1973-Statistical Note 112, Table 1;

4) Admissions 1965 and 1966 - Mental Health Statistics, Current Facility Reports, Provisional Patient Movement and Administrative Data - State and County Mental Hospitals, United States, July 1, 1968-June 30, 1969, Table 4;

5) Admissions, 1967-1968-Statistical Note 60, Table 5;

6) Admissions, 1969 - Statistical Note 77, Table 5;

7) Admissions, 1970-73 - Statistical Note 106, Table 4;

8) Deaths, 1965-1973-NIMH Current Facility Reports or Statistical Notes showing Provisional Data for State and County Mental Hospitals for each respective year;

9) 1974-Statistical Note 114, Table 1.

Appendix Table 4

Resident patient rates per 100,000 population, State and county mental hospitals, by sex and age: United States 1965-1975

Year and sex	Total	Under 15	15-24	25-34	35-44	45-54	55-64	65+
Both sexes								
1965...	247.6	10.2	95.5	197.2	276.2	406.8	603.5	772.9
1966...	233.4	10.5	90.3	190.4	260.9	373.1	564.1	729.6
1967...	217.8	11.0	83.1	172.2	239.2	345.7	529.5	682.9
1968...	202.0	10.7	79.9	157.8	226.4	312.2	486.7	627.9
1969...	185.3	11.4	76.6	146.2	206.0	278.3	440.9	572.3
1970...	167.4	11.3	77.7	139.7	188.3	247.5	378.0	491.1
1971...	151.3	11.1	73.7	131.3	173.7	221.9	334.7	431.4
1972...	133.1	10.2	66.6	115.7	152.9	190.8	290.8	375.8
1973...	119.4	9.6	62.1	106.3	137.2	166.3	254.7	331.1
1974...	102.8	9.2	65.7	102.3	132.6	134.1	200.8	250.5
1975...	90.5	8.0	53.7	85.7	103.1	118.9	174.1	241.9
Male								
1965...	251.0	14.6	126.6	244.0	290.3	417.2	636.2	713.9
1966...	236.9	14.7	120.6	238.6	280.7	382.0	589.9	670.8
1967...	223.6	15.5	113.6	217.9	257.4	353.3	565.5	648.8
1968...	209.3	15.3	109.6	204.7	252.8	321.3	518.9	587.1
1969...	192.8	16.4	105.4	189.2	231.9	284.7	469.6	540.2
1970...	176.5	15.9	107.2	182.1	215.1	253.7	404.3	473.6
1971...	160.5	15.2	101.4	170.9	200.6	227.3	357.8	419.0
1972...	142.9	14.4	92.7	154.2	182.6	196.9	310.4	364.1
1973...	130.7	13.2	88.9	144.1	165.9	173.7	268.9	334.5
1974...	113.3	12.1	81.6	128.0	145.6	146.0	217.8	282.6
1975...	101.2	11.1	76.6	120.5	127.7	125.7	181.4	246.5
Female								
1965...	244.5	5.7	66.8	154.2	263.2	397.0	573.4	818.7
1966...	230.1	6.1	63.1	146.3	242.5	364.7	540.4	775.1
1967...	212.4	6.3	55.8	130.1	221.9	338.6	497.2	714.8
1968...	195.2	5.8	53.3	114.4	201.9	303.8	457.6	658.8
1969...	178.3	6.2	50.7	106.4	181.9	272.3	415.0	596.1
1970...	158.9	6.6	50.8	100.4	163.5	241.7	354.4	503.7
1971...	142.8	6.8	47.9	94.4	148.8	216.8	314.0	440.3
1972...	124.0	5.8	41.9	79.5	125.3	185.1	273.2	384.1
1973...	108.9	5.9	36.5	70.7	110.5	159.4	242.0	328.7
1974...	93.0	6.2	50.3	78.0	120.6	123.0	185.7	228.1
1975...	80.6	4.8	31.5	52.8	80.8	112.6	167.5	238.8

APPENDIX TABLE 5

Number and percent distribution of resident patients 65 years of age and over in psychiatric hospitals by type of hospital, and number of residents 65 years and over with chronic condition of mental disorder 1/ in nursing homes; United States, 1969 and 1973

Type of facility	1969	1973	Percent change 1969-1973	Percent Distribution 1969	1973
State and county mental hospitals	111,420 4/	70,615 6/	-36.6	50.7	26.0
Private mental hospitals	2,460 4/	1,534 6/	-37.6	1.1	0.6
VA hospitals 2/	9,675 4/	5,819 6/	-39.9	4.4	2.1
Nursing homes 3/	96,415 5/	193,900 7/	101.0	43.8	71.3
Total	219,970	271,868	24.0	100.0	100.0

1/ Includes mental illness (psychiatric or emotional problems) and mental retardation but excludes senility.

2/ Includes VA neuropsychiatric hospitals and general hospital inpatient psychiatric services.

3/ Data on residents with chronic condition of mental disorder used rather than data on residents with primary diagnosis of mental disorder at last examination, since latter data were not available by age in 1969.

4/ Source: Selected publications of Division of Biometry and Epidemiology, National Institute of Mental Health

5/ Source: National Center for Health Statistics. "Chronic Conditions and Impairments of Nursing Home Residents: United States - 1969." DHEW Publication No. (HRA) 74-1707. Washington, D.C.: U.S. Government Printing Office.

6/ Source: Unpublished data, Division of Biometry and Epidemiology, NIMH.

7/ Source: Unpublished data, National Center for Health Statistics

Appendix Table 6

Admissions with no prior inpatient care who were admitted to State and county mental hospitals, United States: 1962, 1965, 1969, 1972, and 1975

Sex and age at admission	Number of first admissions					Rate per 100,000 population				
	1962	1965	1969	1972	1975	1962	1965	1969	1972	1975
Both sexes, all ages	129,698	144,090	163,984	140,813	120,690	70.6	75.1	82.1	68.2	57.1
Under 15	3,460	4,510	6,553	7,661	8,304	6.0	7.5	11.0	13.5	15.5
15-24	19,473	25,878	37,507	35,111	35,858	76.9	88.6	114.4	95.1	91.8
25-34	22,761	25,625	26,614	27,767	27,938	105.1	118.5	111.4	103.8	92.2
35-44	23,146	25,669	30,779	24,069	16,812	96.0	106.6	134.3	107.2	74.6
45-54	19,243	21,205	24,676	19,618	13,114	91.2	96.6	106.8	83.3	55.3
55-64	13,280	14,597	18,264	12,097	10,442	82.4	86.1	100.3	63.3	52.8
65+	28,335	26,606	19,591	14,490	8,222	163.7	146.5	100.6	60.2	36.7
Males, all ages	72,663	82,536	98,885	95,755	80,279	81.4	84.5	102.7	96.0	78.6
Under 15	2,339	2,971	4,036	6,713	5,235	7.9	9.7	13.4	23.2	19.1
15-24	11,330	15,352	22,552	24,337	24,124	94.4	109.3	145.5	135.0	125.7
25-34	12,301	14,361	16,389	17,857	20,275	119.1	138.7	142.7	137.8	137.4
35-44	12,938	14,774	17,292	17,635	11,551	111.6	127.3	156.6	162.9	106.3
45-54	11,442	12,711	16,805	12,286	8,193	111.0	119.3	151.2	108.7	71.5
55-64	7,731	8,749	10,229	8,851	6,045	99.5	107.7	118.6	98.5	64.7
65+	14,582	13,618	11,582	8,076	4,856	188.8	171.7	139.6	93.1	52.9
Females, all ages	57,035	61,554	65,099	45,058	40,411	60.4	62.4	63.0	42.2	37.0
Under 15	1,121	1,539	2,517	948	3,069	3.9	5.2	8.7	3.4	11.7
15-24	8,143	10,526	14,955	10,774	11,734	61.2	69.4	86.5	57.1	59.1
25-34	10,460	11,264	10,225	9,910	7,663	92.3	100.0	82.4	71.9	49.2
35-44	10,208	10,895	13,487	6,434	5,261	81.5	87.4	113.5	55.3	45.1
45-54	7,801	8,494	7,871	7,332	4,921	72.2	75.2	65.7	59.9	40.1
55-64	5,549	5,848	8,035	3,246	4,397	66.5	66.2	83.8	32.1	42.1
65+	13,753	12,988	8,009	6,414	3,366	143.5	127.0	71.7	52.2	25.4

SCOPE 97

APPENDIX TABLE 7
NUMBER, PERCENT DISTRIBUTION AND RATE PER 100,000 POPULATION - FIRST ADMISSION BY DIAGNOSIS AND SEX AND RATIOS OF MALE TO FEMALE FIRST ADMISSIONS BY DIAGNOSIS, STATE AND COUNTY MENTAL HOSPITALS, UNITED STATES 1946 and 1972.

Diagnosis and Sex	Number 1946	Number 1972	Percent 1946	Percent 1972	Rate per 100,000 Population 1946	Rate per 100,000 Population 1972
Both Sexes						
Total - All Diagnoses	95,996	140,813	100.0%	100.0%	69.4	68.2
Mental Retardation	1,764	6,082	1.8	4.3	1.3	2.9
Alcohol Disorders	8,411	36,788	8.8	26.1	6.1	17.8
Drug Abuse	788	9,093	0.8	6.5	0.6	4.4
Organic Brain Syn. (excl. alcohol & drug)	41,908	13,987	43.7	9.9	30.3	6.8
Organic Brain Syn. Assoc. with Syphilis	6,562	1/	6.8	1/	4.7	1/
Schizophrenia	18,459	19,607	19.2	13.9	13.3	9.5
Other Psychoses	13,118	4,573	13.7	3.2	9.5	2.2
Psychoneuroses	3,495	17,406	3.6	12.4	2.5	8.4
Personality Disorders	2,164	14,784	2.3	10.5	1.6	7.2
Trans.Sit.Dis. & Adjustment Reaction to Infancy & Childhood	614	9,128	0.6	6.5	0.4	4.4
All Other	5,275	9,365	5.5	6.7	3.8	4.5
Males						
Total - All Diagnoses	50,172	95,755	100.0%	100.0%	74.1	96.0
Mental Retardation	1,098	4,250	2.2	4.4	1.6	4.3
Alcohol Disorders	6,976	32,873	13.9	34.4	10.3	33.0
Drug Abuse	401	6,383	0.8	6.7	0.6	6.4
Organic Brain Syn. (excl. alcohol & drug)	23,163	8,168	46.2	8.5	34.2	8.2
Organic Brain Syn. Assoc. with Syphilis	4,697	1/	9.4	1/	6.9	1/
Schizophrenia	7,787	11,183	15.5	11.7	11.5	11.2
Other Psychoses	4,251	2,001	8.5	2.1	6.3	2.0
Psychoneuroses	1,376	5,776	2.7	6.0	2.0	5.8
Personality Disorders	1,524	11,035	3.0	11.5	2.3	11.1
Trans.Sit.Dis.& Adjustment Reaction to Infancy & Childhood	431	6,801	0.9	7.1	0.6	6.8
All Other	3,165	7,285	6.3	7.6	4.7	7.3
Females						
Total - All Diagnoses	45,824	45,058	100.0%	100.0%	64.8	42.2
Mental Retardation	666	1,832	1.5	4.1	0.9	1.7
Alcohol Disorders	1,435	3,915	3.1	8.7	2.0	3.7
Drug Abuse	387	2,710	0.8	6.0	0.5	2.5
Organic Brain Syn. (excl. alcohol & drug)	18,745	5,819	40.9	12.9	26.5	5.5
Organic Brain Syn. Assoc. with Syphilis	1,865	1/	4.1	1/	2.6	1/
Schizophrenia	10,672	8,424	23.4	18.7	15.1	7.9
Other Psychoses	8,867	2,572	19.3	5.7	12.5	2.4
Psychoneuroses	2,119	11,630	4.6	25.8	3.0	10.9
Personality Disorders	640	3,749	1.4	8.3	0.9	3.5
Trans.Sit.Dis.& Adjustment Reaction to Infancy & Childhood	183	2,327	0.4	5.2	0.3	2.2
All Other	2,110	2,080	4.6	4.6	3.0	1.9

APPENDIX TABLE 7 (CONT.)

NUMBER, PERCENT DISTRIBUTION AND RATE PER 100,000 POPULATION - FIRST ADMISSION BY DIAGNOSIS AND SEX, AND RATIOS OF MALE TO FEMALE FIRST ADMISSIONS BY DIAGNOSIS, STATE AND COUNTY MENTAL HOSPITALS, UNITED STATES 1946 and 1972 (Continued)

Diagnosis	1946	1972
	Ratio of Male 1st Admissions per 100 Female 1st Admissions	
Total - All Diagnoses	109.5	221.0
Mental Retardation	164.9	232.0
Alcohol Disorders	486.1	839.7
Drug Abuse	103.6	235.5
Organic Brain Syn. (excl. alcohol & drug)	123.6	140.4
Organic Brain Syn. Assoc. with Syphilis	251.8	1/
Schizophrenia	73.0	132.8
Other Psychoses	47.9	77.8
Psychoneuroses	64.9	49.7
Personality Disorders	238.1	294.3
Trans.Sit.Dis.& Adjustment Reaction to Infancy & Childhood	235.5	292.3
All Other	150.0	350.2
	Ratio of Male to Female 1st Admission Rate	
Total - All Diagnoses	1.14	2.27
Mental Retardation	1.78	2.53
Alcohol Disorders	5.15	8.92
Drug Abuse	1.20	2.56
Organic Brain Syn. (excl. alcohol & drug)	1.29	1.49
Organic Brain Syn. Assoc. with Syphilis	2.65	1/
Schizophrenia	.76	1.42
Other Psychoses	.50	.83
Psychoneuroses	.67	.53
Personality Disorders	2.56	3.17
Trans.Sit.Dis.& Adjustment Reaction to Infancy & Childhood	2.00	3.09
All Other	1.57	3.84

1/ Data were not available for this diagnostic category in 1972 but based on past years trends it is estimated that the number of first admissions would be approximately only 100 or so.

SCOPE 99

APPENDIX TABLE 8

Number, percent distribution and rate per 100,000 population - resident patients by diagnosis and sex, State and county mental hospitals, United States, 1955 and 1973

Diagnosis and Sex	Number 1955	Number 1973	Percent 1955	Percent 1973	Rate per 100,000 Population 1955	Rate per 100,000 Population 1973
Both Sexes						
Total - All Diagnoses	558,922	248,518	100.0%	100.0%	344.4	119.4
Mental Retardation	47,620	30,237	8.5	12.2	29.3	14.5
Alcohol Disorders	17,258	15,606	3.1	6.3	10.6	7.5
Drug Abuse	1,011	2,492	0.2	1.0	0.6	1.2
Organic Brain Syndromes (excluding alcohol and drug)	137,991	46,910	24.7	18.9	85.0	22.5
Organic Brain Syndromes Associated with Syphilis	29,017	3,996	5.2	1.6	17.9	1.9
Schizophrenia	267,995	122,587	47.9	49.3	165.1	58.9
Other Psychoses	65,785	14,178	11.8	5.7	40.5	6.8
Psychoneuroses	5,366	4,597	1.0	1.8	3.3	2.2
Personality Disorders	8,552	5,501	1.5	2.2	5.3	2.6
Trans. Sit. Dis. & Adjustment Reaction to Infancy & Childhood	1,062	2,797	0.2	1.1	0.7	1.3
All Other	6,282	3,613	1.1	1.5	3.9	1.7
Males						
Total - All Diagnoses	269,405	131,410	100.0%	100.0%	340.6	130.7
Mental Retardation	26,048	16,756	9.7	12.8	32.9	16.7
Alcohol Disorders	14,024	11,815	5.2	9.0	17.7	11.8
Drug Abuse	596	1,889	0.2	1.4	0.8	1.9
Organic Brain Syndromes (excluding alcohol and drug)	72,157	22,152	26.8	16.9	91.2	22.0
Organic Brain Syndromes Associated with Syphilis	19,211	2,415	7.1	1.8	24.3	2.4
Schizophrenia	122,416	64,096	45.5	48.7	154.8	63.7
Other Psychoses	22,489	4,311	8.3	3.3	28.4	4.3
Psychoneuroses	2,109	1,643	0.8	1.2	2.7	1.6
Personality Disorders	6,021	4,287	2.2	3.3	7.6	4.3
Trans. Sit. Dis. & Adjustment Reaction to Infancy & Childhood	646	1,733	0.2	1.3	0.8	1.7
All Other	2,899	2,728	1.1	2.1	3.7	2.7
Females						
Total - All Diagnoses	289,517	117,108	100.0%	100.0%	347.9	108.9
Mental Retardation	21,572	13,481	7.5	11.5	25.9	12.5
Alcohol Disorders	3,234	3,791	1.1	3.2	3.9	3.5
Drug Abuse	415	603	0.1	0.5	0.5	0.6
Organic Brain Syndromes (excluding alcohol and drug)	65,834	24,758	22.7	21.2	79.1	23.0
Organic Brain Syndromes Associated with Syphilis	9,806	1,581	3.4	1.4	11.8	1.5
Schizophrenia	145,579	58,491	50.3	50.0	174.9	54.4
Other Psychoses	43,296	9,867	15.0	8.4	52.0	9.2
Psychoneuroses	3,257	2,954	1.1	2.5	3.9	2.7
Personality Disorders	2,531	1,214	0.9	1.0	3.0	1.1
Trans. Sit. Dis. & Adjustment Reaction to Infancy & Childhood	416	1,064	0.1	0.9	0.5	1.0
All Other	3,383	885	1.2	0.8	4.1	0.8

APPENDIX TABLE 9

Number and Percent Distribution of Admissions to Selected Mental Health Facilities by Age, United States, 1975

Age (in yrs.)	State & County mental hosp.	Private mental hosp.	General hosp. psychiatric inpt. unit	Outpatient psychiatric services	Community mental health centers	Total – All facilities
Total – all ages	385,237	129,832	515,537	1,406,065	919,037	3,355,708
Under 18	25,252	15,426	42,690	358,061	213,607	655,036
18-24	71,841	19,476	43,239	230,634	172,747	587,937
25-44	165,970	47,169	220,266	569,722	354,561	1,357,688
45-64	101,615	34,844	121,202	194,561	141,215	593,437
65+	20,559	12,917	38,140	53,087	36,907	161,610

Percent distribution by age

Total – all ages	100.0	100.0	100.0	100.0	100.0	100.0
Under 18	6.6	11.9	8.3	25.5	23.2	19.5
18-24	18.6	15.0	18.1	16.4	18.8	17.5
25-44	43.1	36.4	42.7	40.5	38.6	40.5
45-64	26.4	26.8	23.5	13.8	15.4	17.7
65+	5.3	9.9	7.4	3.8	4.0	4.8

Percent distribution by facility type

Total – all ages	11.5	3.8	15.4	41.9	27.4	100.0
Under 18	3.9	2.4	6.5	54.6	32.6	100.0
18-24	12.2	3.3	15.9	39.2	29.4	100.0
25-44	12.2	3.5	16.2	42.0	26.1	100.0
45-64	17.1	5.9	20.4	32.8	23.8	100.0
65+	12.7	8.0	23.6	32.9	22.8	100.0

Source: Unpublished data, Division of Biometry and Epidemiology, NIMH

SCOPE 101

APPENDIX TABLE 10

Number and Percent Distribution of Admissions to Selected Mental Health Facilities by Mental Disorder, United States, 1975

Diagnosis	State & county mental hospital	Private mental hospital	Gen. hosp. psych. inpt. unit Numbers	Outpatient psychiatric services	Community mental health centers	Total – All facilities
Total	385,237	128,832	515,537	1,406,065	919,037	3,355,708
Alcohol disorders	106,615	10,827	35,932	53,125	89,338	295,837
Drug disorders	14,435	3,077	17,849	22,094	28,638	86,093
Organic brain syndromes	20,372	5,195	18,981	30,821	22,443	97,812
Depressive disorders	44,965	55,068	194,399	180,735	122,948	598,115
Schizophrenia	129,425	28,315	124,458	148,303	91,914	522,415
Childhood disorders	5,987	1,564	4,625	143,462	120,642	276,280
Social maladjustments	1,139	164	1,818	143,278	66,395	212,794
All other diagnosis	57,163	24,783	114,622	526,926	242,155	965,649
No mental disorder	5,136	839	2,853	157,321	134,564	300,713

Percent distribution by diagnosis

Total	100.0	100.0	100.0	100.0	100.0	100.0
Alcohol disorders	27.0	8.3	7.0	3.8	9.7	8.8
Drug disorders	3.7	2.4	3.5	1.6	3.1	2.6
Organic brain syndromes	5.3	4.0	3.7	2.2	2.4	2.9
Depressive disorders	11.7	42.5	37.7	12.9	13.4	17.8
Schizophrenia	33.6	21.8	24.1	10.5	10.0	15.6
Childhood disorders	1.6	1.2	0.9	10.2	13.1	8.2
Social maladjustments	0.3	0.1	0.4	10.2	7.2	6.3
All other diagnosis	14.8	19.1	22.1	37.4	26.6	28.8
No mental disorder	1.3	0.6	0.6	11.2	14.6	9.0

Percent distribution by facility type

Total	11.5	3.8	15.4	41.9	27.4	100.0
Alcohol disorders	36.0	3.7	12.1	18.0	30.2	100.0
Drug disorders	16.8	3.6	20.7	25.7	33.2	100.0
Organic brain syndromes	20.8	5.3	19.4	31.6	22.9	100.0
Depressive disorders	7.5	9.2	32.5	30.2	20.6	100.0
Schizophrenia	24.8	5.4	23.8	28.4	17.6	100.0
Childhood disorders	2.2	0.6	1.7	51.9	43.6	100.0
Social maladjustments	0.5	0.1	0.9	67.3	31.2	100.0
All other diagnosis	5.9	2.6	11.9	54.6	25.0	100.0
No mental disorder	1.7	0.3	0.9	52.3	44.8	100.0

Source: Unpublished data, Division of Biometry and Epidemiology, NIMH

SCOPE 102

APPENDIX TABLE 12

Age adjusted admission rates a/ by race, sex and type of facility, selected mental health facilities, b/ United States 1975

race & sex	State & county mental hospitals	Private mental hospitals	Inpatient psychiatric services — Non-Federal general hospitals c/ Total	Public	Nonpublic	Federally funded CMHCs	Outpatient psychiatric services
Total-all races	182	61	244	66	178	435	665
Male.........	245	55	209	70	139	427	611
Female.......	124	67	276	62	214	441	709
White	160	65	243	61	182	415	639
Male.........	213	57	206	64	142	404	588
Female.......	110	71	278	58	220	425	683
All other races	340	39	238	98	140	571	834
Male.........	477	40	219	108	111	593	747
Female.......	226	39	253	89	165	550	890

Ratios of rates for all other Races to Whites

Males	2.24	.70	1.06	1.69	.78	1.47	1.27
Females	2.05	1.82	.91	1.53	.75	1.29	1.30

Ratio of rates for Males to Females

Whites	1.94	.80	.74	1.10	.65	.95	.86
Other races	2.11	1.03	.87	1.21	.67	1.08	.84

If rate = ratio = 1

Scope 192

TABLE 13

Number, percent distribution and rate per 100,000 population of persons in institutions by type of institution: United States, 1950, 1960, 1970 [1] [2]

Type of institution	1950	1960	1970
	\multicolumn{3}{c}{Number of persons}		
Total all institutions	1,566,846	1,886,967	2,126,719
Correctional institutions	264,557	346,015	328,020
Mental hospitals & residential treatment centers	613,628	630,046	433,890
Tuberculosis hospitals	76,291	65,009	16,912
Chronic disease hospitals (excl. TB & mental)	20,084	42,476	67,120
Homes for the aged and dependent	296,783	469,717	927,514
Homes & schools for the mentally handicapped	134,189	174,727	201,992
Homes & schools for the physically handicapped	20,999	24,291	22,739
Homes for dependent & neglected children	96,300	73,306	47,594
Homes for unwed mothers	3,135	3,497	4,209
Training schools for juvenile delinquents	36,986	45,695	66,457
Detention homes	3,894	10,821	10,272
Diagnostic & reception centers	(N.A.) [3]	1,367	(N.A.) [3]
	\multicolumn{3}{c}{Percent}		
Total all institutions	100.0	100.0	100.0
Correctional institutions	16.9	18.3	15.4
Mental hospitals & residential treatment centers	39.2	33.4	20.4
Tuberculosis hospitals	4.9	3.4	0.8
Chronic disease hospitals (excl. TB & mental)	1.3	2.3	3.2
Homes for the aged and dependent	18.9	24.8	43.6
Homes & schools for the mentally handicapped	8.6	9.3	9.5
Homes & schools for the physically handicapped	1.3	1.3	1.1
Homes for dependent & neglected children	6.1	3.9	2.2
Homes for unwed mothers	0.2	0.2	0.2
Training schools for juvenile delinquents	2.4	2.4	3.1
Detention homes	0.2	0.6	0.5
Diagnostic & reception centers	(N.A.) [3]	0.1	(N.A.) [3]
	\multicolumn{3}{c}{Number per 100,000 Population}		
Total all institutions	1,035.4	1,052.3	1,046.6
Correctional institutions	174.8	193.0	161.4
Mental hospitals & residential treatment centers	405.5	351.3	213.5
Tuberculosis hospitals	50.4	36.3	8.3
Chronic disease hospitals (excl. TB & mental)	13.3	23.7	33.0
Homes for the aged & dependent	196.1	261.9	456.4
Homes & schools for the mentally handicapped	88.7	97.4	99.4
Homes & schools for the physically handicapped	13.9	13.5	11.2
Homes for dependent & neglected children	63.6	40.9	23.4
Homes for unwed mothers	2.1	2.0	2.1
Training schools for juvenile delinquints	24.4	25.5	32.7
Detention homes	2.6	6.0	5.1
Diagnostic & reception centers	(N.A.) [3]	0.8	(N.A.) [3]

[1] As of date of decennial census of 1950, 1960, and 1970.

[2] Source: U.S. Bureau of the Census: 1953, 1963, 1973.

[3] N.A. = Not Available

SCOPE 104

TABLE 14 Number of persons in institutions per 100,000 population, by type of institution, by sex and color for all ages, under 20 years, and 20 years and over: United States, 1950 and 1970

Sex, Color, and Age	All Types	Type of Institution 1950					All Types	Type of Institution 1970				
		Mental Insti- tutions	Homes- Aged & Depen.	Correc- tional Inst.	School- Juvenile Delinq.	Inst.- Men'lly Handicap.	TB Hospi- tals	All Other 1/	Mental Insti- tutions	Homes- Aged & Depen.	Correc- tional Inst.	School- Juvenile Deling.	Inst. Men'lly Handicap.	TB Hospi- tals	All Other 1/

Rates per 100,000 Population

Both Sexes-Total	1035.4	405.5	196.1	174.8	24.4	88.7	50.4	95.5	1046.6	213.5	456.4	161.4	32.7	99.4	8.3	74.9
Under 20 years	469.0	21.5	7.5	37.9	67.7	90.1	13.2	231.1	387.9	45.6	4.2	47.1	77.1	107.1	1.1	105.7
20 years & over	1326.3	602.7	293.0	245.1	2.2	87.9	69.6	25.8	1448.1	315.9	732.2	231.1	5.6	94.7	12.7	55.9
20-24 years	902.9	162.9	12.3	466.3	12.5	154.5	70.7	23.7	910.7	146.7	19.4	535.2	26.1	155.0	3.7	24.6
25-44 years	939.7	417.2	24.2	312.1	2/ 1.8	102.9	71.9	9.6	726.8	216.0	42.1	332.9	2/ 5.9	108.2	7.1	14.6
45-64 years	1333.1	823.4	204.9	144.3	-	62.4	71.9	26.2	867.1	377.9	251.4	96.2	-	75.4	16.7	49.5
65 years & over	3134.8	1149.7	1769.3	41.8	-	34.0	53.6	86.4	4822.3	563.4	3966.0	20.9	-	53.5	25.3	193.2
Males-Total	1263.0	437.3	197.4	334.6	31.9	91.4	63.1	107.3	1138.7	247.5	307.0	317.3	53.3	114.9	11.7	87.0
Under 20 years	556.5	26.2	7.3	69.5	87.2	102.4	10.9	253.0	516.7	58.1	4.8	86.9	118.5	126.7	1.2	120.5
20 years & over	1637.6	655.3	298.2	475.1	2.6	85.5	90.9	30.0	1546.0	371.5	504.9	468.1	10.7	107.2	18.6	65.0
20-24 years	1402.2	212.6	12.7	906.0	19.3	164.1	63.1	24.4	1564.6	209.6	23.6	1059.8	52.2	188.5	3.5	27.4
25-44 years	1319.7	487.9	29.1	603.8	2/ 0.7	101.4	83.3	13.5	1145.6	280.3	47.6	654.8	2/ 9.7	123.0	10.2	20.0
45-64 years	1664.4	882.7	298.4	277.9	-	54.8	115.3	35.3	1089.4	444.2	273.5	193.4	-	80.1	27.3	70.9
65 years & over	3015.2	1126.3	1607.1	84.4	-	29.6	82.1	85.7	3728.9	605.3	2782.0	43.9	-	50.6	35.5	211.6
Males-White	1176.3	428.5	209.9	245.7	26.5	96.7	58.7	110.3	1005.0	231.2	325.1	206.9	35.5	116.0	9.2	81.1
Under 20 years	544.7	23.5	7.7	53.1	73.8	109.0	8.5	269.1	432.0	54.3	4.7	52.3	81.2	125.6	0.8	113.1
20 years & over	1500.8	636.5	313.8	344.7	2.2	90.3	84.5	28.8	1362.8	341.7	525.2	303.4	7.1	109.9	14.5	61.0
20-24 years	1111.0	186.1	11.3	647.3	16.7	173.6	53.6	22.4	1116.6	179.7	22.6	665.1	31.7	189.1	2.7	25.7
25-44 years	1102.2	454.6	28.7	424.1	2/ 0.7	108.2	73.7	12.2	867.5	241.4	44.5	423.0	2/ 7.6	127.6	6.2	17.2
45-64 years	1598.5	865.1	303.9	226.8	-	57.7	111.4	33.6	995.2	415.9	269.7	140.7	-	82.9	21.2	64.8
65 years & over	3097.3	1138.8	1686.1	73.7	-	30.9	83.2	84.6	3798.4	585.7	2889.2	34.8	-	54.0	31.7	203.0
Males-Nonwhite	1998.1	512.4	91.2	1087.9	77.3	46.3	100.6	82.4	2089.8	363.0	178.3	1102.2	180.0	107.4	29.4	129.5
Under 20 years	640.5	45.2	4.2	185.6	181.4	55.2	27.3	141.6	1002.9	79.8	5.3	285.3	332.6	133.3	3.2	163.4
20 years & over	2929.0	832.7	150.8	1706.6	5.8	40.3	150.9	41.9	3078.2	620.5	335.7	1844.9	41.3	83.9	53.3	98.6
20-24 years	3750.1	426.2	23.8	2991.2	40.6	87.1	139.1	42.1	4748.8	422.1	30.1	3865.4	198.1	183.7	9.4	40.0
25-44 years	3216.8	778.4	32.8	2171.9	2/ 0.9	41.9	167.2	23.8	3287.4	579.4	71.4	2440.7	2/ 26.0	88.4	41.3	40.2
45-64 years	2354.5	1066.6	241.4	812.5	-	24.5	156.1	53.4	1964.4	706.3	308.1	683.2	-	54.1	84.4	128.3
65 years & over	2031.4	976.5	660.5	211.9	-	13.8	68.2	100.5	3039.2	799.7	1718.1	134.2	-	16.9	72.5	297.8

TABLE 14 (CONT.)

Number of persons in institutions per 100,000 population by type of institution, by sex and color for all ages, under 20 years, and 20 years and over: United States, 1950 and 1970 (Continued)

Sex, Color, and Age	All Types	Mental Insti- tutions	Homes- Aged & Depen.	Correc- tional Inst.	School- Juvenile Delinq.	Inst.- Men'lly Handicap.	TB Hospi- tals	All Other 1/	All Types	Mental Insti- tutions	Homes- Aged & Depen.	Correc- tional Inst.	School- Juvenile Delinq.	Inst. Men'lly Handicap.	TB Hospi- tals	All Other 1/
	\multicolumn{8}{c}{Type of Institution 1950}	\multicolumn{8}{c}{Type of Institution 1970}
	\multicolumn{16}{c}{Rates per 100,000 Population}
Females-Total....	810.6	374.1	194.9	17.1	17.1	86.0	37.9	83.5	959.2	181.3	598.1	13.6	13.1	84.7	5.1	63.3
Under 20 years.	378.8	16.6	7.8	5.4	47.6	77.5	15.5	208.4	254.7	32.7	3.5	5.9	34.3	86.8	1.0	90.5
20 years & over	1025.5	551.9	287.9	22.9	1.9	90.3	49.0	21.6	1360.1	265.9	936.5	18.1	1.1	83.5	7.4	47.6
20-24 years..	425.3	115.5	12.0	45.8	5.9	145.4	78.1	22.6	298.3	87.8	15.5	43.8	1.6	123.7	3.8	22.1
25-44 years..	573.1	349.0	19.5	30.6	2/ 2.8	104.4	60.9	5.9	326.7	154.7	37.0	25.5	2/ 2.4	94.0	4.1	9.0
45-64 years..	1001.3	763.9	111.1	10.6	-	69.9	28.5	17.3	663.8	317.4	231.2	7.1	-	71.1	7.0	30.0
65 yrs.& over	3242.1	1170.6	1914.8	3.6	-	38.0	28.1	87.0	5612.1	533.1	4821.4	4.3	-	55.5	17.9	179.9
Females-White....	824.8	373.0	212.7	10.8	16.0	91.8	33.6	86.9	1003.6	176.0	657.4	8.5	9.8	87.0	4.1	60.8
Under 20 years.	390.3	15.2	8.4	3.6	45.5	83.2	12.3	222.1	239.0	31.1	3.5	4.2	26.0	86.6	0.7	86.9
20 years & over	1033.7	545.1	311.0	14.2	1.8	95.9	43.8	21.9	1418.9	254.7	1012.6	10.9	1.0	87.2	5.9	46.6
20-24 years..	395.4	105.8	12.5	26.4	5.8	155.5	67.3	22.1	274.1	80.8	17.0	24.6	1.3	126.0	2.2	22.2
25-44 years..	544.7	331.5	20.0	18.7	2/ 2.6	112.1	54.1	5.7	305.9	140.8	37.7	15.3	2/ 2.4	99.6	2.5	7.6
45-64 years..	987.7	747.2	115.2	8.0	-	74.2	26.7	16.4	648.7	301.4	235.2	4.7	-	67.8	5.1	34.5
65 yrs.& over	3365.8	1183.0	2023.2	3.1	-	39.8	28.2	88.5	5843.2	515.9	5071.8	3.9	-	58.3	16.9	176.4
Females-Nonwhite.	694.0	382.4	47.7	68.8	26.1	38.6	73.1	57.3	654.5	217.9	191.0	48.6	35.8	68.9	12.2	80.1
Under 20 years.	301.1	26.1	3.7	17.5	61.7	38.6	37.5	116.0	341.6	41.5	3.1	15.2	80.1	87.8	3.0	110.9
20 years & over	949.7	614.4	76.4	102.2	2.9	38.6	96.2	19.0	896.8	354.5	336.6	74.5	1.5	54.2	19.2	56.3
20-24 years..	640.2	184.9	8.5	185.2	6.4	72.8	155.6	86.8	458.4	133.5	6.0	170.9	3.6	108.7	14.4	21.3
25-44 years..	806.6	492.8	15.3	128.7	2/ 4.0	40.8	117.0	8.0	465.8	247.5	31.9	93.3	2/ 2.2	56.6	15.2	19.1
45-64 years..	1148.3	944.4	74.7	38.1	-	24.1	48.1	18.9	797.9	459.6	195.3	27.8	-	36.2	23.5	55.5
65 yrs.& over	1644.0	1010.9	515.3	10.5	-	14.6	26.6	66.1	3054.3	722.9	2048.6	8.4	-	24.9	28.3	221.2

1/ Includes detention homes, homes for unwed mothers, homes for neglected and dependent children, chronic disease hospitals, and homes and schools for the physically handicapped. (The rates for each type of institution specific for age, sex and race are given in Appendix table 2.)

2/ Since training schools for juvenile delinquents are primarily for persons under 25 years and detailed age breaks for persons 25 years and over are not available, it is assumed that all of the persons aged 25 years and over in these institutions would be in the group aged 25-44 years.

Source: U.S. Bureau of the Census, Persons in Institutions, 1950 and 1970

Table /5. Institutionalization rates per 100,000 population and percent distribution of persons 20-24 years of age in institutions, by type of institution, sex and color: United States, 1950 and 1970

Type of Institution	Males White 1950	Males White 1970	Males Nonwhite 1950	Males Nonwhite 1970	Females White 1950	Females White 1970	Females Nonwhite 1950	Females Nonwhite 1970
	Rates per 100,000 population							
All Types........	1,111	1,117	3,750	4,749	395	274	640	458
Mental..........	186	180	426	422	106	81	185	134
Aged & Dependent....	11	23	24	30	13	17	9	6
Correctional.......	647	665	2,991	3,865	26	25	185	171
Mentally Handicapped	174	189	87	164	156	126	73	109
Tuberculosis.......	54	3	139	9	67	2	156	14
All other.........	39	57	83	239	27	23	32	24
	Percent distribution of persons in institutions							
All Types........	100.0	100.0	100.0	100.0	100.0	100.0	100.0	100.0
Mental..........	16.7	16.1	11.4	8.9	26.8	29.6	28.9	29.3
Aged & Dependent....	1.0	2.1	0.6	0.6	3.3	6.2	1.4	1.3
Correctional.......	58.2	59.5	79.8	81.4	6.6	9.1	28.9	37.3
Mentally Handicapped	15.7	16.9	2.3	3.9	39.5	46.0	11.4	23.8
Tuberculosis.......	4.9	0.3	3.7	0.2	17.0	0.7	24.4	3.1
All other.........	3.5	5.1	2.2	5.0	6.8	8.4	5.0	5.2

SCOPE 107

TABLE 16 Institutionalization rates per 100,000 population and percent distribution of persons 65 years of age and over in institutions, by type of institution, sex and color: United States, 1950 and 1970

Type of Institution	Males White 1950	Males White 1970	Males Nonwhite 1950	Males Nonwhite 1970	Females White 1950	Females White 1970	Females Nonwhite 1950	Females Nonwhite 1970
	Rates per 100,000 population							
All types........	3,097	3,798	2,031	3,039	3,366	5,843	1,644	3,054
Mental..........	1,139	586	977	800	1,183	516	1,011	723
Aged & Dependent..	1,686	2,889	661	1,718	2,023	5,072	515	2,049
Correctional.....	74	35	212	134	3	4	11	8
Mentally Handicapped	31	54	14	17	40	58	15	25
Tuberculosis.....	83	32	68	73	28	17	27	28
All other........	84	202	99	297	89	176	65	221
	Percent distribution of persons in institutions							
All types........	100.0	100.0	100.0	100.0	100.0	100.0	100.0	100.0
Mental..........	36.8	15.4	48.1	26.3	35.2	8.8	61.5	23.7
Aged & Dependent..	54.4	76.1	32.5	56.5	60.1	86.8	31.3	67.1
Correctional.....	2.4	0.9	10.4	4.4	0.1	0.1	0.7	0.3
Mentally Handicapped	1.0	1.4	0.7	0.6	1.2	1.0	0.9	0.8
Tuberculosis.....	2.7	0.9	3.4	2.4	0.8	0.3	1.6	0.9
All other........	2.7	5.3	4.9	9.8	2.6	3.0	4.0	7.2

TABLE 17 — Distribution of persons 65 years of age and over by living arrangement and marital status by sex, United States March 1970

Living arrangement	Total	Married spouse present	Married spouse absent	Widowed	Divorced	Single
MALE			Number (in 000's) 1/			
Total 65 years and over	8,364	5,721	281	1,510	199	653
Head of family	5,961	5,642	19	218	7	76
Wife of head	-	-	-	-	-	-
Child of head	48	-	2	3	2	41
Other relative of head	626	79	31	369	39	108
Living alone	1,129	-	102	695	116	217
Living with non-relatives	297	-	36	132	23	106
Inmate of institution	302	-	91	93	12	105
FEMALE						
Total 65 years and over	11,349	3,824	200	6,196	259	871
Head of family	1,114	-	13	964	33	104
Wife of head	3,824	3,824	-	-	-	-
Child of head	64	-	9	10	3	41
Other relative of head	1,639	-	21	1,391	39	189
Living alone	3,829	-	85	3,256	141	348
Living with non-relatives	367	-	11	242	12	101
Inmate of institution	512	-	61	333	31	88
MALE			Percent			
Total 65 years and over	100.0%	100.0%	100.0%	100.0%	100.0%	100.0%
Head of family	71.3	98.6	6.8	14.4	3.5	11.6
Wife of head	-	-	-	-	-	-
Child of head	0.6	-	0.7	0.2	1.0	6.3
Other relative of head	7.5	1.4	11.0	24.4	19.6	16.5
Living alone	13.5	-	36.3	46.1	58.3	33.2
Living with non-relatives	3.5	-	12.8	8.7	11.6	16.2
Inmate of institution	3.6	-	32.4	6.2	6.0	16.2
FEMALE						
Total 65 years and over	100.0%	100.0%	100.0%	100.0%	100.0%	100.0%
Head of family	9.8	-	6.5	15.6	12.7	11.9
Wife of head	33.7	100.0	-	-	-	-
Child of head	0.6	-	4.5	0.2	1.2	4.7
Other relative of head	14.4	-	10.5	22.4	15.1	21.7
Living alone	33.8	-	42.5	52.5	54.4	40.0
Living with non-relatives	3.2	-	5.5	3.9	4.6	11.6
Inmate of institution	4.5	-	30.5	5.4	12.0	10.1

1/ Sum of individual figures may not add to group totals due to rounding

Source: U.S. Bureau of the Census, Current Population Reports, Series P-20, No. 212, Table 6

TABLE 18 U.S. populations, actual 1970 [1] and estimated 1985, [2] and numerical and percent change in U.S. populations: 1970-1985, by age and color

Age (Years)	1970 Total	1970 White	1970 Nonwhite	1985 Total	1985 White	1985 Nonwhite
	Population in Thousands					
Total............	203,212	177,749	25,463	234,069	200,548	33,521
Less than 15 years	57,900	49,002	8,898	53,892	44,382	9,510
15-24 years.......	35,441	30,652	4,789	38,496	32,087	6,409
25-34 years.......	24,907	21,779	3,128	39,846	33,989	5,857
35-44 years.......	23,089	20,328	2,761	31,332	27,334	3,998
45-64 years.......	41,810	37,658	4,152	43,844	38,673	5,171
65 years & over...	20,065	18,330	1,735	26,659	24,083	2,576
	Change in Number of Persons (in thousands) 1970-85			Percent Change in Number of Persons 1970-85		
Total............	30,857	22,799	8,058	15.2	12.8	31.6
Less than 15 years	-4,008	-4,620	612	-6.9	-9.4	6.9
15-24 years.......	3,055	1,435	1,620	8.6	4.7	33.8
25-34 years.......	14,939	12,210	2,729	60.0	56.1	87.2
35-44 years.......	8,243	7,006	1,237	35.7	34.5	44.8
45-64 years.......	2,034	1,015	1,019	4.9	2.7	24.5
65 years & over...	6,594	5,753	841	32.9	31.4	48.5

[1] Source: U.S. Bureau of the Census, U.S. Census of Population, 1970, General Population Characteristics PC(1)-B1, Table 52.

[2] Source: U.S. Bureau of the Census, Current Population Reports, Series P-25, No.601, Oct.1975, Table 8 (Series II projection -- projection is based on the estimated July 1, 1974 population and assumes a slight reduction in mortality, an annual net immigration of 400,000 per year and an ultimate cohort fertility level (average number of lifetime births per woman) at the replacement level figure of 2.1.

Appendix Table 19

NUMBER OF ADMISSIONS AND ADMISSION RATES PER 100,000 POPULATION, PSYCHIATRIC FACILITIES,1/ BY AGE AND COLOR: UNITED STATES, 1971

Age (years)	Color Total	White	Nonwhite
Number of Admissions			
Total................	2,541,552	2,106,811	434,741
Less than 18 years....	449,319	369,572	79,747
18-24 years..........	461,152	382,164	78,988
25-44 years..........	957,435	767,706	189,729
45-64 years..........	550,375	478,211	72,164
65 years and over.....	123,271	109,158	14,113
Admission Rates Per 100,000 Population			
Total................	1,244.3	1,179.2	1,699.1
Less than 18 years....	646.3	627.4	751.1
18-24 years..........	1,914.9	1,827.5	2,491.7
25-44 years..........	2,002.7	1,828.8	3,254.9
45-64 years..........	1,299.6	1,253.7	1,716.6
65 years and over.....	601.7	583.1	798.7

1/ Includes State and county mental hospitals, private mental hospitals, VA psychiatric inpatient services, general hospital psychiatric inpatient services, community mental health center inpatient and outpatient services, and all other outpatient psychiatric services except those of Veterans Administration.

Source: Unpublished data from Survey and Reports Branch, Division of Biometry and Epidemiology, NIMH.

Appendix Table 20 Effect of population changes expected to occur in the U.S. between 1970 and 1985 on annual admissions to psychiatric facilities[1] assuming no change in annual age-color specific admission **rates during interval**

Age (Years)	1970 (Estimated)[2]			1985 (Projected Estimate)[3]		
	Total	White	Nonwhite	Total	White	Nonwhite
	Number of admissions					
Total............	2,529,586	2,095,927	433,659	3,134,753	2,506,087	628,666
Less than 18 years..	450,036	370,555	79,481	419,090	333,607	85,483
18-24 years.........	453,686	376,319	77,367	538,807	425,734	113,073
25-44 years.........	961,734	770,053	191,681	1,442,245	1,121,475	320,770
45-64 years.........	543,391	472,118	71,273	573,608	484,843	88,765
65 years and over...	120,739	106,882	13,857	161,003	140,428	20,575
	Change in number of admissions 1970-85			Percent change in number of admissions 1970-85		
Total............	605,167	410,160	195,007	23.9	19.6	45.0
Less than 18 years..	-30,946	-36,948	6,002	-6.9	-10.0	7.6
18-24 years.........	85,121	49,415	35,706	18.8	13.1	46.2
25-44 years.........	480,511	351,422	129,089	50.0	45.6	67.3
45-64 years.........	30,217	12,725	17,492	5.6	2.7	24.5
65 years and over...	40,264	33,546	6,718	33.3	31.4	48.5

[1] Psychiatric facilities include State and county mental hospitals, private mental hospitals, V.A. psychiatric inpatient services, general hospital psychiatric inpatient services, community mental health center inpatient and outpatient services and all other outpatient psychiatric services except those of the Veterans Administration.

[2] Calculated by applying the admission rates for 1971 to the U.S. population for 1970. (Source: U.S. Bureau of the Census, U.S. Census of Population, 1970, General Population Characteristics, PC(1)-B1, Table 52).

[3] Calculated by applying the admission rates for 1971 to the projected U.S. population for 1985 (Source: U.S. Bureau of the Census (1975): Current Population Reports, Series P-25, No. 601, Table 8, (Series II Projection)).

SCOPE 112

Appendix Table 21

Number of new cases of schizophrenia reported to register and treated incidence rates per 1,000 population specific for age, sex and color: Monroe County 1970[1]/

Age (years)	Total	White Both Sexes	White Male	White Female	Nonwhite Both Sexes	Nonwhite Male	Nonwhite Female
Treated Incidence Rates per 1,000 Population							
Total	0.72	0.62	0.72	0.54	1.41	1.45	1.37
Age Adj.[2]/	0.72	0.63	0.74	0.53	1.44	1.60	1.31
<15	0.08	0.05	0.07	0.03	0.32	0.27	0.37
15-24	1.77	1.68	2.57	0.98	2.73	3.58	2.07
25-34	1.37	1.25	1.21	1.30	2.61	1.89	3.22
35-44	0.74	0.69	0.49	0.88	1.41	1.46	1.37
45-54	0.60	0.52	0.51	0.54	2.23	2.80	1.67
55-64	0.26	0.22	0.18	0.25	1.51	2.10	0.97
65+	0.06	0.06	-	0.09	-	-	-
Number of New Cases							
Total	485	412	230	182	73	36	37
<15	17	10	7	3	7	3	4
15-24	214	188	131	57	26	15	11
25-34	126	105	50	55	21	7	14
35-44	59	51	18	33	8	4	4
45-54	49	41	19	22	8	5	3
55-64	16	13	5	8	3	2	1
65+	4	4	-	4	-	-	-

[1]/ Source: Babigian, H.M. (1975): Schizophrenia: Epidemiology Chapter 15.2, Table II, p.862 in Freedman A.M., Kaplan, H.I. and Sadock, B.J. (eds.): Comprehensive Textbook of Psychiatry--Vol.II Baltimore: Williams and Williams

[2]/ Population of Monroe County, as enumerated by age, sex, and color in 1970 Census is used as standard.

Appendix Table 22

Effect of population changes expected to occur in the U.S. between 1970 and 1985 on annual number of new cases of schizophrenia coming under care, assuming no change in annual age-color specific treated incidence rates during interval.1/

Age (Years)	1970 (Estimate)2/ Total	White	Nonwhite	1985 (Projected Estimate)3/ Total	White	Nonwhite
	New cases during year					
All ages............	147,139	110,982	36,157	185,649	133,998	51,651
Less than 15 years	5,297	2,450	2,847	5,262	2,219	3,043
15-24 years.......	64,569	51,495	13,074	71,403	53,906	17,497
25-34 years	35,388	27,224	8,164	57,773	42,486	15,287
35-44 years	17,919	14,026	3,893	24,497	18,860	5,637
45-64 years	22,866	14,687	8,179	25,269	15,082	10,187
65 years and over.	1,100	1,100	-	1,445	1,445	-
	Change in number of new cases 1970-85			Percent change in number of new cases 1970-85		
All ages............	38,510	23,016	15,494	26.2	20.7	42.9
Less than 15 years	-35	-231	196	-0.7	-9.4	6.9
15-24 years.......	6,834	2,411	4,423	10.6	4.7	33.8
25-34 years.......	22,385	15,262	7,123	63.3	56.1	87.2
35-44 years	6,578	4,834	1,744	36.7	34.5	44.8
45-64 years.......	2,403	395	2,008	10.5	2.7	24.6
65 years and over.	345	345	-	31.4	31.4	-

1/ Computations are based on the assumption that the 1970 age-color specific treated incidence rates for Monroe County, N.Y., applied to the actual population of the United States in 1970 and the projected population of the U.S. in 1985.

2/ Calculated by applying the 1970 age-color specific treated incidence rates for Monroe County, N.Y., to the age-color specific population of the U.S. for 1970, (U.S. Bureau of the Census, U.S. Census of Population, 1970 General Population Characteristics, PC(1)-B1, Table 52).

3/ Calculated by applying the 1970 age-color specific treated incidence rates for Monroe County, N.Y., to the projected U.S. age-color specific population for 1985 (U.S. Bureau of the Census, 1975: Current Population Reports, Series P-25, No. 601, Table 8 (Series II Projection)).

Appendix Table 23

Number of cases of schizophrenia under care (hospitalized and not hospitalized) and treated prevalence rates per 1,000 population, specific for age, sex, and color: Monroe County 1970[1/]

Age (years)	Total	White Both Sexes	White Male	White Female	Nonwhite Both Sexes	Nonwhite Male	Nonwhite Female
\<colspan=7\> Treated Prevalence Rates per 1,000 Population						
Total.........	4.78	4.55	4.49	4.61	6.08	6.91	5.32
Age Adj.[2/]..	4.78	4.53	4.46	4.59	6.94	7.89	6.15
<15..........	0.36	0.34	0.47	0.20	0.51	0.64	0.37
15-24	5.35	5.34	6.69	4.11	5.47	8.60	3.00
25-34........	9.13	8.94	8.74	9.13	11.18	12.46	10.09
35-44........	10.78	10.39	9.30	11.44	15.90	17.11	14.75
45-54........	7.25	6.88	6.16	7.53	15.31	14.57	16.05
55-64........	3.77	3.65	2.75	4.45	7.55	8.37	6.80
65+..........	0.96	0.93	0.63	1.13	2.07	3.03	1.27
\<colspan=7\> Number of Cases						
Total........	3,319	3,003	1,428	1,575	316	172	144
<15..........	73	62	44	18	11	7	4
15-24........	649	597	357	240	52	36	16
25-34........	840	750	362	388	90	46	44
35-44........	861	771	339	432	90	47	43
45-54........	596	541	231	310	55	26	29
55-64........	234	219	78	141	15	8	7
65+..........	66	63	17	46	3	2	1

[1/] Source: Babigian, H.M. (1975): Schizophrenia: Epidemiology Chapter 15.2, Table IV, p. 863 in Freedman A.M., Kaplan, H.I. and Sadock, B.J. (eds.): Comprehensive Textbook of Psychiatry--II Baltimore: Williams and Williams

[2/] Population of Monroe County as enumerated by age, sex, and color in 1970 Census is used as standard.

Appendix Table 24

Effect of population changes expected to occur in the United States between 1970 and 1985 on annual number of cases of schizophrenia under care (hospitalized and unhospitalized) assuming no change in annual age-color-specific treated prevalence rates during interval[1]

Age (Years)	1970 (estimate)[2] Total	White	Nonwhite	1985 (Projected estimate)[3] Total	White	Nonwhite
	Number of cases receiving care during year					
All ages............	974,972	809,668	165,304	1,247,806	1,008,622	239,184
Less than 15 years	21,199	16,661	4,538	19,940	15,090	4,850
15-24 years.......	189,878	163,682	26,196	206,402	171,345	35,057
25-34 years	229,675	194,704	34,971	369,343	303,862	65,481
35-44 years.......	255,108	211,208	43,900	347,568	284,000	63,568
45-64 years.......	258,474	206,366	52,108	276,824	211,928	64,896
65 years and over	20,638	17,047	3,591	27,729	22,397	5,332
	Change in number of cases receiving care, 1970-85			Percent change in number of cases receiving care, 1970-85		
All ages............	272,834	198,954	73,880	28.0	24.6	44.7
Less than 15 years	-1,259	-1,571	312	-5.9	-9.4	6.9
15-24 years.......	16,524	7,663	8,861	8.7	4.7	33.8
25-34 years.......	139,668	109,158	30,510	60.8	56.1	87.2
35-44 years.......	92,460	72,792	19,668	36.2	34.5	44.8
45-64 years.......	18,350	5,562	12,788	7.1	2.7	24.5
65 years and over.	7,091	5,350	1,741	34.4	31.4	48.5

[1] Computations based on the assumption that the 1970 age-color specific treated prevalence rates for Monroe County, N.Y., applied to the actual population of the United States in 1970 and the projected population of the United States in 1985.

[2] Calculated by applying the 1970 age-color specific treated prevalence rates for Monroe County, N.Y., to the age-color specific population of the U.S. for 1970, (U.S. Bureau of the Census, U.S. Census of Population, 1970 General Population Characteristics, PC(1)-B1, Table 52).

[3] Calculated by applying the 1970 age-color specific treated prevalence rates for Monroe County, N.Y., to the projected U.S. age-color specific population for 1985 (U.S. Bureau of the Census, 1975: Current Population Reports, Series P-25, No. 601, Table 8 (Series II Projection)).

Appendix Table **25**

Inmates of correctional institutions 1970: Number of inmates and number per 100,000 population by age, color and sex.

Age in Years	Population of the U.S. 1970 (000's) [1] Total	White	Nonwhite	Number of Inmates 1970 [2] Total	White	Nonwhite	Number Inmates per 100,000 Population Total	White	Nonwhite	Ratio of Rates (Nonwhite/white)
Both Sexes										
Total..	203,212	177,749	25,463	328,020	187,199	140,821	161.4	105.3	553.0	5.3
<18.	69,644	59,062	10,582	10,180	4,883	5,297	14.6	8.3	50.1	6.0
18-24	23,697	20,592	3,105	113,650	61,856	51,794	479.6	300.4	1668.1	5.6
25-34	24,907	21,779	3,128	102,133	57,455	44,678	410.1	263.8	1428.3	5.4
35-44	23,089	20,328	2,761	57,651	33,608	24,043	249.7	165.3	870.8	5.3
45-64	41,810	37,658	4,152	40,212	26,318	13,894	96.2	69.9	334.6	4.8
65+..	20,065	18,330	1,735	4,194	3,079	1,115	20.9	16.8	64.2	3.8
Males										
Total..	98,912	86,721	12,191	313,800	179,434	134,366	317.3	206.9	1102.2	5.3
<18.	35,483	30,174	5,309	9,411	4,398	5,013	26.5	14.6	94.4	6.5
18-24	11,572	10,099	1,473	108,495	59,198	49,297	937.6	586.2	3346.7	5.7
25-34	12,218	10,775	1,443	98,037	55,316	42,721	802.4	513.4	2960.6	5.8
35-44	11,231	9,978	1,253	55,493	32,470	23,023	494.1	325.4	1837.4	5.7
45-64	19,992	18,049	1,943	38,672	25,393	13,279	193.4	140.7	683.4	4.9
65+..	8,416	7,646	770	3,692	2,659	1,033	43.9	34.8	134.2	3.9
Females										
Total..	104,300	91,028	13,272	14,220	7,765	6,455	13.6	8.5	48.6	5.7
<18.	34,161	28,888	5,273	769	485	284	2.3	1.7	5.4	3.2
18-24	12,125	10,493	1,632	5,155	2,658	2,497	42.5	25.3	153.0	6.1
25-34	12,689	11,004	1,685	4,096	2,139	1,957	32.3	19.4	116.1	6.0
35-44	11,858	10,350	1,508	2,158	1,138	1,020	18.2	11.0	67.6	6.2
45-64	21,818	19,609	2,209	1,540	925	615	7.1	4.7	27.8	5.9
65+..	11,649	10,684	965	502	420	82	4.3	3.9	8.5	2.2

[1] Source: U.S. Bureau of the Census, U.S. Census of Population, 1970. General Population Characteristics, PC(1)-B1, Table 52.

[2] Source: U.S. Bureau of the Census, U.S. Census of Population, 1970. Persons in Institutions and Other Group Quarters. Subject Reports PC(2)-4E, Table 3.

SCOPE 117

Appendix Table **26**

Effect of population changes expected to occur in the United States between 1970 and 1985 on number of inmates of correctional institutions, assuming no change in number of inmates in such institutions per 100,000 population during interval (i.e. that number of inmates per 100,000 population in 1985 specific for age, color and sex was identical to that in 1970).

Age (Years)	1970 (Actual)[2]			1985 (Projected estimate)[3]		
	Total	White	Nonwhite	Total	White	Nonwhite
	Number of inmates					
Total..............	328,020	187,199	140,821	464,925	244,070	220,855
Less than 18 years	10,180	4,883	5,297	10,160	4,420	5,740
18-24 years.......	113,650	61,856	51,794	149,930	71,991	77,939
25-34 years.......	102,133	57,455	44,678	175,038	90,954	84,084
35-44 years.......	57,652	33,608	24,044	80,171	45,636	34,535
45-64 years.......	40,212	26,318	13,894	44,155	27,160	16,995
65 years and over.	4,193	3,079	1,114	5,471	3,909	1,562
	Change in number of inmates 1970-85			Percent change in number of inmates 1970-85		
Total..............	136,905	56,871	80,034	41.7	30.4	56.8
Less than 18 years	-20	-463	443	-0.2	-9.5	8.4
18-24 years.......	36,280	10,135	26,145	31.9	16.4	50.5
25-34 years.......	72,905	33,499	39,406	71.4	58.3	88.2
35-44 years.......	22,519	12,028	10,491	39.1	35.8	43.6
45-64 years.......	3,943	842	3,141	9.8	3.2	22.3
65 years and over.	1,278	830	448	30.5	27.0	40.2

1/ Includes prisons and reformatories, local jails and work houses.

2/ Source: U.S. Bureau of the Census (July 1973): U.S. Census of Population 1970, Persons in Institutions and Other Group Quarters, Subject Reports PC(2), Table 3.

3/ Calculated by applying the 1970 number of residents in correctional institutions per 100,000 population specific for age, sex, and color, to the projected U.S. age-sex-color specific population for 1985 (Source: U.S. Bureau of the Census, 1975: Current Population Reports, Series P-25, No. 601, Table 8, (Series II Projection)).

SCOPE 118

Appendix Table **27**

Effect of population changes expected to occur in the United States between 1970 and 1985 on number of residents in homes for the aged and dependent, assuming no change in number of residents in such institutions per 100,000 population during interval (i.e. that number of residents per 100,000 in 1985 specific for age and color was identical to that in 1970).

Age (Years)	1970 (Actual)2/			1985 (Projected estimate)3/		
	Total	White	Nonwhite	Total	White	Nonwhite
	Number of residents					
Total 25 years and over	921,135	874,886	46,249	1,201,169	1,134,240	66,929
25-44 years............	20,220	17,276	2,944	30,128	25,202	4,926
45-64 years............	105,108	94,805	10,303	110,162	97,388	12,774
65 years and over......	795,807	762,805	33,002	1,060,879	1,011,650	49,229
	Change in number of residents 1970-85			Percent change in number of residents 1970-85		
Total 25 years and over	280,034	259,354	20,680	30.4	29.6	44.7
25-44 years............	9,908	1,926	1,982	49.0	45.9	67.3
45-64 years............	5,054	2,583	2,471	4.8	2.7	24.0
65 years and over......	265,072	248,845	16,227	33.3	32.6	49.2

1/ Includes homes with and without nursing care

2/ Source: U.S. Bureau of the Census, U.S. Census of Population, Persons in Institutions, PC(2)-4E, Table 6

3/ Calculated by applying the 1970 number of residents in homes for the aged and dependent per 100,000 population specific for age and color to the projected U.S. age-color specific population 1985 (Source: U.S. Bureau of the Census, 1975: Current Population Reports, Series P-25, No. 601, Table 8, (Series II Projection)).

Appendix Table 11

Admission rates [a] per 100,000 population [b] by race and age, selected mental health facilities, [c] United States 1975

Age	Total all races	White	All other races	Ratio of all other races to white rate
Total-all ages	1587.0	1523.4	2009.8	1.3
Under 18......	988.6	936.2	1253.4	1.3
18-24.........	2224.4	2159.1	2523.4	1.2
25-44.........	2569.1	2436.0	3494.0	1.4
45-64.........	1363.8	1339.7	1573.1	1.2
65+...........	721.5	696.0	977.9	1.4

[a] Discharge rates from non-Federal general hospital inpatient units.

[b] Population estimates used as denominators for rate computations are from the Current Population Reports of the Bureau of the Census, Series P-25, No. 614.

[c] Excludes VA psychiatric services, residential treatment centers for emotionally disturbed children and day/night services.

ACKNOWLEDGEMENTS

The Task Panel on the Nature and Scope of the Problems is especially grateful for the major contribution of Beatrix A. Hamburg, M.D., Commission Director of Studies, in all aspects of the preparation of this report. We appreciate also the highly competent professional support services of Gene Broumas, Marie Killilea, and Gretchen Marvin.

The task panel would like to express its deep appreciation to the following individuals who worked closely with Dr. Barbara Snell Dohrenwend and Dr. Bruce Dohrenwend in the preparation of the Special Working Report; Madelyn Schwartz Gould, M.P.A.; Bruce G. Link, M.A.; Richard Neugebauer, Ph.D.; Robin Wunsch, M.A.; from the Research Training Program in Psychiatric Epidemiology, Columbia University, New York, New York, and Martha Tam who provided valuable research assistance throughout.

In addition, the panel wishes to give special recognition for their substantial contributions to Richard C. Redick, Ph.D., Division of Biomety and Epidemiology, National Institute of Mental Health; George Wahrheit, M.D., University of Florida, Gainsville, Florida, with special thanks for his generosity and wisdom; Linda LeReche, Sc.D., School of Hygiene and Public Health, The Johns Hopkins University, Baltimore, Maryland.

We also wish to acknowledge the generous assistance of the following persons and organizations: Elizabeth Douvan, Richard Kulka, and Joseph Veroff of the Survey Research Center, University of Michigan, Ann Arbor, Michigan, with special thanks for the opportunity to meet with them and discuss their exciting survey, "Americans View Their Mental Health"; Office of Drug Abuse Policy and its staff, with special thanks to Pamela Thurber, Julia Taft, and Lee Dogoloff; the Drug Abuse Council, with special thanks to Thomas E. Bryant, M.D., J.D., Jane Silver, and Robert Carr; and to Michael Cohen, M.D., Montefiore Hospital and Medical Center, New York, New York.

BIBLIOGRAPHY

American Psychiatric Association, Committee on Nomenclature and Statistics. Diagnostic and Statistical Manual, Mental Disorders. 2d ed. Washington, D.C.: American Psychiatric Association, 1968.

Babigian, H., and Odoroff, C. The mortality experience of a population with psychiatric illness. American Journal of Psychiatry, 126(4):470-480, 1969.

Babigian, H. M. Schizophrenia: Epidemiology. In: Freedman, A. M.; Kaplan, H. I.; and Sadock, B. J., eds. Comprehensive Textbook of Psychiatry. Vol. II. Baltimore: William and Wilkins, 1975.

Bachrach, L. L. Utilization of services in organized mental health settings in the United States. Draft report for the President's Commission on Mental Health, 1978.

Beck, A. T.; Ward, C. H.; Mendelson, M.; Mock, J.; and Erbaugh, J. An inventory for measuring depression. Archives General Psychiatry, 4:561-571, 1961

Blashfield, R. K., and Draguns, J. G. Toward a taxonomy of psychopathology: The purpose of psychiatric classification. British Journal of Psychiatry, 129:574-583, 1976.

Bower, E. M. Early Identification of Emotionally Handicapped Children in School. Springfield, Ill.: Charles C. Thomas, Publisher, 1960.

Bremer, J. A. A social psychiatric investigation of a small community in northern Norway. Acta Psychiatrica et Neurologica Scandinavica, suppl. 62, 1951.

Brenner, M. H. Personal stability and economic security. Social Policy. May/June 1977.

Brodman, K.; Erdman, A. J.; Lorge, I.; Gershensen, C. P.; and Wolff, H. G. The Cornell Medical Index - health questionnaire III: The evaluation of emotional disturbance. Journal of Clinical Psychology, 8:119-124, 1952.

Cahalan, D. Problem Drinkers: A National Survey. San Francisco: Jossey-Bass, Inc., 1970.

Cahalan, D., and Room, R. Problem Drinking Among American Men. Rutgers Center of Alcohol Studies, Monograph 7, 1974.

Davie, R.; Butler N.; Goldstein, H. From Birth to Seven. London: Longman Publishers, 1972.

Davis, A. E.; Dinitz, S.; and Pasamanick, B.. Schizophrenics in the new custodial community--five years after the experiment. Ohio State University Press, 1974.

Diggs, R. "Mental health issues in mental retardation: Policy implications." Working paper prepared for the President's Commission on Mental Health. Norfolk State College, 1977.

Dohrenwend, B. P. Some issues in the definition and measurement of psychiatric disorders in general populations. In: Proceedings of the 14th National Meeting of the Public Health Conference on Records and Statistics (DHEW Publication No. 74-1214). Washington, D.C.: Superintendent of Documents, U.S. Government Printing Office, 1973.

Dohrenwend, B. P. Sociocultural and socio-psychological factors in the genesis of mental disorders. Journal of Health and Social Behavior, 16:365-392, 1975.

Dohrenwend, B. P., and Dohrenwend, B. S. Psychiatric disorders in urban settings. In: Arieti, S., ed. American Handbook of Psychiatry. Vol. III., 2d ed. New York: Basic Books, Inc., 1974, pp. 424-447.

Dohrenwend, B. P., and Dohrenwend, B. S. Sex differences and psychiatric disorder. American Journal of Sociology, 81:1447-1454, 1976.

Dohrenwend, B. P., and Dohrenwend, B. S. Social and cultural influences on psychopathology. Annual Review of Psychology, 25:417-452, 1974.

Dohrenwend, B. P.; Dohrenwend, B. S.; Gould, M. S.; Link, B. G.; Neugebauer, R.; and Wunsch, R. "Scope of the Problem." Working paper prepared for the President's Commission on Mental Health, January 1978.

Dohrenwend, B. P.; Egri, G.; and Mendelsohn, F. S. Psychiatric disorder in general populations: A study of the problem of clinical judgment. American Journal of Psychiatry, 127:1304-1312, 1971.

Dohrenwend, B. P.; Oksenberg, L.; Dohrenwend, B. S.; and Cook, D. "What psychiatric screening scales measure in the general population." Unpublished manuscript. 1978. Available from Dr. Bruce Dohrenwend, Social Psychiatry Research Unit, Tower 3-19 H, 100 Haven Avenue, New York, New York 10032.

Douglas, J. W. B., and Mulligan, D. G. Emotional adjustment and educatonal achievement: The preliminary results of a longitudinal study of a national sample of children. Proceedings of the Royal Society of Medicine, 54:885-891, 1961.

Dunham, H. W. Community and Schizophrenia: An Epidemiological Analysis. Detroit, Michigan: Wayne State University Press, 1965.

Dupuy, H. Utility of the National Center for Health Statistics General Well-Being Schedule in the assessment of self-representations of subjective well-being and distress. National Conference on Education in Alcohol, Drug Abuse and Mental Health Programs. Department of Health, Education, and Welfare, 1974.

Endicott, J., Spitzer, R. L. A diagnostic interview: "The schedule for affective disorders and schizophrenia." Presented at the American Psychiatric Association Meeting, Toronto, Canada, May 1977.

Evans, J. R.; Rodnick, E. H.; Goldstein, M. J. Premorbid adjustment, phenothiazine treatment, and remission in acute schizophrenics. Archives of General Psychiatry. 27:486-490, 1972.

Fink, R.; Goldensohn, S. S.; Shapiro, S.; and Daily, E. F. Changes in family doctors' services for emotional disorders after addition of psychiatric treatment to a prepaid group practice program. Medical Care, 7(3), 1969.

Frank, J. D. Persuasion and Healing. Baltimore: Johns Hopkins University Press, 1973.

Glidewell, J. C., and Swallow, C. S. The Prevalence of Maladjustment in Elementary Schools. A report prepared for the Joint Commission on the Mental Health of Children. Chicago: University of Chicago Press, 1968.

Goldberg, D. P. The Detection of Psychiatric Illness by Questionnaire. London: Oxford University Press, 1972.

Gordon, S. Middlesex County Schools Mental Health Survey: Covering 25 Districts, 125 Elementary Schools, 53,995 Pupils in Grades Kindergarten through Sixth. New Brunswick, N.J.: County Superintendent of Schools in association with the Middlesex County Mental Health Clinic, 1962.

Gottesman, I.; Shields, J. Schizophrenia and Genetics. New York: Academic Press, 1972.

Graham, P., and Rutter, M. Psychiatric disorder in the young adolescent: A follow-up study. Proceedings of the Royal Society of Medicine, 66:1226-1229, 1973.

Gruenberg, E. N., and Turns, D. M. Science of human behavior: Quantitative experimental and research methods in psychiatry. In: Freedman, A. M.; Kaplan, H. I.; and Sudock, B. J., eds. Comprehensive Textbook of Psychiatry--II, 2d ed. Baltimore, Maryland: William and Wilkins, 1975.

Gruenberg, E. N. "The epidemiology of senile dementia." Unpublished manuscript. Copies available from author. Department of Mental Hygiene, Johns Hopkins University, Baltimore, Md., 1978.

Gurin, G.; Veroff, J.; and Feld, S. Americans View Their Mental Health. New York: Basic Books, 1960.

Hagnell, D. A Prospective Study of the Incidence of Mental Disorder. Stockholm: Svenska Bokforlaget Norstedts-Bonniers, 1966.

Haese, P. N., and Meile, R. L. The relative effectiveness of two models for scoring the Midtown Psychological Index. Community Mental Health Journal, 3:335-342, 1967.

Hein, K.; Cohen, M. I.; and Lih, I. F. "Illicit drug use among urban adolescents: A decade in retrospect." Unpublished manuscript, 1978. Available from Dr. Hein, Adolescent Medicine Division, Department of Pediatrics, Stanford University Medical Center.

Institute of Medicine. *A Policy Statement: The Elderly and Functional Dependency*. National Academy of Sciences. Washington, D.C., June 1977.

Jablensky, A. Personality disorders and their relationship to illness and social deviance. *Psychiatric Annals*, 6(8), 1976.

Johnston, L. D. Drug use during and after high school: Results of a national longitudinal study. *American Journal of Public Health*, suppl., 29-37, 1974.

Joint Commission on Mental Illness and Health. *Action for Mental Health*. Final report of the Joint Commission. New York: Basic Books, 1961.

Kandel, D.; Single, E.; and Kessler, R. The epidemiology of drug use among New York State high school students: Distribution, trends and change in rates of use. *American Journal of Public Health*, 66, 1976.

Kandel, D. B. Convergences in prospective longitudinal surveys of drug use in normal populations. In: Sells, S.; Pollin, W.; Strauss, J.; and Roff, M., eds. *Life History Research in Psychopathology*, in press.

Kety, S.; Rosenthal, D.; Wender, P.; Schulsinger, F. The types and prevalence of mental illness in the biological and adoptive families of adopted schizophrenics. In: Rosenthal, D.; Kety, S. *The Transmission of Schizophrenia*. New York: Pergamon Press, 1968.

Klerman, G. L. Depression and Adaptation. In: Friedman, R., and Katz, M., eds. *The Psychology of Depression: Contemporary Theory and Research*. Washington, D.C.: V. H. Winston & Sons, 1974.

Klerman, G. L.; DiMascio, A.; and Weissman, M. M., et al. Treatment of depression by drugs and psychotherapy. *American Journal of Psychiatry*, 131:186-191, 1974.

Klinge, V., and Vaziri, H. Characteristics of drug abusers in an adolescent in-patient psychiatric facility. *Diseases of the Nervous System*, 38, 1977.

Kramer, M. The history of the efforts to agree on an International Classification of Mental Disorders. In: American Psychiatric Association, Committee on Nomenclature and Statistics. *Diagnostic and Statistical Manual, Mental Disorders*. 2d ed. Washington, D.C.: American Psychiatric Association, 1968.

Kramer, M. Diagnosis and classification in epidemiological and health-services research. In: Hobbs, N., ed. *Issues in the Classification of Children*, Vol. 1. San Francisco: Jossey-Bass, 1975.

Kramer, M. Issues in the development of statistical and epidemiological data for mental health services research. *Psychological Medicine* 6:185-215, 1976.

Kramer, M. "Psychiatric services and the changing institutional scene." Presented at the President's Biomedical Research Panel, National Institutes of Health, 1975.

Kramer, M.; Taube, C. A.; and Redick, R. W. Patterns of use of psychiatric facilities by the aged: Past, present and future. In: Eisdorfer, C., and Lawton, M. P., eds. The Psychology of Adult Development and Aging. Washington, D.C.: American Psychiatric Association, 1973.

Kringlen, E. Twins--still our best method. Schizophrenia Bulletin, 2:429-433, 1976.

Langner, T. S., and Michael, S. T. Life Stress and Mental Health. New York: Free Press of Glencoe, 1963.

Langner, T. S.; Gersten, J.; Green, E. L.; Eisenberg, J. G.; Herson, J. H.; and McCarthy, E. Treatment of psychological disorders among urban children. Journal of Consulting and Clinical Psychology, 42:170-179, 1974.

Langner, T. S. A twenty-two item screening score of psychiatric symptoms indicating impairment. Journal of Health and Human Behavior, 3:269-276, 1962.

Leighton, D. C.; Harding, J. S.; Macklin, D. B.; Macmillan, A. M.; and Leighton, A. H. The Character of Danger. New York: Basic Books, 1963.

Leslie, S. A. Psychiatric disorder in the young adolescents of an industrial town. British Journal of Psychiatry, 125:113-124, 1974.

Macmillan, A. M. The health opinion survey: Technique for estimating prevalence of psychoneurotic and related types of disorder in communities. Psychological Reports, 3:325-329, 1957.

Mangus, A. R., and Seeley, J. R. Mental Health Needs in a Rural and Semi-Rural Area of Ohio. Ohio State Department of Public Welfare, Division of Mental Hygiene, 1950.

Manis, J. G.; Brawer, M. J.; Hunt, C. L.; and Kercher, L. Estimating the prevalence of mental illness. American Sociological Review, 29:84-89, 1964.

Mechanic, D. "Considerations in the design of mental health benefits under National Health Insurance." Unpublished manuscript. Copies available from author. Department of Sociology, University of Wisconsin, Madison, 1978.

Mechanic, D. "Explanations of mental illness." Working paper prepared for the President's Commission on Mental Health. University of Wisconsin-Madison, 1977.

Mechanic, D. "Social factors affecting psychotic behavior." Prepared for the Anniversary Symposium of the 100th meeting of the National Mental Health Advisory Council.

Mechanic, D. Sociology of mental health. In: Mechanic, D. *Politics, Medicine and Social Science*. New York: Wiley-Interscience, 1974. pp. 179-202.

Miller, L. L.; Hampe, E.; Barrett, C. L.; and Noble, H. Children's deviant behavior within the general population. *Journal of Consulting and Clinical Psychology*, 37:16-22, 1971.

Murphy, H. B. M. "The meaning of symptom-check scores in mental health surveys: A testing of multiple hypotheses." Unpublished manuscript, April 1977. Available from Dr. Murphy, Department of Psychiatry, McGill University, Montreal P.Q., Canada H3G IA8.

Murphy, H. B. M. Two stress measures in three cultures--their prognostic efficiency, significance and incongruities. In: Leigh, D.; Noorbakhsh, J.; and Izadi, C., eds. International Symposium on Epidemiological Studies in Psychiatry, Tehran, May 20-22, 1974. Available from Dr. H. B. M. Murphy, McGill University, Department of Psychiatry, Montreal, P.Q., Canada H3G IA8.

National Institute of Mental Health. *Services to the Mentally Disabled of Metropolitan Community Mental Health Center Catchment Area*, Series B, No. 10. DHEW Publication No. (ADM) 76-373. Washington, D.C.: Superintendent of Documents, U.S. Government Printing Office, 1976.

National Institute of Mental Health. *Services to the Mentally Disabled of Selected Catchment Areas in Eastern New York State and New York City*. DHEW Publication No. (ADM) 76-372. Washington, D.C.: Superintendent of Documents, U.S. Government Printing Office, 1976.

National Institute of Mental Health. *Utilization of Mental Health Facilities, 1971*. DHEW Publication No. NIH-74-657. Washington, D.C.: Superintendent of Documents, U.S. Government Printing Office, 1973.

Pasamanick, B.; Roberts, D. W.; Lemkau, D. W.; and Krueger, D. B. A survey of mental disease in an urban population: Prevalence by race and income. In: Pasamanick, B., ed. *Epidemiology of Mental Disorder*. Washington, D.C.: American Association of the Advancement of Psychiatry, 1959.

Phillips, D. C. The "true prevalence" of mental illness in a New England State. *Community Mental Health Journal*, 2:35-40, 1966.

Philips, D. L., and Clancy, K. J. Some effects of "social desirability" in survey studies. *American Journal of Sociology*, 77:921-940, 1972.

Piotrowski, A.; Henisz, J.; and Gnat, T. Individual interview and clinical examination to determine prevalence of mental disorders. *Proceedings of the Fourth World Congress of Psychiatry*, Madrid, No. 150, 2477-2478, 1966.

Prien, R. F.; Caffey, E. M.; and Kleh, C. J. Prophylactic efficacy of lithium carbonate in manic-depressive illness. *Archives General Psychiatry*, 28:337-341, 1973.

Radloff, L. S. The CES-D Scale: A Self-Report Depression Scale for research in the general population. *Applied Psychological Measurement*, 1:385-401, 1977.

Regier, D. A.; Goldberg, I. D.; and Taube, C. A. "The *de facto* U.S. mental health services system: A public health perspective." Unpublished manuscript, February 1978. Available from Dr. Regier, Division of Biometry and Epidemiology, NIMH, Rockville, Maryland.

Robins, L. N. *Deviant Children Grown Up: A Sociological and Psychiatric Study* of Sociopathic Personality. Baltimore: Williams and Wilkins, 1966.

Robins, L. N.; Murphy, G. E.; Woodruff, R. A.; and King, L. J. Adult psychiatric status of Black school boys. *Archives of General Psychiatry*, 24:338-345, 1971.

Robins, L. N. "Mental Disorders in Childhood." Working paper prepared for the President's Commission on Mental Health, February 1978.

Room, R. "The scope and definition of alcohol-related problems." Working paper prepared for the President's Commission on Mental Health, University of California, Berkeley, 1977.

Rosenthal, D. *Genetic Theory and Abnormal Behavior*. New York: McGraw Hill, 1970.

Rutter, M. Why are London children so disturbed? *Proceedings of the Royal Society of Medicine*, 66:1221-1225, 1973.

Rutter, M.; Cox, A.; Tupling, C.; Berger, M.; and Yule, W. Attainment and adjustment in two geographical areas: I - The prevalence of psychiatric disorder. *British Journal of Psychiatry*, 126:493-509, 1975.

Rutter, M., and Graham, P. Psychiatric disorder in 10-11 year old children. *Proceedings of the Royal Society of Medicine*, 59:382-387, 1966.

Rutter, M.,; Shaffer, D.; and Shepherd, M. *A Multi-Axial Classification of Child Psychiatric Disorders*. Geneva: World Health Organization, 1975.

Ryle, A.; Pond, D.; and Hamilton, M. The prevalence and pattern of psychological disturbance in children of primary age. *Journal of Child Psycology and Psychiatry*, 6:101-113, 1965.

Sartorius, N. Classification: An international perspective. *Psychiatric Annals*, 6(8), 1976.

Sartorius, N. The cross-national standardization of psychiatric diagnoses and classification. In: Pflanz, M., and Schach, E., eds. *Cross-National and Sociomedical Research: Concepts, Methods, Practice*. Stuttgart: Thieme, 1976.

Sartorius, N. The programme of the World Health Organization on the epidemiology of mental disorders. In: Excerpta Medica International Congress Series, No. 274. Proceedings of the World Congress of Psychiatry, V, Mexico. Amsterdam: Excerpta Medica, 1971.

Schwab, J. J.; McGinnis, N. H.; and Warheit, G. J. Social psychiatric impairment: Racial comparisons. American Journal of Psychiatry, 130:183-187, 1973.

Schwab, J. J., and Warheit, G. J. Evaluating southern mental health needs and services. Journal of Florida Medical Association, pp. 17-20, January 1972.

Segal, J.; Boomer, D. S.; and Bouthilet, L., eds. Research in the Service of Mental Health--Report of the Research Task Force of the National Institute of Mental Health. DHEW Publication No. (ADM) 75-236. Washington, D.C.: Superintendent of Documents, U.S. Government Printing Office, 1975.

Shepherd, M. General practice, mental illness, and the British National Health Service. American Journal of Public Health, 64(3), 1974.

Shepherd, M., and Sartorius, N. Personality disorder and the International Classification of Diseases. Psychological Medicine, 4(2), 1974.

Shepherd, M.; Cooper, B.; Brown, A. C.; and Kalton, G. W. Psychiatric Illness in General Practice. London: Oxford University Press, 1966.

Shore, J. H.; Kinzie, J. D.; Hampson, J. L.; and Pattison, E. M. Psychiatric epidemiology of an Indian village. Psychiatry, 36:70-81, 1973.

Spitzer, R. L.; Endicott, J.; and Robins, E. "Research diagnostic criteria: Rationale and reliability." Presented at the American Psychiatric Association Meeting, Toronto, Canada, May 1977.

Srole, L.; Langner, T. S.; Michael, S. T.; Opler, M. K.; and Rennie, T. A. C. Mental Health in the Metropolis. New York: McGraw Hill, 1962.

Star, S. A. The screening of psychoneurotics: Comparison of psychiatric diagnoses and test scores at all induction stations. In: Stouffer, S. A.; Guttman, L.; Suchman, E. A.; Lazarsfeld, P. F.; Star, S. A.; and Clausen, J. A., eds. Measurement and Prediction. Princeton, N.J.: Princeton University Press, 1950.

Stengel, E. Classification of mental disorders. Bulletin of the World Health Organization, 21, 1959.

Stennett, R. G. Emotional handicap in the elementary years: Phase or disease? American Journal of Orthopsychiatry, 36:444-449, 1966.

Strauss, J. S. "The problem of schizophrenia." Working paper prepared for the President's Commission on Mental Health. Yale University, 1977.

Strauss, J. S., and Gift, T. E. Choosing an approach for diagnosing schizophrenia. Archives of General Psychiatry, 34:1248-1253, 1977.

Strauss, J.; Carpenter, W. Prediction of outcome in schizophrenia III. Five year outcome and its predictors. A report from the International Pilot Study of Schizophrenia. Archives of General Psychiatry. 34:159-163, 1977.

Strauss, J.; Carpenter, W. Characteristic symptoms and outcome in schizophrenia. Archives of General Psychiatry. 30:429-434, 1974.

Straus, R. Problem drinking in the perspective of social change, 1940-1973. In: Filstead, W. J.; Rossi, J. J.; and Keller, M., eds. Alcohol and Alcohol Problems: New Thinking and New Directions. Cambridge, Mass.: Ballinger Publishing Co., 1976.

Summers, G. F.; Seiler, L. H.; and Hough, R. L. Psychiatric symptoms: Cross validation with a rural sample. Rural Sociology, 36:367-378, 1971.

Thomas, A., and Chess, S. Evolution of behavior disorders into adolescence. American Journal of Psychiatry. 133:539-542, 1976.

Toohey, J. V., and Dezelsky, T. L. A six-year analysis of patterns on nonmedical drug use behavior. The Journal of School Health, January 1978.

Tousignant, M. G. D., and Lachapelle, R. Some considerations concerning the validity and use of the health opinion survey. Journal of Health and Social Behavior, 15:241-252, 1974.

Trussell, R. E.; Elinson, J.; and Levin, M. L. Comparisons of various methods of estimating the prevalence of chronic disease in a community--the Hunterdon County study. American Journal of Public Health, 46:173-182, 1956.

U.S. Department of Commerce, Bureau of the Census. Statistical Abstract of the United States, 1975. 96th edition. Washington, D.C.: Superintendent of Documents, U.S. Government Printing Office, 1975.

U.S. Department of Health, Education, and Welfare. Health: United States 1975. DHEW Publication No. (HRA) 76-1232. Washington, D.C.: Superintendent of Documents, U.S. Government Printing Office, 1976.

Warheit, G. J.; Arey, S. S.; and Buhl, J. M. "Mental health needs and services utilization: Some implications for national health policy." Unpublished manuscript, 1977. Available from Dr. Warheit, Depts. of Sociology and Psychiatry, University of Florida.

Weissman, M. M. "Depressive disorders." Working paper prepared for the President's Commission on Mental Health, Yale University, 1977.

Weissman, M. M.; Kasl, S. V.; and Klerman, G. L. Follow-up of depressed women after maintenance treatment. American Journal of Psychiatry, 133:757-760, 1976.

Weissman, M. M. and Klerman, G. L. "Epidemiology of mental disorders: Emerging trends." Unpublished manuscript. Copies available from Dr. Weissman, Dept. of Psychiatry, Yale University, New Haven, Conn.

Weissman, M. M., and Klerman, G. L. Sex differences and the epidemiology of depression. Archives of General Psychiatry, 34:98-111, 1977.

Weissman, M. M.; Myers, J. K.; and Harding, P. S. Psychiatric disorders in a United States urban community: 1975-76. American Journal of Psychiatry, in press, 1978.

Weissman, M. M., and Myers, J. K. Rates and risk of depressive symptoms in a U.S. urban community, Acta Psychiatrica Scandinavica, in press, 1978.

Weissman, M. M., and Myers, J. K. "The New Haven community survey 1967-75: Depressive symptoms and diagnosis." Presented at the Society for Life History Study of Psychopathology Meeting, Fort Worth, Texas, October 6-8, 1976.

Weismann, M. M., and Paykel, E. S. The Depressed Woman: A Study of Social Relationships. Chicago: University of Chicago Press, 1974.

Weissman, M. M.; Prusoff, B.; and Newberry, P. Comparison of the CES-D with standardized depression rating scales at three points in time. Technical report from Yale University under Contract ASH 74-166, Center for Epidemiologic Studies, National Institute of Mental Health, 1975.

Weissman, M. M.; Sholomskas, D.; Doltenjer, M.; Prusoff, B.; and Locke, B. "Assessing depressive symptoms in five psychiatric populations: A validation study." Unpublished manuscript, January 1977. Available from Dr. Weissman, Dept. of Psychiatry, Yale University School of Medicine, New Haven, Conn.

World Health Organization. Organization of Mental Health Services in Developing Countries, Sixteenth Report of the WHO Expert Committee on Mental Health. World Health Organization Technical Report Series, No. 564. Geneva: World Health Organization, 1975.

World Health Organization. Manual of the International Statistical Classification of Diseases, Injuries, and Causes of Death, Vol. 1. Geneva: World Health Organization, 1977.

Yancey, W. L.; Rigsby, L.; and McCarthy, J. D. Social position and self-evaluation: The relative importance of race. American Journal of Sociology. 78:338-359, 1972.

Yolles, S. F., and Kramer, M. Vital statistics. In: Bellak, L., and Loeb, L., eds. The Schizophrenic Syndrome. New York: Grune and Stratton, 1969.

Young-Masten, I. Behavior problems of elementary school children: A descriptive and comparative study. Genetic Psychology Monographs, 20:123-181, 1938.

Zung, W. W. K. A self-rating depression scale. <u>Archives General Psychiatry</u>, 12:63-70, 1965.

LOCATION OF PATIENTS

ADDENDUM BIBLIOGRAPHY

Alcohol, Drug Abuse, and Mental Health Administration, Legislative Services Unit. "Current status of state community mental health services legislation." Unpublished report, 1976.

American Public Health Association, Program Area Committee on Mental Health. Mental Disorder: A Guide to Control Methods. New York: American Public Health Association, 1962.

American Thoracic Society. Intermittent chemotherapy for adults with tuberculosis. Official statement. Am Rev Respir Dis, 110:373, 1974.

Arnhoff, F. N. Social consequences of policy toward mental illness. Science, June 27, 1975. pp. 1277-1281.

Arnhoff, F. N., and Kumbar, A. H. The Nation's Psychiatrists - 1970 Survey. Washington, D.C.: American Psychiatric Association, 1973.

Arnhoff, F. N.; Rubinstein, E. A.; and Speisman, J. C., eds. Manpower for Mental Health. Chicago: Aldine Publishing Co., 1969.

Babigian, H. M. Schizophrenia: Epidemiology. Chapter 15.2, pp. 862-863. In: Freedman, A. M.; Kaplan, H. I.; and Sadork, B. J., eds. Comprehensive Textbook of Psychiatry - II. Baltimore, Maryland: Williams and Wilkins, 1975.

Babigian, H. M., and Odoroff, C. L. The mortality experience of a population with psychiatric illness. Am J Psychiatry, 126:470-480, 1969.

Bahn, A. K. Methodological Study of Population of Outpatient Psychiatric Clinics, Maryland 1958-59. Public Health Monograph No. 65. PHS Publicacation No. 821. Washington, D.C.: U.S. Government Printing Office, 1961.

Becker, A., and Schulberg, H. C. Phasing out State hospitals - A psychiatric dilemma. N Engl J Med, Vol. 294, No. 5, pp. 255-261, 1976.

Benenson, A. S. Control of Communicable Diseases in Man: Tuberculosis. Washington, D.C.: The American Public Health Association, pp. 265-269, 1970.

Breslow, L. Chronic disease and disability in adults. Chapter 16. In: Sartwell, P. E., ed. Maxcy-Rosenau Preventive Medicine and Public Health. Ninth Edition. New York: Appleton-Century-Crofts, 1965.

Cole, J. O., and Gerard, R. W., eds. Psychopharmacology: Problems in Evaluation. Washington, D.C.: National Academy of Sciences - National Research Council, 1959.

Committee on Finance, U.S. Senate. The Social Security Act (As Amended Through January 4, 1975) and Related Laws. Washington, D.C.: U.S. Government Printing Office, 1975.

Committee on Interstate and Foreign Commerce. Title III Community Mental Health Centers: pp. 34-37. In: Health Revenue Sharing and Health Services Act of 1975. House of Representatives Report No. 94-192. Washington, D.C.: U.S. Government Printing Office, 1975.

Comstock, G. W. Frost revisited: The modern epidemiology of tuberculosis. Am J Epidemiol, 101:363-382, 1975.

Deutsch, A. The Shame of the States. New York: Harcourt, Brace and Co., 1948.

Efron, D. H.; Cole, J. O.; Levine, J.; Wittenborn, J. R., eds. Psychopharmacology: A Review of Progress (1957-1967). Proceedings of the Sixth Annual Meeting of the American College of Neuropsychopharmacology, December 1967. PHS Publication No. 1836. Washington, D.C.: U.S. Government Printing Office, 1968.

Feldman, S., and Goldstein, H. H. Community Mental Health Centers in the U.S.A.: An overview. Int J Nurs Stud, 8:247-257, 1971.

Felix, R. H. Mental Illness: Progress and Prospect. New York: Columbia University Press, 1967.

Fink, R.; Goldensohn, S. S.; Shapiro, S.; and Dailey, E. F. Changes in family doctors' services for emotional disorders after addition of psychiatric treatment to a prepaid group practice program. Medical Care, Vol. VII, No. 3, 1969.

Galioni, E. F.; Adams, F. H.; and Tallman, F. F. Intensive treatment of backward patients: A controlled pilot study. Am J Psychiatry, 109:576-583, 1953.

Gallant, D. M., and Simpson, G. M., eds. Depression: Behavioral, Biochemical, Diagnostic and Treatment Concepts. New York: Halstead Press Division of John Wiley & Sons, Inc., 1976.

Giesler, R.; Hurley, P. L.; and Person, P. H., Jr. Survey of General Hospitals Admitting Psychiatric Patients. Public Health Service Publication No. 1462. Washington, D.C.: U.S. Government Printing Office, 1966.

Glaser, D. Routinizing Evaluation: Getting Feedback on Effectiveness of Crime and Delinquency Programs. Crime and Delinquency Issues: A Monograph Series (NIMH), DHEW Publication No. (HSM) 73-9123, Washington, D.C.: Superintendent of Documents, U.S. Government Printing Office, 1973.

Glaser, D. Strategic Criminal Justice Planning. Crime and Delinquency Issues: A Monograph Series (NIMH) DHEW Publication No. (ADM) 75-195, Washington, D.C.: U.S. Government Printing Office, 1975.

Glasscote, R. M., and Kanno, C. K. A National Survey - General Hospitals Psychiatric Units. Washington, D.C.: Joint Information Service of the American Psychiatric Association and the National Association for Mental Health, 1965.

Greenblatt, M., and Glazier, E. The phasing out of mental hospitals in the United States. Am J Psychiatry, 132:11, 1975.

Gruenberg, E. M., and Huxley, M., eds. Causes of Mental Disorders: A Review of Epidemiological Knowledge, 1959. New York: Milbank Memorial Fund, 1961.

Gruenberg, E. M., and Huxley, M., eds. The failures of success. Health and Society, Vol. 1, No. 1 in press, 1977.

Hersch, C. Social history, mental health, and community control. Am Psychol, 27:749-754, 1972.

Jenkins, R. Alabama prisons ruled unconstitutionally cruel. The New York Times, January 14, 1976. pp. 1, 36.

Joint Commission on Mental Illness and Health. Action for Mental Health. Final report of the Joint Commission. New York: Basic Books, 1961.

Keehn, R. J.; Goldberg, I. D.; and Beebe, G. W. Twenty-four year mortality follow-up of army veterans with disability for psychoneurosis in 1944. Psychosom Med, Vol. 36, 1974. pp. 27-46.

King, W. Rise in inmates strains jails in South; Florida jams 10 into 12-by-15 foot cells. The New York Times, October 24, 1975. pp. 1, 12.

King, W. Prison officials ask reforms for South to avert crowding. The New York Times, January 25, 1976. pp. 1, 24.

Klein, D. F., and Davis, J. M. Diagnosis and Drug Treatment of Psychiatric Disorders. Baltimore, Maryland: The Williams & Wilkins Co., 1969.

Kramer, M. A discussion of the concepts of incidence and prevalence as related to epidemiologic studies of mental disorders. Am J Public Health, 47:826-840, 1957.

Kramer, M. Some Implications of Trends in the Usage of Psychiatric Facilities for Community Mental Health Programs and Related Research. Public Health Service Publication No. 1434. Washington, D.C.: U.S. Government Printing Office, 1966.

Kramer, M. Epidemiology, biostatistics and mental health planning. In: Monroe, R. R.; Klee, G. D.; and Brody, E. R., eds. Psychiatric Epidemiology and Mental Health Planning. Psychiatric Research Reports No. 22. Washington, D.C.: American Psychiatric Association, 1967.

Kramer, M. Applications of Mental Health Statistics. Geneva: World Health Organization, 1969.

Kramer, M. Some perspectives on the role of biostatistics and epidemiology in the prevention and control of mental disorders. Health and Society, The Milbank Memorial Fund Quarterly, Summer 1975.

Kramer, M.; Rosen, B. M.; and Willis, E. M. Definitions and distributions of mental disorders in a racist society. In: Willie, C. V., Kramer, B. M., and Brown, B. S., eds. Racism and Mental Health; Essays, Chapter 11. Pittsburgh: University of Pittsburgh Press, 1973.

Kramer, M.; Taube, C. A.; and Redick, R. W. Patterns of use of psychiatric facilities by the aged: Past present and future. In: Eisdorfer, C., and Lawton, M. P., eds. The Psychology of Adult Development and Aging. Washington, D.C.: American Psychological Association, 1973.

Kramer, M.; Taube, C. A.; and Starr, S. Patterns of use of psychiatric facilities by the aged: Current status, trends, and implications. In: Aging in Modern Society, Psychiatric Research Report No. 23, Washington, D.C.: American Psychiatric Association, 1968, pp. 89-150.

Lieberman, E. J., ed. Mental Health: The Public Challenge. Washington, D.C.: American Public Health Association, 1975.

MacMahon, B.; Pugh, T.; and Ipsen, J. Epidemiologic Methods. Boston: Little, Brown and Company, 1960.

Mechanic, D. Mental Health and Social Policy. Englewood Cliffs, New Jersey: Prentice-Hall, Inc., 1969.

Milbank Memorial Fund. An Approach to the Prevention of Disability from Chronic Psychoses: The open mental hospital within the community. Proceedings of thirty fourth annual conference, 1957, Part I, New York: Milbank Memorial Fund, 1958. pp. 5-80.

National Center for Health Statistics. Nursing care and related homes. Chapter 40. In: Health Resources Statistics. DHEW Publication No. (HRA) 75-1509. Washington, D.C.: U.S. Government Printing Office, 1974.

National Institute of Mental Health. Proceedings of the First Research Conference on Psychosurgery. PHS Publication No. 16, Washington, D.C.: U.S. Government Printing Office, 1951.

National Institute of Mental Health. Second Research Conference on Psychosurgery. PHS Publication No. 156, Washington, D.C.: U.S. Government Printing Office, 1952.

National Institute of Mental Health. Third Research Conference on Psychosurgery. PHS Publication No. 221, Washington, D.C.: U.S. Government Printing Office, 1954.

National Institute of Mental Health. Psychiatric Services in General Hospitals 1969-70. Mental Health Statistics Series A, No. 11, DHEW Publication No. (HSM) 73-9099, Washington, D.C.: U.S. Government Printing Office, 1972.

Oppenheimer, J. Federal prisons so overcrowded they've passed 1986 projection. Washington Star, March 15, 1976, p. A-3.

President of the United States (1963). Message relative to mental illness and mental retardation: February 5, 1963; 88th Congress, Document No. 58. Washington, D.C.: House of Representatives.

Public Law 79-487--79th Congress, Chapter 538--2d Session, July 3, 1946. National Mental Health Act.

Public Law 84-182--84th Congress, Chapter 417--1st Session, July 28, 1955. Mental Health Study Act of 1955.

Public Law 88-164--88th Congress, S. 1576, October 31, 1963. Mental Retardation Facilities and Community Mental Health Centers Construction Act of 1963.

Public Law 90-351--90th Congress, H.R. 5037, June 19, 1968. Omnibus Crime Control and Safe Streets Act of 1968.

Public Law 93-83--93d Congress, H.R. 8152, August 6, 1973. Crime Control Act of 1973.

Public Law 94-63--94th Congress, S. 66, July 29, 1975. Title III Community Mental Health Centers Amendments of 1975.

Redick, R. W. Referral of Discontinuations from Inpatient Services of State & County Mental Hospitals, United States, 1969. Statistical Note 57, November 1971. Rockville, Maryland: Biometry Branch, National Institute of Mental Health, 1971.

Regier, D. A., and Goldberg, I. D. "National Health Insurance and the Mental Health Services Equilibrium." Paper presented at annual meeting of the American Psychiatric Association, Miami, Florida, 1976.

Regional Office for Europe, WHO. Psychiatry and Primary Medical Care (Euro 5427 I). Copenhagen: Regional Office for Europe, 1973.

Segal, J.; Boomer, D. S.; and Bouthilet, L., eds. Research in the Service of Mental Health - Report of the Research Task Force of the National Institute of Mental Health. Chapter 12. Research on treatment of mental disorders. pp. 309-349. DHEW Publication No. (ADM) 75-236. Washington, D.C.: U.S. Government Printing Office, 1975.

Shapiro, S., and Fink, R. Methodological considerations in studying patterns of medical care related to mental illness. In: McKinlay, J. B., ed. Research Methods in Health Care. Milbank Memorial Fund. New York: Prodist, 1963.

Shepherd, M.; Cooper, B.; Brown, A. C.; and Kalton, G. W. Psychiatric Illness in General Practice, pp. 1-21. London: Oxford University Press, 1966.

Swazey, J. P. Chlorpromazine in Psychiatry - A Study of Therapeutic Innovation Cambridge, Mass.: The MIT Press, 1974.

Sykes, G. M. The future of criminality. Am Behav Sci, 15:403-419, 1972.

U.S. Bureau of the Census. U.S. Census of Population: 1950. Vol. IV, Special Reports, Part 2, Chapter C, Institutional Population. Washington, D.C.: U.S. Government Printing Office, 1953.

U.S. Bureau of the Census. Census of Population: 1960 Subject Reports. Inmates of Institutions. Final Report PC(2)-8A. Washington, D.C.: U.S. Government Printing Office, 1963.

U.S. Bureau of the Census. Census of Population: 1970 Subject Reports. Persons in Institutions and Other Group Quarters. Final Report PC(2)-4E. Washington, D.C.: U.S. Government Printing Office, 1973.

U.S. Bureau of the Census. Current Population Reports, Population of the United States, Trends and Prospects: 1950-1990. Series P-23, No. 49. Washington, D.C.: U.S. Government Printing Office, 1974.

U.S. Bureau of the Census. Current Population Reports, Marital Status and Living Arrangements: March 1974, Series P-20, No. 271. Washington, D.C.: U.S. Government Printing Office, 1974.

U.S. Bureau of the Census. Current Population Reports, Projections of the Population of the United States: 1975-2050. Series P-25, No. 601. Washington, D.C.: U.S. Government Printing Office, 1975.

U.S. Department of Health, Education, and Welfare. Health: United States 1975. DHEW Publication No. (HRA) 76-1232. Washington, D.C.: U.S. Government Printing Office, 1976.

U.S. Department of Justice. Uniform Crime Reports for the United States - 1971, p. 30-33. Washington, D.C.: U.S. Government Printing Office, 1971.

Yolles, S. F., and Kramer, M. Vital Statistics. In: Bellack, L., and Loeb, L., eds. The Schizophrenic Syndrome. New York: Grune & Stratton, Inc., 1969.

Report of the Task Panel

on

COMMUNITY SUPPORT SYSTEMS

Submitted to

THE PRESIDENT'S COMMISSION ON MENTAL HEALTH

February 15, 1978

Task Panel: Community Support Systems

MEMBERS

June Jackson Christmas, M.D., Coordinator
Commissioner
New York Department of Mental Health and
　Mental Retardation Services
New York, New York

Nelba Chavez, D.S.W.
Director, La Frontera Center
Administrator, Outpatient Facility
Tucson South Behavorial Health Services
Tucson, Arizona

Sanford M. Dornbusch, Ph.D.
Professor of Sociology
Stanford University
Stanford, California

Audrey Finkelstein
National Vice-President
Girl Scouts of U.S.A.
Coral Gables, Florida

Robert Haggerty, M.D.
Roger I. Lee Professor of Public Health
Chairman, Department of Health Services
Harvard School of Public Health
Boston, Massachusetts

Nicholas Hobbs, Ph.D.
Professor of Psychology and Preventive
　Medicine
Director, Center for the Study of Families
　and Children
Vanderbilt University
Nashville, Tennessee

Robert L. Kahn, Ph.D.
Program Director
Institute for Social Research
University of Michigan
Ann Arbor, Michigan

Berton H. Kaplan, Ph.D.
Professor of Epidemiology (Sociology)
University of North Carolina
Chapel Hill, North Carolina

Reverend Herbert Leslie
University Christian Church
Berkeley, California

Arthur Naparstek, Ph.D.
Director
University of Southern California
  Public Affairs Center
Washington, D.C.

Frank Riessman, Ph.D.
Co-Director
New Human Services Institute
Graduate Center - City College of New York
New York, New York

Joseph Schneider
Judge of the Circuit Court of Cook County
Chicago, Illinois

Donald Smith, D.Min.
President
Institutes of Religion and Health
New York, New York

H.C. Townsley, M.D.
Chief, Mental Health Programs
Indian Health Service, U.S. Public
  Health Service
Albuquerque, New Mexico

Donald I. Warren, Ph.D.
Chairman
Department of Sociology and Anthropology
Oakland University
Rochester, Michigan

Robert Woodson
Resident Fellow
American Enterprise Institute
Washington, D.C.

TABLE OF CONTENTS

	Page
Executive Summary	6
Community Support Systems	14
Principles	16
Objectives	16
Action Strategies	17
Helping Networks, Neighborhoods, and Community Organizations	21
including: Social and Community Supports for Chronically Mentally Ill Patients	25
Recommendations	28
"New" Forms of Support Systems	30
including: Mutual Help Groups	33
"New" Forms of Volunteer Activity	37
Recommendations	40
Social Support Systems, Health, and Medical Care Systems	42
Recommendations	48
Work, Occupational Stress, and Social Support	50
Recommendations	53
Religious Support Systems	54
Recommendations	58
An Expanded Role for Public Schools	59
including: School Volunteer Programs	60
Youth Participation Programs	61
Recommendations	62
The Justice System and Community Support Systems	63
Recommendations	69
Implications For Mental Health and Human Services Delivery Systems	70

CSS 4

Acknowledgements 81

References 83

EXECUTIVE SUMMARY

To be connected to others, to belong, to receive social support when it is needed and to be able to give it in return is an important part of mental health. A healthy society provides opportunities for people to be connected in these ways, in forms and associations of their own choosing, and provides special help for those unable to avail themselves of such opportunities.

Social and community support systems can help to contribute to a sense of well-being and of competent functioning (and thus be preventive). They can aid in reducing the negative consequences of stressful life events and thus bridge the treatment and rehabilitative levels of prevention. They can provide an ongoing source of skills in living and interpersonal relationships so needed by the chronically mentally ill. What is even more significant is that utilization of social and community support systems can provide for constructive innovation and systemic change in the mental health system, moving toward a comprehensive human service system with a holistic orientation that would remedy some of the defects of our present fragmented and uncoordinated efforts.

The Task Panel on Community Support Systems recommends a major new Federal initiative in community mental health to achieve the following objectives:

- Recognize and strengthen the natural networks to which people belong and on which they depend--families; kin, kith, friendship, and neighborhood social networks; work relationships; religious denominations and congregations; and self-help groups and other voluntary associations based on principles of intimacy and mutual aid.

- Identify and strengthen the potential social support functions of formal caregiving institutions.

- Improve the linkages between natural helping networks and the more formal sources of help--professional and institutional.

- Develop educational strategies to inform the general public and caregiving professionals on the nature and function of natural helping networks and on the importance of attachments and mutuality for well-being.

- Initiate research to provide national data periodically on social support and on natural helping networks in American society, to monitor the direction and magnitude of changes in these aspects of American life, and to increase knowledge of how best to attain the above objectives.

Recognition of the strength of naturally occurring social and community support systems should not be an occasion, in a time of scarce resources, for the development of public policy which would withhold resources from people to obtain needed professional and formal institutional services.

In order to accomplish these objectives, the task panel strongly recommends that the President's Commission on Mental Health adopt the following action strategies, summarized as follows:

1. Allocation of manpower and service delivery demonstration monies by the Federal Government to train and retrain personnel on the nature and function of social support systems and natural helping networks, and for the development of models of articulation between professional systems of care and natural helping systems.

2. Experimentation, with program evaluation, to develop new mechanisms for reimbursement of social support services and for community support systems programming as a legitimate part of health and mental health services delivery.

3. Initiation by the Federal Government of the measurement of the quality of life, including social support, in American society. The instruments developed would be shared with any community wanting to evaluate its own progress in enhancing the giving and receiving of social support.

4. Mandate all Federal and federally funded State programs for the delivery of mental health services to incorporate plans for the development of social and community support systems for the chronically mentally disabled, especially the deinstitutionalized patient.

5. Allocation of Federal funds to educate the general public and the health professions on attachment behavior, mutuality and health, through a national TV series linked to local discussion groups, and through the development of model curricula and audiovisual materials.

6. Establishment of a Cabinet-level Federal interagency Task Force on social and community support systems which would cut across agency, disciplinary and categorical disease/problem bariers.

7. Periodic White House Conferences on Community and Mental Health.

In addition, the Task Panel on Community Support Systems recommends other policy options in specific areas, summarized as follows:

Helping Networks, Neighborhoods, and Community Organizations

The "gatekeeping" role of the neighborhood is a critical one. The nature of the local neighborhood can be defined in terms of its richness or its lack of resources for problem solving. Neighborhoods can serve to isolate individuals from the resources of society or help tie them to its mainstream.

8. Community mental health centers should be mandated to link needs assessment and program evaluation to "environmental impact" analyses (including social and cultural factors) of their programs on neighborhood natural helping networks.

9. National legislation is required to prohibit discriminatory zoning which prevents appropriate placement of the mentally disabled in the community, and to direct that community placement programs be based on research information on the diverse nature of communities and their different capacities to solve problems, both on a formal and informal basis, as a way to generate new types of community support systems for the mentally ill.

10. Amend Title XX legislation to allow local community institutions and organizations to receive funds for mental health consultation and education services and community support systems programming.

11. A national telecast, with local discussion groups, by the President's Commission on Mental Health and Mrs. Rosalynn Carter, on the work of the Commission, and to provide feedback on major community and individual needs and locally available mental health formal and informal resources.

12. Establish a hotline program with a single, **nationwide telephone** number that any citizen can call locally to gain advice and information from neighborhood helpers.

"New" Forms of Support Systems

Community support systems, self-help mutual aid groups and peer-oriented helping networks, are unique in that they capitalize on resources that are already present in the community and multiply them. The services provided by these support systems and social networks are participatory in nature and are a cost-effective way to increase much needed human services.

13. Mandate that community mental health centers provide directories of mutual help groups and peer-oriented support systems as part of their resource base, and encourage other community organizations to disseminate them widely to the public.

CSS 8

14. Develop clearinghouses in each Federal region on mutual help groups and peer-oriented support systems which would provide information and technical assistance to professionals and to members of these groups and support systems.

15. Develop curricula on social and community support systems in all undergraduate and graduate training programs in the professions related to mental health services delivery. Inclusion of such curricula should be considered an essential element in the accreditation process for approval status in these training programs.

16. Federal monies should be made available to State mental health associations to help catalyze a citizen-controlled statewide strategy for the development of locally based peer-oriented supportive networks.

17. Convene a national conference of directors of volunteer programs to identify ways volunteer programs can be linked both to the community's natural support networks and the formal caregiving institutions.

Social Support Systems, Health, and Medical Care Systems

The concept of social support has a rich set of meanings and strikes at the very heart of the relationship between social bonds and their health consequences, particularly emotional well-being.

18. Provide research funds to increase knowledge of the mechanisms whereby social support is effective in reducing mental distress and physical illness.

19. Demonstration projects should be conducted in the health care delivery system to assist individuals not only in recovery from illness but also in the maintenance of health, and in coping with life-cycle transitions and major stresses.

20. Allocate funds for the training of health workers about social support and health, especially the development of projects on the appropriate utilization of support systems as a part of primary care training, residency programs, and continuing medical education programs.

21. Health Systems Agencies (HSAs) should be required to include planning for social support systems within their local and state five year plans. Professional Standards Review Organizations (PSROs) should be re-

quired to review social support systems that relate to health services as part of their developing review of the quality of ambulatory care services.

22. Demonstration programs, with an evaluative component, to experiment with reimbursement mechanisms for general health and medical services which include payment for social support services as part of their approved benefits should be initiated. Future national health insurance should provide for payment of such social support services.

Work, Occupational Stress and Social Support

Work is not only a source of products and services, it is itself a public good and a key element in mental health. It should, therefore, be regarded as an entitlement, and its allocation and availability should be prime concerns in public policy. Good jobs are health-enhancing; bad jobs are not.

23. Fund and establish within the Federal Government the continuing review, assessment, and interpretation of innovations in job and organizational design undertaken to improve the quality of work experience.

24. Develop criteria for the gradual enactment of Federal standards for the quality of employment.

25. Conduct experiments and demonstration projects to test and to explain the contributions of work to mental health and well-being and to strengthen the natural supportive networks in places of work.

Religious Support Systems

Religious groups and institutions are committed to helping people fulfill their potentialities. The mental health movement has a similar commitment to people. These two networks of people-serving and people-enhancing institutions in our society are natural, complementing allies in the struggle to make greater wholeness an attainable reality for all.

26. Develop mechanisms to link the personnel and buildings owned by religious groups and institutions to community mental health centers and other social service agencies.

27. Initiate pilot projects, with an evaluation component, for demonstration of the actual functioning of religious support systems and to employ indigenous local clergy and lay people in developing community support systems.

28. Establish a conference mechanism to examine the relationship between religion and mental well-being and to clarify the role of religious support as to actual behavior, inter-personal provisions of support, and models of coping and competence.

29. Recommend the creation of a national voluntary register to process board examinations for clergy mental health professionals.

30. Declare clergy eligible for staff positions in all mental health centers, as providers of services, and as educators about religious support systems.

An Expanded Role for Public Schools

The universality of public education, the presence of underutilized physical and human resources, established funding mechanisms, and local control congruent with the diverse needs of urban, rural, and minority groups can be the advantages of a school-based delivery system to facilitate the healthy physical and mental development of children and their families in their communities.

31. Provide research and demonstration funds to test the feasibility of merging the community education, community mental health and public health systems within the public school network; and to examine options for the development of a community-based health and mental health delivery system in which public schools are the locus of responsibility in providing, obtaining or assuring preventive and rehabilitive care for children and their families.

The Justice System and Community Support Systems

Minimally, the justice system should be constrained from damaging the mental health of those people it affects. Maximally, it should be reshaped to feature individualized attention and appropriate help to promote and sustain the mental health of those potentially and already involved with police, courts, and correctional institutions.

32. Supportive services and community ties sensitive to ethnocultural diversity should be bolstered or created for groups with special emotional problems and with special risks of contact with the justice system, especially juvenile and alienated youth populations.

33. A variety of advocacy services for people with mental disabilities should be mandated through

Federal legislation in order to affirm basic rights and entitlements and to promote adequately funded services.

34. The Federal Government should fund research and demonstration projects in the development of non-judicial mechanisms for resolving disputes and settling grievances within the community and with institutions, with special attention to the unique needs of mental patients and former mental patients.

35. Federal legislation should be passed setting humane standards for correctional facilities. Such standards should also encourage deinstitutionalization when appropriate, relate to the requirements of justice and due process within the institutions, and provide for the diverse mental health needs of correctional clients and staff.

36. The Federal Government should provide funds to promote the use of existing recruiting techniques to identify persons for police work who have empathetic responses to human need and suffering; to train recruits and other police officers, including middle managers, in the techniques of crisis management; and to educate critical gatekeepers in the justice system, such as judges, attorneys, probation officers, on the needs and rights of mentally disabled persons involved in the justice system.

Social and community support systems concepts can be a potent addition and supplement to existing models of mental health practice. Professionals who are knowledgeable about social networks and natural helping systems theory and practice can generate not just more or different services but also more relevant and more easily accessible services.

Utilizing social and community support systems in conjunction with other, formal systems of care:

- can have a multiplier effect on professional and institutional resources.

- can help to provide services which are inherently sensitive to socio-cultural diversity.

- can transcend specific professional ideologies and organizational/structural modalities of service.

- can help to bridge public and private systems of care in the social services, vocational, religious, justice, health, and mental health fields.

- allows services to be population-at-risk, catchment-area or neighborhood-oriented; common interest, age or particular ethnic or minority group focused; have an emphasis on specific problems or life predicaments.

- permits appropriate services to be delivered in the least restrictive environment.

- allows for variance in the intensity and duration of help offered, the kinds of services provided, and for the direction of the help process: natural $\rightleftarrows$ formal.

- promotes individual and community participation in the design and implementation of services on either a voluntary or paid employment basis.

- can provide coherent and responsive rehabilitative services and long-term care in the community for the chronically mentally ill patient.

- can provide the combined resources to precisely design and implement programs for primary prevention, secondary treatment, and rehabilitative services, in life-cycle crises and transitions; in situational and social stress; and for chronic deficits.

- are consumer participatory and therefore cost-effective.

- can permit specifically targeted use of highly trained and costly professional resources.

Social and community support systems should not be viewed as a panacea for all problems in mental health delivery systems. However, an understanding of their characteristics can reveal them as strategic links between individual and community needs and the appropriate deployment of professional and institutional services.

COMMUNITY SUPPORT SYSTEMS

Attachment theory states the essential nature of positive interaction with trusted others for well-being (Bowlby 1977). People rely naturally, and differentially, for everyday support and for emergency assistance on relatives, neighbors, and friends (Barnes 1954; Bott 1957; Litwak and Szelenyi 1969; Mitchell 1969; Wellman et al. 1971). Each person probably requires a set of relationships, in varying degrees of intensity in different phases of life, which provides:

- meaningful attachment to significant others;

- social integration in a network of common interest relationships;

- an opportunity for the nuturance of others, especially children;

- reassurance of individual worth gained through the performance of a social role;

- a sense of reliable alliance with kin;

- access to the obtaining of guidance from a trustworthy and authoritative person in times of stress.

The absence of any one relationship would probably be signaled by distress specific to the nature of the provision of the relationship, e.g., loneliness in the absence of an intimate relationship (Weiss 1969; 1974).

Various elements of an individual's support system naturally emerge from his/her own needs via the social responses of those in his/her network and community, and the values and traditions of his/her subculture (G. Caplan 1974). Mutual intimacy and reciprocal services are an essential part of this supportive matrix.

Recent research evidence suggests that those who have social supports are protected in crisis from a wide variety of pathological states, both mental and physical. It is thought that these supports buffer the individual from the potentially negative effects of undergoing crises and changes, and can facilitate coping and adaptation (Cassel 1974a; Kaplan, Cassel, Gore 1977). Social support has been defined as information that tells a person he is valued and is part of a functioning social network based on a commitment of reciprocity and exchange (Cobb 1976). These social networks are also a key resource in daily coping for the average person (D. Warren 1976). Among the important functions of these networks are:

- the maintenance of social identity;

- the provision of emotional support;

- the provision of mutual aid and services;
- access to information; and
- access to new social contacts and new social roles.

In a crisis situation, a small dense network with strong ties is probably most important in providing a sense of social identity, emotional support, and material aid. During psychosocial transitions, access to information and to new social roles may be even more important (Walker et al. 1977). Hence the notion of the strength of weak ties and the necessity for diversity within the social matrix (Granovetter 1973).

A wide range of professional and formal community institutions, as well as natural systems, can provide elements in an individual's support system and supportive network. These can be placed on a continuum moving from individual self-help to kinship networks, to lay service systems, to quasi-institutional services through voluntary associations and religious denominations, to professional services (D. Warren 1976). In addition to a person's primary group and intimate social network, natural systems of delivery exist, usually in neighborhoods, within which an individual with a need or deficit receives help without professional intervention, often through the direct service of a central figure, a natural neighbor, who provides the assistance himself/herself to those known to him/her.

The central figures who provide these neighborhood-based services occupy a pivotal linkage role to other providers in the informal and in the formal delivery systems. Often the people who benefit most from these neighborly services are the young and the old, many of whom are unserved or underserved by formal agencies (Collins 1973; Collins and Pancoast 1976; Smith 1975). Among lay service systems, help may be given not only in person-to-person helping networks but also in mutual aid self help groups.

Naturally occurring social support systems can provide models of the traditional patterns of self help, mutual help, help seeking and help accepting that are customary in specific populations and communities, and are sensitive to cultural and subcultural variations. As such, they constitute models for development of professional therapeutic strategies and delivery systems which may be especially powerful, meaningful, and acceptable (Thomas and V. Garrison 1975).

Mental health services should be offered to individuals which would build first on their own assets and strengths, maintaining and cultivating their membership in social networks and natural communities in the least restrictive environment. This would mean developing methods which could identify and assess the functioning of an individual's natural support systems, and establishing, where appropriate, linkages between the natural support systems and the professional caregiving systems based on a respect for privacy and on genuine cooperation and collaboration, not cooptation and control. As a corollary of this approach, when the natural support system is ineffectual or absent, the appropriate professional role would be to strengthen, supplement, or stimulate the development of social support systems in the natural environment, if at all possible.

Helping people where they are and assisting them to help themselves allows entry into the help giving and receiving system without requiring that a person be labeled patient or deemed "sick." This may help to deal with the significant problem of stigmatization as a barrier to care. It may, equally, help to develop more appropriate and effective means of help (Christmas 1977a).

The achievement of a sound public program directed at strengthening community support networks and their role in mental health requires attention to these principles:

- <u>adequacy</u>--that the range of formal services and natural support systems reflect the basic needs of all individuals and families and take into account social and cultural diversity;

- <u>equity</u>--that a diversity of informal and formal services, and various combinations of each, be developed in accessible form in all community settings, thus permitting individual choice and availability of the most appropriate form of help when needed.

Emphasis should be placed on the development of models of articulation between professional systems and natural support systems, based on an understanding of the contributions, strengths, and weaknesses of both, which would constructively permit people to participate easily in both systems simultaneously or sequentially and in varying degrees of intensity, as need indicates. The conceptual framework thus provided pinpoints the necessity for developing effective linkages between community support systems and formal institutions which can promote realistic community needs assessment and appropriate professional care, and which can foster the social support functions of formal institutions. It leads naturally to a concept of a comprehensive human service approach.

To further this approach, the Task Panel on Community Support Systems recommends a major new Federal initiative in community mental health to achieve the following objectives:

- Recognize and strengthen the natural networks to which people belong and on which they depend--families; kin, kith, friendship, and neighborhood social networks; work relationships; religious denominations and congregations; and self-help groups and other voluntary associations based on principles of intimacy and mutual aid.

- Identify and strengthen the potential social support functions of formal caregiving institutions.

- Improve the linkages between natural helping networks and the more formal sources of help--professional and institutional.

- Develop educational strategies to inform the general public and caregiving professionals on the nature and function of natural

CSS 16

helping networks and on the importance of attachments and mutuality for well-being.

. Initiate research to provide national data periodically on social support and on natural helping networks in American society, to monitor the direction and magnitude of changes in these aspects of American life, and to increase knowledge of how best to attain the above objectives.

In order to accomplish these objectives, the Task Panel on Community Support Systems recommends that the President's Commission on Mental Health adopt the following action strategies.

1. Allocation of manpower and service delivery demonstration monies by the federal government which would mandate:

    * the training and retraining of human service workers on the nature and function of social support systems and natural helping networks;

    * the development of new techniques for non-intrusive assessment of an individual's supportive network;

    * the development of non-stigmatizing techniques for identifying those persons at special risk and whose support systems are deficient;

    * the development of indirect and collaborative methods and models of helping communities stimulate supportive networks for those people whose natural helping networks are deficient;

    * the development of models of articulation between professional systems of care and natural helping systems;

    * the development of models of service delivery which extrapolate from traditional patterns of help seeking and help accepting and which are sensitive to cultural and sub-cultural variations.

2. Experimentation, with program evaluation, to develop new mechanisms for reimbursement of social support systems and for community support systems programming as a legitimate part of health and mental health service delivery. Such Federal experimental mechanisms might include:

    * single-stream funding from a variety of agencies;

* special project support with forward budgeting;

* program approval for formal institutions tied to existing reimbursement mechanisms on a fee-for-service or capitation basis;

* direct program support to community organizations, e.g., schools, religious institutions, neighborhood organizations, voluntary associations;

* contracts by community mental health centers directly to mutual help groups.

3. Initiation by the Federal Government of the measurement of the quality of life, including social support, in American society by:

    * developing valid measures of social support and relatedness;

    * gathering, at appropriate intervals, national data to measure the level of such quality of life, including social support, among Americans, and the changes that are occurring in level and sources;

    * making available to communities, voluntary associations, and other relevant groups the procedures and instruments that will permit any community or neighborhood to evaluate its own progress in enhancing the giving and receiving of social support, and the resulting quality of life.

4. Mandate all Federal and federally funded State programs for the delivery of mental health services to incorporate plans for the development of social and community support systems for the chronically mentally disabled, especially the deinstitutionalized patient, including:

    * an organized program of housing, financial assistance, medical, social, and vocational rehabilitation services;

    * planned linkages to other human service systems such as education, health, social welfare, the world of work, and religious institutions;

* planned linkages to social support systems, mutual help groups, and neighborhood helping networks, to promote optimum personal and social integration.

5. Allocation of Federal funds to educate the general public, and students and professionals of the health professions on natural social support helping networks and mutual help groups through:

    * a national TV series by the Public Broadcasting System on attachment behavior, mutuality and health, linked to local community discussion groups;

    * development of model curricula and audio-visual materials, distributed through the Regional Medical Libraries of the National Library of Medicine and Area Health Education Centers.

6. Establishment of a Cabinet-level Federal interagency Task Force which would cut across agency, disciplinary, and categorical disease/problem barriers to:

    * focus attention on the nature, function, and value of social and community support systems;

    * provide a forum for the ongoing exchange of information about community support systems;

    * provide an arena for the development of a strategy for a communications network about social and community support between natural helping networks and formal professional caregiving institutions;

    * marshall resources, including single-stream funding, so as to increase support for support systems programming.

7. Periodic White House Conferences on Community and Mental Health which would examine:

    * how our life styles impact on well-being;

    * how to reduce societal contributions to psychopathology;

    * how to promote emotional health;

* how to promote attachments, reciprocity, and a sense of community among people, with a respect for differences; and

* how to promote treatment availability, accessibility, visibility, and effectiveness in both natural helping networks and formal caregiving institutions.

In addition to these across-the-board recommendations, the Task Panel on Community Support Systems has other recommendations to make for policy options to be considered specific to neighborhoods; "new" forms of support systems, including mutual help groups; the health care system; the workplace; religious institutions; public schools; and the criminal justice system.

HELPING NETWORKS, NEIGHBORHOODS AND COMMUNITY ORGANIZATIONS

There is extensive evidence of the importance of a sense of neighborhood or belonging for people, and significant research into the meaningful roles played by neighborhood institutions, that is, churches, schools, ethnic clubs, fraternal organizations, community organizations, etc., in people's lives. In a pluralistic society, people solve problems and meet needs in different ways. Thus, a neighborhood-based approach with community support systems designed to address diverse individual needs can be critical to individual well-being (D. Warren 1976; Naparstek and Haskell 1977; Borus et al. 1975; Macht et al. 1977). Strengthening neighborhood networks can provide a means of (a) gaining a sense of control over one's life, (b) reducing alienation from society, (c) gaining capacity to solve new problems, and (d) maintaining the motivation to overcome the handicaps and frustrations which are common to modern society (R. Warren 1977).

It must also be recognized that key interventions by government are necessary to provide the economic, environmental, and formal services many neighborhoods lack.

To intelligently assess the role of neighborhood in people's lives requires placing in proper perspective the strengths and limitations of the residential environment. In order to deliver appropriate services to people an understanding of the range of functions which are performed in local neighborhoods is necessary without, on the one hand, idealizing these units as always capable of autonomy and self-sufficiency, nor, on the other hand, ignoring the important activities which go on in virtually all neighborhoods.

The "gatekeeping" role of the neighborhood is vital. The nature of the local neighborhood can be defined in terms of its richness or its lack of resources for problem solving. Neighborhoods can serve to isolate individuals from the resources of society or help tie them to its mainstream. This critical role of neighborhood is carried out in three distinct ways: (1) by means of a set of social contacts and entry points available through direct contact with neighbors; (2) indirectly through information, knowledge, or referral that contact with a neighbor eventually brings; and (3) in terms of the perception by individuals that their neighborhood is a resourceful base for seeking help, gaining information and, in general, providing a socially supportive atmosphere and environment. There is a basic need to consider the capacity of both local neighborhoods, as well as the local community as a whole, to be able to encourage forms of mutual aid and helping which need not be competitive with, nor totally independent of, formal caregiving agencies, but which need to work often in conjunction with these agencies to provide for a sound quality of life and the delivery of a range of health and social services.

The basic problem then, facing the public sector, is to diagnose and understand the differences in structure and social processes among communities and to be able to identify the human resources and community leadership available in local communities, and to work collaboratively with them in a variety of different situations (Warren and Warren 1975).

The Community Mental Health Centers Act of 1963 heralded new efforts to put the community into mental health decision-making and programming. The results, although creating change, have not fully satisfied either consumers or providers. We still do not know very much about how people of diverse socio-cultural backgrounds solve problems and cope with stress and crisis. We still have not effectively linked the community with the service delivery system. We also have not fully utilized people's positive identification with their neighborhood as a means for overcoming personal and institutional obstacles to seeking and receiving help (Naparstek, Spiro, Biegel, et al., 1977; Naparstek and Kollias, 1976).

The neighborhood can serve important functions for people in their need for and use of mental health services:

- neighborhood as the locus of services;

- neighborhood as a support system and as a vehicle for the development and strengthening of networks, professional, and natural;

- neighborhood as basis for the development of mental health programming;

- neighborhood as a means of citizen/client involvement;

- neighborhood as a basis of citizen empowerment in mental health.

Naparstek, Spiro, Biegel, et al. propose a model for building and rebuilding neighborhood support systems; recognizing and utilizing the unique cultural and structural differences among neighborhoods; and linking neighborhood support systems with professional and institutional systems to create an effective helping network which maximizes neighborhood and formal caregiving resources in order to facilitate prevention, treatment, and rehabilitation. Such a view of neighborhood in the provision of mental health and community support services serves to:

- help overcome the stigma of mental health

- increase utilization of services

- reach people earlier in need

- provide new models of service delivery

- provide a basis for programming in the areas of prevention and deinstitutionalization

- create a constituency for mental health services.

Schematically, this might be illustrated as follows:

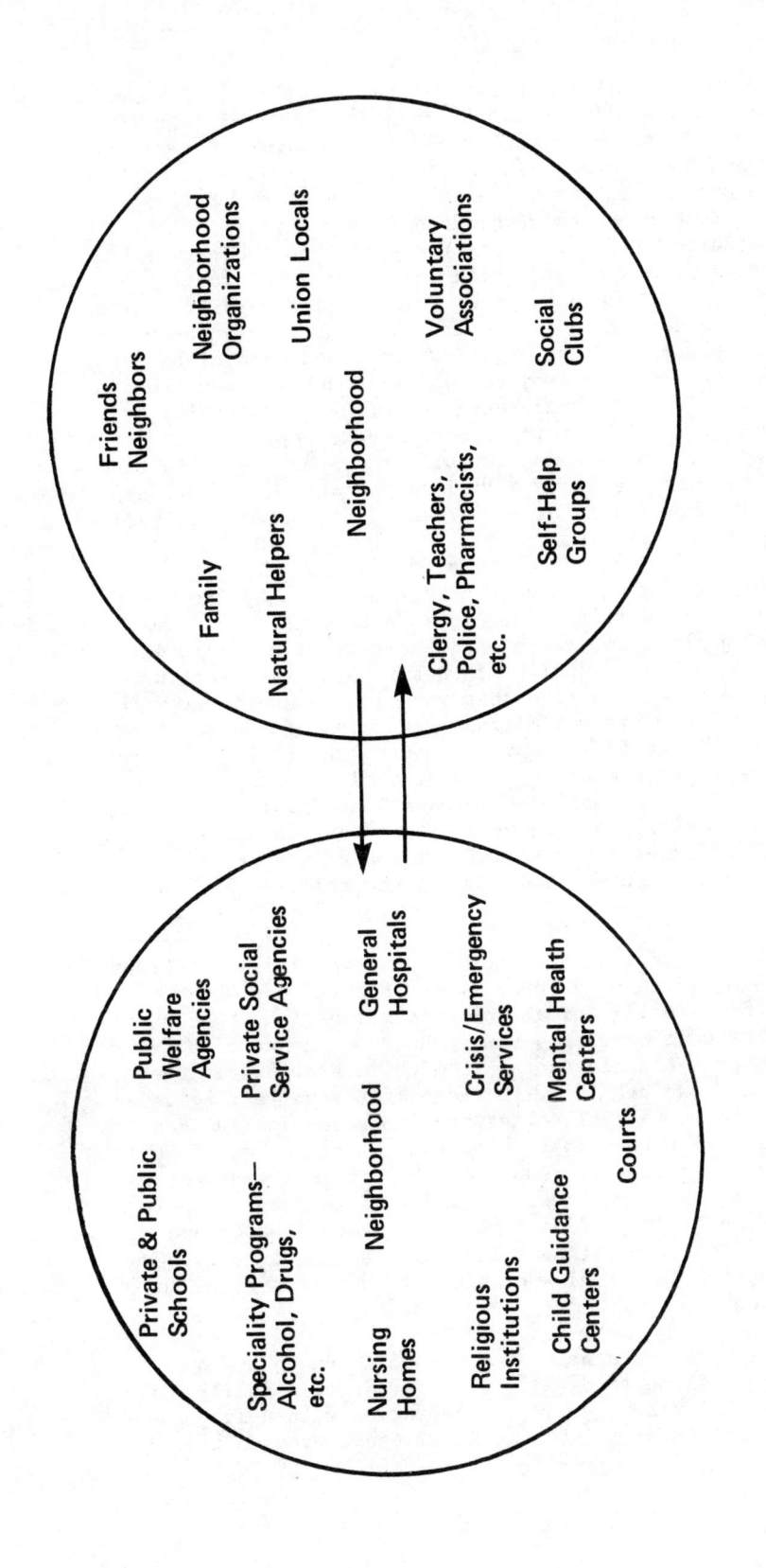

TABLE 1.

Natural Helping Networks
- Friends
- Neighbors
- Neighborhood Organizations
- Union Locals
- Family
- Natural Helpers
- Neighborhood
- Clergy, Teachers, Police, Pharmacists, etc.
- Voluntary Associations
- Self-Help Groups
- Social Clubs

Professional Helping Networks
- Private & Public Schools
- Public Welfare Agencies
- Private Social Service Agencies
- General Hospitals
- Speciality Programs—Alcohol, Drugs, etc.
- Neighborhood
- Crisis/Emergency Services
- Mental Health Centers
- Nursing Homes
- Religious Institutions
- Child Guidance Centers
- Courts

The process for the successful development of this illustrative example, adaptable to all communities and all population groups, is one of capacity-building, through which people in the neighborhood become aware of their own strengths and resources and their own abilities to shape services to meet neighborhood needs. One such "capacity-building" program is the Neighborhood and Family Services Project of the Washington Public Affairs Center of the University of Southern California. The focus of this project is to examine needs and resources from a neighborhood perspective in two ethnic communities in Baltimore and Milwaukee in order to determine ways of linking professional services to the natural helping networks in the neighborhood (churches; ethnic, fraternal, and social organizations; and natural helpers or "gatekeepers"). In each city, the project is designed to work through a local community organization that is representative of, and controlled by, the residents of the community, thus giving neighborhood people more control over human service programs in their communities. Its objective is to refocus previously fragmented services into a working partnership of professional services with the informal helping resources of the community, mediated through a neighborhood organization.

A more direct strategy is being undertaken incrementally by the North Shore Child Guidance Center of Manhasset, New York, a community-based mental health facility serving children, youth, and their families in seven communities. It is attempting to re-design its services by re-directing professional energies by means of a partnership with its communities, with the goal of maximizing service while minimizing escalation of costs. The first step has been a special staff development program which led to a reorganization of its basic services, resulting in a dramatic increase in the number of families in clinical treatment, an elimination of waiting lists, an expansion of community education programs, and the development of new services such as youthful offender programs and child advocacy projects to increase community services to unserved and underserved children and their families.

A pilot survey was then undertaken in one of the communities it serves which looked at the needs of women of diverse ethnic backgrounds who were single parents. Members of existing formal and informal neighborhood support systems were interviewed as well as single female heads of households from five different ethnic groups. A professional from the Center helped the community to organize on its own behalf, with the professional acting as a resource person, and volunteers as data collectors who were also engaged in a constant feedback process with those participating in the survey as well as with a wide range of other community resources that could play important support roles. A series of subsequent meetings was held to involve the community with the professional in providing services, consultation and education as determined by this population's indentification of needs, gaps, and lacks in their neighborhood's formal and informal support systems for women who were single parents.

The Center's currently projected next step, in addition to its ongoing direct treatment services, will be to develop a new project, a Family Life Center, utilizing professional resources in collaboration with neighborhood volunteers to service natural helping networks in all seven communities in ways that will strengthen their ability to be responsive to the needs of families in stressful situations. The proposed Family Life Center will have three components: service, prevention, and community education. Services will be provided through the establishment of groups to give emotional support to families in times of crisis or special life situations such as groups on surviving divorce or separation; life planning groups for adolescents; groups on "negotiating the system" for drop-outs/push-outs so they can be helped "to make it" in school. Members of the groups will be encouraged to develop their own self-help networks to continue after the short-term involvement of the professional resource.

Preventive services will include workshops with professionals and indigenous community leaders on such topics as identifying support systems in local communities; multi-ethnicity and mental health practice; using extended families as a therapeutic resource; organizing self-help mutual aid networks; making advocacy work for clients. Special consultation and orientation programs will be offered to existing institutions, agencies, and clubs such as schools, churches, neighborhood associations, ethnic, and work-related groups in methods of providing support services.

Community education programs will be developed by the planned preparation, wide distribution, and organization of discussion groups around publications on such topics as neighborhood resources for families with special needs; coping through the use of individual and group strengths; and making natural helping systems work in a community. A special speaker's bureau will feature people from all sections of these communities who have developed successful coping strategies with particular difficulties or life situations. For this next step in the restructuring of the Guidance Center's services, the major staff person involved in the Family Life Center project will act as a broker between community volunteers, the community at large, and a resource pool of professionals from the North Shore Guidance Center and other community agencies. These professionals will be reimbursed through minimal charges made to community groups requesting the professional help with a specific focus for a limited period of time. The project will take a research and demonstration approach, with special evaluative focus on single parent families to determine the impact of the Family Life Center approach, the involvement of support systems within the community and an assessment of the cost to the North Shore Guidance Center.

Mobilizing Social and Community Supports for the Chronically Mentally Ill Patient

Although there is a separate Commission Task Panel on Deinstitutionalization, Rehabilitation, and Long-Term Care, it is important to emphasize here the special relevance of community support systems for the former mental hospital patient. Appropriate placement in the community of discharged patients is basic to an orderly discharge system and to the establishment of effective aftercare programs. It is necessary not only for the purpose of satisfacorily serving the mentally disabled, but also to facilitate integration of discharged patients into the community. Cooperation with community groups is essential to reduce or avoid community opposition and, more positively, to mobilize voluntary and civic resources to enable former patients to live independently and constructively in the community.

For many years, in the absence of alternative inexpensive housing, SROs (single room occupancy hotels), especially in large cities, have become the repositories of the unwanted and unfortunate in our society, whether they are drug addicts, or welfare clients, or former mental patients. The placement of those discharged from State institutions into SROs exacerbates both the issue of clustering problematical populations to the detriment of the neighborhood as well as the issue of providing adequate care for deinstitutionalized persons. The backlash to concentrations of discharged patients left to shift for themselves without appropriate aftercare services and social supports has been a weakening of citizens' support for necessary mental health and social services. Public education and community involvement could develop local strategies to:

- persuade commercial and residential real estate companies to create or expand a supply of affordable apartments to accomodate 1-3 chronically mentally ill persons per apartment and/or program sites in commercial areas for social and vocational rehabilitation programs.

- seek private and Federal funds to convert selected buildings to mixed residential/commercial use which will include housing for a fixed number of elderly chronically mentally disabled (Christmas 1977b).

Simultaneously, service programs must be developed for the present occupants of SROs. For example, recent research (O'Connor et al. 1977) in three SROs for ex-mental patients and indigent elderly indicates the special importance of peer social support systems for a sense of well-being and effective adaptation, quite apart from the necessary financial, health, and formal social services these populations require and/or use. The enhancement of these peer support systems by professionals could provide a means for improving the ability of these socially marginal individuals to maintain themselves more effectively in extraordinarily difficult circumstances.

It is clear that a systematic use of the full array of social and community support systems, formal and informal, on behalf of the mentally ill is essential. Budson (1977; 1978) suggests, based on his own work with half-way houses and on a review of the work of other professionals in community care of the chronically mentally ill, that successful programs have at their core the sustenance or fostering of an extended psychosocial kinship system. Professionals have sustained it when it was intact but shaky (Stein and Test, 1975); aided and assisted it when it was weak (Polak and Kirby in press); and introduced it where it was not present (Budson et al. in press). Some examples of comprehensive innovative programs for community care of severely mentally ill patients are:

- The model of "The Lodge," an innovative social system in the community, was established more than 10 years ago by George

Fairweather in Santa Cruz, California. The lodge society is initiated in the hospital, made up of patients who then move together into the community. It is a non-profit self-governing program, usually based on a business operated by the group. Preparation for the business venture and the living situation is made by the patients with the help and consultation of hospital staff. Patients function together as a cooperative communal society, with mobile entry and exit, running the household and working together to earn money. Individuals can move up and down levels of social responsibility without leaving the organization. The social principles involved in the lodge society include: each person has a stake in the system; the structure is non-hierarchical; its members have as much autonomy as possible consistent with role performance; internal norms for behavior are established appropriate to its population; group performance of tasks as much as possible, with a differentiated role for each member. The professional's function is to give consultation to members and to create a system which permits individuals to care for one another. The lodge program has been replicated in various parts of the United States, based on research demonstrating its effectiveness in reducing re-admission rates of former patients to mental institutions (Fairweather, Sanders and Maynard 1969; Sanders 1972).

The Discharged Patient Advocacy Project of the Mental Health Association of Essex County, New Jersey, is a patient-focused study, looking at the life of a previously institutionalized person and at the formal and informal support systems around him/her. The findings of this study show that most discharged patients are unconnected with community resources, mental health, and otherwise. They are vulnerable, low-income, passive people who too often must arrange their lives, organize for their needs, and find their way to community resources on their own. Preliminary data from the third year of the project indicate that where an informal support system exists in the client's life there is indeed a higher level of functioning, a lower re-admission rate and/or length of stay. Mutual help groups, church or religious groups, "significant others," and the telephone (primarily with friends and family, though usage with "hotlines" or mental health providers has also been reported) have been utilized as part of a supportive matrix. What the Discharged Patient Advocacy Project demonstrated in the research and patient-tracking efforts of the first phase of its study was that all the necessary elements exist in the formal mental health network of services but that the "system" is failing to meet the comprehensive needs of the discharged patient, including social, clinical/medical, housing, financial maintenance, and vocational rehabilitation. Based on these findings, the staff of the Project, in its current phase, are functioning in the roles of ombudsman and advocate, beginning with pre-discharge planning, to actively link persons discharged into the community to formal and informal resources and services.

- Hansell describes (1977; in press) a program of local services at the Champaign Mental Health Center in Urbana, Illinois, for the long-term outpatient treatment of 575 schizophrenic patients based on an approach which includes these components: an understanding that services must be designed for multiple-episode users of service with a life-long biological disorder; reliability of medication for decades, with careful and precise attention to informed consent; patient education on the nature of their condition and in self-regulation of medication within a range of dosage, probably best done in groups of patients where there is sharing of reports on control of symptoms and side-effects, with the setting of objectives for self regulation; and crisis-oriented intervention services during adaptational episodes, including the convening of social networks, linkages to community mutual help groups, and non-residential clubs and lodges for otherwise isolated persons.

- The Dane County Mental Health Center of Madison, Wisconsin, uses a training-for-community-living model which has been demonstrated to be an economically feasible and clinically effective alternative to mental hospital treatment for almost all patients. A highly skilled staff work with patients, families and community organizations to mobilize every available social and community support for the patient. Staff make home visits, teach daily living and social skills, catalyze neighborhood helping efforts, help patients find jobs and to keep them, and stimulate recreational activities (Stein, Test and Marx 1975; Test and Stein, 1976a,b).

Unquestionably social support systems are sorely needed for the chronically mentally ill (Gruenberg 1967). They can be most efficient if integrated into a comprehensive approach to helping them during episodes of acute illness, recovery, and integration into the community. To achieve this goal, liaison among all elements of help, formal and informal, is of crucial importance.

The established research data and developing mental health program strategies of strengthening community support capacities as expressed by neighborhood, peer group, and primary group ties should be integrated within agencies responsible for mental health service delivery programs. These units would be responsible for further research development, pilot and demonstration projects, as well as staff training activities related to community support systems.

RECOMMENDATIONS

8. Community mental health centers should be mandated to link needs assessment and ongoing program evaluation to "environmental impact" analyses (including social and cultural factors) of their programs

in terms of their complementing, supplementing, or supplanting neighborhood natural helping networks.

9. National legislation is required to prohibit discriminatory zoning which prevents appropriate placement in the community of the mentally disabled and to direct that community placement programs for the mentally disabled be based on research information on the diverse nature of communities and their different capacities to solve problems, both on a formal and informal basis, as a way to generate new types of community support systems in which the local initiatives, as well as the form of the service, reflect these local conditions.

10. Amend Title XX legislation to allow local community institutions and organizations, e.g., schools, religious organizations, voluntary associations, etc., to receive funds for mental health consultation and education services and community support systems programming.

11. There should be a special nationwide telecast by the President's Commission on Mental Health and Mrs. Rosalynn Carter on the work of the Commission, followed by live local discussion groups in as many cities, towns, and neighborhoods as possible, and a national "call-in." The basic concept is to provide nationwide response and feedback on major community and individual needs and locally available mental health helping resources, including mutual help groups.

12. Establish a hotline program with a single, nationwide telephone number that any citizen can call locally, to gain advice, information or referral from neighborhood helpers who would also be encouraged to develop communications with other neighborhood helpers, service agencies, and local organizations.

"NEW" FORMS OF SUPPORT SYSTEMS

Although this Task Panel is not dealing directly with the oldest natural support system, the family, no discussion of support systems would be complete without some discussion of its centrality in people's lives.[1] The pluralism in form and the strengths that typify American families of diverse ethnocultural heritage have just begun to be recognized and appreciated (Billingsley 1968; Comer 1972; DeLoria 1970; Giordano and Giordano 1976; Hill 1972; Padilla and Aranda 1974; Sue and Wagner 1973; Willie 1970). Characteristics of all families as support systems have been described as: collector and disseminator of information about the world; feedback guidance system; source of ideology; guide and mediator in problem-solving; source of practical service and concrete aid; haven for rest and recuperation; reference and control group; source and validator of identity; and contributor to emotional mastery (G. Caplan 1976a).

Ethnic and minority families, especially, have made extensive use of the support systems provided by strong kinship and extended social and community ties. Self help and mutual help is frequently sought and provided in the context of the fluid, unbounded network of family, extended kin, friends, neighbors, co-workers and other associates, or in formal voluntary associations formed on principles other than those of common interest. These principles of organization include, particularly, extended kinship ties, common religious heritage, common place of origin, or a common theory of causation and cure of illness or misfortune. These groupings have mental health significance, although they may not be specifically organized for mental health purposes. For example, Fandetti (1974) in a study of Italians and Poles in a working-class neighborhood found that both groups primarily rely on the family, the church, and to a limited extent on some voluntary associations for aid with child care, care of the aged, personal problems and for financial assistance. Mental health specialists were not identified as possible sources of help. Guttman (1977) at the Catholic University School of Social Service, is currently studying the informal and formal support systems and their effects on the lives of the elderly in eight ethnic groups in Metropolitan Baltimore and Washington: Estonians, Poles, Lithuanians, Latvians, Italians, Jews, Hungarians and Greeks. He and his colleagues are asking: (1) What are the particular problems and needs of the elderly in various ethnic groups? (2) What are the ethnic support systems corresponding to these needs? (3) What is the relationship of the services provided by the general community and by society to the particular ethnic support systems? Are they complementary to each other or are there conflicts involved? and (4) Could the ethnic support systems, both formal and informal, be utilized and reinforced within the framework of the general assistance provided by society to the elderly?

---

[1]There is a separate Commission Task Panel on Mental Health and American Families, with Sub-panels on the Child, Adolescence, Adult Years, and the Elderly.

In a study of kinship networks in a Black neighborhood in a mid-Western city, Stack (1974) has described a system of kinship in which each child at birth acquires a socially recognized kinship network which is not the same as the official family recognized in the registries and agencies of the larger society. This system of socially recognized kinship is based on a principle of "sponsorship" as much as upon the principles of biological kinship. These "personal kindred," which vary somewhat for each child in a single family, consist of those who assume responsibilities for parenting, and those who are related by biological kinship, social kinship, or fictive kinship to those who assume these responsibilities. In a study of informal adoption of children among Black families, Hill (1977) found the extended family to be a source of strength and health for these children.

Another distinctive feature of voluntary associations in Black communities is the traditional importance of the church, of religious leaders, and of quasi-religious practitioners of various forms of healing and personal consultation. Religious participation in the Black community continues to be the statistically most frequent form of voluntary association and the abundance of churchs, large and small, in any Black inner-city neighborhood attests to the continuing importance of the religious life in the support systems of the Black population.

Anyone seeking to understand American Indians must recognize their reliance on the normative principle of non-interference, based on respect for oneself and others (Good Tracks 1973; Lewis and Ho 1975). The inherent strengths of the American Indian lie in his/her individuality, family, clan and traditions as reflected in the many patterns of tribal life. The Indian natural support systems include childrearing practices, extended family and clanship systems, social customs, and traditional healing practices.

Mutual aid in the many distinct Asian-American communities is organized primarily on the basis of kinship and ethnic associations. In Chinese-American communities, for example, there are traditional voluntary associations of persons bearing the same surname of persons who come from the same district of China. There are fraternal associations, social clubs, and modern service societies and agencies similar to those of other communities. There are also highly developed systems of preventive and curative medicine for both physical and mental health problems. The mentally ill in the Chinese-American community traditionally have been cared for within the family, and support and assistance with the problems of living have come from the family or the larger kinship or ethnic associations. This tradition persists with little change and a mental health care system relevant for the Chinese-American community would have to be integrated into this traditional support system.

In Spanish-speaking communities, of which there are a variety of multicultural sub-groupings, the focal point of support systems is found within the family, which extends beyond the nuclear family, including not only parents and children, but also grandparents, aunts, uncles, cousins, and compadres and comadres. In Mexican-American families, particularly, there is a system of relationships which is similar to a system based on kinship.

For example, the padrino network, which is parallel to other social structures, is based on ceremonial sponsorship. This network can be viewed as similar to one which is based on relationships of consanquinity. The padrino network is as clearly organized in its structure as is the nuclear family. Emphasis in this network is on ritual, whereas the emphasis in the nuclear family may be economic. The concept of padrino is based on insurance for the child, should the parents die before the child reaches adulthood. Usually the first set of padrinos are acquired soon after birth through baptism. The obligations of the padrinos are to consult, aid, and intervene when there is trouble. Additionally, in order to understand the Mexican-American-Chicano family, the total environment must be taken into account. The barrio is an intricate network of communication systems and sub-systems which include but are not limited to the nuclear family and the extended family. Moreover, it includes all those other institutions, i.e., panaderia (bakery), bar, corner store, libraries, etc., which impact on the total life of the individual.

This concept of the entire community, El Concepto de la Famila, as a protective and healing support system is of central importance for all Hispanic communities, and includes social and cultural organizations. Among Puerto Rican communities in New York, for instance, there are social clubs of persons who originate from the same town in Puerto Rico. Through the group, the members retain a sense of identity and history. The members are also helpful to each other in the process of adaption to New York City. These clubs organize parties, outings, and other leisure time activities consistent with the interests of the group. They also help each other through sharing experiences and giving advice related to housing, job, schooling, health care, etc.

Public policy in the mental health field and the design of mental health services must take into account the potency of cultural traditions for strengthening the adaptive capacities of individuals and families in their social networks and communities. Mental health workers should support the positive aspects of these varied family support systems and build on their inherent resources, linking them when necessary to culturally acceptable and relevant formal professional and institutional resources.

Among other "old" forms of support systems receiving "new" attention are indigenous healing practices and traditional cultural health belief systems (Beiser et al. 1974; Hall and Bourne 1973; Jilek 1974; Kiev 1964; Mostwin 1976; Weclew 1975). Social, behavioral, and medical scientists are beginning to study all health care systems as composed of three interconnected, locally sited and socio-culturally grounded components: the professional medical care system, the folk care system, and the popular culture system as composed of individual, family, and community health beliefs and practices (Fabrega 1977; Kleinman 1974; Leutz 1977; Snow 1974).

The natural history method of study, a legitimate research tool common to anthropologists and enthnographers in traditional societies and which is sensitive to cultural and subcultural variations, is being used to identify, for example, folk healers, culture brokers and informal community caregivers in indigenous helping networks in urban communities (Thomas and

Garrison 1975). In an ongoing study in New Jersey, the following practitioners were identified: in the Black community of Central Newark, 28 "Spiritualists," "Psychics," "Rootworkers" and other unique or mixed helping practices, and 30 Gypsy "reader-advisors:" in the Hispanic communities, 30 <u>botanicas</u> (religious object stores), where personal consultation is given, spiritist "centers," where group meetings are held to "work" the "spiritual problems" of those who come, and "Santero(a)s," practitioners in the Afro-American syncretic cult of Santeria. In the largely white surrounding suburban towns, more than 60 astrologers, psychics, clairvoyants and others were discovered through an initial survey (V. Garrison 1976).

Throughout all American communities today evangelistic faith healers, spiritualists, psychics, and a plethora of "mind-and-body-healing" or "consciousness altering" cultic and sectarian groups of ancient or recent origin can be readily found. All of these magico-religious or quasi-scientific cult practices, regardless of the attitude of the majority toward them, are ministering to the personal needs of their membership and their significance for the mental health and well-being of their members should be taken into account by the mental health care system.

<u>Mutual Help Groups</u>

Among the more visible "new" forms of support systems are self help and mutual help groups, one form of the rapidly growing peer-oriented helping networks and associations in our society such as children teaching children (Gartner et al. 1971) and elders helping elders (Patterson and Twente 1971). They are associations of people who band together as individuals who share the same problem, predicament or life situation for the purpose of mutual aid. This element of commonality is solely what defines the member's status in the group (Katz 1970). In contrast to professional help, mutual help is extended in these groups on the basis of identification (Katz and Bender 1976; Killilea 1976). The foundation of this mutual assistance is the member's experiential knowledge gained from personal struggle with his/her problem and experiential expertise acquired through competence in coping with his/her predicament (Borkman in press). Silverman (1978) suggests that mutual help groups form as a response to professional failure to meet the needs of particular client or patient groups; as a reaction to a lack of socially sanctioned coping strategies resulting from dislocations in times of rapid social change; and as the consequence of technological advances which prolong life in persons with chronic deficits without parallel attention to the quality of life.

In mutual help groups, the recipient of help can change roles to become the helper (Riessman 1965). On each side of the equation, helper/helped, helping/being helped, the process is dynamic. As one is helping, he/she is being helped by positive reinforcement to maintain change, through identification as a fellow-sufferer or as a veteran of the experience. As one is receiving help, he/she is providing an opportunity to another both to extend concrete aid and to act as a role model, thus providing hope to the recipient for future mastery. Within a matrix of affective support and shared ideology, mutual help groups have a heavy cognitive emphasis offering alternative coping mechanisms from persons of heterogeneous backgrounds (Ablon 1974). This affective and cognitive support is oriented both to individual responsibility for change or mastery and to constructive action toward shared goals. In mutual help groups all decisions about content, organization and external relationships are made by the membership whose chief qualification is that they currently share or have shared the problem or situation (Silverman 1970). These groups may be particularly helpful in managing life-cycle transitions, in dealing with long-term deficits and deprivations, and in changing noxious habits and life-styles (G. Caplan 1974; Caplan and Killilea 1976).

It has been estimated that there are over a half million different self help groups. The National Association for Retarded Citizens has over 1,300 local units and a membership of more than 130,000. Alcoholics Anonymous, together with its auxiliary groups, has a worldwide membership exceeding 750,000. In a two-county area of New York State alone, among six self help organizations (Alcoholics Anonymous, Al-Anon, Gamblers Anonymous, Gam-Anon, Overeaters Anonymous, and TOPS), there are over 180 groups. There is a self help group for nearly every major disease listed by the World Health Organization (Gussow and Tracy 1976). There are groups of the afflicted themselves and of their relatives and friends. There are self help groups of the handicapped, families of schizophrenic patients, drug abusers, Vietnam veterans, of parents who abuse their children, young people in search of identity and jobs, widows, parents of twins, old people, patients who have had heart attacks or mastectomies, homosexuals, parents of handicapped children, single parents, suicide-prone people, parents of gays and lesbians, families of prisoners, smokers, drinkers, overeaters, patients discharged from mental institutions. The kind of help offered is enormously varied. For instance, some groups, focusing on family concerns, use mail and the telephone as well as face-to-face meetings to help each other. The Candlelighters, a mutual help group of parents of children with cancer, includes among its activities a parent-to-parent correspondence program for those who live in communities which do not have an ongoing group. Another self help group for parents of children with cancer, Lifeline in Connecticut, provides a telephone credit card which members can use to call each other for information, support, and sharing in emergency situations. The telephone bill is paid by the group. In England, a self help group of parents of mentally-handicapped children uses a network of "correspondence magazines," which consist of personal letters, periodically reviewed, from each of them, commenting on shared information in the other letters. Some of the "magazines" have been circulating for several years, with members receiving up to a dozen letters every few weeks, while only writing one.

The trend toward deinstitutionalization in the mental health field has important implications for the mutual aid modality. As they move out into the community, former mental patients need organizations such as Recovery, Inc., and other types of small mutual help units to aid them in their adjustment and transition to everyday life. For example, the Rainbow Club in New York is a club for former patients, now working or in job training. Patients currently at the Harlem Rehabilitation Center are invited to join the Club's activities (on a non-dues paying, non-voting basis) which include socialization and mutual help in all areas of life, including job finding. The role examples the Club members provide for the patients undergoing treatment are a significant contribution toward their rehabilitation. The club uses the facilities of the Rehabilitation Center and the staff of the center are available for consultation and liaison with agencies and clinics.

Many mutual help groups in addition to being supportive of their members are also action-oriented, often focusing on changing public attitudes toward their problem or situation. Outstanding examples of this focus can be found among many groups formed to meet the needs of homosexuals. Some mutual help groups include an emphasis on changing public policy with a concomitant reallocation of resources. In four years, the Center for Independent Living in Berkeley, California, has grown from a small self help group of physically disabled persons to a multipurpose community with a staff, more than half of whom are themselves disabled, which directly serves approximately 2,000 disabled people each month, with material and emotional support in areas including counseling, education, health care, housing and job placement, transportation, financial advocacy, and legal assistance. A major component of its program is political activism by the disabled on their own behalf (Kirshbaum, Harveston and Katz 1976). The Canadian Mental Health Association of Ottawa helped to form a mutual aid group of families and friends of mentally ill or emotionally disturbed patients. This group also seeks to monitor and to influence the quality of treatment services, and works toward the improvement of aftercare facilities for former patients through advocacy for new or better services. Other examples of this activist approach include:

- SHARE (self-help action and rap experience) in New York is a group for post-mastectomy women who share practical information about daily living and follow-up care. They also work actively against job discrimination and rejection for life and health insurance.

- Concerned Relatives of Nursing Home Patients in Cleveland combines educational meetings and group discussions with political and legislative action to affect nursing home policy.

- The Fortune Society in New York and Delancey Street Foundation in San Franciso have as members primarily ex-offenders who assist and are advocates for the ex-offender and offenders whose needs have not been met either by society or the correctional system.

- A small group of women in Boston began meeting in the 1960's for mutual support and to learn more about their bodies and how they might obtain health services more relevant to their needs. They later began sharing the information they gathered with other women, first in small meetings, then through informal publication of their material. The enormously successful and influential book, <u>Our Bodies, Ourselves</u>, was eventually published commercially (1976). The book has educated many women all over the country and in many parts of the world about their bodies and health care. Many women as a result are requesting different kinds of health services from previously unresponsive health care systems.

Professionals have also banded together in groups and in supportive networks to help each other more easily attain common professional goals. Sarason (1977) describes the Essex Network as a mutual aid approach adopted by several hundred people working in different schools, colleges, universities, and private agencies. People in the network exchanged information, resources and in-kind services on a reciprocal basis; they also provided affective support to each other and a sense of belonging to a community of concerned others. Another example of a support system for professionals within a single organization, i.e., a religious denomination, is described by R. B. Caplan (1972) and Richards (1976).

There is clearly a need for much more study of self help mutual aid modalities and practices, as there are few studies to verify their effectiveness (Lieberman and Borman 1976). We do not know whether the usefulness of mutual help group methods apply only to special segments of the population or for help with special problems. We usually do not know whether the reported results reflect consumer satisfaction--a major benefit in itself--or behavioral change. There is beginning to accumulate some research in which objective evidence is provided, such as Stunkard's (1972) study of the success of the weight-reducing group called TOPs, using as indicators loss of weight and the maintenance of that loss. Reduced recidivism has been reported in programs where ex-offenders work with other ex-offenders (Volkman and Cressey 1963; Hampden-Turner 1976). A recent evaluation study (1977) of Parents Anonymous (PA) groups and programs found a significant decrease in physical abuse of children immediately after parents joined PA, a reduction in the social isolation patterns of its members, and an increase in knowledge of child development.

We also need more understanding of the processes by which self help groups render their services. Antze (1976), in a study of three groups (Alcoholics Anonymous, Synanon, and Recovery, Inc.), found that each group develops an ideology and coping strategies which are minutely calibrated to deal with the specific problem or life situation of its members. Levy et al. (1977), in a study of four behavior control groups (AA, TOPS, Emotional Anonymous, Parents Anonymous), and three stress coping groups (Parents Without Partners, Overeaters Anonymous, Make Today Count, a group for cancer patients), found that the behavior control groups had relatively more emphasis on personal goal setting and positive reinforcement for behavioral change than the stress coping groups. Levy also found that in all the groups he studied the following processes occurred most frequently: expressions of empathic understanding; mutual affirmation of worth; explanation; sharing and reassurance. These processes, together with others occurring less frequently, seem to cluster around four activities in all the groups studied: cognitive-emotional interventions; support and relationship building; group sanctioning of behaviors; and normative advice. In addition, he concluded that there seems to be a consensus among people about what kinds of interventions will be most helpful to suffering persons in similar situations.

Efforts are now underway to examine ways in which professionals and self help groups may usefully collaborate. Two such projects are:

The Mutual Help Project, under the direction of Phyllis Silverman at the American Institutes of Research, Cambridge, is working cooperatively with selected self help groups to help them to develop printed materials useful to their work which could serve as models for the development of materials for other similar groups; and, by offering technical assistance, to help them generate partnerships between groups, e.g., a mature group which has successfully solved some common problems might help a new group foundering on these difficulties.

Community Self-Help (CSH) of Toronto, Canada, made up of members who belong to a variety of local self-help groups, offers panel discussions to professionals, community organizations, and individuals on the nature, functioning and availability of self-help groups in Toronto, including presentations in behavioral science seminars for medical school students. CSH also performs clearinghouse communication, linkage, and consultation functions between professionals, people who might benefit from a self-help group, and the groups themselves.

Some newsletters and directories on specific self help groups include: Self-Help Reporter, National Self-Help Clearinghouse, New York; "A resource guide to self help groups in New York," Bill Claflin and Pat Thaler, New York, February, 1977; Action, ed. Shirley Burghard, Self-Help Self-Health Therapeutic Clubs, Syracuse, New York; Self-Help Spotlight, Self-Help Clearinghouse, London, England; The Sunday Times of London Directory of Self-Help Organizations In England, London, 1976.

"New" Forms of Volunteer Activity

In addition to self help groups, there is an enormous increase in "new" forms of volunteer activity combining the use of the concepts of social networks, support systems, peer-oriented and cross-age helping linked to community service. For example, Friends, a group originating in North Dakota but now with groups in 13 States, has a roster of people who have been through various life crises. Through a network of volunteers, persons undergoing a particular stressful situation are matched with veterans of the experience. Haven of Northern Virginia, Inc., a volunteer-staffed organization with the purpose of helping people with life threatening illnesses and members of their families, offers community resource assistance and limited home help care, with efforts being made to tie in to the visiting programs of the Committees for the Sick in operation through the churchs and synagogues in the area; recreation programs for the children of families being helped; and support services provided by professional volunteers (nurses, counselors, psychiatrists, psychologists and clergymen) who are available when needed for consultation with volunteers, as well as those being directly served. Haven also has groups for widows and for parents who have lost children (with future groups planned for adolescents and widowers).[2]

The Parenting Guidance Center of Fort Worth, Texas, serves as a catalyst in the community to develop educational programs for parents and also serves as a focal point to which existing community agencies and institutions can turn for help with parents who abuse their children. As part of its program, volunteers from the community, called Parent Partners, act as a surrogate extended family and also link their partners to the Center's group meetings for mutual exchange and information about child development; a social network with opportunities for friendship and sociability; and information about community resources, including health and recreational services. The Center also trains volunteers to develop and lead parent groups all over the city, e.g., in local churches. In a chain reaction, one staff member to 12 volunteers to 144 young parents in 12 locally based groups in community organizations. A particular preventive focus is taken with an emphasis on isolated newcomers to the city, e.g., white collar business and military base transfers (Marek 1977).

Since 1973, the Program for the Elderly of the Edna McConnell Clark Foundation, now administered by the Academy for Educational Development, has been demonstrating that old Americans are an underutilized resource of major potential, that methods are available to engage them in important service, that very able elders do respond to major challenges, that qualified elders provide superior service in areas of critical national need. So far, demonstrations in over 30 cities have focused on national needs in education, in legal services-and-advocacy, and in health. In education, for example, 6,000 elders have been deployed in seven school districts in New York, Los Angeles, Miami, Seattle, Houston, Boston, and St. Louis, helping children in basic skills, language, career and vocational education, arts, and special education. In legal services, for example, eight Junior Leagues in Seattle, Minneapolis, Grand Rapids, Rochester, Kansas City, Omaha, Orlando and Providence, through the Association of Junior Leagues, are implementing a program called Volunteers Intervening for Equity. The program calls for investigation, service and action by highly competent older citizens in situations where individuals are failing to receive a needed service, a right or an entitlement. Cooperating with a wide range of community agencies, volunteers address themselves to such problems as malfunctioning of the juvenile justice system, deficiencies in the health care system, and the efficiency

---

[2] The hospice movement, which originated more than 10 years ago at St. Christopher's in London, is only now gaining momentum in the United States. The organizers of fledgling hospices in the United States, professionals and volunteers, concentrate first on providing supportive home care to the dying and their families; then, where it is available and necessary, on providing a community facility where the dying are cared for in as pleasant and pain-free an environment as possible during their last days. The emphasis is on the quality of life for the patient, among family and friends.

of emergency health care services. In health, for example, one area of concentration has been the formation of home-health care service agencies, in cooperation with the National Council of Homemaker-Home Health Aide Services, using older community leaders to take charge initially, then recruiting people to provide home care, many of whom are themselves older workers (50 percent over 50; 25 percent over 65).

A substantial number of elders who responded in a 1974 Harris survey sponsored by the Clark Foundation said they would like to become active in "health and mental health services" and in "psychological and social support" services. The Academy for Educational Development (AED) is now engaged in planning a multiple-area demonstration program in which talented older people will be employed as volunteers or paid workers to meet mental health needs in demonstration communities. Elder leaders in all settings (neighborhoods, churches, workplaces) will be identified to enable them to mobilize a network of concerned elders and to support their efforts to maintain contact with people in need. Key people in such a network would be professionals whose prior careers as clergy, social workers, teachers, police, business managers, union officers, and community leaders qualify them as conscientious, caring individuals with the capacity to learn new roles and to lead. If costs are low enough, if results are good enough, and if enough competent old people are meaningfully engaged, then national dissemination of the demonstration would occur. It is anticipated that a variety of private sources will sponsor both phases of this program. A second new thrust of AED will be the use of retirees to assist in developing jobs for hard to employ groups such as urban minority youth, handicapped persons, certain groups of women and older workers.

Sainer (1976) describes the evolution of a Federal national voluntary service program, RSVP (Retired Senior Volunteer Program), from its start in 1966 on Staten Island, New York, sponsored by the Community Service Society of New York, a private social agency. In the beginning 23 elders worked with the retarded at Willowbrook State School. Today more than 700 communities have RSVP programs with more than 165,000 volunteers. The original research conducted by the Community Service Society found that the oldest volunteers took on more assignments and worked more hours; among the major reasons for volunteering initially and for staying on was the need for social contacts and for a useful role. It was also found that a group approach to recruitment, placement, and retention was the most effective because it provided peer contact and support and thus allowed the program to attract and keep the isolated, unaffiliated older person.

Volunteer activity is not just the prerogative of the healthy; the institutionalized and handicapped aged can also contribute usefully. In recent years, the RSVP staff in New York City have developed volunteer programs in institutions such as nursing homes in which more able residents help the less able by visiting them, reading to them, escorting them to other parts of the building. A few years ago the Community Service Society pioneered a program in which blind and visually handicapped older persons work in volunteer service together with sighted volunteers, e.g., at Creedmoore State Hospital for the mentally ill.

Many individuals who do not now receive services or who receive inadequate services may be reached by these community support systems and mutual help groups. They are unique in that they capitalize on resources that are already present in the community and multiply them. The services provided by mutual help groups and these newer forms of community support systems are participatory in nature, increase accountability because they are more determined by consumer satisfaction than by autonomous professional criteria, and can be a cost-effective way to increase much needed human services (Gartner and Riessman 1977). In partnership with professional and institutional resources, the services available to people can be increased geometrically.

RECOMMENDATIONS

13. Mandate that community mental health centers provide directories of mutual help groups and similar peer-oriented support systems as part of their resource base and encourage other community organizations, both public and private, to disseminate these directories in order to make such groups more accessible to the public.

14. Develop clearinghouses on mutual help groups and peer-oriented support systems in each Federal region throughout the country to integrate information, to publish newsletters and other materials, to provide training and technical assistance, to sponsor periodic regional conferences on self help, to enable professionals and members of self help groups to learn from each other.

15. Develop curricula in all undergraduate and graduate training programs in the social, behavioral, educational, and medical sciences and professions related to mental health services delivery on the nature and function of community support systems, natural helping networks, and mutual help groups. The inclusion of such curricula should be considered an essential element in the accreditation process for approval status for graduate professional training programs in medicine, psychology, social work, nursing, pastoral counseling, rehabilitation, psychiatry and other related disciplines.

16. Federal monies should be made available to State mental health associations to help catalyze a citizen-controlled statewide strategy for the development of locally based peer-oriented supportive networks, to give technical assistance in their implementation to their local affiliated associations, and to develop information and referral resources on mutual help groups.

17. Convene a national conference of directors of volunteer programs in health, mental health, educational, and social welfare programs to identify ways volunteer programs can be creatively linked both to the community's natural support networks and the formal caregiving institutions.

SOCIAL SUPPORT SYSTEMS, HEALTH AND MEDICAL CARE SYSTEMS

There is a body of research which suggests that social supports have a direct effect on health. Holmes (1956), for example, demonstrated that the incidence of tuberculosis in Seattle was highest for people who, by the fact of their "social marginality," lacked significant intimate social contacts. Miller and Ingham (1976) found that women lacking a social support network had far more symptoms of tiredness, anxiety, depression, and irritability than those women having an active social support network. Marmot (1975) found that the incidence of coronary heart disease was higher in Japanese living in California than in Hawaii or Japan, and that a key factor accounting for this discrepancy was the loss of a social support system as the individual emigrated progressively farther from the socio-cultural ties of home. Similarly, indices of social disorganization have been associated with increases in stroke mortality (Nesser et al. 1971) and psychological disorders (Leighton 1959).

Unfortunately, studies such as these contain certain conceptual and methodological weaknesses that limit their usefulness with regard to a precise explanation of support systems in disease etiology. Principal among these weaknesses has been the failure of most researchers to relate one set of psychosocial factors (e.g., support systems) to others that have also been shown to influence health, such as stress. Hence, rather than posit a direct relationship between support systems and health, recent authors (Cassel 1974b; Cobb 1976; Kaplan, Cassel and Gore 1977) have argued that the influence of social supports on health can best be understood by referring to their role in modifying the deleterious effects of stress. Animal studies in particular have shown the protective effect of the presence of significant others during times of stress (Conger et al. 1958; Henry et al. 1967; Liddel 1950).

An alternative explanatory mechanism has been suggested in which social supports mediate the impact of stress by strengthening the individual's coping efforts. Social supports provide one of the basic strategies of individual coping (D. Hamburg and Adams 1967; D. Hamburg et al. 1974; D. Hamburg et al. 1976). In circumstances as diverse as early adolescence (B. Hamburg 1974), recovery from severe burns (D. Hamburg and B. Hamburg et al. 1953) and concentration camp imprisonment (Dimsdale 1974), the availability of a supportive network has proved vital for the sustenance of morale, problem-solving, and adaptive behavior.

Just as there is a body of literature assessing the effects of various indices of social support on health, there is a large body of research assessing the effects of stress on health. Holmes and Rahe (1967) emphasize life change per se as the key factor (marriage, job promotion, birth of child, etc.; as well as death in family, school or job failure, arrests, divorce, etc.). Others state that it is the individual's response to life events that is key, with some people having, as a result of constitutional or early life experience, an ability to tolerate well what for others would be very destructive life stress (Engel 1969). Much of the research on stress has been criticized for taking a too narrow theoretical viewpoint, leading to possibly inaccurate accounts of the role of stress in disease onset and duration (Dohrenwend and Dohrenwend 1974; Mechanic 1976; Rabkin and Streuning 1976). Only recently have the two parallel bodies of research become interacting, resulting in studies that simultaneously measure stress and social support systems. For example, Nuckolls, Cassel and Kaplan (1972) found that the absence of social supports was associated with increased complications in pregnancy and delivery only when accompanied by high stress; lack of supports did not, in itself, increase risk. Similar results were obtained by deAraujo et al. (1973) who found that chronic intrinsic asthmatics required much more medication if they had high stress and few social supports. Brown et al. (1975) found that the presence of a confidant, usually male, provided the women they studied significantly greater protection from severe affective disorder in the face of adverse events than women lacking such intimates. Finally, a recent study by Wells et al. (1977) showed that social supports mitigated the effects of occupational stress on health, using such outcome measures as ulcers, angina, and neurotic symptoms.

Stress and social support systems have also been found to play a role in influencing the use of health services. Some research suggests that psychosocial factors may influence utilization independently from their effects on health. With regard to stress, Roghmann and Haggerty (1972) found that daily life stresses increased utilization of some services (e.g., telephone calls, emergency room visits) even when no illness was present. Similarly, Tessler, Mechanic and Dimond (1976) found that, in a prepaid group practice, physician utilization increased significantly in the presence of stress, even when the effects of health status were controlled for. The evidence regarding the effects of social supports on utilization is more diffuse and must be extrapolated from the more broadbased approach investigating the role of social or "lay" factors in utilization. Here a useful distinction has been made between the "lay referral network" and the "lay treatment network." The first concept refers to the collection of informal consultants used by an individual to identify sources of help for a problem (Freidson 1960); the second to the non-professional modes of interpersonal helping which occur in the natural environment (Gottlieb 1976).

The lay referral process was examined empirically by McKinlay (1973) who studied "utilizers" and "underutilizers" of a prenatal clinic. Underutilizers were found to have more relatives living close by and consulted with a dense (i.e., interlocking) network of family and friends. The utilizers, by contrast, were more likely to have separate or differentiated kin and friendship neworks. It would be erroneous, however, to assume, on the basis of the results of this one study that dense social networks serve to defer contact with professional health services. Another study (Geersten et al. 1975) found that tight-knit social networks tended to facilitate use of health services. The content of the referrals obviously differed between the two populations in these studies, with the important point being that support systems can serve a dual role in influencing use of health services; i.e., inhibiting or faciliating. Factors such as social and cultural disparities between providers and clients, trust in professionals, the perceived accessibility and appropriateness of the services offered, etc., may determine which of these roles are played. The dimensions of the lay treatment network could include resources in kinship and friendship networks, neighborhood-based support systems, or mutual/self help groups. To the extent that treatment received in these domains parallels or competes with professional services, utilization may decrease. But to the extent that the help given complements professional services, utilization may be unaffected or even increase. An example of the former comes from a study by Croog et al. (1972) which showed, with post-infarction patients, that these men made minimal use of institutional and professional services (aside from the physician) even when appropriate services were available, but relied on friends and kin instead. An example of the latter would be childbirth education groups, which, while providing a service, also often promote the utilization of professional obstetrical services.

It is clear, therefore, that the relationship between social support systems and utilization is not simple and clear-cut. On the one hand, the absence of an adequate social support system can lead to the inability to use health services or may lead to an increased use of health services when the major problem is not disease, but the need for human support. On the other hand, the presence of social supports, depending on the content of the support given, may lead to increased use (e.g., through a lay referral process) or decreased use (e.g., through the provision of alternative not-professional services).

In terms of health-care policy, a fundamental issue regards the "inappropriate" use of health care services. In the scheme outlined above, both under-utilization of needed services and overutilization for non-medical reasons can be considered inappropriate. Unfortunately, "inappropriate" is often used pejoratively in the sense of "blaming the patient." More constructively, it should be taken to mean the use of health services for situations in which these services are relatively ineffective. The difficulty has been that once a person with a need for social support triggers the response of the medical care system, this system often responds in an "inappropriate" way, utilizing medical technology rather than invoking a potentially more effective and less costly social support system. The inappropriate utilization of medical technology also has attendant risks of increasing likelihood of iatrogenic effects.

Just as social support systems can influence the utilization of health services, they can affect other aspects of health behavior such as compliance with medical regimens. For example:

. The diagnosis and treatment of high blood pressure (hypertension) have reached a state that is both encouraging and frustrating. Available medications produce an impressive drop in blood pressure and in the incidence of strokes and other illnesses associated with uncontrolled high blood pressure--provided, of course, that patients adhere to the prescribed regimen. It has been estimated, however, that only about half the people with high blood pressure obtain proper diagnosis, that only some of those obtain the prescribed drugs, and that only half of that group actually continue to take the medication as prescribed. The major medical problem, in short, has shifted to the question of improving adherence to regimens among hypertensive patients.

A recent study (R. D. Caplan et al. 1976) provided an interesting sequence of findings that bear on this problem: patients who adhered to their medical instructions did indeed have lower blood pressures; patients who had the most accurate knowledge of those regimens and of the consequences of adhering to them were more likely to do so. They were also more likely to be free of symptoms of psychological strain--anxiety, anger, and depression. Finally, social support from the physician was associated with knowledge of consequences, and social support from the spouse was associated with the patient's avoidance of depression and with his or her motivation to adhere to the medical regimen.

A field experiment was conducted in which attempts were made to increase the patients' knowledge and motivation to adhere to prescribed regimens, by means of lectures and increases in social support. The increases in social support were introduced through a sort of "buddy system" among the patients themselves. Results showed decreases in blood pressure in the lecture and support groups, as compared to control groups. Moreover, social support was more effective than lecture in the percentage of patients brought into "clinical control" (that is, blood pressures less than 140/90).[3]

It must also be recognized that the medical care system itself can be a social support system, and at times is the only resource some people have in times of stress. The notion that social support is important to the delivery of personal medical services has been emphasized in the sensitive work of Balint (1964), Freidson (1961), and Shuval (1970). It is now widely accepted, following from studies on the doctor-patient relationship, that the personal qualities of the provider and the mode of interaction with the patient may have as much therapeutic value for some problems as other more technological interventions, such as drugs.

Studies assessing patient satisfaction with medical services also point to the importance of emotional support in patients' assessment of the quality of medical care, as measured attitudinally (Ben-Sira 1976), or more behaviorally by such criteria as "doctor-shopping" or appointment-breaking (Alpert 1964; Kasteller et al. 1976). Patients may in fact not always distinguish between the "caring" and "curing" aspects of medical care (Ware and Snyder 1975). While studies such as these point to the importance of social support in the medical care setting, it is clear that the ability and willingness of providers themselves to give social support depends not only on the individual provider's personality characteristics, prior experience, or even training, but also on the organizational constraints of the medical setting that may serve to facilitate or inhibit such supportive interchanges. One of the great needs in this area is to devise methods to increase the capacity of medical settings in recognizing when social support is needed by patients, and then providing access to an effective social support system. In family practice medicine, for instance, there are some predictable situations that require assessment of a patient's and family's social support systems.

---

[3]An important aspect of the spectrum of health care receiving increased attention today is self-care, including patient participation in professional care (Levin et al. 1976).

TABLE 2
SOME PRESENTING PROBLEM SITUATIONS WHICH NECESSITATE ASSESSMENTS OF SUPPORTIVE NETWORKS
(adapted from Medalie, forthcoming)

1. Bereavement
2. Care of the elderly
3. First pregnancy
4. Major illness in patient or immediate family
5. Adolescence
6. Newcomer to community
7. Multi-problem family

Acceptance by medical professionals of community support resources is presently greatest for (1) those medical problems that are minimally responsive to traditional medical interventions, such as alcoholism and drug addiction, and for (2) aid in rehabilitation of patients with severe physical illness and long-term disability. Regarding the latter, recent studies have confirmed the impact of informal social support networks (Finlayson 1976; Hyman 1972) and more organized support systems (Guggenheim and O'Hara 1976) in the rehabilitation of severely ill patients. As a result of studies such as these on the contributions of social support systems in major illnesses, many hospitals dealing with chronic care patients or severely injured patients have started to institute programs to maximize group affiliation.

The social support capabilities of the medical settings themselves may need to be enhanced, but an equally important strategy may be to increase the interaction between medical settings and not-professional support systems in communities. Since the recognition of the importance of community support systems is relatively new among medical professionals, and even in the social sciences, it is clearly a topic that has received little emphasis in medical training and practice. As a result, there is often both a failure to identify problems related to deficiencies in patients' social support systems and a lack of knowledge of referral possibilities outside the medical system. In addition to restricting referral possibilities, this lack of knowledge also may affect the efficacy of treatment.

As the importance of social support systems becomes increasingly apparent to medical care providers and policy makers, important issues with regard to the nature of the role of professionals vis-a-vis community support systems will need to be explored. A variety of roles are possible and presently exist, some direct and some indirect (Baker 1977; Powell 1975). Indirect interaction may take place through a referral process, e.g., medical providers advising patients to use existing mutual help groups. For instance, obstetricians may advise women who want to breast-feed their baby to attend LaLeche League meetings, without having any direct contact with these groups themselves. A more direct role might encompass professionals actually initiating a mutual help program for unserved populations (e.g., Widow-to-Widow, as developed by Silverman, 1970), professional consultation to already established support systems (e.g., to TOPS--Take Pounds Off Sensibly--on the medical aspects of obesity), or assisting groups such as Alcoholics Anonymous, Recovery, Inc., etc., in other ways, such as providing them with a place to meet.

While there are not at the present time many models of the medical care system stimulating the development of social and community support systems, some examples do exist and should be further explored. The Family Service of the Bronx Psychiatric Center has developed mutual aid groups of families with a chronic schizophrenic member, beginning in the State hospital, and moving out to members' homes. The groups provide (a) an educational model: "This is what we know helps people suffering from schizophrenia, and this is what makes people worse," (b) an affiliative model: the families are experts in what has worked for them and what has not and teach one another and turn to one another in crises and day-to-day living. In some community mental health centers, staff target certain populations felt to be at risk and help design new forms of social supports appropriate to each group (Snyder 1978). For instance, young mothers, who are raising infants and toddlers in the absence of assistance from an extended family, are offered one morning a week during which the health center provides childcare. The program, Mothers' Morning Out, gives them an opportunity to shop, socialize with neighbors, and get some respite from the demands of child raising. This program is even more important for the young single mother, who has only paltry social support. Other programs focus on the elderly and social isolates who can profit immeasurably by the provision of a quasi-social group comprised of other individuals in the same predicament. Formation of fitness groups in a health care setting can also provide information, emotional support, and assistance in diet, exercise, and activity. The Kaiser Permanente Santa Teresa Medical Center in San Jose, California (Harrington, forthcoming; Harrington et al. 1977) is developing a mental health care delivery system within a medical care delivery system so as to be able to offer appropriate treatment for patients' problems. As part of an overall multiphase examination, assessments are made of patients' life stresses, supports, and coping patterns. Patients who are having problems in living or who have medical illnesses that may be a result of these difficulties are referred by their physician or nurse practitioner to health educators who are part of the medical center or to existing community resources. Resources of all types are utilized, including special junior college courses designed to help individuals learn to cope with life problems (e.g., how to deal with teenage children).

A viable social support system is essential to successful coping and appears highly relevant to morbidity and mortality. The intentional cooperation of the health-care system and social support systems is to be encouraged. Cooperation would appear particularly important in the fields of rehabilitation medicine, psychiatry, and ambulatory medicine. It also must be recognized that the very nature of social and community support systems may set limits in this regard. Some mutual-help health groups (e.g., women's health collectives) have arisen largely in opposition to the existing medical care system.[4] Also, even in circumstances where professional participation is welcomed by community support systems, there is a danger of professionalization which would be counterproductive to their effectiveness. More data are needed on the effectiveness of professionally organized and/or assisted social support services, as well as on naturally occurring ones. We know very little about the natural history of support systems, and how they can be changed or enhanced when deficiencies exist. It is on this level that well-designed scientific studies would be invaluable.

RECOMMENDATIONS

    18. Research funds should be provided to increase knowledge of the mechanisms whereby social support is effective in reducing mental distress and physical illness.

---

[4]A separate study has been conducted for the Commission on parallel services/structures such as free clinics, acupuncture programs, holistic healing centers, patient-run community residences, health collectives, etc: "Special Study on Alternative Mental Health Services," James S. Gordon, M.D.

19. Demonstration projects should be conducted under the rubric of a broad concept: health care as supportive of human development. The health-care delivery system must move toward provision of services to assist the individual not only in recovery from illness, but also in the maintenance of health and in coping with life-cycle transitions and major stresses.

20. Allocate funds for the training of health workers about social support and health, especially the development of projects on the appropriate utilization of support systems as part of primary care residency programs, family practice residency programs, nurse practitioner training programs, and programs for continuing medical education.

21. Health Systems Agencies (HSAs) should be required to include planning for social support systems within their local and State five-year plans. Professional Standards Review Organizations (PSROs) should be required to review social support systems that relate to health services as part of their developing review of the quality of ambulatory care services.

22. Demonstration programs, with an evaluative component, to experiment with reimbursement mechanisms for general health and medical services which include payment for social support services as part of their approved benefits should be initiated. Future national health insurance should provide for payment of such social support services.

WORK, OCCUPATIONAL STRESS AND MENTAL HEALTH

Controversies about the definition of work and its meaning in human life are age-old and likely to persist. The following definition and propositions about work are well supported, we believe, although they are not beyond argument.

- Work is human activity that produces something of acknowledged value. All three of the elements in that definition--activity, production, and value--are important for mental health. Mental health can be enhanced by activity, although all activities are not health-enhancing. Mental health is also enhanced by the reality and experience of producing something, and by the recognition on the part of others that the activity and its outcome have value.

- Work is available to most people only as jobs--paid employment. People do not create jobs to suit their individual needs and abilities; they seek and accept the job that is the best available to them.

- Many people are unable to find jobs and many jobs are deficient on one or another of the dimensions in our definition--activity, production, and valuation. The required activity may be minimal or meaningless in itself; the thing produced may be remote from the worker; or the value assigned by others to the work may be meager. Such deficiencies reduce or nullify the contribution of work to the mental health of the worker.

- Whatever their adequacy on these defining dimensions, jobs have other characteristics that are important for well-being or illness. Among them are dependence or autonomy, powerlessness or control, monotony or variety, hazardousness or safety, appropriateness of workload (as compared to overload or underutilization), and isolation or belongingness.

- Social support on the job, from co-workers and supervisors, contributes to the well-being of workers in two ways--as a direct source of satisfaction and as an aid in coping with stress.

- For most adults in industrial societies there is no satisfactory alternative to work. No alternative within present aspiration and reach offers equivalent prospects for activity, meaningfulness, reward, and recognition.

- It follows that the loss or denial of work is generally damaging to the individual and dangerous for the society, and that mental health and well-being can be increased by increasing the availability of appropriate jobs.

- The qualities of jobs, including the social support that they can provide, are scarcely less important than their availability.

CSS 50

In summary, then, work is not only a source of products and services, it is in itself a public good. It should therefore be regarded as an entitlement, and its allocation should be a prime concern of policy. The possession of a job is a unique source of connectedness, membership, and access to social support. It is therefore a factor in promoting mental health. Work, however, can be a source of stress as well as of well-being, and jobs differ greatly in their health-enhancing or damaging attributes. The quality of employment is second in importance only to the fact of employment, as a factor in mental health. It follows that increasing the quality of employment should become a matter of national policy, and that minimum standards for such quality should be promulgated (Kahn 1977).

A considerable amount of evidence exists indicating that occupational stress (i.e., job dissatisfaction, alienation, pressures, etc.) has a deleterious impact on mental health, and on aspects of physical health as well (Kahn et al. 1964; Kornhauser 1965; French et al. 1974; House et al. 1976). Wherever possible, the source of occupational stress should be addressed directly and remedied or reduced. In addition, recent studies suggest that social support can mitigate the relationship of occupational stress to health (R. D. Caplan 1971; Cobb 1974; Gore 1973; House et al. 1977a; Wells et al. 1977). These studies show that people who have adequate social support from friends, family, and co-workers are able to deal more successfully with such events as unemployment, retirement, and job change. Similar findings have been reported for more chronic kinds of job stress. It appears from these research studies that social support from one significant other person can often be effective in alleviating much and sometimes all of the deleterious impact of occupational stress on health. Thus, applied efforts at enhancing social support ought to concentrate initially on ensuring that as many persons as possible have a supportive relationship with one such significant other, rather than on trying to enhance the social supportiveness of total communities, organizations or networks. From a variety of perspectives, work supervisors appear to be the most promising targets for initial intervention programs designed to reduce the deleterious effect of occupational stress on health by enhancing social support.

Work supervisors have been shown to be effective sources of social support; they can be reached through organizational channels and in many cases through existing programs for supervisory training; and if all work supervisors are effectively reached in this way, all persons in the organization could have at least one supportive other. The effectiveness of work supervisors will be more limited for workers who are self-employed or work in organizations with a minimum of hierarchy (e.g., professional organizations which are organized on a collegial basis). Complementary efforts should be made in all organizations to enhance the supportiveness of union stewards, co-workers (peers and subordinates), as well as supervisors, and these efforts should take precedence over programs for enhancing supervisory support in those contexts where supervisors are absent, less salient, or unresponsive.

Efforts to enhance social support should concentrate on persons and/or contexts in which people experience high levels of stress and/or are especially lacking in social support. Such groups are identifiable from existing knowledge of occupational differences in stress and of the predictable developmental transitions and crises of occupational life (e.g., job entry, job change, retirement, etc.). Families, especially spouses, can constitute very effective sources of support with respect to occupational, as well as more general social, stress. Thus, programs should be developed to enhance the supportiveness of family members toward each other. However, the family should not be assumed always to be ready and able to buffer persons against occupational stress--this is rightly the primary responsibility of work organizations (House et al. 1977b).

Natural networks and social support systems can be utilized in combination with resources from industry, unions, government, and formal local community organizations to moderate the damaging effects of job loss.

. One such experimental trial took place in a moderate-sized Michigan city faced with an acute problem of unemployment. A major employer in the area was proposing to shut down its local facilities, and transfer their functions to other locations. The shutdown was occurring at a time when the local labor market gave little promise of absorbing quickly the displaced workers. An earlier study (Cobb and Kasl 1977) had demonstrated the negative effects of both the anticipation and the fact of such job loss. These effects were not only economic, but extended to the health and psychological well-being of the affected workers. The research further showed that these effects were reduced, and in some cases were wholly absent, among workers who received a great deal of social support from their spouse, their relatives, and their friends. These findings provided the basis for an action program in this Michigan city faced with the prospect of a plant closing. The company contributed facilities and the time of key people who served as counselors. Many local organizations--unions, the United Way, schools, hospitals, and local offices of various State agencies, and others-- joined to provide supportive services and to strengthen those already available. Some of these services were informational, listing available jobs and organizations offering them; some concentrated on discovering job openings in other communities. Some emphasized direct counseling, and others worked through existing membership groups.

Observations by social scientists of this pilot effort suggest that the creation and use of such support networks may mitigate some long-documented human costs of plant closings and job loss. These networks can provide support in informational as well as emotional terms, by helping people to interact appropriately with existing agencies, by making them aware of educational opportunities, by showing them how to cope realistically with many problems, e.g., managing their debts on a reduced income. People who unexpectedly lose their jobs are faced with a complex and interrelated set of problems. The network approach seems useful because it can coordinate the activities of diverse groups and organizations which individually are able to deal only with specific aspects of problems (Taber, Walsh and Cooke 1976).

All programs for enhancing social support in connection with work must be treated initially as intervention trials, the impact and effectiveness of which should be carefully evaluated through research. The Federal Government has a long tradition of providing evidence, demonstration, and service in other areas, e.g., the Department of Agriculture does these things through its program of experimental farms and stations and its network of county agents. This can also be done in the workplace, e.g., by the Department of Labor.

RECOMMENDATIONS

23. Fund and establish within the Federal Government the continuing review, assessment, and interpretation of innovations in job design and organizational design undertaken to improve the quality of work experience.

24. Develop criteria for the gradual enactment of Federal standards for the quality of employment, including such job characteristics as variety or monotony, length of work cycle, control over methods and pace of work, degree of isolation or opportunity to be with others, and the like.

25. Conduct experiments and demonstration projects to test and to explain the contributions of work to mental health and well-being and to strenghthen the natural supportive networks in places of work.

RELIGIOUS SUPPORT SYSTEMS

In a recent study (Veroff 1976), more people (39.2 percent) said they would turn to the clergy than to any other professional if they had a problem and needed to seek professional help. Rabbis, priests, preachers, shamans, etc., have long traditions as sources of spiritual, social, cognitive, and emotional healing. As such, they represent a major, partially-tapped mental health resource (Clinebell 1970). Haugk (1976) has reviewed the unique and cooperative contributions religious institutions and personnel can make to community mental health endeavors. Perhaps the greatest natural asset of clergy is their acknowledged right to care for their congregants and to seek out those in trouble, thus providing a population focus (R. B. Caplan 1972).

One hundred twenty-seven million people belong to religious groupings, reflecting a wide diversity of ethno-cultural traditions. At least 250,000 clergy, in these religious groupings, are available as a resource. Few cities, towns, or hamlets are without such groups and institutions, including many communities which do not have mental health agencies. In minority communities, the church, particularly the storefront church, is often the central, and at times the only, accessible source of local assistance.

Religious leaders, professional and lay, at any one time are in face-to-face relationship with hundreds of thousands of persons who are in emotionally hazardous periods of stress such as are caused by illness, surgery, accidents, divorce, natural disasters, unemployment, moving, and by many forms of loss and grief. Religious institutions possess rich spiritual resources, including many insights about human values and the meaning of life. Such resources can be especially supportive to persons in, for example, acute care hospitals and long-term care facilities such as nursing homes, prisons, State mental hospitals. Clergy in their roles as pastors and as chaplains have traditionally ministered to their needs. The clergy and religious communities have been about their business, "healing," for a long time.

In addition to providing a belief system and shared values, religious groups and institutions by their very nature foster support among individuals, families, and neighbors (G. Caplan 1975). Certain religious social mechanisms have been suggested, in a study of religious behavior and coronary heart disease, as contributing to the maintenance of hope, the regulation of depression and fear, and the protection of social-personal integration: ritual behavior; interpersonal provisions of support; and religious teachings as coping models for effectively dealing with threat, anxiety, and despair (Kaplan 1976). Also, churches and synagogues are the major transgenerational organization in most communities and thus have exceptional opportunities to help people cope creatively with the developmental crises which occur throughout the life-cycle, and to help build communication bridges between the generations.

A relatively new personnel resource for mental health within religious organizations is the growing group of clergy who, in addition to their undergraduate and seminary training, have specialized clinical and academic education in the behavioral sciences and the psychotherapeutic disciplines. There are now several thousand clergy who have met rigorous training standards and are functioning as specialists in pastoral psychology and counseling in a wide variety of institutions and community settings. These specialists also provide a significant amount of cost-effective counseling and psychotherapy for people in need of mental health services. They are also key resource persons in educational programs for other clergy in the mental health aspects of their ministries.

Some examples of programs sponsored by religious groups and institutions are:

Lay Caring Teams in Congregations

Some religious organizations are experimenting with ways of releasing the caring potential of sensitive, mature lay persons--the natural caregivers to whom people gravitate spontaneously when personal crises strike. Two congregations in California--Glendale and Temple City--have recruited and trained small teams of persons to provide care and support to the hospitalized, the sick, the aged, the bereaved, and lonely newcomers in the community. The Virginia Institute of Pastoral Care is training lay persons specifically for a ministry of pastoral care, helping people in times of grief and other critical junctures of life. They are not trained as professional psycho-therapeutic counselors but as listeners and carers. A church in Minneapolis has trained 20 mature young adult and older couples to give support to newly married couples. This approach may provide a strategy for reducing the marital breakdown among teen marrieds.

Congregation-Based Sharing Groups

Some of the types of small groups now being used effectively in churches and synagogues nationally include Grief Recovery Groups to help people bear their losses constructively (e.g., in churches in Temple City, California, and Moline, Illinois). Divorce Recovery Groups and Workshops are also now being developed in various parts of the country. Other support groups include Parents of Handicapped Children Sharing Group, sponsored by a church in Tucson, Arizona; and Living with Dying Groups (for relatives of terminally ill persons), sponsored by a church in the Seattle area.

Marriage Enrichment Groups, Retreats, Workshops, or Classes

Marriage enrichment groups, retreats workshops, or classes are being sponsored by many religious institutions, e.g., Roman Catholic clergy are participating extensively in Marriage Encounter programs for enrichment of marriage relationships and for prevention of marriage breakdowns.

Church-related Counseling and Growth Centers

Many church-sponsored centers combine therapeutic, preventive growth, and training programs. They offer individual, group, couple, and family pastoral counseling services, together with a wide variety of support-growth groups whose aim is to help people learn communication and relationship-building skills, and to engage in mutual help during typical life crises. The Institutes of Religion and Health, New York City, with 27 Centers, provides 300,000 hours of therapy a year, at an average cost of $20 per hour. In Des Moines, a Pastoral Counseling Center sponsors a Grief Clinic, an adjunct service of seminars for clergy, mental health professionals, and funeral directors, focusing on the needs of grieving persons and ways to assist in bereavement.

The Mustard Seed Learning Center for Children, in Harlem, New York City, is a program for children and their parents to help counteract negative self-images and thus reinforce problem solving skills inherent in themselves as individuals and as social groups. In New Mexico, a church-sponsored center has contracts with the Headstart program and a medical clinic for migrants to provide direct client services. Another center, in Closter, New Jersey, is actively involved in community programs and, in particular, the staff works with the County Children's Mental Health Unit for mutual referral and consultation.

Additionally, some church-related counseling services provide consultation for parish clergy who wish to enhance their counseling and caregiving skills.

The Use of Pastoral Counselors by Community Agencies

A group in Glendale, California, is developing a program to link community agencies such as the Red Cross, YMCA, YWCA, with clergy counselors. The leaders of a network of community organizations (which encounter many people with personal and family problems but do not have counselors on their staffs) are being brought together with pastors who are willing to provide counseling for a limited number of hours each to persons referred by these agencies. In Ohio, a pastoral consultant and counselor works with county public agencies, providing educational programs for clergy in helping rural people accept mental health services.

Neighborhood Social and Civic Action

Members of the Accion Civica Evangelica in New York, which includes more than 500 evangelical Hispanic churches, are directly involved in providing services in their local communities such as nutrition programs, youth employment offices, ongoing education classes for pastoral leaders, and minicenters for the elderly. The Campaign for Human Development, an activity of the U.S. Catholic Conference, provides grants to organizations and groups for community self-help efforts. Projects have included a mutual help group in a socially mixed neighborhood in Cleveland, which focuses on making Federal housing programs more responsive to the community, a South

Carolina group of disabled and retired cotton mill workers who are fighting for protection from and appropriate compensation for brown lung disease; a self-help citizens' group of Mexican Americans in San Antonio working to improve the quality of neighborhood life.

In Las Vegas, churches and synagogues jointly sponsor work in potential community conflict situations. Also they distribute a Helping Services Directory to police, hotels, apartment mangers, hospitals, and nursing homes.

Wholistic Health Centers in Churches

Under the leadership of Dr. Granger Westberg of the University of Illinois Medical School, a new model of wholistic health services has been developed in six communities in the mid-West (Holinger and Westberg 1975). The centers are housed in church buildings and staffed by medical personnel and trained pastoral counselors. Many people come to such centers to discuss health issues and their problems in living in the context of their medical problems. The use of trained pastoral counselors to help them with the psychological and interpersonal dimensions of their concerns relieves physicians of the heavy burden of attempting to supply these services (for which they frequently have neither time nor training). Such centers have proved to be effective in both middle-class suburbs and in working class neighborhoods.

The Samaritan Health and Living Center in Indiana has developed a program to help people with stress-related problems. By using a team approach, with care provided by physicians, counselors, and ministers, services offered include marriage and family counseling, individual and group counseling, pastoral counseling, medical consultations, and educational programs. The center uses previously little-used rooms of the church for administration and counseling purposes, and has found that by offering these services in a church building, many people are less threatened, and are seeking help at the onset of their problems. A unique feature of the Samaritan Center is the use of in-kind payment as an alternative for those who are unable to manage the regular fees; under this concept the person being counselled works as a volunteer in a community agency.

Publication Programs

Many religious organizations have an extensive publishing program of books, tapes, pamphlets, films, and life enrichment study courses which could be utilized more fully as a resource for positive prevention.

Religious groups and congregations are committed to helping people fulfill their potentialities. The mental health movement has a similar commitment to people. These two networks of people-serving and people-enhancing institutions in our society are natural, complementing allies in the struggle to make greater wholeness an attainable reality for all.

RECOMMENDATIONS

26. Develop mechanisms to link the personnel and buildings owned by religious groups and institutions to community mental health centers and other social service agencies.

27. Initiate pilot projects, with an evaluation component, for demonstration of the actual functioning of religious support systems and to employ indigenous local clergy and lay people in developing community support systems.

28. Establish a conference mechanism to examine the relationship between religion and mental well-being and to clarify the role of religious support as to actual behavior, interpersonal provisions of support, and models of coping and competence.

29. Recommend the creation of a national voluntary register to process board examinations for clergy mental health professionals.

30. Declare clergy eligible for staff positions in all mental health centers, as providers of services and as educators about religious support systems.

AN EXPANDED ROLE FOR PUBLIC SCHOOLS

Schools are where most children are--55 million of them. The schools are the only social institution that provides services to all children on a universal basis. The long-standing tradition of a free public education has meant that there is no stigma attached to receiving service from or through the school system. Advocates of an expanded role for schools point to the universality of public education, the presence of underutilized physical and human resources, established funding mechanisms, and local control as the advantages of a school-based delivery system.

There are numerous State and Federal programs, some of which are currently school-based, delivering services to an expanded population group, including pre-schoolers, adults, and handicapped children. Several hundred communities, including Galveston, New Orleans, Cambridge, Flint, Nashville, St. Louis, and Jacksonville, are presently delivering limited health care for mothers and children, providing expanded child care before and after regular school hours, and/or including adults and senior citizens in their educational programs. For example, the Cambridge Community Schools in Massachusetts, a tax-supported department of city government, has developed year-round programs that serve infants, elders, and the age groups in between. There are day care, preschool, afterschool programs; senior citizen hot lunches; child care parent cooperatives which provide health, nutrition, and social services; recreational and cultural activities; teen centers; social and educational opportunities for the handicapped. In all programs, there is extensive neighborhood, parent, and volunteer participation, with a tailoring of programs to local needs.

Existing caring networks and innovative programs, including community mental health centers (Miller 1974), health agencies, and community education programs (Seay et al. 1976), lend themselves to the development of a system of health and mental health services delivered through the schools, with citizen participation in the decision-making process. Current State and Federal legislation (e.g., Public Law 88-164, Mental Retardation Facilities and Community Mental Health Center Construction Act of 1963, as amended by Public Law 94-63, Health Revenue Sharing Act of 1975; Public Law 93-380, Education Amendments of 1974 of the Elementary and Secondary Education Act; Public Law 94-63, Special Health Revenue Sharing Act of 1975, an amendment to the Public Health Service Act of 1944; Public Law 94-142, Education of All Handicapped Children Act of 1975; Section 504, Rehabilitation Act of 1973; Public Law 94-317, National Consumer Health Information and Health Promotion Act of 1976) would require a minimum of modification to enable health and mental health services to become school-based. There are a variety of service options that could be provided through the school system (Joint Commission on the Mental Health of Children and Youth 1970). Which ones would be adopted depend on local values and needs, existence of other community services and caregivers, cost, and the availability of technical assistance in implementing the system. The most important consideration, and the one perhaps least responsive to legislative regulation, is the need to develop varied delivery systems that are congruent with the divergent needs of urban, rural, and minority groups. It is essential that parents and other citizens be given a major role in defining the options for solving these problems.

CSS 59

It is not suggested that the health and mental health systems be subsumed under the public school bureaucracy. Rather, community schools could become the service entry point for families not previously in contact with health-care providers, and the agency responsible for identifying the unmet needs of children and their families in the community. The creation of a monolithic service system should be avoided but there are advantages in the creation of an efficient system that could coordinate the numerous services for children and their families that now exist (Mallory and Cottom 1977).

School Volunteer Programs

In recent years, there has been a notable expansion of contacts between schools and their local communities. There has been, for instance, a dramatic increase in community volunteers working in schools. A 1975 survey by ACTION, the Federal agency which coordinates domestic and international volunteer programs sponsored by the U.S. Government, found that 15 percent of the total number of volunteers in the United States, in both public and private programs (during the survey week, about 2,271,000 persons), worked in education on an average of 6 hours each per week. The majority of these volunteers were givers of direct service to children. The use of volunteers in the school can extend the teacher's teaching time, enrich the learning environment, expand the resources of the school, and enlist the community as partner with the school.

School volunteer programs can include cross-age tutoring; the involvement of neighborhood elders as oral historians and transmitters of cultural heritages and customs; the development of friendly and supportive adult relationships with troubled children in order to improve a child's sense of worth and self esteem, e.g., the Listener Program in Miami, Florida, with handicapped children; parent involvement through the development of math materials for use by parent (at-home) volunteers in St. Cloud, Minnesota; the inclusion of volunteers with parents and professionals, both clinical and educational, in planning for children with learning disabilities; the enrichment of curriculum through the addition of community resource persons from the arts, the professions, business and politics, e.g., in Minneapolis 110 community representatives in an average week participate in these kinds of classroom activities. Many older people serve in schools, e.g., DOVES (Dedicated Older Volunteers in Educational Services) is a group of 2,000 senior citizens and retirees who volunteer in 309 Los Angeles schools, helping children in the classroom, teaching them special skills, involving them in cultural and creative arts. Senior volunteers in many schools have been particularly successful working with physically and emotionally handicapped students. With the enactment of P.L. 94-142 (Education for All Handicapped Children Act of 1975), school volunteers have a unique opportunity to act as a bridge between the community and schools which must, in order to receive Federal funds, educate children they have not served before and serve better those handicapped children whose needs they are currently attempting to meet (Cunninggim 1977).

Youth Participation Programs

Schools have also become arenas for youth participation programs, including peer helping and community service, both within the school system and in local communities. Senior honor students at Jamaica High School in New York participate in a structured volunteer program at the Lifeline Center for Child Development, a highly effective day treatment program which provides medical, psychological, social service, special education, and therapeutic recreation services for severely disturbed children 2 to 16 years of age. The Peer Counseling Program in Palo Alto, California, trains high school and junior high school students to help other students by assisting with personal problems; teaching social skills; giving information about jobs, volunteer opportunities, and mental health resources in the community; acting as models; and serving as agents of change where the school atmosphere is characterized by coldness and indifference (B. Hamburg and Varenhorst 1972). In Baltimore, school community volunteers provide tutoring for elementary school children in a local church. The pre-school children of volunteers are cared for in a nursery operated by teenagers whose schools are on double session. In Cleveland, middle school children have been trained to be home-based book buddies for first graders over the summer. The young teenagers were given an opportunity for constructive summer activity and the chance to take on responsibility; the first graders used and improved their newly learned reading skills. Both enjoyed each other as friends. In Virginia, high school students are released from their classes to serve as aides in the elementary school they once attended. The project was designed to accomplish, among other objectives: better communication between the various levels of schools in the system; an increase in cross-age interaction and in the provision of face-to-face role models; the development of skills for the aides in helping processes, particularly in assisting young children with special needs; better school and community relations.[5]

The National Commission on Youth Resources, a private non-profit organization, was founded in 1967 by judges, social workers, educators and business people to address the problems of youth alienation, and to promote opportunities for youth to assume responsible and socially useful roles in their local schools and communities through youth participation. The Commission on Youth Resources has identified four basic types of programs by which this objective is usually accomplished: helping service to others; service to the community; social action; and community internships. The essential elements for a successful youth participation program include:

. maximum decision-making by the youth participants;

. addressing a genuine need as perceived by young people;

. concrete evidence of community respect for the project, such as school credit or payment;

---

[5]Information about youth participation and school volunteer programs can be found in Resources for Youth Newsletter, New York, New York; and in The School Volunteer and in NSVP Information Bank, National School Volunteer Program, Inc., Alexandria, Virginia.

- a structured learning component;

- a challenge and accountability for success or failure;

- promotion of maturity;

- a view of options available for youth in the adult world;

- a common experience of interdependence with other young people and adults;

- an opportunity for a working partnership between adults and youth (Kohler 1976).

Many local youth participation projects have offered students immensely varied roles in their schools and communities: as curriculum builders; as teachers; as community manpower; as business entrepreneurs; as community problem-solvers; as communicators; as resources for other youth (National Commission on Resources for Youth 1974). Such experiences for students have great educational benefits and help to lower barriers between schools and communities.

RECOMMENDATIONS

31. Provide research and demonstration funds to:

    * examine various service, staffing, funding, and program evaluation options for the development of a community-based health and mental health service delivery system in which public schools are the locus of responsibility in providing, obtaining, or assuring preventive and rehabilitative care for children and their families.

    * field test the feasibility of merging the current community education, community mental health, and public health systems within the public school network to facilitate the healthy physical and mental development of children and their families in their own community environments.

    * develop means for parent and consumer participation in the creation, implementation, and evaluation of such community-based systems.

THE JUSTICE SYSTEM AND COMMUNITY SUPPORT SYSTEMS

Rearing children to develop the necessary skills to be able to work, care for self and others, and meet their responsibilities as citizens in society is a difficult task under the best of conditions. It is almost impossible when parents do not have the benefit of a supportive community which promotes positive social behavior. Only full appreciation of the role of families and communities in shaping individual behavior—and the development of social policies which are designed to strengthen these institutions—will significantly reduce delinquency and crime (or any other social problem) among youth and adults (Comer 1977; Elkins 1977; Woodson 1977).

Fundamental concepts of due process and equal justice require a justice system which ensures fairness and equality. It must be a system that cares about the victim and the accused as human beings. Minimally, the justice system should be constrained from damaging the mental health of those people it affects. Maximally, it should be reshaped to promote and sustain the mental health of those potentially and already involved with police, courts, and correctional institutions. There are dangers, however, inherent in changing the justice system without concomitant research and demonstration projects. Historically, changes in justice system procedures which have replaced what appear to be severe, inflexible, and formal sanctioning processes with more humanitarian and informal substitutes often trigger unintended consequences, either in the direction of (1) increasing the number of persons brought under social controls, and decreasing the procedural safeguards surrounding their imposition ("widening the net"); or (2) removing incentives and facilities for official responses to persons with real service needs ("avoidance response") (Greacen and Morris 1977). The justice system cannot function in a vacuum. Its clients need the same kinds of formal and natural social and community support systems that are necessary for people uninvolved with the justice system. Procedures and services should be structured to feature individualized attention and appropriate help.

Police officers on patrol are in a position to observe the whole spectrum of human behavior, some of which involves persons with mental problems. A broad range of options is available to the skillful, resourceful officer in dealing with these situations if he is trained, and if police managers appreciate the value of this police role, including:

- intervention to prevent violence and injury;

- separation of disputing parties, including arrest of one or more if no other means is available;

- transportation of a psychologically disturbed person to a mental facility or to a hospital out-patient or intake unit;

- transportation of the homeless or runaways to shelter facilities;

- suggestion to persons who exhibit unusual behavior or have continuing personal or family problems that they seek help from specific social service agencies or professionals;

- application of dispute resolution techniques to resolve a confrontation;

- invocation of the attention of child welfare services to children who appear to be abused or neglected;

- referral of persons in physical need of basic necessities to appropriate welfare agencies;

- compassionate understanding and empathy with persons in traumatic moments, especially victims of crimes; and

- personal counseling of youth and others in trouble (Greacen and Morris 1977).

The traditional law enforcement role model of the police officer must be changed and incentives, promotions, and informal reward structures developed for the performance of non-crime-related, non-arrest-oriented activities (Greacen and Morris 1977). Research in Norwalk, Connecticut, and Oakland, California, (Bard and Zacker 1976; Muir 1976) has shown that some officers instinctively react in helpful ways in many such situations, even without special training. Many departments have developed effective working relationships with social service agencies; a number have added social workers and counselors directly on the department's staff. The Wilmington, Delaware, department recently completed the first phase of a "split-force" experiment in which two-thirds of the patrol force was assigned exclusively to calls for service, most of which were not related to crime and many of which were related to problems of mental health. Response time for such calls improved and both officer and citizen satisfaction were very high.

Our judicial apparatus, civil and criminal, also has substantial impact on mentally disabled persons and individuals seeking to cope with life stress problems. Judicial personnel (judges, prosecutors, defense counsel, auxilary staff) need to better understand the dynamics of human behavior, including mental illness and mental retardation, and reflect such insights not only in personal functioning but in the operating procedures of judicial agencies (pretrial proceedings, adjudications, sentencing, civil litigation, diversion and release-on-recognizance programs, etc.). This impact goes beyond the substance of laws relating to or affecting mental health system responsibilities (e.g., commitment laws, patient's rights, special education, criminal insanity tests, guardianship, legislatively guaranteed services for the mentally disabled). Courts are official adjudicators of when individuals are deemed "insane," mentally ill, or mentally incompetent for a variety of civil and criminal status purposes. They exercise this responsibility despite a lack of significant mental health expertise, relying, as it filters through the prism of the adversary process, on expert testimony, certifications, etc., from mental health system personnel. A fundamental issue that must be addressed is how justice apparatus can institutionally respond better to these functions and in a manner consistent with modern mental health concepts and theory.

There is a need to review justice system handling of disturbed or troubled youngsters not tied to criminal behavior but based rather on abuse, neglect, or non-criminal behaviors. Recent justice system studies have condemned, for example, delinquency jurisdiction over non-criminal actors--the so-called "status offenders"--yet withdrawal of judicial control leaves gaps in dealing with behaviors of chronic truants, runaways, and emotionally disturbed children that may require additional new community supports or alternate forms of justice system support or supervision. Reform of the juvenile justice system will inevitably require a rethinking of responsibilities and functions by numerous youth-serving institutions. Many juveniles fall between the cracks and are not wanted by either the juvenile correctional system or the mental health system. As an example, as attempts are made to restrict the intake of status offenders into the juvenile justice system, increases in referrals to other youth-serving agencies are inevitable (Rosenheim 1977). In many minority communities, the parent of a runaway child is not likely to report him/her to the police, even in the case of multiple episodes. The parent knows that the child will be maintained within the extended family and indigenous social networks in the community. Programs designed for the deinstitutionalization of the status offender are not aware of this child up to this point because there are no programs which extend into the support systems of minority neighborhoods. Juvenile justice system programs designed for the status offender should be enlarged to include an outreach strategy into the supportive network of minority communities to find and help the minority child before he becomes a felony offender.

The data are not available as to how large a proportion of juveniles dealt with by justice officials should properly be diverted elsewhere or require special treatment within the programs and facilities that the juvenile justice system operates. To encourage appropriate handling will require greater sophistication on the part of the gatekeepers positioned at crucial points in the juvenile justice process: most important, the police; next, court intake staff; then, the judge. As the demand for services in the community and in a variety of types of residential programs increases, it should also be recognized that many of the coping problems of juveniles need not be handled by mental health agencies but through caring and supportive neighborhood endeavors, including low-visibility and fluid forms of service involving such elements as sports and recreation, educational supplements, and caring relationships with non-parent professionals and volunteers (Rosenheim 1977). When appropriate, substitute social structures can be developed specifically for young people to address their developmental needs rather than sending them through the corrections system. For example, The House of Umoja, a non-profit neighborhood organization structured along the lines of the African-extended family, has successfully worked with the toughest youth gang members in Philadelphia. On the island of Puerto Rico, the Community Service Center of Ponce has worked over the past 7 years with the young people of La Playa to unite them in a common struggle to rid their community of crime. The Center tries to provide help instead of despair to its young and poor with programs of job development and other activities geared to uplifting the spirit of the community (Woodson 1977).

Outreach, financial aid, and other specifically tailored supports can be sponsored for communities burdened by young people with recurrent mental health and justice system involvements. In a study of a vagrant population in South Berkeley, predominantly male (4 to 1) and with a median age of 23, it was found that individuals with histories of mental hospitalization were more likely to be arrested and to have contacts with the criminal justice system (Baumohl and Miller 1974; Segal, Baumohl and Johnson 1977). Following their involvements with these two systems, or more accurately, between involvements, these young individuals face the difficult problem of socially integrating themselves in ways which can enable them to pursue less self-destructive lives. Given the difficulty of creating roots for these young people, two major goals are appropriate: (1) the development of social supports which can build some stability into their life situations, and (2) the development of a coordinated service to the transient population in order to reduce the negative consequences of their transiency. The type of agency most successful in dealing with these individuals seems to be one that becomes a surrogate for a natural helping network. Such agencies help by facilitating the attainment of public welfare, providing an address for checks and for correspondence with the "straight" community, providing free local telephone service to help people find lodging, food, a job, or providing point-of-phone contact for out-of-area relatives (Berkeley Support Services 1977; Segal, Baumohl 1977).

The scholarly literature as well as recent class action litigation involving prison systems in Alabama, New Hampshire, and Virginia give ample reason for believing that imprisonment negatively affects the emotional well-being of the confined person. The rate of suicides and suicide attempts of individuals in jails and prison is higher than that of comparably aged, non-incarcerated youths and adults. There are more psychophysiological reactions, situational emotional disorders, and signs of anxiety (Brodsky 1973; D'Atri and Ostfeld 1975). No single pattern of coping responses is apparent among inmates, however, so a diversity of mental health service delivery solutions would appear to be in order (Osterhoff 1973), including experimentation with voluntary utilization of private sector practitioners (Halleck 1977). Part of the explanation is that correctional personnel are not usually trained to respond to the special needs of the prison population. To address this need some significant training models have been developed, e.g., by the Department of Psychology at the University of Alabama, and the Department of Psychiatry at Hahneman Medical College in Philadelphia.

Correctional facilities are closed societies and community mental health principles are relevant. Kagan has suggested that a critical mass of helping skills and positive relationships may be developed within a correctional institution (Gormally et al. 1972). Such programs have been developed in the Berkshire County House of Corrections in Massachusetts and the Vienna Correctional Center in Illinois. Some correctional institutions are developing curricula for the enhancement of life skills. Participation in these curricula is voluntary and the courses are short-term, problem-oriented and directed at specific issues such as insomnia, smoking behavior, and improvement in interpersonal skills (Brodsky 1973, 1976; Hosford and Moss 1975). Such life skills enhancement programs have been instituted in Federal correctional facilities in Lompor, California, and Lexington, Kentucky.

There are conflicting social forces at work in relation to the justice system. On the one hand efforts are being made to limit the discretion of judges in the sentencing process in order to minimize the disparity of sentences being given for similar crimes. On the other hand it is essential for a judge to have discretion and to recognize the impact of imprisonment on people; and to be sensitive to the value to both the defendant and society of considering realistic and sound community-based alternative programs. An effective community program is a priceless commodity from a number of perspectives--public safety, governmental economy, and offender restoration. The Des Moines Community Corrections Program (offering services for both convicted offenders and defendants diverted before trial) is one of an increasing number of community-based programs which demonstrates that the normality of the community setting makes both mental health and correctional sense and can work even for serious and repeat offenders (e.g., Project New Pride in Denver dealing with older juveniles). Community linkages such as work release, educational furloughs, and home leave offer equal promise for offenders who must be in institutions. They are now authorized in most States, and provide valuable community support for these high "at risk" groups in the spectrum of social deviancy. An important additional resource has been programs of service and advocacy for the offender by ex-offenders, e.g., the programs of the Fortune Society in New York.

The American legal system has failed to develop means of resolving the grievances of everyday life. Further, the increasing complexities of our governmental apparatus both at the local and Federal levels have made it difficult for a person to process a claim or even to make a complaint. The hidden costs of ignoring citizens' complaints include crime, illegal self help, apathy, political disenchantment, emotional disturbance, and mental illness. Both Chief Justice Warren E. Burger and Attorney General Griffin Bell recently have acknowledged the need for creating non-judicial methods of resolving citizens' grievances. Recognizing that our overburdened court system cannot function as the only officially sanctioned forum for processing disputes, the Department of Justice is supporting neighborhood justice centers on an experimental basis for 18 months in Atlanta, Los Angeles, and Kansas City, Missouri. The centers are designed to handle neighborhood disputes among individuals who have continuing relationships with one another and hence a stake in developing lasting solutions to their disagreements. The bulk of their caseload is anticipated to consist of minor criminal matters referred by official criminal justice agencies. Whether the centers will succeed in developing sufficient community credibility to attract other types of complaints initiated by community members themselves remains to be seen (Breed and Singer 1977).

Neighborhood justice centers represent an attempt to deal with one type of dispute--that between individuals with ongoing relationships. Yet the largest number of disputes in a complex, industrialized society occur not between people who know each other but between individuals and various institutions. Administrative grievance procedures and mechanisms are needed:

- to resolve disputes between individuals and institutions, e.g., mental health programs, schools, welfare agencies, social security programs, public housing, etc.

- to allow an effective means of channeling the input of clients and consumers into the policy-making institutions that are supposed to serve their needs;

- for the purpose of conflict resolution and problem-solving in all correctional programs--adult, juvenile, institutional, and community-based.

Special attention should be given to explore and develop grievance procedures and techniques which respond to the special difficulties and needs of mental patients and ex-mental patients in both institutions and in the community (Breed and Singer 1977).

Several themes now running through programs for the mentally disabled are respect for the worth of each individual, the right to receive adequate and appropriate services, and the individual's right to minimal intrusion by the government restricting his liberty or self-determination. In furtherance of these principles and in accord with the prevailing mood in our country, new programs must require openness, honesty and greater accountability to assure that mandated services are provided. No matter how wise and comprehensive, laws are not self-executing. Even significant legal decisions handed down by the highest courts require implementation and monitoring. The mentally disabled are not only a neglected group, easily exploited, but in general lack the sophistication necessary to articulate or actively enforce their rights. This is especially applicable to children and youth who are more vulnerable because of their age and immaturity. Accordingly, it is crucial that any imaginative proposals assuring service for the mentally disabled must include advocacy and monitoring components to improve the conditions within institutions which confine persons with mental health problems; to protect the non-mental health interests of the mentally disabled individual, in and out of institutional confinement; and to help the mentally handicapped with daily life within the community.

Existing data strongly suggest the dearth of advocacy programs. Advocacy can take many forms. It can be legal advocacy, the furnishing of services by the legal profession. For example, Minnesota has some of the longest and most successful experience in the design of comprehensive legal advocacy service in the developmental disability field, as demonstrated by the Minnesota Developmentally Disabled Advocacy Project. Non-legal advocacy, involving citizens other than lawyers, can include lobbying for legislative and administrative change and monitoring compliance with the law. The major thrust of these activities should be to recast the delivery of services, based on the consumer model, in order to articulate, expand, and ensure the rights of patients to appropriate services (Minow and Schneider 1977). Another important form of advocacy is volunteer programs of citizen advocacy. The aim is for the individual volunteer to provide companionship, personal guidance, and emotional support in coping with problems of everyday living. The Eastern Nebraska Community Office of Retardation in Nebraska, although its funding has been cut back recently, deserves study. A newly emerging and important form of advocacy is represented by the groups comprised of ex-patients. These important constituencies have been effective in San Francisco, California (Network against Psychiatric Assault); New York (Project Release); Kansas City, Kansas (Advocates for Freedom in Mental Health); West Sommerville, Massachusetts (The Mental Patient's Liberation Front); in Philadelphia, Pennsylvania (The Alliance for the Liberation of Mental Patients).

Unless increased funding follows advocacy efforts, advances in due process standards and individual rights to treatment will exist in name only. Advocacy of all sorts should be solution-oriented with an aim toward better administration of appropriate services, as well as fair and responsive individualized attention. Mechanisms are also necessary to involve both professionals and consumers in techniques to investigate complaints of alleged abuses against the mentally disabled. Improved legal services and advice for the mental health provider agencies is a necessary component for a comprehensive system of advocacy (Minow and Schneider 1977).

RECOMMENDATIONS

32. Supportive services and community ties sensitive to ethnocultural diversity should be bolstered or created for groups with special emotional problems and with special risks of contact with the justice system, especially juveniles and alienated youth populations.

33. A variety of advocacy services for people with mental disabilities should be mandated through Federal legislation in order to affirm basic rights and entitlements and promote adequately funded services.

34. The Federal Government should provide leadership and funding to support research and demonstration projects in the development of non-judicial mechanisms for resolving disputes and settling grievances within the community and with institutions. Special attention should be given to the unique needs of mental patients and former mental patients.

35. Federal legislation should be passed setting humane standards for correctional facilities. Such standards should go beyond minimum physical standards and should encourage deinstitutionalization when appropriate, relate to the requirements of justice and due process within the institution, and provide for the diverse mental health needs of correctional clients and staff.

36. The Federal Government should provide funds to promote the use of existing recruiting techniques to identify for police work persons with empathetic responses to human need and suffering; to train recruits and other police officers, including middle managers, in the techniques of crisis management; and to educate critical gatekeepers in the justice system, such as judges, attorneys, probation officers, on the needs and rights of mentally disabled persons involved in the justice system.

IMPLICATIONS FOR MENTAL HEALTH AND
HUMAN SERVICES DELIVERY SYSTEMS

Until recently, most professionals have had little awareness of and very little understanding of the nature and function of social support systems. Although the importance of supportive others in times of crisis has been recognized for many years (Lindemann 1944), the use of the concept of personal and social networks in mental health clinical practice and research, and in the design of services, is a recent occurence (Erickson 1975; Fine 1973; Garrison et al. 1977; Hansell 1976; Henderson 1977; Pattison 1977; Speck and Attneave 1973; Toldsdorf 1976).

Naturally occurring helping networks exist independently of professional caregivers and formal caregiving institutions. Often they are invisible to professional scrutiny because the assistance given and received is qualitatively different from that offered within disciplinary frames of reference and is rendered outside the structure of the human services agencies within which most professionals work, i.e., within the family, in kin, kith, friendship and neighborhood social networks; religious denominations; common interest and mutual help groups. Professionals need to affirm the existence and worth of these natural helping networks. Linages need to be developed between these social and community support systems, including mutual help groups, and the professional and formal institutional caregiving systems. They should be established on a basis of cooperation and collaboration, not cooptation and control, and without disturbing the potency of their very different helping processes. These linkages can provide people in need of help individual choice and freedom of movement between natural and formal systems of care. They can promote professionally responsive and consumer-accountable services.

In the development of the best methods to help communities strenghthen, supplement, or stimulate natural helping networks and mutual help groups, a partnership should be established: professionals and formal caregiving institutions working with and through natural helpers and persons who are veterans of the problem or life predicaments, and with community institutions such as churches, synagogues, social clubs, etc. Examples of how this can be done are illustrated by Collins' work with natural neighbors who provide neighborhood daycare services for children (1973); by the work of Smith who identified central figures who provided services within their neighborhood to the elderly (1975); by Shapiro (1969; 1971) in identifying and working with the quasi-matriarchal families which formed spontaneously in the single room occupancy hotels in New York; by Pancoast (1970) who discovered and worked with a natural network of boarding homes for discharged mental patients in an urban poverty area; by Silverman (1970) who catalyzed the development of an outreach program to the newly bereaved, the Widow-to-Widow Program; by Ellis (1972) who initiated a program to help needy groups, isolated elderly and "latch key" children, by working with the elderly to develop after school programs staffed by elders, which provided mutually satisfying activities and promoted the development of peer helping networks in each group; by Patterson and Twente (1971) in developing mental health services in a rural area where no professional helping resources existed, using natural helpers and local counselors, such as ministers, lawyers, bankers, and county extension agents; by G. Caplan (1976b) who organized support systems in a time of war and developed a framework for professional involvement, "supporting the supporters."

Martinez (1977) describes an ethnographic and survey approach to the study of help-seeking behavior in a Latino community in Detroit to identify the existing functional networks most preferred and utilized in times of emotional distress. He found that, overall, informal helping systems provided twice as much help as did formal systems. Relatives, friends, and spouses were the preferred informal helpers, and doctors and priests the preferred formal helpers. His findings also indicated that the informal helping system may also operate as a screening and referral source to the formal system. The concepts of social and community support systems are sensitive to cultural diversity and are applicable to developing mental health services which build on the strengths of minority cultural traditions. This can be demonstrated in the work of Attneave (1969) in clan-networks on Indian reservations; in the work of Sussex et al. (1975) in Miami in developing culturally appropriate services for a diverse catchment area which includes large numbers of Haitians, Blacks, and Hispanics; the work of Thomas and Garrison (1975) in their ongoing involvement with community folk healers in a community mental health catchment area in Newark. All of these examples open exciting possibilities for addressing important problems in unserved and underserved populations. For example, there currently exist on Indian reservations few mechanisms which foster communication across generations, build a knowledge and respect for tradition among the young, and which promote integration among extended families. Additionally, 55,000 Indian children are currently enrolled in boarding schools run by the Bureau of Indian Affairs. These schools have been described in a recent report by the American Academy of Child Psychiatry (1975) as a menace to mental health and as contributory to the formation of dysfunctional adults. Ways of addressing these issues, using what we know about natural support systems concepts, could include establishing day care centers on the reservation for the elderly Indian who is often isolated and alienated from the social milieu in a period of rapid socio-cultural change. These day care centers could be organized in such a way as to provide encouragement for the Indian youth to participate actively in a program of service to their elders and which would also engage the old in a program of education through oral history, sharing with the young their accumulated wisdom. Also, young Indians could be trained to work with the elderly, and to assist the elderly as culture brokers and advocates in transactions with off-reservation health and social welfare delivery systems.

In addition to supporting Indian tribes and organizations in their efforts to maintain Indian children in their families and communities, the educational methodologies in Indian Boarding Schools could be reformed in ways which would support and validate the values, identity and modes of expression of Indian children. Indian elders could be utilized in the boarding schools as surrogate parents. This would address the issue of the current high ratio of children to staff, would provide anguished children a culturally sympathetic haven, and would give Indian elders a significant role to enhance their self-esteem and sense of worth. Along with this, a concerted effort could be undertaken to recruit and enthusiastically use Indian teachers to instruct Indian children, with transitional classes conducted by Indian teachers in Indian languages for all children who come to school without fluency in the English language.

Some examples of innovative social and community support systems projects currently in various stages of development are:

- The Indiana State Mental Health Association is implementing, through their local affiliates, a statewide program for the development of mutual help groups and support networks for situational crises such as marital separation; death of spouse, parent or child; birth of a handicapped child; illness of spouse or child with long hospitalization; natural disasters, e.g., flood, fire, earthquake. In the first phase, dozens of counties are developing Widow-to-Widow programs with the technical assistance of the State and local mental health associations.

- The Gray Panthers, a mutual help group of young and old concerned about the needs of the elderly, has field tested the feasibility, and is developing plans for an experiment in neighborhood home health care called <u>The Health Block/Neighborhood</u>, in Philadelphia (Kuhn 1976). The purpose is four-fold: to deliver comprehensive home care in neighborhoods where people live on a coordinated basis, including physical, mental, and environmental health; to identify and organize "natural leaders" and opinion makers in a neighborhood and equip them to be "health builders" and advisors for their neighborhood--assuming some responsibility for their own health and well-being and sensitive to the health needs of their neighbors; to provide a series of informal health forums to increase neighborhood awareness of the need for positive mental, physical, and environmental health; and to provide advocacy for and access to necessary services to maintain and secure maximum health, safety, and well-being for all residents.

- The Chicago Commons Association, a voluntary nonsectarian social agency, in cooperation with the School of Social Service Administration of the University of Chicago and the Taylor Institute, is developing neighborhood self help projects, with research, service and public policy analysis components, to strengthen, support, and expand existing informal self help endeavors and resource networks as alternatives to expanded formal service institutions.

- Vallance and his colleagues at Pennsylvania State University College of Human Development, in collaboration with the Geisinger Mental Health Center in Danville, are developing an experimental model to identify and train natural caregivers in order extend preventive mental health manpower and to reduce costs of service delivery. In the first instance, professional educators will teach trainers to train direct service providers;

next, these trainers in turn will train a group of formal and informal helpers in basic helping skills, crisis intervention skills, and life development skills; finally, these natural helpers will enhance the development of life skills in others in their communities. The goal is to establish an administrative structure within a mental health system that can sustain and expand community helping networks.

The Health Facilitator Program was developed at the Community Health Education Unit of Duke University's Department of Community and Family Medicine (Salber et al. 1976; Service and Salber 1977) in an attempt to improve the health of people through better use of their own and the community's resources. It was based on the idea that in every community people exist to whom their friends and neighbors turn for advice, support, help and counsel with their problems. The Program worked out ways to recognize these unpaid community health facilitators and to offer them carefully designed educational programs (which guard against professionalization) related to information on health and illness, on the effects of lifestyle on health and on appropriate use of community resources. By offering the programs to these selected individuals rather than to the public at large, the program makes use of the network of contacts these people have already established. The idea is that the information offered will travel along these channels and diffuse into the community like the ripples in a pond. The diffusion mechanism works both ways. Problems of individuals will become known to health service agencies through the network, and the assistance they may render flows back.

A health facilitator program can be freestanding and generalized, or it can be attached to an agency and be more specifically defined. It can be used in any community, rich or poor, urban or rural. It can address the problems of all the citizens of a community or concentrate on one segment--the elderly, for instance. It can be directed at health problems, but it can also emphasize housing, social services, the environment, or whatever aspect of living the community defines as a priority. The program has been tried in Durham County, in four Hispanic and Indian communities in New Mexico, and has just begun in a depressed area outside Wellington, New Zealand. Other programs are in the planning stage; for example, the program will be used by a mental health center in a rural area of North Carolina beginning July 1978. Interesting adaptations of the model are its present use by the City of Durham in its HUD-sponsored rehabilitation of housing program; its use by students in an American Medical Student Association summer project in a factory in Bolivar, Tennessee; and its use by North Carolina Central University's department of health education to identify and train natural leaders among out-of-school youth in several counties to advise other youth on available sources of veneral disease diagnosis and treatment.

Social and community support systems concepts can be a potent addition and supplement to existing models of mental health practice. Professionals who are knowledgeable about social networks and natural helping systems theory and practice can generate not just more or different services but also more relevant and more easily accessible services.

Utilizing social and community support systems in conjunction with other, formal systems of care:

- can have a multiplier effect on professional and institutional resources.

- can help to provide services which are inherently sensitive to socio-cultural diversity.

- can transcend specific professional ideologies and organizational/structural modalities of service.

- can help to bridge public and private systems of care in the social services, vocational, religious, justice, health, and mental health fields.

- allows services to be population-at-risk, catchment-area, or neighborhood-oriented; common interest, age or particular ethnic or minority group focused; have an emphasis on specific problems or life predicaments.

- permits appropriate services to be delivered in the least restrictive environment.

- allows for variance in the intensity and duration of help offered, the kind of expertness required, the kinds of services provided, and for the direction of the help process: natural ⇌ formal.

- promotes individual and community participation in the design and implementation of services on either a voluntary or paid employment basis.

- can provide coherent and responsive rehabilitative services and long term care in the community for the chronically mentally ill patient.

- can provide the combined resources to precisely design and implement programs for primary prevention, secondary treatment and rehabilitative services, in life-cycle crises and transitions; in situational and social stress; and for chronic deficits.

- are consumer-intensive and therefore cost-effective.

- can permit specifically targeted use of highly trained and costly professional input.

CSS 74

Social and community support systems should not be viewed as a panacea for all problems in mental health delivery systems. However, an understanding of their characteristics can reveal them as strategic links between individual and community needs and the appropriate deployment of professional and institutional services.

Literature is now beginning to appear which is not only descriptive but which provides a theoretical framework, research findings, and practice principles about social and community support systems which can guide program planning and design. Some of the more recent are: <u>Support Systems and Mutual Help</u>, Gerald Caplan and Marie Killilea (eds.), 1976; <u>Natural Helping Networks</u>, Alice H. Collins and Diane L. Pancoast, 1976; <u>Self-Help in the Human Services</u>, Alan Gartner and Frank Riessman, 1977; <u>The Person-In-Distress: On the Biosocial Dynamics of Adaptation</u>, Norris Hansell, 1976; <u>The Strength in Us: Self-Help Groups in the Modern World</u>, Alfred H. Katz and Eugene I. Bender, 1976; "Special Issue on Self-Help Groups," Morton A. Lieberman and Leonard D. Borman (eds.), <u>Journal of Applied Behavioral Science</u>, 12(3), 1976; "Special Issue on Self-Help," <u>Social Policy</u>, 7(2), 1976; <u>Community Health Education: The Lay Advisor Approach</u>, Connie Service and Eva J. Salber (eds.), 1977; <u>If You Will Lift the Load I Will Lift It Too: A Guide to Developing Widow-to-Widow Programs</u>, Phyllis R. Silverman, 1976; <u>Mutual Help Groups: A Guide for Mental Health Workers</u>, Phyllis R. Silverman, 1978; <u>The Neighborhood Organizer's Handbook</u>, Rachelle B. Warren and Donald I. Warren, 1977.

WORKING GROUPS

The Task Panel on Community Support Systems would like to express its deep appreciation for the enormous contributions made to its work by the following Working Groups.

WORKING GROUP ON THE JUSTICE SYSTEM
AND COMMUNITY SUPPORT SYSTEMS

Joseph Schneider, Coordinator
Judge of the Circuit Court of Cook County
Chicago, Illinois

Allen F. Breed
Special Master for Adult Correctional Institutions
U.S. Courthouse and Federal Building
Providence, Rhode Island

Stanley L. Brodsky, Ph.D.
Professor of Psychology
The University of Alabama
Tuscaloosa, Alabama

James P. Comer, M.D., M.P.H.
Maurice Falk Professor of Psychiatry
Child Study Center
Yale University School of Medicine
New Haven, Connecticut

William Elkins
Special Assistant to the Mayor of Los Angeles
Los Angeles, California

John Greacen
Deputy Director
Police Foundation
Washington, .D.C

Seymour Halleck, M.D.
Professor of Psychiatry
University of North Carolina
Memorial Hospital
Chapel Hill, North Carolina

Martha Minow, M.Ed.
Yale University Law School
New Haven, Connecticut

Norval Morris
Dean
University of Chicago Law School
Chicago, Illinois

John Rector
Administrator of Juvenile Justice and Delinquency
  Prevention
Department of Justice
Washington, D.C.

Margaret K. Rosenheim, J.D.
Professor
School of Social Service Administration
University of Chicago
Chicago, Illinois

Steven P. Segal, Ph.D.
Associate Professor
School of Social Welfare
University of California
Berkeley, California

Daniel L. Skoler
Director of Public Service Activities
American Bar Association
Washington, D.C.

Robert L. Woodson
Resident Fellow
American Enterprise Institute
Washington, D.C.

WORKING GROUP ON "NEW" FORMS OF SUPPORT SYSTEMS

Frank Riessman, Ph.D., Coordinator
Co-Director
New Human Services Institute
Graduate Center - City College of New York
New York, New York

Leonard Borman, Ph.D.
Director
Self-Help Institute
Center for Urban Affairs
Northwestern University
Evanston, Illinois

Robert Farwell
Executive Director
Recovery, Inc.
Chicago, Illinois

Susan Flinn, Ph.D.
Assistant Director of Family Studies
Bronx Psychiatric Center
Rehabilitation Center
Bronx, New York

Vivian Garrison, Ph.D.
Adjunct Associate Professor of Psychiatry and Mental
   Health Sciences
College of Medicine and Dentistry
New Jersey Medical School
East Orange, New Jersey

Alfred H. Katz, D.S.W.
Professor of Public Health and Social Welfare
University of California School of Public Health
Los Angeles, California

Marie Killilea
Assistant Director of Education
Western Psychiatric Institute and Clinic
University of Pittsburgh
Pittsburgh, Pennsylvania

Diane Lacey
Director of Volunteer Services
Sydenham Hospital
New York, New York

Nolan Penn, Ph.D.
Professor of Psychiatry
School of Medicine
University of California - San Diego
LaJolla, California

David Sanders, Ph.D.
Deputy Director for Adult Services
City and County of San Franciso
Department of Public Health
Community Mental Health Services
San Francisco, California

WORKING GROUP ON RELIGIOUS SUPPORT SYSTEMS

Donald Smith, D.Min., Coordinator
President
Institutes of Religion and Health
New York, New York

Peg Aieta
Beverly, Massachusetts

Clark S. Aist, Ph.D.
Director
Protestant Chaplain Activities
St. Elizabeth's Hospital
Washington, D.C.

The Reverend Jose A. Caraballo
Dean of Spanish Concerns
New York Theological Seminary
New York, New York

Canon Lloyd Casson
Washington Cathedral
Washington, D.C.

Howard Clinebell, Ph.D.
Professor of Pastoral Counseling
School of Theology
Claremont, California

The Reverend Carl E. Flemister
Executive Minister
American Baptist Churches of Metropolitan New York
New York, New York

LeRoy Graham, Ph.D.
Director
Washington Pastoral Counseling Center
Washington, D.C.

The Reverend Paul J. Henry
Coordinator
Chaplain Services
United States Catholic Conference
Washington, D.C.

The Reverend Ronald Lee
Northbrook, Illinois

The Reverend Herbert Leslie
University Christian Church
Berkeley, California

The Reverend Patrick Prest
Richmond, Virginia

The Reverend Bruce Ritter
Executive Director
Covenant House
New York, New York

Rabbi Sanford Saperstein
Temple Beth Am
Merrick, New York

Robert Steele, Ph.D.
Assistant Professor of Psychology
University of Maryland
College Park, Maryland

The Reverend Edward V. Stein
San Anselmo, California

In addition to working papers prepared for the Commission which are cited in the text and listed in the references, substantial contributions to this Task Panel report were made by the Reports of the Working Groups on the Justice System and Community Support Systems, on "New" Forms of Support Systems, and on Religious Support Systems, and by a Report, "The Impact of Social Supports on Health," prepared by Joel E. Dimsdale, M.D., Department of Psychiatry, Massachusetts General Hospital, Harvard Medical School, Boston, Massachusetts; John Eckenrode, M.S., Research Assistant, Department of Behavioral Sciences, Harvard School of Public Health, Boston, Massachusetts; Robert J. Haggerty, M.D., Roger I. Lee Professor of Public Health, Harvard School of Public Health, Boston, Massachusetts; Berton H. Kaplan, Ph.D., Professor of Epidemiology, University of North Carolina, Chapel Hill; Frances Cohen, Ph.D., Assistant Professor of Psychology, University of California Medical Center, San Franciso, California; and Sanford Dornbusch, Ph.D., Professor of Sociology, Stanford University Stanford, California.

ACKNOWLEDGEMENTS

The Task Panel on Community Support Systems is especially grateful for the highly competent professional support services and invaluable contributions of Beatrix A. Hamburg, M.D., Study Director; Juel Janis, Ph.D., Staff Liaison to the Panel until November 20, 1977, with Dr. Hamburg; Marie Killilea, a Member of the task panel until November 20, and thereafter Staff Liaison to the Panel, with Dr. Hamburg; Gretchen Marvin, Staff Liaison; and with the assistance of Anita King. Joel E. Dimsdale, M.D., served as a consultant to the task panel.

The Task Panel also wishes to acknowledge the invaluable assistance of the following persons and organizations in the preparation of this report.

John Alden, Ph.D., Executive Director, National School Volunteer Program, Inc., Alexandria, Virginia; Jim Baumohl, M.S.W., Berkeley Support Services, Berkeley, California; David Biegel, A.C.S.W., Project Director, Neighborhood and Families Services Project, Washington Public Affairs Center, University of Southern California, Washington, D.C.; H. Carson Briggs, Editor, Self-Help Reporter, National Self-Help Clearinghouse, New York, New York; Richard D. Budson, M.D., Assistant Professor of Psychiatry, Harvard Medical School and Director, Berkeley House/Waverly House Programs, McLean Hospital, Belmont, Massachusetts; Dorothy Burgoin, President, Relatives and Friends of the Mentally Ill, Mental Health/Ottawa, Canadian Mental Health Association, Ottawa, Ontario, Canada; William Claflin, Alcohol Education Coordinator, The County of Rockland Community Mental Health Center, Pomona, New York; Merrell M. Clark, Senior Vice President, Academy for Educational Development, Inc., New York, New York; Frances Cohen, Ph.D., Assistant Professor of Psychology, Department of Psychiatry, University of California Medical Center, San Francisco, California; Alfred T. Dean, Ph.D., Associate Professor of Psychiatry, Albany Medical School, Albany, New York; John Eckenrode, M.S., Research Assistant, Harvard School of Public Health, Boston, Massachusetts; Gladys Egri, M.D., Chief, Harlem Rehabilitation Center, Harlem Hospital Center, New York, New York; George W. Fairweather, Ph.D., Professor of Psychology, Michigan State University, East Lansing, Michigan; John R. P. French, Jr., Ph.D., Program Director, Institute for Social Research, University of Michigan, Ann Arbor, Michigan; Dorothy N. Garrett, Co-ordinator, Haven of Northern Virginia, Inc., Annandale, Virginia; Alan Gartner, Ph.D., Co-director; New Human Services Institute, Graduate Center--City College of New York, New York; David Giber, Department of Psychology, Duke University, Durham, North Carolina; Willis B. Goldbeck, Director, Washington Business Group on Health, Washington, D.C.; Susan Gore, Ph.D., Professor of Sociology, University of Massachusetts; David Guttman, D.S.W., National Catholic School of Social Service, The Catholic University of America, Washington, D.C.; Barbara Hansel, Director, Cambridge Community Schools, Cambridge, Massachusetts; Norris Hansell, M.D., Medical Director, Champaign County Mental Health Center, Urbana, Illinois, and Professor of Psychiatry, Northwestern University Medical School, Evanston, Illinois; Carol Hogue, Ph.D., Associate Professor of Nursing and Assistant Professor of Medicine, Duke University, Durham, North Carolina; Ralph Horton, Jr., Ph.D., Executive Director, Washington Heights--West Harlem--Inwood Community Mental Health Center, New York, New York; James S. House, Ph.D., Professor of Sociology, Duke University,

Durham, North Carolina; Stanislav V. Kasl, Ph.D., Professor of Epidemiology, Yale University, New Haven, Connecticut; Judge Mary Conway Kohler, Director, National Commission on Resources for Youth, Inc., New York, New York; Deborah Kottle, Chicago Illinois, Maggie Kuhn, Gray Panthers, Philadelphia, Pennsylvania; Cathy Kuttner, Chairman, Community Mental Health Services Committee, Mental Health Association of Essex County, East Orange, New Jersey; Alexander H. Leighton, M.D., Professor Emeritus, Harvard School of Public Health; Boston, Massachusetts; Marion Levine, A.C.S.W., Executive Director, North Shore Child Guidance Center, Manhasset, New York; Morris A. Lipton, M.D., Kenan Professor of Psychiatry, University of North Carolina School of Medicine, Chapel Hill, North Carolina; Bruce L. Mallory, M.E., Research Associate, Center for the Studies of Families and Children, Vanderbilt Institute for Public Policy Studies, Vanderbilt University, Nashville, Tennessee; Gordon Manser, Principal Consultant, Aging Project, Academy for Educational Development, Inc., New York, New York; Ann Marek, Member, Board of Directors, Parenting Guidance Center, Fort Worth, Texas; Leon R. McKinney, M.D., Clinical Director, Harlem Interfaith Counseling Service, Inc., New York, New York; Jack Medalie, M.D., Chairman, Department of Family Medicine, School of Medicine, Case Western Reserve University, Cleveland, Ohio; Harriett Lee Montgomery, Associate Director, Mental Health Association in Indiana, Inc., Indianapolis, Indiana; Jose Morales, Chicago Commons Association, Chicago, Illinois; Margaret Morgan-Lawrence, M.D., Developmental Psychiatric Service, Division of Child Psychiatry, Harlem Hospital Center, New York, New York; Jane Murphy, Ph. D., Professor of Anthropology, Department of Health Administration, Division of Behavioral Medicine, Harvard School of Public Health, Boston, Massachusetts; James Peacock, Ph.D., Chairman and Professor of Anthropology, University of North Carolina, Chapel Hill, North Carolina; Arnold Rabin, Ed.D., Executive Director, Mental Health Association of Essex County, East Orange, New Jersey; Reverend R. J. Ross, Executive Director, Samaritan Health and Living Center, Elkhart, Indiana; Eva J. Salber, M.D., Professor, Community and Family Practice, Duke University Medical Center, Durham, North Carolina; Frank Seever, Executive Director, Chicago Commons Association, Chicago, Illinois; Wendy Sherman, M.S.W., Field Director, Neighborhood and Families Services Project, Washington Public Affairs Center, University of Southern California, Washington, D.C.: Phyllis Silverman, Ph.D., Director, The Mutual Help Project, American Institutes for Research in the Behavioral Sciences, Cambridge, Massachusetts; Linda R. Singer, Executive Director, Center for Commmunity Justice, Washington, D.C.; Vickie Thomas, Special Assistant to the Commissioner, New York City Department of Mental Health and Mental Retardation, New York, New York; Ruel Tyson, Ph.D., Chairman and Professor of Religion, University of North Carolina, Chapel Hill, North Carolina; Theodore Vallance, Ph.D., Professor of Human Development, Institute for the Study of Human Development, The Pennsylvania State University, University Park, Pennsylvania; Rachelle B. Warren, Ph.D., Center for Research on Teaching and Learning, University of Michigan, Ann Arbor, Michigan; James A. Wells, Ph.D., Assistant Professor of Sociology, Washington University, St. Louis, Missouri; Ann M. Wilson, Director, Discharged Patient Advocacy Program, Mental Health Association of Essex County, East Orange, New Jersey; James Wilson, Chicago, Illinois; Robert N. Wilson, Ph.D., Professor of Sociology, University of North Carolina, Chapel Hill, North Carolina; Ethel S. Wyner, Ed.D., Executive Director, Lifeline Center for Child Development, Inc., Jamaica, New York.

REFERENCES

Ablon, J. Al-Anon family groups. *American Journal of Psychotherapy*, 28(1): 30-45, 1974.

Alpert, J. J. Broken appointments. *Pediatrics*, 5:127-132, 1964.

American Academy of Child Psychiatry. "Placement of American Indian Children: Need for Change." Position statement, January 25, 1975.

Antze, P. The role of ideologies in peer psychotherapy organizations: Some theoretical considerations and three case studies. *The Journal of Applied Behavioral Science*, 12(3):323-346, 1976.

Attneave, C.L. Therapy in tribal settings and urban network intervention. *Family Process*, 8:192-210, 1969.

Baker, F. The interface between professional and natural support systems. *Clinical Social Work Journal*, 5(2):139-148, 1977.

Balint, M. *The Doctor, His Patient and the Illness*. New York: International Universities Press, 1964.

Bard, M., and Zacker, J. *The Police and Interpersonal Conflict: Third Party Intervention Approaches*. Washington, D.C.: Police Foundation, 1976.

Barnes, J. A. Class and committees in a Norwegian island parish. *Human Relations*, 7(1):39-58, 1954.

Baumohl, J., and Miller H. *Down and Out in Berkeley*, City of Berkeley--University of California Community Affairs Committee, 1974.

Beiser, M. et al. Special issue on Indian mental health. *Psychiatric Annals*, 4(9), 1974.

Ben-Sira, Z. The function of the professional's affective behavior in client satisfaction: A revised approach to social interactional theory. *Journal of Health and Social Behavior*, 17:3-11, 1976.

Berkeley Support Services. Internal memorandum. Berkeley, California, 1977.

Billingsley, A. *Black Families in White America*. Englewood Cliffs, New Jersey: Prentice-Hall, 1968.

Borkman, T. Experiential knowledge: A new concept for the analysis of self-help groups. *Social Service Review*, in press.

Borman, L.D., American Indian tribal support systems and economic development. In: Cafferty, P.S.J., and Chestang, L., eds. *The Diverse Society: Implications for Social Policy*. Washington, D.C.: National Association of Social Workers, 1976. pp. 151-161.

Borus, J. D. et al. The coordination of mental health services at the neighborhood level. *American Journal of Psychiatry*, 132:1177-1181, 1975.

Bott, E. *Family and Social Network: Norms and External Relationships in Ordinary Urban Families*. London: Tavistock Publications, Ltd., 1957; 2nd ed. revised, 1971.

Boston Women's Health Collective. *Our Bodies, Ourselves: A Book By and For Women*. 2nd ed. New York: Simon and Schuster, 1976.

Bowlby, J. The making and breaking of affectional bonds, Part I. *British Journal of Psychiatry*, 130:201-210, 1977.

Breed, A. F., and Singer, R. "Dispute Resolution: A Mental Health Prescription." Working paper prepared for the President's Commission on Mental Health. Center for Community Justice, Washington, D.C., 1977.

Brodsky, S. L. *Psychology in the Criminal Justice System*. Urbana, Illinois: University of Illinois Press, 1973.

Brodsky, S. L. "The Right to Refuse Treatment." Paper presented at a Conference on Mental Health for the Convicted Offender: Patient and Prisoner, Raleigh, North Carolina, 1976. University of Alabama.

Brodsky, S. L. "Mental Health Needs of Correctional Clients." Working paper prepared for the President's Commission on Mental Health. University of Alabama, 1977.

Brown, G. W.; Bhrolchain, M. N.; and Harris, T. Social class and psychiatric disturbance among women in an urban population. *Sociology*, 9:225-254, 1975.

Budson, R. D. "The Crucial Factor in Community Programs Success." Paper presented at the meeting of the American Psychiatric Association, Toronto, May, 1977.

Budson, R. D. *The Psychiatric Halfway House: A Handbook of Theory and Practice*. Pittsburgh: University of Pittsburgh Press, 1978.

Budson, R. D.; Grob, M. C.; and Singer, J. E. A follow-up study of Berkeley House: A psychiatric half-way house. *International Journal of Social Psychiatry*, in press.

Caplan, G. *Support Systems and Community Mental Health: Lectures on Concept Development*. New York: Behavioral Publications, 1974.

Caplan, G. "Support Systems: A Model for Reaching the Population of a Community Mental Health Program." Keynote address at the Kings View Foundation Symposium on Prevention and Indirect Services, Fresno, California, April 25, 1975.

Caplan, G., and Killilea, M., eds. *Support Systems and Mutual Help: Multidisciplinary Explorations*, New York: Grune and Stratton, 1976.

Caplan, G. The family as support system. In: Caplan, G., and Killilea, M., eds., *Support Systems and Mutual Help*, New York: Grune and Stratton, 1976a. pp. 19-36.

Caplan, G. Organization of support systems for civilian populations. In: Caplan, G., and Killilea, M., eds., *Support Systems and Mutual Help*, New York: Grune and Stratton, 1976b. pp. 273-315.

Caplan, R. B. *Helping the Helpers to Help: The Development and Evaluation of Mental Health Consultation to Aid Clergymen in Pastoral Work*. New York: The Seabury Press, 1972.

Caplan, R. D. "Organizational Stress and Individual Strain: A Social Psychological Study of Risk Factors in Coronary Heart Disease Among Administrators, Engineers and Scientists." Unpublished Ph.D. thesis, University of Michigan, Ann Arbor, 1971.

Caplan, R. D.; Cobb, S.; French, Jr., J.R.P.; Harrison, R. V.; and Pinneau, S. R., *Job Demands and Worker Health: Main Effects and Occupational Differences*, Washington, D.C.: Superintendent of Documents, U.S. Government Printing Office, 1975.

Caplan, R. D.; Robinson, E. A. R.; French, Jr., J. R. P.; Caldwell, J. R.; and Shinn, M. Adhering to medical regimens: Pilot experiments in patient education and social support. Ann Arbor, Michigan: Institute for Social Research, University of Michigan, 1976.

Cassel, J. C. Psychiatric epidemiology. In: Caplan, G., ed. *American Handbook of Psychiatry*. vol. 2. New York: Basic Books, 1974a pp. 401-410.

Cassel, J. C. Psychosocial processes and 'stress': Theoretical formulation. *International Journal of Health Services*, 4(3):471-482, 1974b.

Christmas, J. J. "Testimony on Community Support Systems." President's Commission on Mental Health, Washington, D.C., October 14, 1977a.

Christmas, J. J. Internal document. Department of Mental Health and Mental Retardation, City of New York, 1977b.

Christmas, J. J. "Unresolved Governance Issues as Barriers to Care." Working Paper prepared for Technical Conference on Barriers to Mental Health Care, President's Commission on Mental Health, Airlie, Virginia, July 7-9, 1977c.

Clinebell, H. J. The local church's contribution to positive mental health. In: Clinebell, H. J., ed. *Community Mental Health: The Role of Church and Temple*. Nashville, Abingdon Press, 1970.

Cobb, S. Physiological changes in men whose jobs were abolished. *Journal of Psychosomatic Research*, 18:245-258, 1974.

Cobb, S., and Kasl, S. V. Termination: The consequences of job loss. Cincinnati, Ohio: Center for Disease Control, National Institute for Occupational Safety and Health, 1977.

Cobb, S. Social support as a moderator of life stress. Psychosomatic Medicine, 38(5):300-314, 1976.

Collins, A. H. Natural Delivery systems: Accessible sources of power for mental health. American Journal of Orthopsychiatry, 43(1):46-52, 1973.

Collins, A. H., and Pancoast, D. L. Natural Helping Networks: A Strategy for Prevention. New York: National Association of Social Workers, 1976.

Comer, J. P. Working paper prepared for President's Commission on Mental Health. Yale University, 1977.

Comer, J. P. Beyond Black and White. New York: Quadrangle Books, 1972.

Conger, J.C.; Sawrey, W.; and Turrell, E. S. The role of social experience in the production of gastic ulcers in hooded rats placed in a conflict situation. Journal of Abnormal Psychology, 57:216+, 1958.

Croog, S. H. Health patterns in severe illness: The roles of kin network, non-family resources and institutions. Journal of Marriage and Family, 32-41, February, 1972.

Cunninggim, W. Help for the handicapped. The School Volunteer, National School Volunteer Program, Inc., 2(1):2, 1977.

De Araujo, G.; Van Arsdel, P. P.; Holmes, T. H.; and Dudley, D. L. Life change, coping ability and chronic intrinsic asthma. Journal of Psychosomatic Research, 17:359-63, 1973.

D'Atri, D. A., and Ostfeld, A. Crowding: Its effects on the evaluation of blood pressure in a prison setting. Journal of Preventive Medicine, 4:550-566, 1975.

DeLoria, V. We Talk, You Listen. New York: MacMillan and Co., 1970.

Dimsdale, J. The coping behavior of Nazi concentration camp survivors. American Journal of Psychiatry, 131:792-797, 1974.

Dohrenwend, B. S., and Dohrenwend, B. P. Stressful Life Events. New York: John Wiley, 1974.

Elkins, W. Working paper prepared for President's Commission on Mental Health. Office of the Mayor, City of Los Angeles, 1977.

Ellis, J. B. "Love to Share: A Community Project Tailored by Oldsters for 'Latch-Key' Children." Paper presented at the meeting of the American Orthopsychiatric Association, Detroit, 1972.

Engel, G. L. A life setting inducive to illness: The giving up, given up complex. *Annals of Internal Medicine*, 69:293-300, 1969.

Erickson, G. D. The concept of personal network in clinical practice. *Family Process*, 14(4):487-498, 1975.

Fabrega, H. The scope of ethnomedical science. *Culture, Medicine and Psychiatry*, 1:201-228, 1977.

Fairweather, G. W.; Sanders, D. H.; and Maynard, H. *Community Life for the Mentally Ill: An Alternative to Institutional Care*. Chicago: Aldine, 1969.

Fandetti, D. "Sources of Assistance in a White Working Class Ethnic Neighborhood." Unpublished Ph.D. dissertation, Columbia University Graduate School of Social Work, New York, 1974.

Fine, P. Family networks and child psychiatry in a community health project. *Journal of the American Academy of Child Psychiatry*, 12(4):675-689, 1973.

Finlayson, A. Social networks as coping resources: Lay help and consultation patterns used by women in husbands' post infarction career. *Social Science and Medicine*, 10(2):97-103, 1976.

Freidson, E. Client control and medical practice. *American Journal of Sociology*, 65:374-382, 1960.

Freidson, E. *Patients' Views of Medical Practice*, New York: Russell Sage Foundation, 1961.

French, Jr., J. R. P.; Rodgers, W.; Cobb, S. Adjustment as person-environment fit. In: Coelho, G. V.; Hamburg, D. A.; and Adams, J. E., eds. *Coping and Adaptation: Interdisciplinary Perspectives*. New York: Basic Books, 1974. pp. 316-333.

Garrison, J.; Kulp, C.; and Rosen, S. Community mental health nursing: A social network approach. *Journal of Psychiatric Nursing*, 15(1):32-36, 1977.

Garrison, V. "Inner city support systems." New Jersey College of Medicine and Dentistry, 1976.

Gartner, A.; Kohler, M.; Riessman, F. *Children Teach Children*. New York: Harper and Row, 1971.

Gartner, A., and Riessman, F. *Self-Help in the Human Services*. San Francisco: Jossey-Bass, 1977.

Geersten, R.; Blauber, M. R.: Rindflesh, M.; Kane, R. L.; and Gray, R. A re-examination of Suchman's views of social factors on health care utilization. *Journal of Health and Social Behavior*, 16:426-437, 1975.

Giordano, J., and Giordano, G. P. Ethnicity and community mental health: A review of the literature. *Community Mental Health Review*, 1(3), May/June, 1976.

Good Tracks, J. G. Native American non-interference. *Social Work*, 18(6): 30-34, 1973.

Gore, S. "The Influence of Social Support and Related Variables in Ameliorating the Consequences of Job Loss." Unpublished Ph.D. dissertation, University of Pennsylvania, 1973.

Gormally, J. F.; Brodsky, S. L.; Clements, C. B.; and Fowler, Jr., R. D. "Minimum Mental Health Standards for the Alabama Correctional System." University of Alabama, 1972.

Gottlieb, B. H. Lay influences on the utilization and provision of health services: A review. *Canadian Psychological Review*, 17(2):126-136, 1976.

Granovetter, M. S. The strength of weak ties. *American Journal of Sociology*, 78:1360+, 1973.

Greacen, J., and Morris, N. "Improving the Response of the Police to the Mental Health Problems of Citizens." Working paper prepared for the President's Commission on Mental Health. Police Foundation, Washington, D.C., 1977.

Gruenberg, E. M. The social breakdown syndrome: Some origins. *American Journal of Psychiatry*, 123:1481-1489, 1967.

Guggenheim, F., and O'Hara, S. Peer counseling in a general hospital. *American Journal of Psychiatry*, 133(10):1197-1199, 1976.

Gussow, Z., and Tracy, G. S. The role of self-help clubs in adaptation to chronic illness and disability. *Social Science and Medicine*, 10:407-414, 1976.

Guttman, D. "Informal and Formal Support Systems and their Effect on the Lives of the Elderly in Selected Ethnic Groups." Progress report. National Catholic School of Social Service, Catholic University of America, Washington, D.C., 1977.

Hall, A. L., and Bourne, P. G. Indigenous therapists in a Southern Black urban community. *Archives of General Psychiatry*, 28:137-142, 1973.

Halleck, S. Working paper prepared for President's Commission on Mental Health. University of North Carolina, 1977.

Hamburg, B. Early adolescence: A specific and stressful stage of the life cycle. In: Coelho, G. V.; Hamburg, D. A.; and Adams, J. E., eds. *Coping and Adaptation*. New York: Basic Books, 1974.

Hamburg, B., and Varenhorst, B. Peer counseling in the secondary schools: A community mental health project for youth. American Journal of Orthopsychiatry, 42:566-581, 1972.

Hamburg, D. A., and Adams, J. E. A perspective on coping behavior: Seeking and utilizing information in major transitions. Archives of General Psychiatry, 17:277-284, 1967.

Hamburg, D. A.; Adams, J. E.; and Brodie, H. K. H. Coping behavior in stressful circumstances: Some implications for social psychiatry. In: Kaplan, B. H.; Wilson, R. N.; and Leighton, A. H., eds. Further Explorations in Social Psychiatry. New York: Basic Books, 1976. pp. 158-175.

Hamburg, D. A.; Coelho, G. V.; and Adams, J. E. Coping and adaptation: Steps toward a synthesis of biological and social perspectives. In: Coelho, G. B.; Hamburg, D. A.; and Adams, J. E., eds. Coping and Adaptation. New York: Basic Books, 1974. pp. 403-440.

Hamburg, D. A.; Hamburg, B.; and deGoza, S. Adaptive problems and mechanisms in severely burned patients. Psychiatry, 16:1-20, 1953.

Hampden-Turner, C. Sane Asylum: Inside the Delancey Street Foundation. San Francisco: San Francisco Book Co., 1976.

Hansell, N. The Person-In-Distress: On the Biosocial Dynamics of Adaptation. New York: Behavioral Publications, 1976.

Hansell, N. Evolving services for schizophrenia. Hospital and Community Psychiatry, in press.

Hansell, N., and Willis, G. L. Outpatient treatment of schizophrenia. American Journal of Psychiatry, 134(10):1082-1086, 1977.

Harrington, R. L. The mental health component. In: Multiphasic Health Testing Services. New York: John Wiley, forthcoming.

Harrington, R. L.; Koreneff, C.; Nasser, S.; Wright, C.; and Engelhard, C. "Systems Approach to Mental Health Care in an HMO Model." Three-Year Report. Kaiser Permanente Santa Teresa Medical Center, San Jose, California, March, 1977.

Haugk, K.C. Unique contributions of churchs and clergy to community mental health. Community Mental Health Journal, 12(1):20-28, 1976.

Henderson, S. The social network, support and neurosis: The function of attachment in adult life. British Journal of Psychiatry, 131:185-191, 1977.

Henry, J. P.; Meehan, J. P.; and Stephens, P. M. The use of psychosocial stimuli to induce prolonged hypertension in mice. Psychosomatic Medicine, 29:408+, 1967.

Hill, R. B. The Strength of Black Families. New York: National Urban League, 1972.

Hill, R. B. *Informal Adoption Among Black Families*, Washington, D.C.: National Urban League, 1977.

Holinger, P. C., and Westberg, G. E. The parish pastor's finest hour--revisited. *Journal of Religion and Health*, 14(1):14-21, 1975.

Holmes, T. Multidiscipline study of tuberculosis. In: Sparer, P. J., ed. *Personality, Stress and Tuberculosis*, 1956.

Holmes, T., and Rahe, R. The social readjustment rating scale. *Journal of Psychosomatic Research*, 11:213-218, 1967.

Hosford, R. E., and Moss, C. S., eds. *The Crumbling Walls: Treatment and Counseling of Prisoners*. Urbana, Illinois: University of Illinois Press, 1975.

House, J. S.; McMichael, A. J.; Kaplan, B.; and Wells, J. A. "Effects of Occupational Stress on the Health of Rubber Workers." Paper presented at meeting of American Public Health Association, 1975; Duke University Department of Sociology, revised 1976.

House, J. S.; French, Jr., J. R. P.; Hogue, C.; Kasl, S. V.; Wells, J. A.; Wilson, R. N. "Social Support, Work and Mental Health." Working paper, President's Commission on Mental Health, Duke University, 1977b.

House, J. S., and Wells, J. A. "Occupational Stress, Social Support and Health." Paper presented at a Conference on Reducing Occupational Stress, White Plains, New York, May, 1977a. Duke University.

Hyman, M. D. Social isolation and performance in rehabilitation. *Journal of Chronic Disease*, 25:85-97, 1972.

Jilek, W. G. Indian healing powers: Indigenous therapeutic practices in the Pacific Northwest. *Psychiatric Annals*, 4(9):10-13, 1974.

Joint Commission on Mental Health of Children. *Crisis in Child Mental Health: Challenge for the 1970's*. New York: Harper and Row, 1970.

Kahn, R. L.; Wolfe, D. M.; Quinn, R. P.; Snoek, J. D.; and Rosenthal, R. A. *Organizational Stress*. New York: John Wiley, 1964.

Kahn, R. L. "Work, Social Support and Mental Health." Working paper prepared for President's Commission on Mental Health. University of Michigan, 1977.

Kaplan, B. H. A note on religious beliefs and coronary heart disease. *Journal of the South Carolina Medical Association*, Supplement: 60-64, February, 1976.

Kaplan, B. H.; Cassel, J. C.; and Gore, S. Social support and health. *Medical Care*, 15(5) Supplement: 47-58, 1977.

Kasteller, J.; Kane, R. L.; Olsen, D. M.; and Thetford, C. Issues underlying prevalence of "doctor-shopping" behavior. *Journal of Health and Social Behavior*, 17:328-339, 1976.

Katz, A. H. Self-help organizations and volunteer participation in social welfare. *Social Work*, 15(1): 51-60, 1970.

Katz, A. H., and Bender, E. I. *The Strength in Us: Self-Help Groups in the Modern World*. New York: New Viewpoints, Franklin Watts, 1976.

Kiev, A. *Magic, Faith and Healing*. New York: Free Press of Glencoe, 1968.

Killilea, M. Mutual help organizations: Interpretations in the literature. In: Caplan, G., and Killilea, M., eds. *Support Systems and Mutual Help*. New York: Grune and Stratton, 1976. pp. 37-94.

Kirshbaum, H. R.; Haveston, D. S.; and Katz, A. H. Independent living for the disabled. *Social Policy*, 7(2):59-62, 1976.

Kleinman, A. "Explanatory Models in Health Care Relationships: A Conceptual Frame for Research in Family-based Health Care Activities in Relation to Folk and Professional Forms of Clinical Care." Paper presented at the International Health Conference on "Health of the Family," October 17, 1974. Massachusetts General Hospital.

Kohler, M. C. Citizen concern: Key to youth participation. *Citizen Action in Education/Resources for Youth Newsletter*, 5(3):1, 12-14, 1976.

Kornhauser, W. *The Mental Health of the Industrial Worker*. New York: John Wiley, 1965.

Kuhn, M. Testimony before U.S. Congress Select Committee on Aging, October 7, 1976.

Leighton, A. H. *My Name Is Legion*. New York: Basic Books, 1959.

Leutz, W. N. The informal community caregiver: A link between the health care system and local residents. *American Journal of Orthopsychiatry*, 678-688, 1977.

Levy, L. H.; Knight, B. G.; Padgett, V. P.; and Wollert, R. W. "Patterns of Help-giving in Self-help Groups." Paper presented at meeting of the American Psychological Association, San Francisco, August, 1977.

Levin, L. S.; Katz, A. H.; and Holst, E. *Self-Care: Lay Initiatives in Health*. New York: Prodist, 1976.

Lewis, R. G., and Ho, M. K. Social work with Native Americans. *Social Work*, 20(5):379-382, 1975.

Liddel, H. Some specific factors that modify tolerance for environmental stress. In: Wolff, H. C.; Wolff, Jr., S. G.; and Hare, C. C., eds. *Life Stress and Bodily Disease*. Baltimore: Williams and Wilkins, 1950.

Lieberman, M. A., and Borman, L. D., eds. Special issue on self-help groups. *Journal of Applied Behavioral Science*, 12(3), 1976.

Lindemann, E. The symptomatology and management of acute grief. *American Journal of Psychiatry*, 101(2): 141-148, 1944.

Litwak, E., and Szelenyi, I. Primary group structures and their functions: Kin, neighbors and friends. *American Sociological Review*, 34(4): 465-481, 1969.

Macht, L. B.; Scherl, D. H.; and Sharfstein, S. *Neighborhood Psychiatry*. Lexington, Massachusetts: D.C. Heath and Co., 1977.

Mallory, B. L., and Cottom, C. "An Expanded Role for Public Schools: Community-based Delivery of Comprehensive Health and Mental Health Services." Center for the Study of Families and Children, Vanderbilt University, Nashville, 1977.

Marek, A. "The Enhancement of Parenting Skills." Working paper prepared for Conference on Mental Health and Families, President's Commission on Mental Health. Parenting Guidance Center, Fort Worth, Texas, 1977.

Marmot, M. "Acultural and Coronary Heart Disease in Japanese-Americans." Unpublished Ph.D. dissertation, University of California at Berkeley, 1975.

Martinez, T. "Alternative Mental Health Resources for the Spanish-speaking: Latino Helping Networks." Paper presented at meeting of American Psycological Association, San Francisco, August, 1977.

McKinlay, J. B. Social networks, lay consultation and help-seeking behavior. *Social Forces*, 51(3):275-292, 1973.

Mechanic, D. Stress, illness and illness behavior. *Journal of Human Stress*, 2(2):2-6, June 1976.

Medalie, J. H. Family diagnosis in family practice. In: Kaplan, B. H., and Ibrahim, M., eds. *Family and Health: An Epidemiological Approach*, forthcoming.

Miller, D. H. *Community Mental Health: A Study of Services and Clients*. Lexington, Massachusetts: Lexington Books, 1974.

Miller, P. McC., and Ingham, J. G. Friends, confidants and symptoms. *Social Psychiatry*, 11:51-58, 1976.

Minow, M., and Schneider, J. "Advocacy as a Supportive Survice." Paper prepared for the President's Commission on Mental Health. Circuit Court of Cook County, Chicago, Illinois, 1977.

Mitchell, C., ed. *Social Networks in Urban Situations: Analysis of Personal Relationships in Central African Towns*. Manchester, England: Manchester University Press, 1969.

Mostwin, D. "Differential Values and Attitudes Among Families of Eastern and Central European Background: Implications for Mental Health and Social Services." Paper presented at Baltimore Conference on Ethnicity and Social Welfare, Institute of Pluralism and Group Identity, New York, January 1976.

Muir, W. Police: Street Corner Politicians. Chicago: University of Chicago Press, 1976.

Naparstek, A. J., and Kollias, K. The ethnic and class dimensions in neighborhood: A means for the reorganization of human service delivery systems. Washington, D.C.: National Center for Urban Ethnic Affairs, 1976.

Naparstek, A. J., and Haskell, C. D. Neighborhood approaches to mental health services. In: Macht, L. B.; Scherl, D. J.; and Sharfstein, S., eds. Neighborhood Psychiatry. Lexington, Massachusetts: D.C. Heath Co., 1977. pp. 31-42.

Naparstek, A. J.; Spiro, H.; Biegel, D.; Sherman, W.; Ditzig, H.; Andreuzzi, J.; and Coffey, J. "Neighborhood and Family Services Project." First Annual Report. University of Southern California, Washington Public Affairs Center, Washington, D.C., 1977.

National Commission on Resources for Youth. New Roles for Youth in the School and the Community. New York: Citation Press, 1974.

Nesser, W.; Tyroler, H.; and Cassel, J. Social disorganization and stroke mortality in the Black population of North Carolina. American Journal of Epidemiology, 93:166-175, 1971.

Nuckolls, K. B.; Cassell, J. C.; and Kaplan, B. H. Psychosocial assets, life crisis and the prognosis of pregnancy. American Journal of Epidemeiology, 95:431-441, 1972.

O'Connor, P.; Vogel, N.; Gordan L.; Felton, B.; Lehman, S. "SRO Hotels: Social Support for the Socially Disabled?" Paper presented at the meeting of the American Psychological Association, San Francisco, August 1977. New York University.

Osterhoff, W. E. "MMPI Changes in the Youthful Offender During Incarceration." Unpublished Ph.D. dissertation, University of Alabama, 1973.

Padilla, A., and Aranda, P. Latino Mental Health: Bibliography and Abstracts. Rockville, Maryland: National Institute of Mental Health, 1974.

Pancoast, D. L. "Boarding Home Providers for Released Mental Hospital Patients." Unpublished manuscript, 1970.

Parents Anonymous Self-Help for Child Abusing Parents: Project Evaluation Report. Tucson, Arizona: Behavior Associates, 1977.

Patterson, S. L., and Twente, E. Older natural helpers: Their characteristics and patterns of helping. Public Welfare, Fall issue:400-403, 1971.

Pattison, E. M. Clinical social systems interventions. Psychiatry Digest, 25-33, April 1977.

Polak, P., and Kirby, M. A model to replace psychiatric hospitals. Archives of General Psychiatry, in press.

Powell, T. The use of self-help groups as supportive reference communities. American Journal of Orthopsychiatry, 45(5):756-764, 1975.

Rabkin, J. G., Streuning, E. L. Life events, stress and illness. Science, 194:1013-1020, 1976.

Richards, D. E. Peer consultation among clergy: A resource for professional development. In: Caplan, G., and Killilea, M., eds. Support Systems and Mutual Help. New York: Grune and Stratton, 1976. pp. 261-272.

Riessman, F. The helper therapy principle. Social Work, 10:27-32, 1965.

Roghmann, K., and Haggerty, R. J. Family stress and the use of health services. International Journal of Epidemiology, 1:279-286, 1972.

Rosenheim, M. K. "Juvenile Justice and Mental Health Services." Working paper prepared for the President's Commission on Mental Health. University of Chicago School of Social Service Administration, 1977.

Sainer, J. S. The community cares: Older volunteers. Social Policy, 7(3): 73-75, 1976.

Salber, E. J.; Beery, W. L.; and Jackson, E. J. R. The role of the health facilitator in community health education. Journal of Community Health, 2(1):5-20, 1976.

Sanders, D. H. Innovative environments in the community: A life for the chronic patients. Schizophrenia Bulletin, 6:49-59, 1972.

Sarason, S. B.; Carroll, C. F.; Maton, K.; Cohen, S.; and Lorentz, E. Human Services and Resource Networks: Rational Possibilities and Public Policy. San Francisco: Jossey-Bass, 1977.

Seay, M. F., et al. Community Education: A Developing Concept. Midland, Michigan: Pendell Publishing Co., 1976.

Segal, S. P., and Baumohl, J. "Engaging the Disengaged: Social Integration Following Criminal Justice and Mental Health System Involvements." Working paper prepared for the President's Commission on Mental Health. University of California, Berkeley, 1977.

Segal, S. P.; Baumohl, J; and Johnson, E. Falling through the cracks; Mental disorder and social marginality in a young vagrant population. Social Problems, 24(3):387-400, 1977.

Service, C., and Salber, E., eds. Community Health Education: The Lay Advisor Approach. Durham, North Carolina: Duke University, Community Health Education Program, 1977.

Shapiro, J. Dominant leaders among slum hotel residents. American Journal of Orthopsychiatry, 39(4): 644-650, 1969.

Shapiro, J. H. Communities of the Alone. New York: Association Press, 1971.

Shuval, J. Social Functions of Medical Practice. New York: John Wiley, 1970.

Silverman, P. R. The widow as a caregiver in a program of preventive intervention with other widows. Mental Hygiene, 54(4): 540-545, 1970.

Silverman, P. R. Mutual Help Groups: A Guide for Mental Health Workers. Rockville, Maryland: National Institute of Mental Health, 1978.

Silverman, P. R. If You Lift the Load, I Will Lift It Too: A Guide To Developing Widow-to-Widow Programs. New York: Jewish Funeral Directors of America, 1976.

Smith, S. A. "Natural Systems and the Elderly: An Unrecognized Resource." Unpublished report. Oregon State Programs in Aging and the School of Social Work, Portland State University, 1975.

Snow, L. F. Folk medical beliefs and their implications for care of patients: A review based on studies among Black Americans. Annals of Internal Medicine, 8(1):82-96, 1974.

Snyder, M. Unpublished document. Mental Health and Social Service Department, North End Community Mental Health Center, Boston, Massachusetts, 1977.

Social Policy. Special self-help issue. Social Policy, 7(2), September/October, 1976.

Speck, R., and Attneave, C. Family Networks: Retribalization and Healing. New York: Pantheon, 1973.

Stack, C. All Our Kin: Strategies for Survival in a Black Community. New York: Harper and Row, 1974.

Stein, L. I.; Test, M. A.; and Marx, A. J. Alternative to the hospital: A controlled study. American Journal of Psychiatry, 132:517-522, 1975.

Stunkard, A. J. The success of TOPS, a self-help group. Post-Graduate Medicine, 18:143-147, 1972.

Sue, S., and Wagner, N., eds. Asian Americans: Psychological Perspectives. Palo Alto: Science and Behavior Books, Inc., 1973.

Sussex, J. N., et al. Special issue. Psychiatric Annals, 5(8), 1975.

Taber, T. D.; Walsh, J. T.; and Cooke, R. A. An innovative corporate/community program for reducing the social impact of a plant closing. Institute for Social Research, University of Ann Arbor, Michigan, 1976.

Tessler, R.; Mechanic, D.; and Dimond, M. The effect of psychological distress on physician utilization: A prospective study. Journal of Health and Social Behavior, 17:353-363, 1976.

Test, M. A., and Stein, L. I. Training in community living: A follow-up look at a Gold-Award Program. Hospital and Community Psychiatry, 27: 193-194, 1976a.

Test, M. A., and Stein, L. I. "Practical guidelines for the community treatment of markedly impaired patients." Community Mental Health Journal, 12(1): 72-82, 1976b.

Thomas, C. S., and Garrison, V. A general systems view of community mental health. In: Bellak, L., and Barten, H., eds. Progress in Community Mental Health, Vol. III. New York: Brunner/Mazel, 1975.

Tolsdorf, C. C. Social networks, support and coping: An exploratory study. Family Process, 15(4): 407-417, 1976.

Veroff, J.; Douvan, E.; and Kulka, R. Americans View Their Mental Health. Survey Research Center, University of Michigan, 1976.

Volkman, R., and Cressy, D. Differential association and the rehabilitation of drug addicts. American Journal of Sociology, 69:129-142, 1963.

Walker, K. N.; MacBride, A.; Vachon, M. L. S. Social support networks and the crisis of bereavement. Social Science and Medicine, 11(1):35-42, 1977.

Ware, J. E., and Snyder, M. K. Dimensions of patients' attitudes regarding doctors and medical care services. Medical Care, 13:669-682, 1975.

Warren, D. I. Neighborhood and Community Contexts in Help Seeking, Problem Coping, and Mental Health. Data Analysis Monograph. Program in Community Effectiveness, University of Michigan, 1976.

Warren, R. B. "Rationale for Multi-Agency Program Recommendations." Unpublished paper. Center for Research on Teaching and Learning, University of Michigan, 1977.

Warren, R. B., and Warren D. I. The Neighborhood Organizer's Handbook. Notre Dame, Indiana: University of Notre Dame Press, 1977.

Warren, R. B., and Warren, D. I. Six kinds of neighborhoods. Psychology Today, 8:75-80, 1975.

Weclew, R. V. Literature, prevalence and level of awareness of "curanderismo" and some of its implications for community mental health. Community Mental Health Journal, 11(2):145-154, 1975.

Weiss, R. S. The fund of sociability. Transactions, 6:36-43, 1969.

Weiss, R. S. The provisions of social relationships. In: Rubin, Z., ed. Doing Unto Others, Englewood Cliffs, New Jersey: Prentice-Hall, 1974. pp. 17-26.

Wellman, B.; Craven, P.; Whitaker, M; Dutoit, S.; and Stevens, H. "The uses of community: Community ties and support-systems." Research paper no. 47. Center for Urban and Community Studies, University of Toronto, 1971.

Wells, J. A.; House, J. S.; McMichael, A. J.: Kaplan, B. H. "Effects of Social Support on the Relatiohship Between Occupational Stress and Health." Paper presented at meeting of Southern Sociological Association, 1976. Duke University Department of Sociology, Durham, North Carolina, revised 1977.

Willie, C. V., ed. The Family Life of Black People. Columbus, Ohio: C.E. Merrill Publishing Co., 1970.

Woodson, R. L. "The Criminal Justice System: Community Alternatives - Adults and Juveniles." Working paper prepared for the President's Commission on Mental Health. American Enterprise Institute, Washington, D.C., 1977.

Report of the Task Panel

on

PLANNING AND REVIEW

Submitted to

THE PRESIDENT'S COMMISSION ON MENTAL HEALTH

February 15, 1978

Task Panel: Planning and Review

MEMBERS

William Allerton, M.D., Coordinator
Director
Department of Mental Health and
  Mental Retardation
Atlanta, Georgia

Paul Ahr, Ph.D., M.P.A.
Assistant Commissioner for Planning,
  Evaluation and Training
Virginia Department of Mental Health
  and Mental Retardation
Richmond, Virginia

Cora M. Christiansen
Mental Health Service Coordinator
Los Angeles County Department of
  Mental Health Service
Los Angeles, California

Eugene Feigelson, M.D.
Director
Department of Psychiatry, St. Luke's
  Hospital
New York, New York

Jerome M. Goldsmith, Ed.D.
Executive Vice President
Jewish Board of Guardians
New York, New York

Uwe Gunnersen
Director
Human Services Horizons
San Leandro, California

Joseph T. English, M.D.
Executive Coordinator, Service
  Delivery Task Area
Director, Department of Psychiatry
St. Vincent's Hospital and Medical
  Center
New York, New York

Margaret Hastings, Ph.D.
Executive Director
The Commission on Mental Health
  and Developmental Disabilities
State of Illinois
Kenilworth, Illinois

Mary A. Marshall
Virginia Legislator
Arlington, Virginia

Dane G. Prugh, M.D.
Director, Child Psychiatry Train-
  ing
University of Colorado
Denver, Colorado

Sheila W. Wellington
Director
Hill West Haven Community Mental
  Health Center
New Haven, Connecticut

PREFACE

The panel's activities and deliberations focused on three primary areas for review and analysis: (1) governmental legislation and regulations which impact on mental health services; (2) mental health planning processes as they are currently being carried out; and (3) accountability and regulatory mechanisms utilized to assure the quality and measure the outcome of mental health services.

The panel had 10 members. One was a State legislator; two were Ph.D.'s with considerable planning experience; three were M.D.'s (one in private practice, one child psychiatrist in an academic setting, and one State administrator); one member had had considerable experience in standards, having worked for the Joint Commission on Accreditation of Hospitals and now in a private consulting role; one member with a doctorate in education has had a wealth of experience in Professional Standards Review Organization (PSRO) and peer review; two members came from local service delivery settings, one being the director of a mental health center and one involved in a county mental health system. There was a good mixture of experience with Federal, State, and local programs and the planning and review requirements at all levels.

The panel identified and analyzed Federal legislation and regulations as they have been promulgated. These Federal initiatives and mandates proved to be often in conflict with one another. Moreover, their interpretation and implementation at the State and local level are often both inconsistent and conflicting. The conflict and confusion stem in no small part from the multiplicity of standards, requirements, and reviews mandated through a multiplicity of legislation and regulations, and tend to inhibit the most effective and efficient delivery of mental health services at the local level.

Much of the data concerning local and State planning processes derived from a detailed questionnaire distributed by the panel. We received an excellent response to the questionnaire (a return rate of 75-80 percent). In addition to the wide variety of interpretations given Federal regulations by individual States, there emerged various and quite different patterns of service delivery and planning mechanisms. It became clear that there is a multiple range and a questionable amount of funding delineated for mental health. Support for various systems of service delivery and planning derive from wholly different funding sources than those defined as principally mental health. They come from a mixture of social and human service categories, as well as from general health. The necessity for interdisciplinary work and coordination was patent.

The panel also dealt with those unique aspects of mental health practice that tend to complicate the function of both planning and review mechanisms. These include such issues as the interdisciplinary nature of the mental health profession, the relationship to other fields of practice--particularly health, and the role and responsibility of the physician as a mental health practitioner.

We evaluated alternative models for the delivery of mental health services and how aspects of these alternatives might be utilized and incorporated into the present system to add strength and vitality.

We explored the multiple elements that go into the planning process and the knowledge we must possess or develop to plan effectively within a multidisciplinary and intersystem environment. We attempted to direct attention to all the people participating in the planning process, but specifically at the needs of actual staff planners, public officials and State legislators, and those involved with programs for the child and the elderly.

Similar types of problems as identified with the planning process emerged when we analyzed accountability and review mechanisms. Many of these mechanisms originally derived from other fields and thus have not been fully adapted to the unique characteristics of mental health services. There are real problems with establishing a unified data base which will allow for reliable reporting. Once again the problems of multiple and conflicting requirements emerged from an analysis of review mechanisms.

In the deliberations of the panel the recent report of the Government Accounting Office (GAO) on deinstitutionalization was discussed. The necessity of improving coordination between all health components of Health, Education, and Welfare (HEW), Housing and Urban Development (HUD), the newly reorganized Welfare Department, and the Department of Labor was emphasized. Problems of States with categorical mental health departments and with mental health operations in human service umbrellas were noted. The multiplicity of Federal, State, and local funding sources for mental health programs and the fact that mental health straddles a fence with one foot in the health service sector and one foot in the social sector was recognized. The need for improved throughput or process standards and for outcome standards was emphasized.

SUMMARY OF RECOMMENDATIONS

The following recommendations were derived from inventory and analysis of the problems related to planning and review. It is hoped that they will provide a starting point from which to develop a systems approach to planning for service delivery, to standard setting, and to appropriate evaluation.

I. Planning

   a. A mental health advisory planning system should be implemented at the State level with members appointed by the Governor. This system should parallel and be coordinated with the local State Health Systems Agency (HSA) system.

   b. The President should direct the Secretary of HEW to require that the governing boards and executive committees of Health Systems Agencies have an appropriate number of providers and consumer members representing mental health, alcohol, and drug abuse. A minimum of 30-percent representation from these fields is advised.

 c. Staffs of HSA's should be required to develop expertise in mental health, alcohol, and drug programs.

 d. Mental health planning efforts should be reorganized providing for a coordinated mental health planning process parallel to the health planning system.

  1. All efforts in mental health planning should be targeted through the development of a consolidated planning model which utilizes a series of dual purpose modules. These modules would be developed in the area of health related mental health services, social services related mental health services, rehabilitation related mental health services, and educational related mental health services. Other possible modules would be housing related mental health services and specialty related mental health services like those for the aged, children, or the developmentally disabled.

  2. A comprehensive plan for comprehensive mental health services should be organized according to the taxonomy currently used in the Comprehensive Health Planning Act.

  3. Public Laws 93-641, 93-647, 92-142, 93-112 should be amended so as to require the inclusion in their planning formats of a mental health/illness related module describing what services are being made available to the potentially and actually mentally ill under this program.

  4. A State Mental Health Advisory Council should be appointed by the Governor and must participate in, review, and approve a comprehensive plan for comprehensive mental health services.

  5. The mental health planning activity should be redirected so that it conforms to a bottom-up format in which the Health Service Area is the smallest reporting unit, except when a State Mental Health Authority justifies the use of another smaller unit such as a State designated catchment area, a federally designed catchment area, city,

or county. In no case should the sub-State planning unit be larger than the Health Service Area.

6. Local plans should be aggregated at the HSA level and at the State level for submission to the Mental Health Advisory Council.

7. The State Mental Health Agency should encourage the development of regional Mental Health Advisory Councils at HSA level. These councils should be composed of consumers and providers of mental health services, who oversee and approve the preparation of the local mental health plan input.

8. Prior to submission of the Plan for Comprehensive Mental Health Services this plan should be reviewed and approved by the Governor or his designee.

II. Standards and Quality Assurance

a. There should be a National Board for Quality Assurance in Mental Health. The Board would have the responsibility for developing model standards responsive to the views of professional groups, the needs of State and Federal agencies, and the concerns of consumer organizations. The standards should be such that they can replace existing Federal monitoring, State licensing, and professional accreditation functions. The Board would have quasi-governmental status, with its members appointed by the President and placed under the Secretary of HEW. Representation on the Board would be by Federal, State, and local government, professional organizations, and consumer and volunteer interests.

The standards would be proposed to States as a "model act" that can be modified to flexibly respond to the specific and unique needs of each individual State. Completed State standards and implementation procedures should be subject to review and approval by the National Board.

Implementation of surveys in accordance with approved standards would be a State government function. Approval and accreditation of surveyed programs would fall under the auspices of a State board appointed by the Governor and similar in composition to the National Board. Concomitant with State implementation, the National Board would continuously and routinely monitor the results of State government and State board functions under these standards. The monitoring of these functions should be an integral part of an ongoing research and evaluation process leading to planning and development for the future and specific modifications of national standards.

    b. The Federal Government should provide sufficient fiscal incentives to ensure that State adoption of model standards does not result in an unreasonable fiscal burden on the States. Therefore, beyond the financial investment for the operations of the National Board, incentive grants should be provided to the States for development of standards and block grants to the States to support ongoing implementation. Over a 3- to 5-year period, we would anticipate the necessary expenditures to increase from $100 million to $450 million annually, approximately .8 to 2.5 percent of the projected cost of most national health insurance proposals. This effort should be anchored in Federal legislation that precedes any national health insurance bill. Linkages with P.L. 93-641 and section 249F of P.L. 92-603 must be established to assure complementarity.

    c. Standards should emphasize throughput (process) and output and not confine themselves to "input" considerations.

III. Evaluation and Review

    a. A form of "prospective review" for ambulatory and other types of community care should be implemented in the peer review process. This will involve the setting of explicit goals and schedule for treatment. Moreover it would mandate involvement in the planning of continuity of care in the community for the patient. These followup plans must be prospective and must precede the patient's discharge.

    b. The peer review process should involve a multidisciplinary team approach. It should cut across professional lines and include appropriate paraprofessionals who provide and are knowledgeable about the community resources and services. These review teams should involve individuals from the various community agencies and services. A named psychiatrist should serve as chairman of the peer review group to assure medical responsibility. The multidisciplinary review process should incorporate a multidisciplinary appeals procedure.

    c. The peer review process, to be fully comprehensive, should include review of community support systems. The peer review team itself should include persons from the community, be they advocates, neighbors, religious leaders, etc. As is the case with the review of professional practitioners, persons directly involved in the case under review should not be members of the peer review team.

    d. Participation in the peer review process should be regarded as a professional obligation. A parallel may be drawn to the duty to serve on juries. Just as the average citizen sits on juries in judgment of his peers, so too professionals who serve on the peer review team evaluate professional activities and patient care.

    e. Reviewers must not only be uninvolved in the practice under review, but must be rotated on a routine basis through review assignments which will both spread the responsibility and ensure an "arm's length" relationship to programs or practitioners under review.

IV. Uniform Information System

    a. A selected uniform set of definitions concerning mental health services and programs should be refined and utilized as a primary step in a useful, national data collection system.

    b. The National Institute of Mental Health (NIMH) should accelerate its current program to develop and implement a uniform non-client-identified data system so that information will be available on clients who receive mental health services and on the programs, units, and persons in the Nation providing these services.

    c. The NIMH Demographic Profile System should be refined and expanded as an available and feasible means of indicating what needs exist for mental health and social service. The system should be employed for this purpose by planning units established under P.L. 93-641. Inclusion of relevant demographic items in the 1980 census should be planned.

    d. As a means of meeting the long-term need for national data on the prevalence of mental illness, specialized studies aimed at the development of generally accepted epidemiologic survey techniques should be encouraged and supported financially.

    e. A program of onsite technical assistance should be mounted by NIMH to train State and local service units in the implementation of mental health information systems.

f. Training of personnel in management information skills should be viewed as an essential part of the Federal mental health manpower training effort.

V. <u>Special Focus Areas</u>

a. We recommend seminars be held for State legislators and other public officials. The seminars should address the following subjects:

1. unified delivery of mental health services
2. rights of patients
3. mental health of children
4. mental health of the elderly
5. provision for long-term care
6. planning for mental health services

b. HEW should require the implementation of the recommendation of the Joint Commission on Mental Health that the funding of specialized services for children and adolescents in community mental health centers be tied to the actual percentage ratio of the population in the catchment area served, with special regard for minority children. Proportional funding is the basic principle involved, and it should apply to the elderly as well in future legislation.

c. Child mental health advocates and advocates of the elderly should have proportional representation in the HSA and PSRO planning systems.

d. The proposed National Commission on Mental Health Standards and all other official standard-setting bodies at regional, State, and local levels should have proportioned representation of advocates for child and geriatric mental health programs.

e. The guidelines for State mental health planning should be amended to mandate the analysis of the mental health needs of children and adolescents and the elderly and the development of a specific plan to meet those needs.

f. Sufficient budgetary and recruiting autonomy should be required for children's and adolescents' programs to carry out their mission in community mental health centers or other institutions in which children's programs are part of larger units.

The panel fully recognizes that while our recommendations are intended to help solve some of the more serious problems of mental health planning and review, implicit in these recommendations are potential problems which

P/R 9

must be monitored. A few of these potential problems, identified at random, might include the politicization of the peer review process to the extent that it works against the best interests of clients; the multiplicity of monitoring and surveyor teams which by their sheer numbers may paralyze service delivery mechanisms; the balance between mental health as a unique special interest vs. the general health approach to mental health planning; the development of a set of central standards for the purpose of accreditation.

We firmly believe, however, that these problems are manageable within the more specific parameters of our recommendations.

INTRODUCTION

I. OBSTACLES IN FUTURE EVOLUTION OF COMPREHENSIVE
    MENTAL HEALTH PLANNING AND EVALUATION

The recent report by the GAO on deinstitutionalization appropriately points out the contributions to a somewhat chaotic posture by multiple Federal programs in health and social services which provide for erratic impact on service delivery because of multiple funding sources, often not geared to appropriate needs of recipients.

The GAO report is very critical of the lack of coordination between the various Federal agencies involved. It is also critical of State governments in failing to coordinate in many instances the various agencies involved at State level. Following this report NIMH has attempted to work out a model of planning for community alternatives. This model contemplates considerably improved coordination with other health components of HEW, with HUD, components of the newly reorganized welfare systems in HEW, and with the Department of Labor.

Today 26 States' mental health agencies are located in superagency organizations frequently referred to as umbrellas. This should provide for integration of such constituent agencies in planning as well as in implementing service delivery in the human service arena. This has not always been as productive as the architects of such human service agencies would have desired. It certainly adds some further complexity to the planning arena. There is the danger, in even the best human service arrangement, for planning to become so bureaucratized that mental health participation becomes seriously limited. The categorical departments, which were the pattern of the 1940's and the 1950's, frequently had the opposite effect; that is, those individual categorical programs were planned in isolation from others that did or should impact on their service delivery models.

At the local level, where collaboration, coordination, and integration were even more necessary than at State or Federal level, turf protection has resulted in serious fragmentation of comprehensive, holistic planning endeavors. A complex set of problems involving communication from one echelon to another has unfortunately been created at every level. Difficulties in planning, standard setting, and evaluation of existing programs have occurred because Federal coordination has been so lacking and State coordination has been less than optimal. At the same time local attention to turf issues has persisted even when Federal and State coordination has improved. This is impossible when the models at State and Federal levels are in disarray. But it is also impossible unless Federal and State organizational elements encourage the local service deliverers to get their act together. Progress has been and can be made in a more collaborative model for comprehensive planning for mental health service delivery. Obstacles will certainly continue to exist but opportunities for important modifications will be present.

P/R 11

Since the early 1960's attempts to more appropriately plan, set standards, and evaluate mental health programs have gradually evolved. The community mental health center movement, with all of its successes and failures, tended often to view institutional care as an anachronism ideologically. Nonetheless, there has emerged from the development of the comprehensive mental health center concept by the Federal Government various attempts to plan and evaluate service programs in a productive manner. These efforts have most recently evolved into more realistic attempts to create unified or single service delivery concepts. In this evolution, the institution, the community facility, and the community environment were all often considered. In the past several years, the concept of a balanced service system (a concept now utilized by the Joint Commission on Accreditation of Hospitals for Community Mental Health Centers) has invited increased attention and, in some places, implementation of this system approach. In this model, service delivery is given high focus. Locations for treatment are termed the protective environment, the supportive environment, and the natural environment. Therapeutic interventions are termed stabilization, growth, or sustenance. In this model, planning, standard setting, and evaluation can be viewed in a holistic, nonfragmented manner.

II. PLANNING FOR MENTAL HEALTH SERVICES IN RELATION TO HEALTH PLANNING IN GENERAL

Many have pointed out that mental health tends to straddle the fence with one foot in the health service sector, another foot in the social service sector. As pertains to our relationship to health planning, mental health planners have tended to go in their own direction, seemingly little affected by or involved with comprehensive health planning. The comprehensive health planning and regional health programs of the last several decades did not in any great part seek out or show interest in the mental health sector. In turn, mental health planners did not routinely invite themselves into these programs. As measured by many signposts and the present state of the art, health planning has not, for the most part, been notable for its successful contributions.

With the advent of P.L. 93-641 (the Health Planning and Resource Development Act) mental health finds itself in a strange position. Many services and grants must be included in overall health planning and approved by the health planning process, but mental health's portion of the mental health service delivery system (estimated to run from 15 to 50 percent of the total health service programs in this country) is not, to date, well represented in the implementation of P.L. 93-641. This seems to be related to the fact that health planners in general view mental health as a categorical special interest group rather than a major sector of the health delivery system. Also, we are dealing with oftentimes contradictory regulations and statutes regarding mental health planning.

III. STANDARD SETTING

Standards for mental health programs to date suffer from two serious problems. One is external to the mental health system, the other is internal. The external problems relate once again to the multiplicity of the various agencies which impact on mental health service delivery. Statutes set by health programs and by welfare programs are frequently not attentive to the particular problems of the mental disability scope of concern. Considerable progress has been made in some quarters in an endeavor to better orient such standards with consideration of mental health clients in mind. There continues to be much to be done in this area.

Standards for mental health programs have also suffered some internal problems within the mental health system nationally. Until recently, standards for the various types of programs funded by NIMH have not been well developed. Many States have been dilatory in developing realistic standards for their programs. In this regard, however, Government cannot be totally indicted. The various constituency pressures, value judgments on the part of professional peers, and pressures from legislators and the judiciary have seriously complicated standard development. It is imperative that realistic standards for all mental health service programs be evolved in the very near future, or the judiciary at Federal or State level will usurp the responsibilities of the executive and legislative areas of Government to set such standards. One only need look at the frequent litigation against the State and Federal Governments which has resulted in various types of standard setting to recognize this as a definite trend.

Standards of performance or outcome standards may ultimately be far more important than room size, staff ratios, or types of personnel.

IV. EVALUATION

The literature abounds in evaluative efforts and outcome studies that are almost entirely related to specific programs with specific types of therapeutic endeavors. Comparisons between one type of program and another, while not nonexistent, are rare. This in some ways relates to the fact that there has not as yet been developed a consensually validated systems approach to the service delivery program. Outcome studies have been, in many instances, appropriately accomplished, but often the questions of "in relation to what" and "in comparison to what" remain unanswered. When planning becomes more rational and standard setting more realistic, then more comprehensive evaluation attempts can be productive.

To date, many evaluation attempts address the problem of changes in psychopathology of the individual as measured by various clinical studies. What is needed is a more systematic methodology to evaluate gradations of disability. Individuals labeled as schizophrenics often perform well despite their degree of psychopathology, while schizophrenics with a similar psychopathology are totally disabled. A systems approach to planning for service delivery and to setting standards can ultimately lead to more appropriate evaluation techniques geared to a measurement of relative disability.

P/R 13

CHAPTER I. PLANNING

Planning in the public sector is the process through which public policies are translated into a series of time-limited measurable and achievable action steps. These steps are ultimately derived from the consideration of a variety of factors, including legislative intent, demonstrable need, public expectations, and available resources.

At its best, planning is a part technical, part political process which is future oriented and which allows all affected parties to determine how public policies will be implemented.

Twenty years ago there were virtually no federally initiated planning activities in the area of mental health services. Ten years ago the majority of Federal planning mandates focused on facilities planning. Even at the height of the community mental health centers movement there were few Federal requirements for State governments to plan for statewide or regional mental health services.

Since 1975, however, two major federal laws require extensive mental health planning activities. These laws are the National Health Planning and Resources Development Act of 1974 (P.L. 93-641) and the Community Mental Health Centers Amendments of 1975 (P.L. 94-63).

Each of these laws requires the preparation of statewide and regional mental health plans. The National Health Planning and Resources Development Act considers mental health needs and services within the context of comprehensive health services. At the State level these plans constitute less than one-fourth of the federally mandated human service and education plans which directly or indirectly address the needs of mentally handicapped individuals.

In Illinois the Commission on Mental Health and Developmental Disabilities has invented eight federally mandated State plans which affect the delivery of comprehensive services to the mentally disabled. Table 1 presents an outline of those plans and a checklist of surveyed components. It was noted that similar types of data were requested and collected several times through different planning mechanisms.

The statement of program objectives, the identification of target groups, and a survey of existing services were required in most mandates. Incentives for consolidated planning, the articulation of evaluation measures or activities, and the identification of realistic and enforceable sanctions were infrequent or absent.

The net result of these uncoordinated planning efforts is that Federal funds are not put to their best use and federally funded programs are not responsive to the needs of the individual they have been developed to serve.

P/R 14

TABLE I

ANALYSIS OF FEDERAL PLANNING MANDATES	TITLE XX	93-641	94-63	92-255 (Drugs)	94-103 (DD)	Alcoholism 91-616	Special Ed 94-142	314d	Voc Rehab 93-112
1. Objectives	X	X	X	X	X	X	X	X	X
2. Target Groups	X	X		X			X	X	X
3. Survey of Existing Services	X	X	X	X	X	X	X		
4. Inventory of Services Under Other Federal Programs					X				
5. Planning, Evaluation and Reporting Activities	X								X
6. Program Effectiveness				X	X	X			
7. Administrative Structure	X		X						X
8. Available Resources	X	X					X		X
9. Expenditures on Services	X	X							
10. Coordination	X	X			X		X		X
11. Implementation		X					X	X	
12. Survey of Facilities Utilization		X			X	X	X		
13. Facilities Plan		X			X				
14. Criteria Governing Funding Choices									
15. Survey of Non-Institutional Services			X		X				
16. Report on Quality of Care in Institutions			X		X				
17. Manpower Requirements		X	X				X	X	X
18. Client Rights					X		X		X
19. Public Review	X	X	X	X			X	X	
20. Sanctions	X	X			X				X

P/R 15

TABLE 2
AN ANALYSIS OF MENTAL HEALTH AND RELATED
SERVICES AVAILABLE UNDER FOUR FEDERAL ACTS

	P.L. 94-63 Community Mental Health Centers Amendments of 1975	P.L. 93-112 Vocational Rehabilitation Amendments of 1974	P.L. 94-142 Education of All Handicapped Children Act of 1975	P.L. 93-647 Title XX of the Social Security Act
Community Health Promotion and Protection Services	Public Education Consultation			Public Education Training Family Planning
Prevention and Detection Services	Consultation Education		Child Identification Program	Information & Referral Protective Services Respite Care Infant Stimulation Companion Services Homemaker Services Chore Services Nutrition
Diagnosis and Treatment	Court Services Inpatient Services Outpatient Services Emergency Services Partial Hospital Services Diagnostic Services	Evaluation of Rehabilitation Potential Including Diagnostic and Related Services Counseling/Guidance Services	Diagnosis/Evaluation Counseling	Counseling and Treatment: Outpatient and Residential
Habilitation and Rehabilitation Services	Inpatient Services Outpatient Services Partial Hospitalization Services	Physical and Mental Restoration Services Vocational and Other Training Services	"Related Services"	Sheltered Workshop Employment Services Adult Day Care
Maintenance Services & Support Services	Follow-up Services Alternative Living	Maintenance Services Transportation Placement in Suitable Employment	Transportation Room and Board	Homemaker Services Chore Services Home Delivered Meals Foster Care Companion Services Employment Services Adult Day Care

P/R 16

RECOMMENDATIONS

FOR

INTEGRATED MENTAL HEALTH PLANNING

Despite this general lack of human service coordination the Planning and Review Task Panel chose to direct their attention and recommendations to improve the relationships between State mental health planning and State health, rehabilitation, social services, and education planning activities.

Recommendation:

>Mental health and health planning activities should be consolidated.

Rationale:

There are at least four models for describing the possible organizational relationships between State level health planning and State level mental health planning: separation, coordination, consolidation, and integration. A separated health/mental health approach would be one in which the State Mental Health Authority and its affiliates operate independently from the Statewide Health Coordinating Council and the Health Systems Agencies and submit to them only the minimum information necessary for their various approvals. At the other extreme, in an integrated approach the planning would be done by a single agency without regard for the specific categorical interest or specialized program requirements of the mental health system. Both of these alternatives are unsatisfactory.

Separated planning is unsatisfactory because it unrealistically ignores the legal requirements of the Statewide Health Coordinating Council and Health Systems Agencies to coordinate their activities with those of the State Mental Health Authority and its local affiliates, and to approve mental health related grants under the Public Health Service Act and the Community Mental Health Centers Act.

Integrated health/mental health planning is unsatisfactory because it does not recognize that mental health is an independent health care delivery system which is:

A. a significant (up to 40 percent) portion of the total health care supersystem, and

B. a complex system which includes at least a health related component, a social services related component, and a rehabilitation component.

A coordinated relationship between health and mental health planning would be one in which the Statewide Health Coordinating Council and the State Mental Health Authority operated in some isolation, utilizing separate reporting formats, separate data sets, and/or separate personnel for the collection, analysis, and presentation of data and service program plans. In a coordinated relationship these agencies and their affiliates would exchange memoranda of agreement for the ready transfer of goodwill and good data to facilitate compatible program plans. However, such a relationship would likely result in two separate mental health plans, one as displayed in the State Health Plan as prepared by the State Health Planning and Development Agency staff for the Statewide Health Coordinating Council

P/R 18

and one as presented in the Comprehensive Mental Health Services Plan as prepared by the State Mental Health Authority staff.

A consolidated health/mental health planning activity would be one in which there was a significant sharing of authority in the decisionmaking around mental health priorities and programs and in which there was significant sharing of planning resources, including data sets, program models, and staff. Under a consolidated approach there would likely be a close approximation between the mental health components of the State Health Plan and the health related component of the State Comprehensive Mental Health Services Plan.

Adjustments to the National Health Planning and Resources Development Act and the Community Mental Health Centers Act and other human resource legislation which impact upon the delivery of services to potentially or actually mentally ill persons should target toward a consolidated approach to mental health planning. This recommendation is made recognizing that the mission of the Statewide Health Coordinating Council as presented in its title is one of coordination.

Recommendation:

> The guidelines for the preparation of the State Comprehensive Mental Health Services Plan should be amended to permit the development of a consolidated plan which contains the following modules: health component, social services component, rehabilitation component, and education component.

Rationale:

Current requirements for planning mental health services within the States are articulated under section 237 of the Community Mental Health Centers Amendments of 1975 and under the 314-d requirements of the Public Health Service Act. The National Institute of Mental Health has compassionately consolidated the requirements for 314-d and section 237 in one set of mental health planning guidelines. The product of these guidelines is identified as the "Comprehensive Mental Health Services Plan".

"Comprehensive" in the title of the plan in practice defines neither the term "services" or "plan." Actually, with the exception of the 314-d requirements, the plan is really a plan for community mental health centers.

Reference to Table 2 will show that those services which are provided under community mental health centers programs are an important but small portion of the total range of services which would constitute a comprehensive mental health program. State Mental Health Planning Guidelines should be amended to require a plan document which identifies those services which are provided under at least the following programs: Community Mental Health Centers Act (P.L. 94-63); Title XX of the Social Security Act (P.L. 93-647); the Vocational Rehabilitation Amendments of 1974 (P.L. 93-112); and the Education for All Handicapped Children Act of 1975 (P.L. 94-142).

P/R 19

Recommendation:

> Guidelines for the plans required under the National Health Planning and Resources Development Act, Title XX of the Social Security Act, the Vocational Rehabilitation Amendments, and the Education for All Handicapped Children Act should be amended to require the development and publication of an identified component detailing services to potentially or actually mentally ill persons.

Rationale:

Considerable amounts of Federal funds are made available to mentally ill persons under the National Health Planning and Resources Development Act, Title XX of the Social Security Act, the Vocational Rehabilitation Amendments, and the Education for All Handicapped Children Act.

Therefore the planning requirements for these acts should be consolidated in such a fashion that there would be a health related component of the Comprehensive Plan for Mental Health Services which would also be an identifiable module in the Comprehensive Health Plan (93-641), a social services component of the Comprehensive Plan for Mental Health Services which is identifiable within the State Comprehensive Annual Social Services Plan (93-647), a rehabilitation component of the State Comprehensive Mental Health Plan which is compatible with a mental health component in the State Vocational Rehabilitation Plan (93-112), and an educational component in the Comprehensive Plan for Mental Health Services which is an identifiable aspect of the State's Annual Program Plan (94-142).

Recommendation:

> The planning format for a revised Comprehensive Mental Health Services Plan should conform to the format of the State Health Plan required under P.L. 93-641.

Rationale:

This format has the following seven elements:

1. community health promotion and protection
2. prevention and detection
3. diagnosis and treatment services
4. habilitation and rehabilitation services
5. maintenance services
6. support services
7. health system enabling services

The 93-641 taxonomy is recommended for two reasons:

1. because it better captures the wide range of primary, secondary, and tertiary prevention activities which State and community mental health programs should provide, and

2. because the use of this taxonomy will greatly facilitate the consolidation of the State Comprehensive Mental Health Services Plan and the State Health Plan.

Recommendation:

> State mental health planning activities should originate at a local level, be consolidated at the Health Systems Agency regional level and be integrated at the State level.

Rationale:

At the present time the two major human services planning activities impacting on mental health activities are conducted from a bottom-up or local-to-State perspective. Mental health planning is currently conducted as a top-down activity. Bottom-up mental health planning would facilitate plan consolidation and would enhance the contributions and responsibilities of local mental health service providers and consumers in the overall State mental health planning process.

Using a bottom-up approach, the base unit of this plan should be the area served by a Health Systems Agency except when the State Mental Health Authority justifies the use of a smaller unit such as a city, county, or a community mental health center catchment area or some other indigenous service delivery unit. (For example, the 648 boards in Ohio or Chapter 10 Boards in Virginia.) In no case should the local planning unit be larger than the Health Systems Agency. All local planning should be aggregated at the Health Systems Agency level and all Health Systems Agency plans should be aggregated at the State level.

Recommendation:

> The State Mental Health Advisory Council should be appointed by and act as the agent of the Governor and should review and approve the State Mental Health Plan.

Rationale:

The overall planning effort should be supervised at the local level by a community mental health center governing body or some other body which is composed of individuals who are competent in the planning and delivery of mental health services. At the State level the overall supervision of the planning process should be under the authority of a newly constituted Mental Health Advisory Council, which is appointed by the Governor and which submits the comprehensive plan for mental health services to the Governor. This council, which now has a consumer majority, should also have among its members the representatives of the State education agency, the State social

P/R 21

services agency, the State rehabilitation agency, and a representative of the Statewide Health Coordinating Council.

As currently required under the Community Mental Health Centers Act, the council should remain responsible for participating in the development of the State Plan, but unlike current councils the newly constituted Mental Health Advisory Council should have the authority to review and approve the State Comprehensive Mental Health Services Plan and the authority to review and comment on the mental health components of other plans. This authority should derive from the Governor and this council should compete as minimally as possible with existing operational and advisory councils to State mental health programs.

In addition to a local oversight body and the State Mental Health Advisory Council, the State Mental Health Authority should encourage the development of advisory councils at the Health Systems Agency level, especially in those areas where the local planning unit is a portion of the Health Systems Agency.

Recommendation:

> The President should direct the Secretary of Health, Education, and Welfare to require that the governing boards and executive committees of Health Systems Agencies consist of a minimum of 20 percent of knowledgeable provider members and 20 percent of informed consumer members representing mental health, alcohol, and drug abuse interests. Members of community mental health center boards should be permitted to serve as consumer representatives on Health Systems Agencies boards and executive committees. Staffs of Health Systems Agencies should be required to develop expertise in alcohol, drug abuse, and mental health services.

Rationale:

P.L. 93-641 requires that the Health Systems Agencies be the responsible planning authority for all health care in their regions. For the first time alcohol, drug abuse, and mental health planning is brought into the general health planning authority and is not treated as a special interest, as it appears many Health Systems Agencies have an inclination to do. Community mental health center grants must be approved by Health Systems Agencies. In order that alcohol, drug abuse, and mental health interests have representation on the governing boards and executive commitees of the Health Systems Agencies appropriate to the national expenditures in these areas, the above recommendation is made since the cost of mental health care was approximately 20.5 percent of the Nation's health expenditures in fiscal year 1975. Other studies demonstrate that between 15 and 50 percent of visits to physicians' offices are for mental health reasons, and the medication most prescribed by physicians is a psychotropic medication.

P/R 22

Furthermore, a recent study (The Orkand Study) reveals that:

- 84 percent of HSA boards have fewer than 15 percent alcohol, drug abuse, and mental health members;

- 89 percent of HSA boards have fewer than 15 percent alcohol, drug abuse, and mental health consumer members;

- 77 percent of HSA boards have fewer than 15 percent alcohol, drug abuse, and mental health provider members;

- only 4.7 percent of executive committee members of HSA's represent alcohol, drug abuse, or mental health.

> It is recommended that members of community mental health center boards be permitted to serve as consumer representatives on HSA's as a way of increasing the pool of knowledgeable mental health representation.

Planners of general health care exclusive of mental health, alcohol, and drug abuse have a tendency to treat these areas as special interest areas, not as a part of general health care. It is possible that general health care planners would want to continue to do so and would, therefore, disagree with the above recommendation. However, because of the magnitude of the public health problem and the national expenditures in these areas it is unrealistic to continue the practice of regarding mental health, alcohol, and drug abuse as special interest areas.

Recommendation:

> Grants should be made to the State Mental Health Authorities to conduct comprehensive mental health planning activities.

Rationale:

The State Mental Health Authority or the State Mental Health Advisory Council should be allocated an annual sum which is equivalent to the population of the State multiplied by $.20. This money would be used for the activities of the Mental Health Advisory Council to help defray the costs of regional councils, local councils, the hiring of local, regional and State planning staff, for the development and analysis of data, and for the preparation and publication of the Comprehensive Mental Health Services Plan.

At the present time State Mental Health Authorities receive planning and development funds under provisions of section 314-d of the Public Health Service Act. These monies amount to about 5 to 7 cents per capita. A major portion of the 314-d funds could be set aside for this planning activity. In addition, approximately $.15 per capita of funds allocated under the National Health Planning and Resources Development Act could be

P/R 23

set aside for the State regional and local mental health planning activities. These funds should be under the control of the State Mental Health Authority or the Mental Health Advisory Council.

It is important to recognize that with $.20 per capita grant, the State Mental Health Authorities could accomplish the objectives of the State Mental Health Improvement Act, which was targeted at $25 million by the staff of the National Institute of Mental Health. At $.20 per capita the total operation of this program would be in the vicinity of $40 million, and probably $10 to $15 million are already being made available under the 314-d provisions of the Public Health Service Act.

With this level of support, it would be possible to eliminate completely the planning grant program under the Community Mental Health Centers Act and make available some additional funds for a truly comprehensive statewide mental health planning program.

P/R 24

CHAPTER II. REGULATORY MECHANISMS

A. PEER REVIEW

Introduction

The recognition that the peer review process at the local level should involve social and support agencies for chronic care cases reflects a changing philosophy of mental health care in the United States. The impetus of this philosophy of deinstitutionalization parallele the impetus for peer review. The dual goals of both are quality assurance of care and cost control. However there has not yet been developed a peer review system which accommodates the new service delivery patterns engendered by deinstitutionalization.

The compelling concept behind deinstitutionalization is that a person should receive treatment or care in the least restrictive setting possible appropriate to his or her needs, and that such a setting, particularly community based, can provide the social and caring support systems that are most important to the maintenance of health. This has been a national goal since 1963.

The other side of deinstitutionalization is prevention. The prevention of institutionalization involves assessing the need for it and developing appropriate alternatives in the community for treatment, training, rehabilitation, education, and housing. This prevention process must utilize the entire system of community supports and services. Local service systems must assume responsibility for the planning and integration of services. At the same time there must be coordination with institutional systems.

Peer review has been with us for quite some time, in both health and mental health settings. The use of case conferences and similar clinical reviews of treatment were intended to assure quality of care. More recently in 1972 with the passage of P.L. 92-603, Professional Standards Review Organizations (PSRO's) were authorized to review inpatient health services reimbursed particularly through Medicare and Medicaid. Most of the experience with peer review still resides in the health field, although there is expanding experience within the mental health field, including onsite review at psychiatric facilities, clinical care evaluation as a component of the Joint Commission on Accreditation of Hospitals accreditation of mental health programs, and peer review mandated by the 1975 Community Mental Health Center (MHC) Amendments. This trend toward quality assurance now must be extended to mental health support services if we are to attain a continuum and continuity of care.

Peer review on the local level must be expanded to cover social and other support agencies as well as nonprofessional community support. Such a peer review process will not only have to be multidisciplinary but also interservice in nature.

The Unique Case of Chronic Illness and Long-Term Care

Peer review has not been tailored to cope with the special needs associated with chronic illness and long-term care. The emphasis of peer review has been on acute care cases in hospitals providing short-term hospitalization. The review of chronic care treatment is no less important, and requires a very different context of perception and procedure.

Chronic and long-term care is usually wedded to a single agency or service. The underlying concept is of maintenance, of sustaining and stabilizing the client at the maximum possible degree of independence and functionality. For both institutionalized and community care patients, chronicity demands a type of care which accepts the possibilities of limited progress and of relapse and rehabilitation, but which anticipates and integrates, to the degree possible, full life experiences, such as marriage, parenting, and seeking and sustaining friendships.

Care for the chronically ill must be comprehensive and continuous if it is to be quality care. This requires the full utilization of the natural support system of the community. We need the concept, of a "hospital without walls," where the chronically ill have natural community supports as well as the full range of medical and social services, while living in the community.

For chronic patients returning to and being maintained in the community, the entire support system must be utilized. Where appropriate, this may mean that in addition to physician, nurse, social worker, or psychologist there may be need for a physical therapist, recreation aide, employment counselor, or homemaker, as well as friends, neighbors, religious leaders, and family. The list must be flexible enough to include all available community resources appropriate for the client. What is important, however, is that these principles and realities be incorporated in the peer review process.

Principles of Peer Review

A. Components of Review

The process of review for quality assurance may involve a member of different kinds of review. Under the PSRO legislation and the CMHC Amendments both retrospective review and concurrent review are mandated. Under the PSRO review system, retrospective reviews would include Medical Care Evaluation (MCE) studies and profile analysis. Both types of studies are designed to identify local problems upon which concurrent reviews may then concentrate. The CMHC amendment guidelines also call for retrospective in-depth care evaluation studies.

Nevertheless, the main emphasis and concern of the peer review team is on concurrent review. Within the hospital setting this review has focused on the necessity and appropriateness of admission and on the length of stay. The concern is for the necessity, quality, and level of care being provided.

P/R 26

Recommendation #1:

>   The extension of concurrent review of ambulatory care (optional for PSRO's and now mandated for CMHC's) and to other forms of community care requires a form of "prospective review". This will involve the setting of explicit goals and schedule for treatment. These followup plans must be prospective and must precede the patient's discharge to achieve maximum utility.

Rationale:

The prospective aspect of review for chronic care patients is particularly important since planning is of a more long-range nature. At the same time, it must be more comprehensive and involve a diversity of support systems. The ability to maintain continuity requires prospective review.

Recommendation #2:

>   ### Multidisciplinary Review
>
>   The peer review process shall involve a multidisciplinary team with a unidisciplinary appeal mechanism.

Rationale:

The effectiveness of this approach has been documented by Dr. Dane Prugh in its application to the Civilian Health and Medical Program for the Uniformed Services (CHAMPUS) program. It will cut across professional lines and include appropriate paraprofessionals who provide and are knowledgeable about the community resources and services. Furthermore, these review teams will involve individuals from the various community agencies and services. This type of collaboration should not only be able to carry out the traditional role of peer review but will be uniquely suited to stimulate prospective case planning. With a psychiatrist serving as chairman of the peer review group, medical responsibility is assured.

Recommendation #3:

>   ### New Member of the Team
>
>   ### Rationale
>
>   The review team shall include persons from the community, be they advocates, neighbors, religious leaders, etc. As is the case with the review of professional practitioners, persons directly involved in the case under review should not be members of the peer review team.
>
>   Because the chronically ill live in the community, close to neighbors, friends, and family who perform the important functions of friendship, socialization, and personal

assistance, good case management dictates that these elements must be integrated into the treatment plan for the individual. Accordingly, the peer review process, if it is to be fully comprehensive, should include review of this community support system as well.

Recommendation #4:

<u>Resources for the Peer Review Team</u>

Participation in the peer review process should be regarded as a professional obligation.

Rationale:

A parallel may be drawn to the duty to serve on juries. Just as the average citizen sits on juries in judgment of his peers, so too professionals who serve on the peer review team should evaluate professional activities and patient care.

By drawing upon this broad pool of talent, new professional resources will be made available to the peer review process. Broadening participation should serve to: diminish the current overreliance on retirees and others detached from practice; discourage the development of elitism and intellectual rigidity; develop among practitioners an investment in the efficiency and effectiveness of peer review; and more readily translate new sensitivities and knowledge emerging from the review process into altered professional practice, as reviewers become practitioners once again.

In order to spread the responsibility, and to ensure an "arm's length" relationship to programs or practitioners under review, reviewers must not only be uninvolved in the practice under review, but must be rotated on a routine basis through review assignments.

Potential Impact on Service

1. <u>Case Management</u>

The interdisciplinary-interagency peer review mechanism will stimulate development of the case management function. Accountability for the full range of services provided and under review can only be located in a case manager. Each element of service provision should be linked with other elements through the professional decisions made by the case manager. The key criteria in the review process will include not only the appropriateness and quality of each service element provided, but the degree to which the various elements are consistent with and integrated with each other. Moreover, and this is crucial in long-term care, the consistency and compatibility of service elements must be reviewed in the long-term time frame, in order to ensure that the sequence of service provision meets minimal standards of continuity of care.

2. Expanded Use of Natural Community Support Systems

The primary impact of peer review is on the service delivery and treatment aspects of clinical care. A multidisciplinary, multiservice orientation to the review process should open new, less traditional approaches and promote the utilization of community supports in the delivery of services.

We can no longer afford, from either a treatment or a fiscal point of view, the overmedicalization and overprofessionalization of care. Every problem need not be turned over to a specialist. If the phrase "least restrictive setting" is to bear full fruit, it must refer not only to physical settings but to professional intervention as well. "Least restrictive" must come to mean "minimally necessary professional intervention." We will have to learn how to contain problems in our families and in our communities. We may then begin to focus our scarce professional resources on education, consultation, and case management, in addition to direct intervention where indicated.

At the same time, the deemphasis on professionalism will require a renewed emphasis on volunteerism. The support system needs the participation of the volunteer whether he is a neighbor, family member, religious leader, etc. Volunteerism constitutes a critical support system of a nonprofessional nature which strengthens the possibility of stability for the chronically ill patient if he is to remain in the community. Volunteers are the caretakers.

Reassumption of caring functions by families and neighbors, under professional supervision and subject to peer review, will help as well to reinstate our communal and ethical obligation to assist the mentally disabled. The loss of this commitment has been perhaps the most devasting and far-reaching effect of overutilization of institutional care and overreliance on professionals. We must no longer put the mentally disabled out of our minds by putting them out of sight and into other hands.

3. Service Coordination

Peer review at the local level will provide impetus for service coordination and collaboration. Because it will monitor the integration of various health, mental health, social service, and other formal and informal systems, it will develop a new awareness of the importance of service linkage. By monitoring practitioners who are accountable for good case management it will work through them to assure that the agencies within which they work will actively and effectively pursue coordination with other agencies.

4. Feedback to the Planning Process:
   Peer Review and the HSA

Interdisciplinary and interagency peer review teams will produce on a case-by-case basis information nowhere else gathered about the presence or absence of service coordination, service gaps and duplication, etc. Taken in the aggregate, such findings will have planning and policy implications.

This aggregate information should be fed into the committees of the local Health Systems Agencies where the authority for local health service planning rests. Appropriate linkages between peer review teams and the HSA's will have to be developed. The resulting feedback should be invaluable to the HSA's in assessing needs and promoting reallocation of resources where necessary.

5. Quality Care at Less Cost

A major impact of peer review is on program quality through the provision of better care, clearly the first priority. The other concern of peer review is cost containment and efficiency. The proposed peer review process should result in reduced costs as well as better care. Cost reduction will follow from: demedicalization and deprofessionalization and the full utilization of less expensive and alternative community support systems; decreased use of institutionalization; and discovery and elimination of duplicative services.

B. REPORTING AND DATA SYSTEMS

At present, we lack uniform data on mental health resources and their utilization, as well as valid indicators of need for mental health services. Without such information, it will be difficult to promote rational planning and resource allocation under P.L. 94-63 and P.L. 93-641. Accordingly, the panel recommends that:

1. A selected uniform set of definitions concerning mental health services and programs should be refined and utilized as a primary step in a useful, national data collection system.

2. The National Institute of Mental Health should accelerate its current program to develop and implement a uniform non-client-identified data system so that information will be available on clients who receive mental health services, and on the programs, units, and persons in the Nation providing these services.

3. The NIMH Demographic Profile System should be refined and expanded as an available and feasible means of indicating what needs exist for mental health and social service. The system should be employed for this purpose by planning units established under P.L. 93-641. Inclusion of relevant demographic items in the 1980 census should be planned.

4. As a means of meeting the long-term need for national data on the prevalence of mental illness, specialized studies aimed at the development of

P/R 30

> generally accepted epidemiologic survey techniques
> should be encouraged and supported financially.
> (e.g., Gruneberg et al.)

To promote effective use of a uniform national data base for planning mental health services, workable statistical systems must be deployed at the local level. Technical capacity to do this is lacking in all but a few areas of our Nation.

The panel therefore recommends that:

1. A program of onsite technical assistance should be mounted by NIMH to train State and local service units in the implementation of mental health information systems.

2. Training of personnel in management information skills should be viewed as an essential part of the Federal mental health manpower training effort.

CHAPTER III. STANDARDS FOR MENTAL HEALTH PROGRAMS

Concern over the quality of health care has become one of the constants that characterizes virtually all discussion of health care provision, stimulated in part by new public funding through Medicare and Medicaid legislation; by anticipated further funding through national health insurance; and by the increased demand for health care, with corresponding inflationary cost increases and unexplainable variability in quality, as well as racial, sexual, and geographical maldistribution of service. Of late, the ultimate quality assurance mechanism, the malpractice suit, is vying with governmental and professional regulation for the position of the most powerful and costly external motivation to quality service delivery.

Reviewing the quality of health care has largely resided in two overlapping and, in practice, often duplicative functions: licensure of facilities and accreditation. Licensure is generally a legislated function administered and performed by State government personnel. Normally based upon a facility-oriented survey that emphasizes life safety and health code requirements and only minimally evaluates treatment process, licensure is essentially permission to operate a service within a particular State. The standards are usually set by State officials.

Accreditation is a voluntary process administered and performed by such private, nonprofit corporations as the Commission on Accreditation of Rehabilitation Facilities, the American Osteopathic Association, the Joint Commission on Accreditation of Hospitals, and the Occupational Health and Safety Program Accreditation Commission. Unlike licensure, accreditation constitutes professional (peer) rather than governmental recognition. The accreditation survey generally tends to be facility-oriented, placing great emphasis on environmental safety and esthetics, as well as instrumentation and ancillary or support services. However, the accreditation survey involves more evaluation of the treatment process (primarily through patients' records) than do most State licensing procedures. Further, the accreditation standards are developed with maximum possible input from the field and based upon national norms of performance.

Licensure and accreditation each have been particularly problematic in their implementation, as well as somewhat duplicative of each other. Licensure has been plagued with poorly trained inspectors, often political appointees, who compensate for poor training by rigidly applying regulations--regulations which are themselves frequently inflexible and which are developed with insufficient input from providers and practitioners.

Accreditation has similar problems with poorly trained surveyors, who range on a continuum from rigidity to creativity. Standards tend to follow only the medical model, lack normative validation, bear little, if any relationship to patient care outcome, and tend to overlook regional and local variations.

Finally, increasing contention between accreditation and licensure authorities over duplication of effort and contradictory findings have

P/R 32

embroiled providers and consumer groups in ever-escalating controversies that further polarize their positions.

To state the issue boldly: health care in general, and mental health care in specific, differ significantly from other goods and services in that the pattern of "free market" choices of consumers which acts to monitor the quality of those goods and services simply does not exist in health care. Consumer control of quality is limited by the structure of health care, which follows the public utility model; the culture of health care provision, in which the provider of service sees it as his highest professional duty to make choices for the consumer; and the nature of health care needs, in which the consumer believes it to be in his own self-interest to forego his choices. This latter problem is excerbated in mental health care, where the competence of the consumer to decide may itself, to a greater or lesser degree, be in question.

These characteristics of mental health care require that quality assurance be overseen on behalf of the individual consumer (though the mechanism itself should include generic consumer input). Moreover, the process must have both the legitimacy of statutory authority and the benefit of provider and practitioner participation. It is equally important, on the negative side, to protect the process from political interference as well as from provider bias.

Recommendation:

> There should be established a National Board for Quality Assurance in Mental Health.

Rationale:

The Board would have the responsibility for developing model standards responsive to the views of professional groups, the needs of State and Federal agencies, and the concerns of consumer organizations. The standards should be such that they can replace existing Federal monitoring, State licensing, and professional accreditation functions. In order to maintain maximum visibility, independence, and influence, the Board should have quasi-governmental status, with its members appointed by the President and placed under the Secretary of Health, Education, and Welfare. The Board would be composed of representatives of Federal, State, and local government, professional organizations, and consumer and volunteer interests. The Board would be charged with the conduct of applied research in the development of reliable, valid, and realistic standards for mental health programs. The staff supporting the activities of the Board should be multidisciplinary in nature.

The standards would be proposed to States as a "model act" that can be modified to flexibly respond to the specific and unique needs of each individual State. Staff to the Board would provide technical assistance, as necessary, to States in the development of State mental health standards consistent with the model. Staff would also, as necessary, provide assistance in developing implementation procedures and in surveyor training on the State level. Completed State standards and implementation procedures should be subject to review and approval by the National Board.

Whereas implementation of surveys in accordance with approved standards would be a State government function, approval/accreditation of surveyed programs would fall under the auspices of a State board appointed by the Governor and similar in composition to the National Board. Concomitant with State implementation, the National Board would continuously and routinely monitor the results of State government and State board functions under these standards. The monitoring of these functions should be an integral part of an ongoing research and evaluation process leading to planning and development for the future and specific modifications of national standards.

Recommendations:

> The Federal Government should provide sufficient fiscal incentives to ensure that State adoption of model standards does not result in an unreasonable fiscal burden on the States.

Rationale:

Beyond the financial investment for the operations of the National Board, incentive grants should be provided to the States for development of standards and block grants to the States to support ongoing implementation. Over a 3- to 5-year period, we would anticipate the necessary expenditures to increase from $100 million to $450 million annually, approximately .8 to 2.5 percent of the projected cost of most national health insurance proposals. This effort should be anchored in Federal legislation that precedes any national health insurance bill. Linkages with the National Health Planning and Resources Development Act (P.L. 93-641) and section 249F of P.L. 92-603 must be established to assure complementarity.

The organization of the National Board should involve broad participation. We suspect that broad consensus can be expected from governors, county officials, consumer groups, and health planners, among others. The inclusion on the National Board of representatives from professional organizations that presently oversee accreditation, (i.e., American Hospital Association, American Medical Association), should reduce their otherwise almost certain opposition.

Two approaches to organizing the Board are suggested. One alternative would be to charge an existing agency with the responsibility of developing and implementing mental health standards. However, this might effectively exclude consumer, private health sector, and State interests, while significantly decreasing the visibility and influence of this very important effort. The second approach would be to restructure the Joint Commission on the Accreditation of Hospitals along the lines of the proposed National Board. However, the Board organization should be established in law, with stipulations regarding membership composition and funding.

P/R 34

CHAPTER IV. MENTAL HEALTH TRAINING OF ELECTED OFFICIALS AND OTHER PLANNING OFFICIALS

State legislation is the principal determinant of who has access to mental health care and the terms of that access. Commitment, voluntary and involuntary, licensing of professionals and paraprofessionals, rights of patients, confidentiality of records, standards for personnel and treatment, all are set by State legislation.

State and local appropriations supply at least half of the mental health dollar as a result of action by elected officials.

But education and training of political leaders in mental health is almost nonexistent. An elected official is lucky to find a helpful mental health association leader or a friendly and knowledgeable bureaucrat. Mental health professionals, except for public employees in delivery and management systems, play almost no role in developing public policy other than protection of their turf. Schools of psychiatry have tended to avoid contact or involvement with the public system of delivering mental health care. Academic institutions and professional organizations seldom answer requests for aid in the planning of programs beyond the limits of their own self-interest.

State legislators often do not even know how much Federal money they are getting or what they are getting it for, and do not include Federal funds in their budgets. Some categorical programs are funded by the Federal bureaucracies and are never reviewed by or even known to any elected official on any level. Ignorance of existing programs and how they are funded makes successful State planning difficult.

> We recommend seminars be held for State legislators, each seminar dealing with one of the following subjects:
>
> 1. Unified delivery of mental health services
> 2. Rights of patients
> 3. Mental health of children
> 4. Mental health of the elderly
> 5. Provision for long-term care
> 6. Planning for mental health services

The seminars would be organized through the National Conference of State Legislatures (NCSL), and their proceedings would be published and circulated.

Since State governments would pay most of the expenses for people attending, the cost would be relatively low. Each seminar would cost about $20,000, requiring a total appropriation of $120,000.

In accomplishment of this objective, the following activities could be implemented by the NCSL:

P/R 35

1. Survey key legislators to determine problems and/or concerns caused by the subject mandate areas where objective information would be helpful in the process of drafting legislation and/or developing programs to assure the rights of mental patients.

2. Organize a planning committee to develop seminar format, identify seminar speakers and panelists, select a site for holding the subject seminar, and formalize other general logistics. The planning committee would, for example, include two to three State legislators, representatives of health agencies and associations responsible for overseeing health, educational and other organizations associated with mental patients, and others as may be suggested by NCSL, including appropriate NCSL staff. The planning committee will also select legislators to serve as seminar co-chairman and/or panel moderators.

3. Develop a seminar announcement and registration brochure and mail to legislators designated in a mailing list to be furnished by NCSL, and to other government, community representatives, and mental health agency leaders, etc., as may be determined by the seminar planning committee.

4. Invite national, regional, and appropriate community and congressional leaders to participate as principal seminar speakers and/or panelists according to their area of expertise as related to the component issues to be discussed at the subject seminar.

5. Compile registrations to determine planning seminar attendance.

6. Direct and present the seminar in behalf of NCSL.

7. Tape record the seminar proceedings. Type the proceedings and submit to seminar speakers and panelists for editorial changes. Type the final draft of proceedings, and publish and distribute same to seminar attendees and other State legislators.

8. Prepare an evaluation questionnaire for submittal to seminar participants to determine value and usefulness of information provided and topics that should be considered for discussion at future seminars.

9. Compile the final report of seminar activities and evaluation questionnaire and submit same to NCSL.

The seminar proceedings could be published in booklet form and distributed to each seminar participant, including legislators of each of the States represented at the seminar, Governors, and congressional legislators. To distribute the proceedings beyond those attending the seminar will tend to increase the utilization of the information that is presented, as well as to maximize the factor of education and information dissemination inherent in such meetings for giving and discussing information on pressing policy issues.

Utilizing the issues that are discussed and information that is provided in the multi-State seminar, efforts could be made to determine the actions that are, or will be, taken by attending legislators as a whole to

P/R 36

resolve such issues. Evaluation will include the efforts that are made by legislators to change present legislation approved during regularly scheduled legislative sessions as a result of their having attended the seminar. A questionnaire will also be submitted to each seminar participant to determine the anticipated value of the information that is presented and how State legislators will utilize such information.

CHAPTER V. PLANNING FOR CHILDRENS' MENTAL HEALTH

The panel felt great concern for the special plight of children in this country with regard to mental health and mental retardation services. The fact that childrens' mental health and mental retardation services are conspicuous areas of neglect compelled the panel to discuss them in some detail. Because these matters were somewhat beyond the original mandate of this panel, it is forwarding its recommendations with regard to children to the task panel specifically concerned with children. Nevertheless, the panel also wishes to record recommendations as part of its report to emphasize their critical importance in the general scheme of developing a national policy with regard to childrens' services.

PLANNING FOR MENTAL HEALTH SERVICES TO THE ELDERLY

The panel had a similar concern for the special problems of the elderly in this country as has previously been discussed regarding children. The fact that community mental health services in particular have tended to ignore the elderly must be recognized in planning efforts. The fact that the percentage of United States citizens over the age of 60 is projected to be a consistently growing group lends great importance to the need for special emphasis on planning for mental health services for our elderly citizens.

ACKNOWLEDGMENTS

The Task Panel wishes to acknowledge the invaluable assistance of F. Dee Goldberg, M.H.A., Staff Liaison, in the preparation of this report.

We wish also to thank the following persons and organizations for their contributions to our work: Julia Hysom, Veterans Administration; Barbara Ritz, George Washington University, Washington, D.C.; Joan Perrault, Washington, D.C.; Peter Gilbert, Nick Bollman and Tillie Carlin, Jewish Board of Guardians; Harry Schnibbe, and Susan Manduke, National Association of State Mental Health Program Directors.

Report of the Task Panel

on

ORGANIZATION AND STRUCTURE

Submitted to

THE PRESIDENT'S COMMISSION ON MENTAL HEALTH

February 15, 1978

TASK PANEL: ORGANIZATION AND STRUCTURE

MEMBERS

Charles B. Wilkinson, M.D., Coordinator
Executive Director
Greater Kansas Mental Health Foundation
Kansas City, Missouri

Joseph J. Bevilaqua, Ph.D.
Director, Rhode Island Department
  of Mental Health, Mental Retardation
  and Hospitals
Cranston, Rhode Island

Leona Egeland
Assemblywoman, California Assembly
Sacramento, California

Archie Givens, Jr.
President
Willows Convalescent Center
Minneapolis, Minnesota

Ruth Lewis, R.N., M.A.
Coordinator, Division on Psychiatric
  and Mental Health Practice
American Nurses Association
Kansas City, Missouri

Donald G. Miles, Ed.D.
Superintendent
Georgia Mental Health Institute
Atlanta, Georgia

Milton N. Silva, Ph.D.
Deputy Chairman
Department of Psychiatry and Mental
  Health Sciences
Medical College of Wisconsin
Milwaukee, Wisconsin

Joseph T. English, M.D.
Executive Coordinator
Service Delivery Task Panels
Director, Department of Psychiatry
St. Vincent's Hospital
New York, New York

Robert Campbell, M.D.
Director
Gracie Square Hospital
New York, New York

Ken Gaver, M.D.
Commissioner, Department of Mental
  Health and Mental Retardation
Austin, Texas

Dorothy Huntington, Ph.D.
Chief of Child and Family Services
Penninsula Hospital
Burlingame, California

William Liu, Ph.D.
Director, Asian American Mental
  Health Research Center
Chicago, Illinois

Lee Macht, M.D.
Director
Department of Psychiatry
Cambridge Hospital
Cambridge, Massachusetts

O&S 2

EXECUTIVE SUMMARY

The Task Panel on Organization and Structure of the President's Commission on Mental Health was charged with the responsibility for identifying gaps and barriers to service for those in need, inventorying present and available services, developing principles for models of service delivery systems, and developing appropriate models of service delivery.

Drawing upon the vast experience of each of the panel members, the panel dissected presentations describing all types of systems and extracted the barriers to currently available services. The list included the lack of a clear national policy, legislative dilemmas, professional conflicts, institutional rigidities, stereotyping and stigma, training biases and funding inconsistencies.

Reviewing these barriers and experiences allowed the panel to identify certain principles upon which to base a sound mental health system.

PRINCIPLE I.

There should be active programs at all levels related to the general goals of:

Promotion--The assistance and collaboration in creation of conditions and the conduct of activities which will be conducive to the growth and development of effective and durable emotional capacities to cope with the exigencies of living.

Prevention--The development and implementation of activities which reduce the incidence of mental disability.

Identification--The provision of early case finding, and when indicated, establishing relationships between consumers and providers.

Crisis Stabilization--Activities which reduce the effect of accute mental disability to a level which is at least minimally socially acceptable.

Growth--Services designed to return the individual to either his former state or to an improved level of functioning.

Sustenance--Maintenance of the mentally impaired or handicapped individual at his/her maximum level of functioning.

PRINCIPLE II.

Services should be delivered to critical points of emergence. Therapeutic or interventive efforts should, as often as possible, begin at the point and in the exact location in which the prospective consumer is first identified by either self or social network for possible entry into the service system.

PRINCIPLE III.

There should be facilities available for persons of all ages and cultural groups, with the understanding that there is a need for many organizational patterns of service and preservation of options and an individual's right to choice. No single service delivery approach should be forced on, or mandated for, all communities. The uniqueness of the client population being served should be reflected in the delivery system.

PRINCIPLE IV.

Incentives should be provided to insure that resources and services are equitably distributed as to client groups and geographic areas, and to insure that only those services which can be demonstrated effective be continued.

PRINCIPLE V.

Maximum use should be made of support systems available outside the formal mental health or health care system. Community mechanisms should integrate the totality of human needs (e.g., social services, housing, religion, employment, legal, etc.) so that mental health services will be an integral part of the total life of a community in both its informal structure and its organized systems.

PRINCIPLE VI.

Service delivery mandates should be directed to objectives and outcomes rather than to specific service functions.

PRINCIPLE VII.

A simple but concise means of continual monitoring and evaluating based on changing needs and outcomes must be developed and applied as a condition for continued funding. Evaluation results should determine the continuation of, or change in, the delivery or organization of services.

PRINCIPLE VIII.

The creation of new social, health, and political agencies through statute or regulation should be minimized.

PRINCIPLE IX.

Programs should be responsive to constitutional and civil rights issues now identified in the courts.

PRINCIPLE X.

Special categorical funding for specific purposes should continue but specific types of programs should not be mandated.

PRINCIPLE XI.

Existing service delivery institutions, such as State mental hospitals, Veterans Administration hospitals and other such facilities must be integrated into the total delivery system and not be allowed to be freestanding entities.

PRINCIPLE XII.

An active program of outreach should be part of all mental health programs.

PRINCIPLE XIII.

In the organization and structure of services, the "catchment area" should be viewed primarily as a planning tool unless it clearly conforms to natural communities and neighborhoods, linked to other helping services and to natural support systems.

A Service Delivery Planning Model was accepted as a unitary model for the development of community oriented mental health services. The task panel model is based on the primary use of <u>community support system</u> and the natural family system as most important. It must be noted that the <u>logic</u> of the proposed model has been borrowed from the Balanced Service System as explicated by Dr. Miles, but that the model proposed differs in basic assumptions: The task panel has agreed on the need for a developmental model oriented to health, not illness. The task panel model is not one of deinstitutionalization alone; it is not an accountability model for cost effectiveness. It does not refer necessarily to the mentally ill or disabled, but represents more of a total approach to mental health. It implies a different distribution of funds since it is not based on the assumption that since most funds now go to the care of major mental illnesses that most money should go to the most severely disabled in our society. The task panel model stresses local option in priority of funding distribution and in goals development. It is a logical model relating to needs of individuals, of systems, and of social groups. It is based on a shift in planning from beds and facilities to the whole person, integrating mental health into a human development model.

The task panel model starts from an investigation of organizational structures (large State, small State, rural, private delivery systems, child and family systems, etc.) and moves to the issue of the principles underlying any organizational system, and the incorporation of elements of a variety of provider oriented systems into a more logical consumer/goal oriented system. The basic goal of any mental health system must be defined locally, on the basis of local need. Is it to reduce State hospital utilization, or reduce mental health expenditure, or maximize the potential of the youth in a community, or whatever? What results are expected for the chronic mental patient: to live in the community? to be maintained at minimum living standards? to achieve the maximum level of independent living regardless of the content of the psychosis? Are the priorities on prevention, or on protection of the community from the impact of already developed mental disorders?

The model helps planners formulate vital questions: What changes are needed in regulations in order to establish sheltered living situations in a community? What funding changes and licensing changes are necessary to utilize all appropriate environmental settings, rather than just the most protective and most restrictive? How can quality of care in all settings be assured? What financial constraints are there on developing alternatives to hospitalization, or on developing promotive and preventive programs?

INTRODUCTION

The Task Panel on Organization and Structure of the President's Commission on Mental Health was charged with the responsibility for identifying gaps and barriers to service for those in need, inventorying present and available services, developing principles for models of service delivery systems, and developing appropriate models of service delivery.

The deliberations of the panel occurred during meetings held July 14-15 and September 19-21. Panel members unanimously agreed that mental health services, even after 14 years following passage of the Community Mental Health Centers Act, were still fragmented, poorly coordinated, provided a narrow range of services which were often inappropriate to communities served, were plagued by the absence of continuity between State and local systems, and lacked a systematic approach to service delivery.

In attempting to deal with this myriad of problems and deficiencies, the panel reviewed services available, identified and categorized barriers to services, developed principles that form the structure of a mental health system, and designed a model for planning the delivery of mental health services.

It should be mentioned that in developing a model, an amalgamation of a developmental model and the Balanced Service System was utilized, adopting the best features of both, so that it is neither solely a developmental model nor a rerun of the B.S.S. Further it is not an operational model but rather one used for planning, funding, determining interrelatedness of structures, and administrative alignments. It views potential consumers on a continuum, ranging from minimal noninstitutional support through 24-hours-a-day institutional care. It may also be applied at any organizational level, ranging from local community groups to federal planning agencies.

The Commission may feel that in providing a single model the panel is permitting no other options. The panel opted for this single model which provides sufficient flexibility to adapt itself in a variety of ways and was thus more utilitarian. The options available with this model are dependent upon the needs and creativity of the user.

The major proportion of this report is divided into three sections which depict the way in which the panel carried out its work. These are: Barriers to Service, Principles, and a recommended Model of Service Delivery.

I. WORKING SESSIONS

During its first meeting, July 14 and 15, 1977, the task panel heard presentations by three staff members:

Dr. Harold Pincus: a review of the original Joint Commission on Mental Health and Illness report, and the legislation that followed the report.

Professor Glenn E. Morris: a working classification of the myriad of organizations presently providing services to the mentally ill: State and county mental health programs, Federal mental health programs, private psychiatric hospitals, psychiatric services in mental hospitals, Health Maintenance Organizations and prepaid practice plans, community mental health centers and other local services including private practicing mental health and counseling professionals, specialized categorical treatment programs, services to the courts, church and voluntary agencies, and other medical facilities including physicians, public health nurses, nursing homes and human service agencies.

Dr. Lee Bachrach: current utilization data and their relationship to issues of systems, patients or clients, service delivery staff, and communities. Of striking importance was the increasing utilization of outpatient sources; the transfer of patients from and reduction of census at State hospitals without a clear understanding of where or if these patients are being served; and the sources and confusions in current patterns of funding. Current funding sources support only portions of a total delivery system, and most frequently only those services based in institutions. In addition, services to children, the aged, the non-white, and the poor are limited in scope; these populations are markedly underserved.

Following these staff presentations, task panel members provided information and data concerning several current delivery systems. A brief summary of each presentation appears below.

Small State Systems--Joseph J. Bevilacqua, Ph.D.

States limited in population may experience more ease in achieving balanced programs because of their limited number of facilities, in redistributing resources and in realizing the advantages of model program development. However, because of their size, difficulties in generating effective constituencies and lack of technical and informational capacity may arise. Other issues, such as the relationship of local organizations to State and Federal agencies, patient movement patterns, and fragmentation of responsibilities for the four areas of mental health, mental retardation, drugs, and alcohol are shared with other states regardless of size. Dr. Bevelacqua finds it to his department's advantage to have direct access to the chief executive of the State.

Large State System - Kenneth D. Gaver, M.D.

A large mental health system can benefit from independence of constraints of other agencies in adapting its priorities to the population it serves developing comprehensive data systems, establishing Statewide standards and monitoring systems, equalizing delivery service dollars, involving a variety of agencies and experts, and utilizing legislative clout. It shares disadvantages of many large organizations: distance from the actual delivery of service, problems in communication and information flow, rigidness of State and local laws and regulations, politicization and "bureaucratic barnacleization".

Regional System--Donald Miles, Ed.D.

The Balanced Service System (BSS) offers a foundation for unifying services and management through reallocating of resources and establishing a single point of accountability. Experience with such a system in a Georgia region produced a dramatic increase in service to recipients because of the ability to avoid duplication and fragmentation and to reach an ever increasing population which had not been able to receive help before.

Rural Systems--Ruth V. Lewis, R.N.

A review of several existing models of mental health care providers meeting the needs of the rural population reveals wide disparity in quality, leadership, and creativity. This critique points up the importance of evaluating and, when necessary, improving upon services currently being provided to Americans in need of mental health services.

Child and Family Services--Dorothy S. Huntington, Ph.D.

Changes in the American family lead to needs for changes in public policy and a larger, family view of what must be done to ensure mental health of children. While standards of what is to be accomplished should be appropriately set on the Federal level, local needs and individual differences should indicate how to get there. A new model of service delivery should recognize that in their very nature children differ conceptually from adults and are not just "little people," that the functions and goals of existing public and private agencies, instead of overlapping, should be coordinated, and that mental health providers should aim at being proactive rather than reactive.

Private System--Robert Campbell, M.D.

Mental health services which are not part of any governmental body range from inpatient and outpatient facilities in proprietary hospitals, and office practices of physicians, private practice nurses, and social workers to such agencies as Ask and Recovery, Inc. Thus, the private system provides a plurality of needs. Those private profitmaking multiservice institutions are very cost conscious out of necessity.

Outreach--Milton Silva, Ph.D.

In order to meet Community Mental Health Centers (CMHCs) mandates to treat patients close to their homes and to develop and engage in preventive programs, consultation, education, and community organization as well as the provision of care must be part of a mental health center's objectives. A human service network, within which the center functions, is postulated to identify community needs and examine, upgrade, and coordinate services and create new services or agencies to accommodate unmet needs. Such a program is designed to support the efforts of other human service agencies and community caretakers, assisting other professionals and paraprofessionals in problem solving, helping others to increase capacities and skills in dealing with problems, and supplying technical expertise on a short term basis. One such network has consulted with school systems, developed specific center programs supportive of the network, promoted community organization and consulted with urban planning boards.

Utilizing these presentations, the task panel began identifying:

a. problem areas in the present organization and structure of service delivery systems, and

b. general principles that should govern the organization and structure of service delivery.

After this first meeting, individual panel members took responsibility for explicating principles, barriers to appropriate service delivery, and a model for considering any suggested delivery system. At the second meeting of the task panel, on September 19, 20, and 21, 1977, the principles, model, and barriers were reviewed and elaborated.

II. BARRIERS

Obstacles to obtaining mental health services delivery by consumers were categorized and listed as barriers to care by the panel. Minimal elaboration is provided since another task panel was assigned this task as its major effort. The reviewing of the barriers were, however, important to this task panel. The principles and the delivery model designed by the panel were expected to relieve or remove these barriers.

It should be noted that several of the barriers overlap, which is not unusual since many of the same obstacles may be present in several areas for different reasons. Barriers were perceived as falling into seven major areas.

a. Philosophic or "values" barriers

A lack of a national policy, a national mandate, or a workable commitment, and misplaced priorities have handicapped comprehensive planning policies. The Federal Government has paid for transferring many patients from State hospitals to nursing homes and intermediate care facilities through the Medicare and Medicaid programs, a system of continued institutionalization while it simultaneously funds the Community Mental Health Center program which is designed to promote deinstitutionalization and provide services in the community.

To many the image of mental health is synonymous with mental illness.

Current mental health systems are seen primarily for "crazies," thus enhancing the problem of stigma. The restricted definitions of mental health and the derogation of issues such as life coping skills, parental skills enhancement, together with minimal importance placed on the issues of learning disabilities and the effects of marital disruption, have resulted in a limited approach to conceptual models of mental health.

In keeping with the above failures there is a reluctance on society's part to accept responsibility for children whose parents are unable to unwilling to care for them in such a way that will meet the minimum developmental needs of these children. Children are still regarded as chattel; society thus produces recurrent generations of marginally functional people while maintaining the myth that children are basically responsible for the circumstances in which they find themselves.

It would appear that there is a fear of deliberate social planning and a lack of coordinated planning by different although interrelated agencies. There is a reluctance on the part of planners to make decisions on the basis of research findings or theoretical understandings, and all too often decisions are based primarily on "practical politics."

Further, in planning the opportunity of offering different services at different developmental stages in the life of the child, the adult, a family, a community or larger social groups are ignored. Serving a child or adult alone and not taking a family or natural network support systems approach tends to fragment and alienate the support networks, providing nothing of equal permanence or relevance to replace them. As a result, services are often delivered in vain.

b. Legislative constraints

The gulf of misunderstanding between professional planners and legislators has not noticeably improved. The blame must be borne by both groups. If clarity existed, one would not expect to see the fragmentation and inappropriate organizational structure at national and State levels but rather the introduction of meaningful incentives that would induce appropriate patterns of service instead of the continual "rewarding" of deficiencies and duplication of services. Decisions affecting mental health planning should be based on research findings, evaluation and assessment, as opposed to decisions based on political necessities or bureaucratic inertia.

c. Barriers related to "professionalism"

Despite pronouncement to the contrary there is a lack of trained personnel. The shortage in professional personnel is further compounded by maldistribution and conflicts between professionals themselves and with para-professionals, while vested interest among professional groups leads ultimately to rigidity of service delivery. Even in instances of adequate service delivery there is a lack of communication between providers and consumers. In other instances there are frequent mismatches between provider and client.

A serious error on the part of professionals occurs with unidimensional diagnoses and formulations of treatment plans. The complexity of problems and their solutions are frequently missed when the child or adult is not understood as a biopsychosocial organism and the individual is not seen in a total context.

Equally as serious are the inadequate diagnostic systems relating to individual and special group differences. This is particularly apparent with the minority populations. This can result in a lack of a relationship between mental health services and the client's perception of what he/she needs. On the other side of the coin, extremely heavy workloads among most service deliverers can lead to the "burn-out" phenomena.

d. Institutional barriers

Institutional barriers are innumerable and sometimes appear insurmountable. Principle among these is the rigidity apparent in organizational structures. There is often a lack of flexibility in changing services to meet changing needs, as both individuals and social forces change. Institutional support for innovation is minimized and it seems that there is marked opposition to change for fear of loss of selfesteem related to the belief that developed skills may no longer be appropriate.

Other institutional rigidities are present, in budgetary planning, management practices, service boundaries, and in perception of consumer needs. Further, there is often a lack of communication interchange, and absence of coordination within an institution's own delivery system. These problems may be worsened by unsystematic methods of data collection, resulting in an oversupply of fragmentary, confused data and an almost total absence of useable operating and management information directed toward problem solving.

Accountability of institutions to the community they serve has been erratic. Accountability has traditionally been from bottom to top, with the top of the institution or organizational structure rarely accountable to the community or individual consumers.

e. Community organization barriers or public stereotyping

Community representatives may zealously seek to have an input into institutions serving their community or in establishing services over which they might exert control but are hampered by the absence of sophistication and political clout. Community advocates also have ample reason for complaint about the inadequacy in diagnostic systems related to individual and special group differences, which in the broadest psychosocial sense leads to inadequate treatment modalities and delivery. Part of this is due to the elitism of traditional attitudes, e.g., biases related to class, race, ethnic, and individual differences. As a result, special needs of minorities continue to go unmet, while others have not yet been identified. Nor for that matter are modifications in delivery systems made with any degree of ease when rapid social changes occur in the community.

f. Training barriers

There is a lack of investment in specialized training programs at many levels for many different professional and paraprofessional groups. Interest lags in providing specialized training in "marginal" but crucial fields, e.g., skills development vs. the "glamorous" insight psychotherapy. Intraprofessional group rivalries lead to isolation in training, e.g., child psychiatrists rarely are taught about normal child development; psychiatrists learn little about sociology, etc. Finally, parochialism of professional "schools of thought" leads to inadequate training of individuals, who are therefore only able to function in a narrow sphere and who become defensive and frightened if change is required.

g. Funding barriers

Problems related to funding are being considered at length by another task panel and are mentioned here only in relationship to the principles provided in this report. These barriers are longstanding and relate to both the public and private sectors.

Presently both third-party and Federal funding support the most expensive form of medical care. The more prolonged care for chronic ailments for which ambulatory status can be maintained at far more reasonable costs are funded less adequately. Also, no consistent support has been identified for preventive activity.

III. PRINCIPLES

The task panel concluded that certain principles must underlie any service delivery system and form the structure around which the model for organization and structure of services is to be built.

These principles are discussed below.

PRINCIPLE I.

There should be active programs at all levels related to the general goal of:

Promotion--The assistance and collaboration in creation of conditions and the conduct of activities which will be conducive to the growth and development of effective and durable emotional capacities to cope with the exigencies of living. (The collaboration should take place among agencies such as the Office of Human Development, the Office of Education, the Public Health Service, and the agencies of the Alcohol, Drug Abuse, and Mental Health Administration, to name but a few examples).

Prevention--The development and implementation of activities which reduce the incidence of mental disability.

Identification--The provision of early case finding, and when indicated, establishing relationships between consumers and providers.

Crisis Stabilization--Activities which reduce the effect of acute mental disability to a level which is at least minimally socially acceptable.

Growth--Services designed to return the individual to either his former state or to an improved level of functioning.

Sustenance--Maintenance of the mentally impaired or handicapped individual at his/her maximum level of functioning.

If mental health services are to deal with mental health in its entirety they must then address themselves to encouraging, developing, and sustaining mental abilities; to identifying conditions which diminish mental abilities, and to intervening and providing assistance when mental function is declining due to stress. If all these fail, then services should assist the individual to attain maximal use of residual abilities. Finally, if irreparable loss has occurred, the services should be provided to assist in the maintenance of each person at the maximal level of functioning.

PRINCIPLE II.

Services should be delivered to critical points of emergence. Therapeutic or interventive efforts should, as often as is possible, begin at the point and in the exact location in which the prospective consumer is first identified by either self or social network for possible entry into the service system. Today's systems frequently fail to recognize what the points of emergence are for various special groups. An improved mental health model should assist in defining these points and delivering service to them.

PRINCIPLE III.

There should be facilities available for persons of all ages and cultural groups, with the understanding that there is a need for many organizational patterns of service and preservation of options and an individual's right to choice. No single service delivery approach should be forced on, or mandated for, all communities. The uniqueness of the client population being served should be reflected in the delivery system.

PRINCIPLE IV.

Incentives should be provided to insure that resources and services are equitably distributed as to client groups and geographic areas, and to insure that only those services which can be demonstrated effective be continued.

Guidelines for funding should be flexible enough to meet local needs and to deploy resources toward different priorities at different times. Funding mechanisms must have the degree of elasticity that will allow the development of a wider variety of services (nonmedical, natural community setting, sheltered and respite housing, etc.) in keeping with the uniqueness of the area served.

Fiscal incentives should be established to promote innovation and the shifting of resources and programs from less to more effective formats.

PRINCIPLE V.

Maximal use should be made of support systems available outside the formal mental health or health care system. Community mechanisms should integrate the totality of human needs (e.g., social services, housing, religion, employment, legal, etc.) so that mental health services will be an integral part of the total life of a community in both its informal structure and its organized systems.

PRINCIPLE VI.

Service delivery mandates should be directed to objectives and outcomes rather than to specific service functions. The Community Mental Health Act requires a series of essential services. If the requirements were instead focused on the expectations or outcomes that would accrue from the successful delivery of such services, it would permit flexibility on the part of the "local deliverers" in the design of their services such that the focus and thought would be on meeting the needs of age, ethnic, socioeconomic, and disability-type groups. At present, services tend to become an end in themselves instead of a means to the end of improving the life functioning of consumers.

The Federal Government should provide consultation and technical assistance which reinforces the capacities of local levels to organize themselves.

PRINCIPLE VII.

Services once established tend to create forces that primarily ensure their own longevity and only secondarily respond to the needs of the clientele for whom they were originally intended. A simple but concise means of continual monitoring and evaluating based on changing needs and outcomes must be developed and applied as a condition for continued funding. Evaluation results should determine the continuation of, or change in, the delivery or organization of services.

PRINCIPLE VIII.

The creation of new social, health, and political agencies through statute or regulation should be minimized. At the operational level, there is often the tendency to proliferate new, autonomous organizational structures for new or different tasks. Many, if not most, of these new offerings can or should be an integral part of an existing structure, thus decreasing fragmentation. At the same time, existing service delivery institutions such as State mental hospitals, Veterans Administration hospitals, and other such facilities must be integrated into the total delivery system and not be allowed to be freestanding entities.

PRINCIPLE IX

Programs should be responsive to constitutional and civil rights issues now identified in the courts.

PRINCIPLE X

Special categorical funding for specific purposes should continue but specific types of programs should not be mandated. It is recognized that at the operational level, certain direly needed services are often ignored. This has frequently been dealt with by categorical funding which, while it successfully places the needed emphasis on topical areas, also frequently results in fragmentation of services and rigidity of delivery modalities at the local level.

There is an absolute need to develop a mechanism for the coordination of services in order to obviate problems of fragmentation, overlap, confusion, and gaps in service. The elimination of present conflict among Federal categorical programs is essential.

PRINCIPLE XI.

Existing service delivery institutions, such as State mental hospitals, Veterans Administration hospitals, and other such facilities must be integrated into the total delivery system and not be allowed to be freestanding entities. Integrating these facilities into the larger mental health system would (1) help alleviate their second class status, (2) stimulate the identification of their proper role in the continuum of services, and (3) allow equitable application of service standards for both public and private facilities.

PRINCIPLE XII.

An active program of outreach should be part of all mental health programs. Outreach programs should be built on the base of the natural community and should include dissemination of information about the availability of services located in the community, not necessarily tied to physical facilities such as State hospitals or community mental health centers. Such outreach services must be based on the premise that an individual has the right to refuse services, but should have easy access to information about these services.

PRINCIPLE XIII.

In the organization and structure of services, the "catchment area" should be viewed primarily as a planning tool unless it clearly conforms to natural communities and neighborhoods, linked to other helping services and to natural support systems. The use of catchmenting in community mental health has often failed to focus services on natural population groups, has been used inflexibly and rigidly and has thereby impeded decentralizaiton of services on the one hand, and sharing of services for low incidence problems across on the other.

IV. THE RECOMMENDED MODEL OF SERVICE DELIVERY

A Developmental Model for Mental Health and Retardation Services

In its selection of a structural model from which the Nation's mental health and retardation services could be planned, funded, administered, and evaluated, two primary design factors were considered essential:

    a. Scope. The capacity to apply to all human service systems, thereby permitting a logical integration, coordination, and reorganization capacity essential for the development of nonoverlapping, noncompeting, comprehensive Federal programs.

    b. Comprehensiveness. An applicability to all mental disabilities and all age groups. The comprehensiveness of the developmental model, adapted from the Balanced Service System, is illustrated by the following diagram of the human services system.

	HUMAN SERVICES SYSTEM	
	HEALTH	EDUCATION WELFARE
FUNCTIONAL AREAS	MENTAL GENERAL ENVIRONMENT	
	MENTAL HEALTH / MENTAL RETARDATION / SUBSTANCE ABUSE	
SERVICES		
ADMINISTRATION		
CITIZEN PARTICIPATION		
RESEARCH & EVALUATION		
STAFF DEVELOPMENT		

O&S 18

V. THE NEED FOR A MODEL

The price currently being paid by the lack of a comprehensive model for the organization of services and the conceptualization of needs, and the relationships of needs to service, is considerable. Without a comprehensive model with which to identify needed services and gaps in services, indicated legislative and appropriations decisions cannot be made. Continuation of the present pattern of fragmentation, discontinuity, and inadequacy of services can be anticipated if a conceptual model is not applied. Virtually all of the present plans for mental health coverage under national health insurance bear the imprint of our historical error in uncritically extending the physical illness model and the provider-oriented system; the model proposed in this report attempts to avoid this error.

VI. ASSUMPTIONS OF THE SUGGESTED MODEL

The model is based on the assumption that there is more to the delivery of mental health care than just the mental health sector. This involves changing concepts of mental health and mental health treatment from a purely intrapsychic model to one of understanding the social, psychological, hological, and economic forces and their interrelatedness in mental health and mental illness. This model also involves funding implications: there should not be a total dependence on the mental health dollar; multiple sources of funding must be considered. The model allows identification of where money is not.

VII. IMPORTANCE OF THE MODEL

The suggested model makes primary use of community support systems--the family, the neighborhood, the church, housing, the medical care system, the social network, schools, community-based public and private services--before turning to institutional forms of care.

It is based on the principles of cultural pluralism, of local option, of adjusting programs to cultural and minority issues and needs, including, at every point, the right of individuals to refuse services.

It is based on a developmental model, both by age and by social organization.

It addresses functions and objectives of a mental health system rather than specific services mandated on a universal basis.

The greatest utility of the suggested model is as a tool--it is a planning model, not a service delivery model. It is not a provider-oriented system, but a model for conceptualizing what functions must be fulfilled, where services might be delivered, and what these services might best take on a local level.

VIII. THE MODEL

1. In stepping back and viewing mental health systems (or nonsystems) from the point of view of organization, the task panel agreed that certain functions must be performed, no matter what form the services might take to fulfill these functions.

These goals or functions are:

a. Promotion--The assistance and collaboration in creation of conditions, and the conduct of activities, which will be conducive to the growth and development of effective and durable emotional capacities to cope with the exigencies of living.

b. Prevention--The development and implementation of activities which aim at reducing the probability of occurrence of mental disabilities.

c. Identification--Activities aimed at determining who needs services, using the natural environment whenever feasible as the locus of identification.

d. Growth/Intervention/Restoration--Activities oriented to improving a person's general level of functioning by the development of new skills. These programs also require an identification of the elements of the environment that are growth supportive.

e. Crisis Stabilization--Activities serving people with severe, usually sudden, decreases in their normal level of functioning. The goal is to restore, as quickly as possible, a level of functioning sufficient to allow these people to remain in their natural settings, to return home if removal has already occurred, or to receive services in the least restrictive and structured setting.

f. Sustenance--Programs for people who need help to remain at their current level of functioning. Without assistance they would "backslide." The degree and duration of help given will vary with the individual's needs, but the goals are to give the minimum help required in order to encourage independence, and to move the individual as soon as possible to the least structured environments and the least restrictive programs.

2. These functions or goals could be carried out in a variety of settings, ranging from a person's home to a 24-hour locked facility such as a State hospital. The next step in formulating the model was to investigate carefully the environments in which service might be offered, and to conceptualize the types of environments in which people generally find themselves. This was done on the basis of degree of structure and the degree of restriction involved. Using this analysis, the following functional environments were specified:

a. Regular--The regularly occurring family and other social network systems in which an individual ordinarily lives, sometimes destructive and sometimes powerfully constructive. The understanding of and linking with the regular environment is of primary importance in the delivery of human services.

b. Augmented--These are the family and the other naturally occurring social networks which have been augmented by consultation and assistance from system providers. Augmentation is the strengthening of natural systems including schools, nursing homes, and families, which themselves may then be enabled to provide climates which promote healthy human development.

c. Devised--This is a social network and support system which does not occur ordinarily but which has been devised with assistance from the service system. It joins people together in the types of groupings which promote healthy human development.

Only when the folk-support system is not able to provide an effective service is there utilization of the professional system. It is seen as preferable for the mental health worker to go to the natural environment to provide the professional service. Consistent with this philosophy, if services cannot be offered in the natural environment it is preferable to offer them in the least restrictive supportive environment of a mental health center or agency than in the protective environment provided by hospitalization or some other 24-hour protective care setting. Definition of the supportive and the protective environments are as follows:

d. Supportive--This environment includes all those service functions and activities which are provided by the organized service system and are performed within facilities operated by the system. These involve services which support an individual's capacity to care for him- or herself and thus do not include 24-hour protective care.

e. Protective--These are the locations in which a person is cared for 24-hours a day, either for his or her own protection or for that of the larger community. It is operated by the service system, by definition, and may be an institution or any other type of facility capable of providing 24-hour protective care.

The most important goal is to move individuals as rapidly as possible to the least restrictive and least structured environment.

3. Having analyzed the functions or goals of a mental health system, and the environments in which these goals could be achieved, the task panel considered the third crucial element, that of the principles underlying the services to be delivered. It was agreed that the developmental model best organized these underlying principles:

a. The human development model--The developmental model is not a treatment model, but a model of growth. It implies an approach to issues or problems in living, to growth facilitation, not simply an approach to "curing" major intrapsychic pathology. Development is an interactional construct, implying a set of emergent functions, structures progressively evolved by continuous interaction between an individual with all his biological givens and past psychological history, and the external world. The implications of the human development model are:

1) Needs differ at varying developmental stages—by age, by developmental task, by social demands. Services appropriate at one age or stage may not be appropriate at another.

2) Individual differences in development and expectation are crucial.

3) There is a strong relationship between what a person is structurally at an early stage and what he is at a later stage.

4) Motivation plays a crucial role in development, and is intimately related to a pervasive sense of hopefulness vs. hopelessness. What is crucial to future development at any age are issues such as self image, self confidence, independence, freedom to try new activities, and the enjoyment of master of new tasks.

5) Psychological development cannot be separated from biological, neurophysiological, or social factors.

6) There is an enormous range of psychological functions that make up mental health: self, sense of competence, ability to communicate needs, a sense of trust, ability to think, to learn, sensitivity and understanding in social relationships, appropriate regulation of antisocial behavior, appropriate social and economic behavior, relationship to authority, to cite only a few examples. The status of these functions determines whether a person is functional or dysfunctional in society at any one time. Mental health is not simply the absence of psychosis, but involves, for example, the ability to work, to play, to love oneself and others. Dysfunctions in these areas have major implications economically and socially in our society.

7) What happens in the real world—War, violence, poor housing, poor medical care, unemployment, loss of a child, marital disruption, being on welfare—whatever the individual perceives as a social stress determines in a major way the course of future development.

8) Cognitive functions cannot be separated from psychological or emotional functions. For example, children growing up in severely disadvantaged families who show symptoms of pseudo-retardation, or children with learning disabilities, have mental health problems which should be addressed within the mental health system.

9) A total reorganization of service delivery might be contemplated around the focus of "point of emergence"—that services would be delivered at the time of the move to a new developmental stage (the move from home to school, the birth of a developmentally disabled child, the time of marital disruption, etc.) or at the place at which this new development centered (the pediatrician's office, the juvenile court, the divorce court, the schools, etc.).

The service delivery model must be related to a theoretical conceptualization of human development or it becomes a model in search of a problem.

The basic assumption about the formation of personality strengths and stability is that it takes place within the context of a relative sense of gratification, effectiveness and competence, within a series of social

O&S 24

networks. Fragmented people exist within fragmented families, and fragmented families exist within fragmented social structures in which meanings are inconsistent. There is, thus, an important place for environmental interventions in reducing or preventing disabilities early on and in attending to issures that lead to lifelong restriction or disability but are generally not defined as of concern to the mental health field: the effects of economic disadvantage on a child's development, physical abuse, parent loss, the high level of violence in society, marital disruption, lack of motivation to join the work force, the social isolation of single parent families, the lack of social integration of newly immigrant families, and the like. These are not usually regarded as major mental health issues, but they cripple society personally and economically.

 b. The social development model--Just as people are at different places developmentally by age or task faced, so are social groups, whether these groups be defined by membership in class, ethnic or geographic terms, or terms referring to common status, such as parents of adult schizophrenics, single parent families, or individuals sharing a problem such as chronic illness.

 These different groups are at very different places in terms of organization and political sophistication at any one time, yet their needs as they perceive them must inform and direct any model of a service delivery system.

 At one point in social development the major need may be for assistance in defining problems as well as needs; at another point the group may be more active as advocates for additional services; at another point, they may be exercising consumer power to change the entire model of service delivery.

 In the past, professionals decided what they thought was best. Sometimes they were right, sometimes very wrong. At best, the consumer could acquiesce and passively use the service. At worst, he could go away. The decisionmaking process is now being reshaped. It is community that wants to decide what is desirable and appropriate to its own individual needs, and it is through this process of decisionmaking and responsibility that groups are experiencing--many for the first time--a sense of effectiveness and competence.

 The implication of this model is that different groups within different communities, at different times, must be able to establish their own goals, difficult as this may be for the traditionally organized mental health system. While certain structured functions are essential, such as protection of those unable to care for themselves, there should be flexibility in how a community meets these goals and specifies these functions and a flexibility in setting priorities for services. It is impossible to mandate an organizational structure, and extremely unwise to specify or mandate the locus of organization.

 This model also implies a need to maintain support systems via deliberate social planning and not breaking up community patterns that are part of support systems. There is a need also for a clear analysis of what maintains human networks. A further implication is that decisionmaking networks will never match "lines" drawn on rigid catchment area concepts. There is no "one road to Rome," and there is a corollary need for the reinforcement of the capacity of the local level to organize itself. Delivery mandates would thus be directed to goals, objectives, and outcomes, rather than to specific services.

The systems delivery model of intensity of services at different levels--Given the foregoing analysis, it follows that needs at certain times would require self-help groups, rap sessions with community outreach workers, peer counseling or the like. Under other circumstances, work with trained nonprofessionals is more appropriate, while certain conditions require the most highly skilled efforts of mental health professionals. Exquisitely expensive individual long term psychotherapy is frequently inappropriate.

Also it follows that work with individuals alone or in groups is not always the answer: early childhood intervention programs, respite centers, child care programs, sheltered workshops, skills training programs, and a host of other settings are most valuable. The principle to be followed is that the service must meet the need of the individual, not the need of the service delivery system.

While the developmental model served to organize the principles of mental health delivery the logic of the proposed model was borrowed from the Balanced Service System.

4. The task panel agreed that the model must be capable of being applied to all human service systems, thereby permitting a logical integration, coordination, and reorganization essential for the development of nonoverlapping, noncompeting, and comprehensive programs.

The Model

The model must accommodate the following conditions:

1. An individual may enter the system at any point developmentally:

--by age

--by situation (becoming a parent, marital separation, newly immigrant, unemployment, severe personal stress, high risk of psychological disorder on basis of severely disadvantaged psychological or socioeconomic circumstances of family, etc.)

--by severity of symptoms

--by neurophysiological status (high risk infants, minimal brain dysfunction, toxic psychosis, etc.)

2. Full use is made of all available natural social networks and support systems, in addition to the mental health system, in delivery of services:

family

educational system

friendship networks

church

medical care system

public health nurses

neighborhood organizations

social/cultural groups

legal system

welfare system

adult and child protective services

housing

employment/vocational rehabilitation

3. The level of service relates to the problem and the need: the more restrictive or structured services are not employed where less restrictive alternatives are appropriate. For example, one does not use 24-hour inpatient care for adolescents who could be placed in group homes.

4. Delivery mandates are directed to the goals and functions:

promotion

prevention

identification

growth/intervention/restoration

crisis stabilization

sustenance

and outcome (fewer inpatient hospital days, fewer adolescents in the juvenile justice system, etc.) rather than to specific forms of service, which will vary according to local needs and conditions. Employing this model, different forms of service might meet the same goals of responsibility of the mental health system for a range of functions along a continuum from sustenance to restoration of preexistant functioning to the enhancement of abilities to cope with the exigencies of living (promotion).

5. This model encourages the use of paraprofessionals, widely distributed in the community with successively more sophisticated and professional backup at each level as one progresses from the levels of the natural to the protective environment, and from the functions of promotion to sustenance.

6. The application of this model encourages the use of natural social networks, and thereby speaks against the rigid application of catchment area concepts.

7. The logic of funding that accompanies this model is that money follows the individual through the system (this is a crucial element), and that there must be funding at all points of entry into the system for a variety of types of providers: visiting nurses, homemakers, neighborhood helpers, etc.

8. A human services system conceptualization is necessary (rather than "mental health" conceptually divorced from the human services system model). The system implicit in this model emphasizes collaborative work in terms of the needed function for an individual or family (from promotion to sustenance), which then leads to the specific assignment of responsibility according to skills, resources, and local situations.

9. The application of this model allows for the analysis of services and gaps in service for each level of functional outcome and each level of service environment at every developmental level. It does not determine priorities, nor does it address such issues as funding or equity. Any planning for implementation must include prioritization, funding, and equity separately from the application of the model. Also to be addressed are the training/staff development implications.

10. The application of this model provides incentive for the identification of crucial issues impacting on service delivery:

   a. The organization of Federal, State, county, local money; the legislative organization of resources; budgetary problems due to Federal, State, or county regulations.

   b. The existant organizational structure of services: State hospitals, nursing homes, community mental health centers, private practice, etc.

   c. The existant organization of socio-cultural factors, sources of strengths and problems, in collaboration with such agencies as Housing and Urban Development, the Medical Services Administration, etc.

11. There are many direct implications of this model for the organization of Health, Education, and Welfare (HEW) services and funding. A lack of reorganization within the current HEW system leads to easily demonstrable problems; a reorganization could support the best implementation of the model. There are far more appropriate structural models than exist at the current time; suggestions regarding what would be appropriate might well be conveyed to the Committee on Reorganization of Governmental Function.

EXAMPLES OF USE OF THE MODEL

At every administrative level--Federal, State, county, local--this model may be used to plan by asking the questions, "What do we have and what do we need?" for each of the cells of the matrix. Examples of programs for each age level that might be developed as specific services are given in the following pages.

Ages 0-18 — Natural Environment

Objective	Regular	Augmented	Devised	Organized/Supportive	Protective
Crisis Stabilization	Parental stress hotlines. Adolescent talk lines. 24-hour ER services for children of all ages.	Mobile crisis teams to go into the home. Crisis homemaker services.	Child protective services-special support systems to maintain children in home if appropriate.	Group homes for adolescents. Adolescent drop-in centers. Emergency child care centers.	Shelters for parents children-protected places to "cool off".
Sustenance	Rap sessions in churches.	Homemaker support services for a family with a chronically psychotic single mother.	Respite centers for families with children who are chronically "ill"- autistic, SED, m.r., d.d., etc.	Long term group or foster family living situations for children and adolescents who cannot remain with their own families.	24-hour hospital facilities.
Collaboration/ Coordination	At every point of entry into the system and for every service environment, there would be mandated collaboration with all other supportive networks: educational, legal, social welfare, housing, employment, the church, etc., particularly including pediatricians, GP's seeing children, schools, etc. Importance of educational system.				
Case Management	Individual differences; motivational state; assessment; social system impact; advocacy.	Community organization. Mental health education. Strengthening of social/cultural groups, of neighboring networks of friendship networks to break down isolation, of self help groups.	Aiding communities seek funds for childservice care projects: for special counselling programs. Placing individuals in appropriate supportive networks.	Assurance that gaps in service do not exist/ Strenuous attempt to prevent movement into protective settings by organization and mobilization of all support networks.	Care of patient in 24 hour facility with constant attempt to move pt. to the least structured environments and the least restrictive programs.

Ages 10-18 — Natural Environment

Objective	Regular	Augmented	Devised	Organized/Supportive	Protective
Promotion	Informational materials for points on child development, child rearing. Parental self help groups.	Mass media. Befriending programs for isolated families very young adolescent parents, etc.	Child care centers. Rap groups for children whose parents are going through a divorce.	Education programs in a CMHC for adolescent parents. Activity groups in schools for special populations.	Family planning information for hospitalized women.
Prevention	Attention to preventable disorders- environmental, nutritional, etc. factors in mental retardation, other developmental disabilities.	Visiting nurse, etc. support systems for stressed families. Schools-Magic Circle, Inside-Out programs.	Therapeutic tutoring programs for children with learning disabilities.	Mental health counselling programs in genetic screening centers. Programs for infants and young children in MH centers.	
Identification	Neonatal nursery early detection procedures. Parent education materials. Pediatrician's offices.	Training for teachers on identifying children with difficulties.	Screening and assessment program (EPSDT/CHAP).	Diagnostic program in a MH setting. Adolescent rap groups, special centers and phone lines.	Training or detection of MH problems for personnel in the juvenile justice system, courts, etc.
Intervention/ Growth/ Education/ Restoration	Courses for parents. Parent programs on dealing with hyperactive children, aggression, sibling problems, etc.	Home based intervention programs for high risk infants. Special Rx education programs for children of psychotic parents. Special school programs for severely emotionally disturbed children, for autistic, for educationally handicapped, mentally retarded, etc.	Head Start, day care centers—MH services and personnel training. Special training for teachers. Special education and treatment programs for autistic children- speech, socialization, skills for living, etc. MH oriented socialization programs for	Juvenile Justice System. Individual, group, and special treatment programs for children of all ages in MH centers. Treatment programs in MH centers oriented to children with long-term characterological problems- asocial, delinquent, isolated, etc.	Treatment for children in long-term foster care, other out of home placement. Residential care for psychotic children and adolescents for MR, dd, etc. MH services to status and non-status offenders in protective custody.

Ages 19-64 (Cont'd)   Natural Environment

Objective	Regular	Augmented	Devised	Organized/Supportive	Protective
Crisis Stabilization	Parental stress hot lines. Talk lines.	Homemaker services. Mobile crisis teams. Suicide prevention hot lines.	Police family crisis intervention programs. Drop-in centers. Adult protective services.	Temporary services. MH crisis intervention services in CMHCs, in hospital emergency rooms.	Shelters for battered wi and children. 72-hour holds for crisis observation, etc.
Sustenance	Courses on dealing with mentally ill family members.	Homemaker support services for a chronic psychotic. Transitional volunteer program.	Respite centers. Community care programs. Friendship centers.	Sheltered vocational workshops. Intermediate care facility.	24-hour care in hospital
Collaboration/ Coordination	At every point of entry into the system and for every service environment, there would be mandated collaboration with all other supportive networks: educational, legal, social welfare, housing, employment, the church, etc.				
Case Management	Individual differences. Motivational state. Assessment. Social system impact. Advocacy.	Community organization. MH education. Strengthening of social/cultural groups, of neighborhood networks, of friendship networks to break down isolation, of self help groups.	Aiding communities to seek funds for child care projects for special counselling programs. Placing individuals in appropriate supportive networks.	Assurance that gaps in service do not exist. Strenuous attempts to prevent movement into protective settings by organization and mobilization of all support networks.	Care of patient in 24-ho facility with constant attempt to move patient the least structured environments and the lea restrictive programs.

Ages 19-64   Natural Environment

Objective	Regular	Augmented	Devised	Organized/Supportive	Protective
Promotion	Activity groups; recreation centers, dance groups, art groups, horticultural societies, etc.	Mass media. TV programs incorporating successful skills for living.	Rap groups for people facing marital separation, unemployment, retirement, being a single parent, etc.	Drop-in centers in CMHC - to rap about the exigencies of life.	Family planning informat for mentally ill patient
Prevention	Attention to mental health aspects of physical care, general hospitals, physicians' offices. Church groups.	Rap sessions on stress reduction and techniques. Self help groups.	MH oriented programs in divorce courts. Alcohol education programs. Family planning programs.	MH counselling programs in genetic screening centers. CMHC programs.	Programs for children an spouse of mentally ill.
Identification	MH orientation in work settings (re MH problems, alcoholism, etc.)	MH triage and referral training for bartenders, hairdressers, etc. Places of employment, general hospitals, etc.	Special training for professional groups and organizations. Where people take their troubles-ministers, lawyers, physicians, etc.	Diagnostic programs in MH settings. Training programs for police.	MH services in jails, th prison system.
Intervention/ Growth/ Education/ Restoration	Courses in churches, Red Cross, schools. Vocational rehabilitation services. Housing services.	Mass media. Home visits by public health nurses. Befriender programs. Adult education courses on MH issues.	Friendship Centers in churches. Task oriented group therapy. Rap groups on self assertion, surviving with a depressed spouse, dealing with mid-life crises, etc.	Entire range of treatment modalities in MH settings-out-patient individual and group psychotherapy; partial care programs; alternatives to hospitalization, etc. Community day care programs.	Skills for living course for hospitalized patient Full range of treatment modalities for patients 24-hour care.

305

O&S 31

Ages 65 and Over — Natural Environment

Objective	Regular	Augmented	Devised	Organized/Supportive	Protective
Promotion	Activity groups; senior citizen centers, recreation programs; transportation programs.	Visiting nurse for family with aged member. Volunteer programs for seniors to work with children in day care centers, RSVP, etc.	Rap groups re how to cope with retirement, with the problems of aging, losing self-esteem, etc.	Education programs in a CMHC programs on dealing with object loss, death and dying, etc.	Attention to MH aspects in long term care hospitals, nursing homes, etc.
Prevention	Church groups. Physicians offices. Senior citizens centers. Retirement communities, housing complex.	Self help groups. Homemaker service. Cooperative programs.	Day care centers for the ambulatory; activity groups emphasizing the contributions of the aged to others.	MH counselling programs in senior citizen centers.	Training for personnel in nursing homes, chronic care facilities.
Identification	Physicians' offices. General hospitals. Church groups.	Outreach programs to the isolated, the lonely, the physically ill.	Respite centers for families with aged members. Nutrition and MH programs in churches, Y's, etc. in libraries.	Diagnostic programs in MH settings, in general hospitals. Training program for social security workers, etc.	Training for personnel in nursing homes, mental health centers, etc. to identify neurological, MH nutritional problems.
Intervention/ Growth/ Education/ Restoration	Mass media programs for families with aged members. Nutritional information. Information regarding recreational and vocational opportunities.	Home visits by public health nurses. Development of programs to restore self esteem through valued activities.	Out-patient individual and group psychotherapy. Special housing programs.	Day care centers for patients already needing special care and support. Sheltered workshops.	Evening care programs. Special forms of partial hospitalization.

Ages 65 and Over — Natural Environment

Objective	Regular	Augmented	Devised	Organized/Supportive	Protective
Crisis Stabilization	24-hour call lines for advice on medical crises, on dealing with sleep cycle reversals, etc.	Homemaker services. Public health nurses. Befriender programs.	Respite centers.	Emergency day care centers. Crisis intervention services in CMHC; hospital emergency rooms.	24 to 72-hour hold facilities.
Sustenance	Self-help groups. Senior citizen centers. Creative arts programs.	Homemaker support services.	Respite centers in churches, Y's, etc.	Intermediate care facilities.	24-hour hospital facility. Chronic care for the aged psychotic.
Collaboration/ Coordination	At every point of entry into the system and for every service environment, there would be mandated collaboration with all other supportive networks: educational, legal, social welfare, housing employment, the church, etc.				
Case Management	Individual differences. Motivational state. Assessment. Social system impact. Advocacy.	Community organization. MH education. Strengthening of social/cultural groups, of neighborhood networks, of friendship networks to break down isolation, of self help groups.	Aiding communities to seek funds for special counselling programs. Placing individuals in appropriate supportive networks.	Assurance that gaps in service do not exist. Prevent movement into protective settings by organization and mobilization of all support networks.	Care of patient in 24-hour facility with constant attempt to move patient the least structured environments and the least restrictive programs.

O&S 32

ADMINISTRATION, RESERACH AND EVALUATION, STAFF
DEVELOPMENT, AND CITIZEN PARTICIPATION

Success in achieving the service goal of the model depends to a substantial degree upon the functioning of administration, research and evaluation, staff development, and citizen participation. The relationship of each functional area to effective and efficient delivery of service is spelled out in this section.

Administration

The function of administration is to make the most cost effective and cost efficient use of human and material resources to meet the system's goal.

Community Involvement in Planning

The three constituent groups, consumers, providers, and social institutions interact to carry out an ongoing analysis of mental health needs of the community. Environmental and cultural factors as well as the interests and expectations of all three groups are translated into the mission and goals of the system. The next step in the planning process is to determine strategies, structures, and resources for accomplishing the mission. Short and long range plans for each organizational unit are jointly established.

Putting the Plan Into Action

Through the processes of organizing, directing, and coordinating the structures and functions of the system the plans begin to take concrete form. However, in order to insure that the system is a dynamic one and capable of adjustment, a monitoring function occurs to correct for underutilization or overutilization of the component parts. It is important to look at the organizational structure to determine if it facilitates the achievement of objectives.

Research and Evaluation

Innovation and orderly evolution seldom occur spontaneously within complex organizational systems. The lag between newly discovered knowledge and its effective application throughout a system presents a continual challenge to administrators responsible for managing a balanced array of service programs.

The research and evaluation function is primarily aimed at understanding and improving the operating capacity of all five functional areas. The emphasis is upon objective information and analysis related to the outcome or impact upon the population served. Such outcome information is crucial if the system is to remain responsive and accountable. Equally

O&S 33

crucial is the emphasis upon research and evaluation as a major, interdependent functional component of the total delivery system.

Management Information System Essential

Effective, integrated program analysis and evaluation in human services depends on comprehensive, basic information which identifies (1) the needs of a target population, (2) the resources available to meet such needs, and (3) the results from applying the resources to the identified needs. Such information must be organized to allow for continual updating, ready access at highly individual as well as system-wide levels, and analysis of simple, complex, short range as well as long range patterns of events. The management information system's most critical output, then, is communication between a variety of service providers and administrative decisionmakers; communication (feedback) regarding current staff, program and total organizational objectives, and communication regarding current and prospective imbalances which will require further organizational, program level, and staff level planning and development.

Systematic Looking at What We Are Doing

Effective evaluation procedures are dependent upon: (1) establishing common terminology, methodology, and objective criteria for all functional areas and programs, and (2) the provision of information necessary to determine if current activities are meeting current objectives.

Find Better Ways to Offer Services

It is important that the system's continuing evaluation as well as other research findings be available to providers. The ultimate goal is to expand the capacity of the system to meet identified needs and to move toward the development of a general theory of mental health and an effective, comprehensive system of mental health services.

Capacity for Development of Standards

Also inherent within the model is a methodology for establishing an evaluative approach whereby objective standards may be set for an entire human services system based on the mode.

Staff Development

The human resources required to operate the model are the most essential as well as the most expensive factors in meeting the system's goals.

Train and Retrain

Some providers have not worked in a mental health system before. Others have had varying degrees of training in traditional therapeutic approaches usually with middle class and less seriously disturbed clients. Such training does not prepare them for working with the population usually served by a Balanced Service System. The major emphasis of the model is on providing services for individuals suffering major disabilities often with long term impairment and on stabilization of acute crisis states. To reach this population, staff need training in procedures more appropriate to the goals of sustenance and stabilization. In addition, training is needed for outreach interventions into the natural environment. In order to provide adequate service to the often underserved, client staff must become capable of performing a greater variety of services than those typically offered in the primarily psychotherapy oriented clinic. The function of staff development is to provide each employee a personalized development and utilization plan to achieve this end. A modular series of education, training, and experiential opportunities should enhance individual growth and career development plans. Periodic review and revision of learning experiences will enable the staff to be more responsive to changing demands of a dynamic system.

V. IN SUMMARY

The model and the accompanying principles have been outlined and discussed. It must be noted that the logic of the proposed model has been borrowed from the Balanced Service System as explicated by Dr. Miles, but that the model proposed differs in basic assumptions: The task panel has agreed on the need for a developmental model oriented to health, not illness. The task panel model is not one of deinstitutionalization alone; it is not an accountability model for cost effectiveness. It does not refer necessarily to the mentally ill or disabled, but represents more of a total approach to mental health. It implies a different distribution of funds since it is not based on the assumption that since most funds now go to the care of major mental illnesses that most money should go to the most severely disabled in our society. The task panel model stresses local option in priority of funding distribution and in goals development. It is a logical model relating to needs of individuals, of systems, and of social groups. It is based on a shift in planning from beds and facilities to the whole person, integrating mental health into a human development model.

The task panel model starts from an investigation of organizational structures (large State, small State, rural, private delivery systems child and family systems, etc.) and moves to the issue of the principles underlying any organizational system, and the incorporation of elements of a variety of provider oriented systems into a more logical consumer/goal oriented system. The basic goal of any mental health system must be defined locally, on the basis of local need. Is it to reduce State hospital utilization or reduce mental health expenditure, or maximize the potential of the youth in a community, or whatever? What results are expected for the chronic mental patient: to live in the community? to be maintained at minimum living standards? to achieve the maximum level of independent living regardless of the content of the psychosis? Are the priorities on prevention, or on protection of the community from the impact of already developed mental disorders?

The model helps planners formulate vital questions: What changes are needed in regulations in order to establish sheltered living situations in a community? What funding changes and licensing changes are necessary to utilize all appropriate environmental settings, rather than just the most protective and most restrictive? How can quality of care in all settings be assured? What financial constraints are there on developing alternatives to hospitalization, or on developing promotive and preventive programs?

The task panel model is based on the primary use of community support system and the natural family system as most important.

ACKNOWLEDGMENTS

The Task Panel on Organization and Structure wishes to acknowledge the invaluable assistance of F. Dee Goldberg, Staff Liasion to the panel, in preparation of this report.

The panel appreciates also the generous help of Ms. Julia Hysom, Veterans Administration; Professor Glenn E. Morris, George Washington University; and Leona Bachrach, Ph.D. and Harold Pincus, M.D., Commission Staff.

Report of the Task Panel

on

COMMUNITY MENTAL HEALTH CENTERS ASSESSMENT

Submitted to

THE PRESIDENT'S COMMISSION ON MENTAL HEALTH

February 15, 1978

Task Panel: Community Mental Health Centers Assessment

MEMBERS

Peter B. Edelman
Task Panel Coordinator
Director
New York State Division for Youth
Albany, New York

James Ciarlo, Ph.D.
Consultant, Research and Evaluation
Northwest Denver Mental Health Center
Denver, Colorado

Howard Gurevitz, M.D.
Acting Director
Department of Health and Welfare,
   San Mateo County
San Mateo, California

Thomas W. Gwyn
Director
Public Service Programs
University of California
San Francisco, California

Loraine Henricks, M.D.
Medical Director
The Door - A Center of Alternatives
New York, New York

Alan Levenson, M.D.
Professor and Head
Department of Psychiatry, Arizona
   Health Sciences Center
Tucson, Arizona

Joseph T. English, M.D.
Executive Coordinator, Service
Service Delivery Task Panels
Director
Department of Psychiatry
St. Vincent's Hospital
New York, New York

David F. Musto, M.D.
Associate Professor, Psychiatry
   and History
Yale University
New Haven, Connecticut

Lindbergh S. Sata, M.D.
Professor and Chairman
Department of Psychiatry, St.
   Louis University
St. Louis, Missouri

Vivian Smith, M.S.W.
Acting Director, Area D Community
   Mental Health Center
St. Elizabeths Hospital
Washington, D.C.

Marta Sotomayor, D.S.W.
Associate Dean
Graduate School of Social Work,
   University of Houston
Houston, Texas

Henry Tomes, Ph.D.
Director
Community Mental Health Center
Meharry Medical College
Nashville, Tennessee

INTRODUCTION

The community mental health center program is at a crossroads. Developed on the premise that a declining Federal contribution would produce stable financing after a period of time, it is now "graduating" centers into a world of fiscal constraint and uncertain expectations. To merely discuss establishing further centers would seem rather self-defeating, so long as the premise of the community mental health center (CMHC) program makes possible the disappearance or diminution of proven programs 8 years after they are established. And yet there is a clear need for additional community mental health centers and services.

Substantively, there is a crossfire of criticism. Observers point to the relatively limited role the centers have played in key areas like prevention, services to populations at special risk, and services to the previously institutionalized. Furthermore, it is contended that this proves, variously, the overpromising of the program; the impossibility of performing these tasks; the fundamental racial, ethnic, and income cleavages in American society; the lack of commitment of the mental health professions; or the political reality of the appropriations process at all levels of government.

We take a rather different view. We strongly support community mental health services and community participation in the planning and oversight of such services. We believe a significant number of the community mental health centers have made substantial contributions to the development of needed community mental health services. And we think absurd priorities in any field can be altered if adequate efforts are made over a period of time.

In the constellation of Federal programs, the CMHC's have been, in fact, a distinctly small item, currently costing less than a quarter of a billion dollars a year for their categorical appropriation. The program has recevied a total of approximately $1.5 billion in categorical Federal funding during the entire 14 years it has been in existence.

Yet this relatively small funding has brought 590 operational community mental health centers to areas around the country, with another 85 funded but not yet operational. With all the criticism that has been leveled about the failure of the centers to attract other resources, every dollar put in by the CMHC program itself leverages three other dollars of support. The bulk of this additional support is from non-Federal sources. In community after community around America, the CMHC program has created important, useful mental health services that would not be in existence if the program had not produced them.

At the same time, there are serious problems that remain throughout the entire country in regard to delivering mental health services. Overall, neither the quantity nor quality of available services is sufficient. Some areas have virtually no community mental health services; others have gaping deficiencies for certain populations. Even where there are CMHC's, there is often a distressing lack of service for previously institutionalized patients returning to the community. In addition, not enough is being done to prevent initial institutionalization. The populations especially at risk, as recognized in the 1975 CMHC legislation--children and youth, the elderly, and substance abusers--are frequently underserved. While the CMHC program has made generally successful efforts from the outset to target services toward minorities and the poor, there are still gaps in these areas.

A special problem is the connection of some centers to the communities of which they are supposed to be an integral part. The nature of this problem in any given community, in those instances where it is a problem, will depend on the form of the CMHC in that community. If it is run by a State or local governmental authority that has historically tended to bureaucracy and lack of capacity to reach out to people who need to know there is a way they can get help, the problem of connection is of one sort. If, at the other extreme, the CMHC is a freestanding program governed by people from the community, the problem may be the exact opposite: failure to be part of a functioning network of human services in the relevant geographical area.

This, in turn, highlights two key introductory points: the tremendous diversity of the program that is encompassed in the community mental health center concept in terms of auspices, governance, location, size, pattern of service, and all the rest; and the fact that many of the program dilemmas are hardly the fault of individual centers. Over the past years there has been a failure of Federal oversight, technical assistance, evaluation, and leadership that is at the heart of the current matter. It is important to note that over these same years previous administrations had sought to end the program, arguing that a successful demonstration project no longer needed to be demonstrated. In the face of this erosion of support (manifested most strikingly by the administration's impoundment of congressionally authorized funds) and diminishing resources for program support, there has been an increasing need for such services and leadership. In many ways, to criticize the centers themselves for many (but not all) of their failings is to "blame the victim."

To the same end we would stress as strongly as we possibly can that there will never be any real hope of adequate community mental health services so long as over half the American mental health dollar is spent on State institutions and mental-health-related nursing home care. If the Commission is unable to point a clear path toward Federal policy that will alter the current balance of expenditures, we doubt the efficacy of anything that it might recommend regarding community mental health centers and services.

Our deliberations elicited a cascade of observations about the changes in the context of the CMHC program over the past 14 years: changes in expectations about what the program can accomplish; changes in the financial and economic environment; changes in the professions and the public's attitude toward them; changes in the "medical model" of treatment and associated changes in the manpower mix; the development of consumerism, advocacy, and legal rights in health and mental health care; and many others.

If there is one change we could point to above all, however, it is this: when the CMHC program was instituted, the centers were the visible symbol of mental health services in the community. Now there are many new services and programs which are often unassociated with CMHC's.

HISTORY

On February 5, 1963, President John F. Kennedy sent to Congress the first Presidential "Message on Mental Illness and Mental Retardation." In it, he proposed a "national mental health program to assist in the inauguration of a wholly new emphasis and approach to care for the mentally ill."

President Kennedy's program was, in a sense, the culmination of a century of struggle to gain Federal support for mental health services. President Franklin Pierce had, in 1854, vetoed legislation which would have made Federal land grants available to facilitate the development of public mental hospitals, stating that he could find no constitutional authority for the Federal Government to be "the great almoner of public charity throughout the United States."

The Depression of the 1930's, which created a new Federal role as initiator and supporter of national social welfare programs, eroded that constitutional position. After World War II, accounts gathered from among the three thousand conscientious objectors who had served in State mental hospitals helped reveal to the public the abysmal conditions among the neglected civilian mentally ill. The returning military clinicians also helped stimulate a new wave of interest in treatment for mental illness. This led first to the establishment of the National Institute of Mental Health in 1946, and then to the creation in 1955 of the Joint Commission on Mental Health and Mental Illness, the report of which was a major underpinning of President Kennedy's message.

The Kennedy administration's program, while sharing many of the assumptions and proposals of the Joint Commission, differed in certain key ways. For one thing the administration proposals emphasized primary prevention and treatment in community mental health centers, moving the primary locus of treatment for the mentally ill away from the State hospitals, as opposed to using Federal institutions and funding for State hospital improvement (although in the interim existing authorization for demonstration grants to them would be continued). The population areas to be served by the community mental health centers were larger than the Joint Commission had proposed, and thus the ultimate number to be established was lower. Moreover, the concept of a community mental health "center" was broader than that of the community mental health "clinic" which the Joint Commission had spelled out.

While it recommended large increases in Federal funding, the legislation sought to specifically designate funding for construction and initial staffing of the community mental health centers, with at least 50 percent of the cost borne by the States. Further, this Federal assistance was to diminish over time. It was asserted that the centers would ultimately be financed by increased State and local funds made available through the phasing out of State hospitals and, it was hoped, by the private sector through voluntary insurance.

The Community Mental Health Center Act was ultimately passed by the Congress, but the law which was signed by President Kennedy on October 31, 1963, authorized substantially less money for construction of centers than originally was requested and also eliminated Federal support for initial staffing and operation of the centers. In any case, the National Institute of Mental Health (NIMH) immediately set out to provide for State mental health planning and to draw up the required regulations. The regulations established in 1964 state that "to qualify for Federal construction...grants, an applicant, which by law must be a public or private nonprofit agency, must present a plan for a coordinated program of at least five essential mental health services: inpatient services, emergency services, partial hospitalization (such as daycare), outpatient services, and consultation and educational services." There were also several services that were recommended but not required. These included specialized diagnostic services, rehabilitation, preadmission and postdischarge services for State hospital patients, research and evaluation programs, and training and education activities. In addition, the regulations mandated linkages of information, staff, and patients among those services so as to insure continuity of care.

With the regulations in effect, NIMH began to fund construction of community mental health centers. This responsibility was augmented with the passage of the Community Mental Health Center Amendments of 1965, which authorized grants to assist in paying for professional and technical personnel to staff the centers in the initial 51 months of operation. In 1967, the initial construction and subsequent staffing programs were renewed by Congress for 3 more years.

By 1970, it had become apparent that the original estimate of the length of time that community mental health centers would need Federal support had been overly optimistic. As such, the Community Mental Health Center Amendments of 1970 not only extended the Act for 3 more years, but also increased the maximum Federal share for construction and staffing grants. All centers became eligible for support over a total period of 96 months (8 years) rather than the 51 months that had originally been authorized. Those in designated poverty areas could receive more aid than others. Additional grants called "Part F Grants" were allocated for specific services for child mental health, alcoholism, and drug abuse.

In 1975, Congress passed legislation which provided for a substantial revision of the original Community Mental Health Centers Act. For the first time there was prescribed within the legislation, as opposed to simply regulations, a definition of a "community mental health center" and of the comprehensive mental health services which such a center must provide. The definition contained requirements for the organization and operation of such centers; provision of services; coordination of services with other entities and the development of an integrated system of care; staffing; availability of services; responsiveness to the community served; governing bodies; quality assurance; and related matters.

The services that a CMHC is required to provide include not only the "essential services"--inpatient services, outpatient services, daycare and partial hospitalization, emergency services, and consultation and education services for a wide range of individuals and entities involved with mental health services, including health professionals, schools, law enforcement and correctional agencies, public welfare agencies, and the like--but also specialized services for children and the elderly, assistance to courts and other public agencies in screening individuals being considered for admission to

State mental hospitals, followup care for those discharged from State mental hospitals, halfway houses for those discharged from mental institutions, and programs for alcoholism and drug abuse.

To fund new centers and assist existing centers to make the transition, the new 1975 law consolidated and replaced numerous categories of aid to centers with six new grant programs: (1) planning grants; (2) initial operating grants for the support of a center's first 8 years of operation; (3) grants for consultation and education services to individuals and entities involved with mental health services; (4) conversion grants to existing centers so that they can meet the standards and requirements for the provision of services under the new law; (5) financial distress grants (no more than three may be awarded to any one center) to centers which have reached the end of their Federal support period and which demonstrate they would have to reduce the quality and number of services; and (6) facilities grants to provide for the acquisition, remodeling, leasing, and construction of facilities.

CURRENT STATUS

Federal funds have assisted in the initiation of 675 CMHC's (590 are actually operating in whole or in part) which, when fully operational, will make services available in areas where 93 million persons reside, 43 percent of the population of the United States.

It is difficult to describe a typical center. In terms of the catchment areas they serve, 58 percent are in urban, 17 percent are in inner city, 17 percent in rural, and 8 percent in suburban areas. They are distributed throughout most of the country: 22 percent are in the Northeast, 25 percent in the Southeast, 21 percent in the Midwest, 10 percent in the Southwest, 13 percent in the Far West, and 5 percent in the Northwest. Fifty-seven percent of the centers are serving designated poverty areas. Organizationally, they vary enormously: from freestanding facilities offering a full array of required services under a central administration to simple associations of preexisting services and facilities. Overall 19 percent are general hospital based, 3 percent are State mental hospital based, 2 percent are private psychiatric hospital based, 64 percent are hospital affiliated, and 12 percent are freestanding mental health centers.

Major differences also exist in staff composition, but some information on overall trends is available. In 1976, the full-time equivalent staff of the CMHC program nationally numbered 48,466, averaged 92 full-time equivalents (FTE's) per center, and accounted for 11.5 percent of the staff in all mental health facilities. Of these, 4.7 percent were psychiatrists, 9.4 percent psychologists, 13.9 percent social workers, 9.5 percent registered nurses, 21.8 percent paraprofessionals, 13.7 percent all other patient care staff, and 26.4 percent administrative and maintenance personnel. In recent years, the average size of center staffs has increased somewhat, in terms of FTE's, with increases mostly in administration, maintenance, and clerical personnel, psychologists, and social workers. While the average number of FTE psychiatrists has diminished, the overall ratio of professional to paraprofessional staff has slightly increased.

In 1975, the centers and their staffs served 1.6 million people, providing nearly 2 million episodes of care, or 29 percent of the total episodes of inpatient and outpatient care provided by mental health facilities. In general, patient care in CMHC's has been largely outpatient care. In 1975, 81 percent of all CMHC patient care episodes were outpatient; inpatient care and partial hospitalization comprised 13 percent and 7 percent of total patient care episodes, respectively.

Of those people admitted to care in 1975, 13 percent had a diagnosis of substance abuse, 10 percent schizophrenia, 13 percent depressive disorders, 5 percent organic brain syndrome or other psychoses, 3 percent mental retardation, 13 percent childhood disorders, 21 percent neuroses and personality disorders, and 22 percent social maladjustment, no mental disorder, deferred diagnosis, or nonspecific condition. The major trend in the diagnostic composition of the centers' clients has been the decreasing percent of those diagnoses with depressive disorders and schizophrenia, counterbalanced by an increase of those classified as socially maladjusted, no mental disorder, deferred diagnosis, or nonspecific disorder.

CMHC 8

Out of 919,000 persons entering the CMHC system of care in 1975, 52 percent were females and 48 percent were males. The largest percentage of total additions was in the 25-44 age group, which accounted for 38.5 percent of all additions. Approximately one-fourth were under 18 years of age; 4 percent were over 65; 19 percent were 18-24; and 15 percent were 45-65 years old. Relative to their numbers in the catchment areas, children are served at roughly one-third the rate and the elderly at less than one-fourth the rate of the 25-44 age group. Almost 83 percent of all additions in 1975 were white, with the remaining 17 percent representing all other races. Over 54 percent of the additions reported weekly family incomes of less than $100.00 among those centers reporting.

In terms of the total cost of services provided by CMHC's, in 1975 the expenditures accounted for $776 million. In 1974 (the latest year for which data are available) the CMHC program represented only 4.2 percent of the $14.5 billion expended for mental health care in the United States. (This can be compared to the expenditures for direct care of the mentally ill in nursing homes or in State, county, and public mental hospitals, which represented 29.3 percent and 22.8 percent, respectively, of the total costs.) Overall two-thirds of the costs of CMHC's were financed by Government sources, with 30 percent from Federal and 29 percent from State monies. An additional 30 percent is accounted for by receipts from services, with 4 percent from patient fees, 8 percent from private third-party carriers, 2 percent from Medicare, and 10 percent from Medicaid.

REVIEW OF EVALUATIVE DATA

An evaluation perspective necessarily involves relating information about program processes and results to the goals of that program. Thus, we examined the evaluative data about the community mental health centers program, grouping our analysis of the findings around seven general goals:

- increasing the range and quantity of public mental health services
- making services equally available and accessible to all
- providing services in relation to existing needs in the community
- decreasing State hospital admissions and residents
- maximizing citizen participation in community programs
- preventing the development of mental disorders
- coordinating mental-health-related services in catchment areas

Two additional areas were also reviewed because of their timeliness and importance, even though formal goals in these areas for the CMHC program were not clearly articulated in CMHC legislation:

- providing services in as efficient a manner as possible
- providing services which reduce suffering and increase personal functioning to the maximum level possible

In all these areas we found both substantial strengths and observable weaknesses.

1. INCREASING THE RANGE AND QUANTITY OF MENTAL HEALTH SERVICES

On the positive side, there appears to be agreement that CMHC's have increased substantially the volume of services to catchment residents, particularly outpatient care and partial hospitalization. NIMH data show CMHC episodes increasing sharply since 1966, while other facilities' episodes appear to be increasing more slowly or leveling off. Studies focusing on specific areas of the country also show that areas receiving CMHC's develop more services more rapidly than areas which do not. The CMHC's have substantially increased the amount of non-inpatient care available in the mental health system (outpatient, partial hospitalization, and consultation and education services), and newer, specialized services are now being added (halfway houses, sheltered workshops, and so on). Thus, the CMHC's have become a major factor in public mental health care.

On the negative side, there is evidence that, after the termination of Federal grants, centers begin to retrench their programs and show signs of compromising the CMHC objectives of providing essential mental health services

CMHC 10

to all catchment area residents regardless of their ability to pay. In many of the centers that have not yet achieved "graduate" status, growth is especially slow in the development of specialized services.

2. MAKING SERVICES EQUALLY AVAILABLE AND ACCESSIBLE TO ALL

The CMHC program aimed at alleviating the "two-class" system of care, in which the well-do-do received primarily private outpatient care and the disadvantaged received custodial State hospitalization. This topic is complex, but will be restricted here to issues involving rich-poor, minority-nonminority, male-female, and urban-rural dimensions.

The majority of CMHC clients (52 percent) could be considered "poor"; their family incomes are less than $100 per week, which is just about at the official poverty level for an urban family of four. This may be partly a result of NIMH's funding more CMHC's in "poverty" areas than in "nonpoverty" areas in the earlier years of the program, but even in nonpoverty areas 48 percent of CMHC clients have family incomes below poverty level.

Male and female utilization rates were almost exactly equal in 1973; young males under 15 have higher rates, but rates for female adults are higher and thus balance the total rates.

While the large majority of CMHC clients are whites (about five-sixths), the utilization rates per 100,000 catchment residents are more nearly equal, with nonwhites (Blacks, Orientals, Native Americans) actually using the CMHC at a 30 percent higher rate (1,300 vs. 1,000 per 100,000 residents). In any case, availability and accessibility of CMHC services to minority races appear to be favorable by this utilization criterion.

In terms of barriers to accessibility, one that is important is the degree to which the community and its other caregivers are aware of the CMHC and the services it offers. It has been found that publicly identifying a CMHC with its catchment area of responsibility resulted in less sociodemographic bias in its clientele, including more nonwhites, welfare recipients, and lowest social class persons than in comparable noncatchmented services. In general, studies have indicated a fair to good awareness by residents and other caregivers as to the availability of CMHC services.

On the negative side, accessibility barriers do exist. For example, a survey of open hours for CMHC outpatient and partial care services indicated only a minority were open evenings when many employed persons would want to use those services. There is relatively thin coverage of rural catchment areas--fewer centers, less manpower, and lower utilization. Recently the relative proportion of poorer areas funded has been decreasing. Finally, there is significant underrepresentation of some minorities in many of the various professional groups working in CMHC's. This may influence both the minorities' willingness to use CMHC services and the appropriateness of the treatment given them.

3. PROVIDING SERVICES IN RESPONSE TO COMMUNITY NEEDS

On the positive side, since poverty is well established as being associated with need for mental health services, the early NIMH thrust toward funding "poverty-area" centers was well directed toward meeting citizens' needs. A sophisticated analysis of all U.S. catchment areas in terms of needs and resources showed that in 1969, catchment areas highest in need also had the highest percentage of "adequate service structures" (31 percent) in terms of service availability and accessibility. Federally funded CMHC services undoubtedly contributed to this situation; in Colorado, for example, Federal funding helped the neediest catchment area (Northwest Denver) to establish a very large service system capable of meeting most of the need assessed.

In terms of the diagnostic population served by CMHC's, there is a strong similarity between the clients seen by CMHC's and public outpatient psychiatric clinics, with the largest groups being neurosis, schizophrenic, and personality disorders. In comparison to State hospitals, however, the clientele is less impaired in terms of fewer instances of alcoholism, schizophrenia, and organic brain syndrome. A Kansas City study compared the clients of a metropolitan CMHC with a private practice clientele. It showed that the CMHC clients were far more diagnostically diverse and were more socially disengaged. Thus, there is evidence that the CMHC program is indeed serving a needy population in the United States.

On the negative side, higher income areas have disproportionately high representation in those catchment areas recently funded for CMHC's. NIMH has long been criticized for failing to see that services were planned and funded in relation to needs; Comptroller General (Government Accounting Office) reports to Congress in 1971 and 1974 both list this deficiency. The former notes the lack of funding for CMHC's in areas of greatest need and the latter refers to programs not addressing specific catchment area needs.

There has also been a declining percentage of severe diagnoses (schizophrenia and depression) in the total program. While this appears to be attributable mainly to patterns in the newer centers, the issues involved are complex and the meaning of these data is not clear. In addition, the data on rates of additions to CMHC's suggest that children under 15 and adults over 45--and especially adults 65 and over--are underserved by CMHC's in the light of a probable need at least comparable to young adults. Rates for the elderly are less than one-fourth those for younger adults, and for children only one-third the adult rate.

4. DECREASING STATE HOSPITALIZATION

A sizable number of studies indicate that CMHC's have had at least some impact upon reducing admissions to State hospitals. Unpublished NIMH data which show lower State hospital utilization from CMHC catchments than from the Nation as a whole are quite compelling because of the likelihood that CMHC catchments would normally generate higher rates because of their relatively less favorable sociodemographic characteristics--greater poverty, more overcrowding, etc. In addition, several longitudinal studies indicate that CMHC's make a positive contribution to lowering State hospital admission rates.

Finally, the data indicate that fewer psychiatric clients of the CMHC's are going to the State hospitals than was true in the past.

On the other hand, it is remarkable that the data reviewed are as mildly positive as they are, considering the importance of this objective to the CMHC program. A recent Comptroller General (Government Accounting Office) report to Congress cites an NIMH contract study to the effect that 175 CMHC's ranked "decreasing state hospital utilization" next to last in a list of 10 CMHC program goals. It does appear from CMHC additions data that the total program is moving away from caring for the most severely mentally disabled, the type most likely to spend time in a State hospital. Furthermore, the data strongly support the inference that CMHC's are not picking up State hospital discharges adequately. The absence of continuity of care for seriously ill people is a critical issue. In many instances State hospital systems seldom work with the CMHC's in providing continuity of care.

A survey of both CMHC's and various public and private agencies in the human service area conducted by one of our panel members clearly underscores the often inadequate and fragmentary services to deinstitutionalized patients. The problems that were noted basically involved the provision of little service, particularly aftercare services, including outreach, housing, and transitional residences. In addition, it was found quite common for patients to "get lost" or "fall between the cracks" and not have access to those services that do exist.

5. INCREASING CITIZEN PARTICIPATION

There has, especially in recent times, been considerable high-level support for citizen participation, with increasing activities headed toward this goal. In Public Law 94-63 Congress set requirements for "representative" governing or advisory bodies; the National Council of Community Mental Health Centers has reorganized its board of directors to include "community directors" from each region on an equal footing with "staff directors"; a non-mental-health provider is now president of that organization; annual evaluation reports which incorporate citizen board and community input, and the responsiveness of the CMHC managers to that input, are now required of all CMHC's. At lower levels, interest in the topic of community participation in CMHC program affairs is also growing.

However, incorporation of citizen input into CMHC programs has been slow in coming. The Comptroller General's report of 1974 observed significant community involvement in only 2 of 12 centers reviewed. NIMH has also noted in 1977 that "boards are not sufficiently representative of the communities they serve."

6. PREVENTING MENTAL DISORDERS

On the positive side, there are studies which document that consultation and education efforts have had positive effects upon the knowledge, attitudes, and, sometimes, behavior of CMHC consultees, including police, other health professionals, and schoolteachers. CMHC consultation has long been directed primarily at schoolteachers, and this focus on children should help maximize any disorder-prevention potential of the consultation process. While evidence of impact on the children is absent from most reports, a number of behavior changes, in social interaction, learning effort, and academic performance, have been noted in a few studies.

Overall, however, this is an area of weakness. Consultation and education activities are extremely low in volume and are declining. In graduate centers facing financial constraint this is the first area to be cut back. Finally, and possibly most problematic, there is a paucity of data supporting the effectiveness of consultation in preventing mental disorders.

7. COORDINATING MENTAL-HEALTH-RELATED SERVICES

The CMHC itself, by definition, is comprehensive (multiservice). Some early studies show intra-CMHC continuity of care. In terms of coordinating with existing catchment area services, P.L. 94-63 set new requirements for CMHC's regarding screening clients being considered for hospitalization, followup care to discharged clients, promoting rape prevention, and coordination with other health and social service agencies and State hospitals. It remains to be seen whether this legislation will have any real impact.

In general, a great deal has been written about the problems in coordination of CMHC services with other community facilities. Most recently the Government Accounting Office completed a study of deinstitutionalization which found that while a number of CMHC's were discussing individual clients' needs with State hospital caregivers, frequently there was insufficient communication which later resulted in an untimely or inappropriate admission to the State hospital. The report noted that CMHC's and State hospitals had developed independently of each other, were accountable to different authorities (State vs. Federal, local, or private organizations), tended to serve different populations, and had different funding contingencies (again State vs. Federal). There was little incentive to collaborate closely; hence, too little joint planning has been done for dischargees from the State hospitals and in-community care for such persons has often been inadequate. In addition, both CMHC's and related agencies reported serious coordination deficiencies in response to the previously described survey by one member of our panel.

8. DELIVERING EFFICIENT SERVICES

On the positive side, CMHC's show a low program cost relative to total care episodes and a declining cost in constant dollars per care episode. Calculations from NIMH data on episodes of care per center and expenditures per center show that in current dollars, the average episode cost $328 in 1971 and rose to $355 in 1975, a 2 percent annual rate of increase. In constant dollars, corrected for inflation, the cost per episode decreased from $328 to $270, about a 5 percent annual decline. This was accomplished through more rapid growth in outpatient episodes (up 78 percent) and partial care episodes (up 101 percent) than in more costly inpatient episodes (up only 21 percent). Still greater efficiency is likely in the future as partial care continues its rapid expansion and further replaces inpatient stays.

In terms of administrative staffing costs, the CMHC program compares quite favorably with all other mental health facilities in administrative or maintenance staff; only 26 percent are administrative or maintenance staff, in comparison to an average of 32 percent for all other facilities.

Cost-finding techniques are now being employed quite frequently in CMHC's and other facilities, and it should not be too long before costs per unit of service for inpatient, outpatient, and partial care are available on a large scale. Some early figures for Colorado CMHC's and clinics (the latter provide only outpatient care) show that a 30-45-minute outpatient visit costs $26, a 4-hour partial care day just slightly more, and an inpatient day about $120. These figures are generally below the prevailing rates for similar services in the private sector in Colorado. This is to be expected, however, since CMHC's also utilize lower-paid nonprofessionals in their service delivery programs.

On the negative side, there is information to suggest unduly low percentages of clinical staff time spent on face-to-face client or consultee contact in some CMHC's. The Nader group's report on CMHC's criticized these programs for devoting nearly half of all working hours to administration, staff meetings, consultation, teaching, and other non-patient-care activities. An analysis of direct and indirect service hours in a large western CMHC showed that only 35 percent of all staff time went into client or consultee contact. Administrators have defended this percentage as reasonable considering vacations, necessary staff meetings, staff education, supervision, administration, recordkeeping, and substantial time lost to "no-shows."

9. REDUCING SUFFERING AND INCREASING PEOPLE'S ABILITY TO FUNCTION

An increasing number of treatment outcome studies on CMHC populations specifically are being conducted and published. Most studies show evidence of probable positive impact upon client functioning, and a few show improvement in clients to functional levels approaching those of the normal community. However, despite the encouraging trends in outcome studies, most CMHC's are quite far from being able to regularly study and document their programs' effectiveness. This is partly because the task is difficult, but it is also partly because CMHC's, not unlike other mental health facilities, have devoted few resources to evaluation.

STRENGTHS AND WEAKNESSES OF THE PROGRAM--AN ANECDOTAL VIEW

Since our panel reflects direct experience with community mental health centers in at least a half dozen areas of the country, we shared our own anecdotal experiences with one another. We found ourselves a microcosm of the evaluative data. Our comparison of experiences produced examples of everything from superb innovation to poor implementation. <u>We all reported many services in danger of disappearing</u>. Nearly all of us could identify some things being done well for substantial numbers of people, others being done poorly or not at all in the same catchment areas, and some others being done well but for very few of those who need the service in the particular area.

CMCH 15

One panel member, for example, reported excellent but small-scale services for chronic patients, including help in socialization and in vocational referrals and some good halfway house residential programs. "Beyond these examples, there is warehousing" in her city. Services for the elderly were described as particularly weak.

Another reported that 24-hour emergency service is good in his city but only one of three centers has weekend services. That center is in financial jeopardy. He said the centers do seem to have impacted on utilization of inpatient beds but "a better job is being done on the way in as opposed to the way out."

A third stressed that his program has become a center for community activities generally and described excellent programs in the schools and for the foster care of the elderly. He said, however, that many people from outside the catchment seek care from his center because of the inadequacy of services elsewhere in the metropolitan area.

Still another reported special efforts for minorities, with stress on Asians and Native Americans as well as Blacks. He pointed with pride to an affiliated adolescent counseling program, a contract with the local school system, a grant for a neighborhood health station in the catchment area, heavy inservice training, promotional opportunities for minorities, and intensive management efforts at utilization review and peer review. He also indicated, though, that fiscal problems have driven the consultation and education staff from seven down to one half-time person.

All members of the panel emphasized repeatedly the need to indicate that all levels of government must bear their fair share of responsibility for the weaknesses in the program, as well as the share of responsibility that is fairly attributable to the centers themselves.

AN ATTEMPT AT DEFINITION--IN THE PRESENT AND FOR THE FUTURE

We believe the CMHC, as an entity, partakes far more of the field of health than of any broader human service or social service difinition. This is its basic identity. This should be the basic disciplinary background and orientation of its staff, even though they must necessarily be both diverse and broad in their outlook, values, and professional approach. Thus, we define the community mental health center as a health care delivery approach with linkages.

This definition is especially important when the issue of future financing is considered. We believe national health insurance, plus continued Federal categorical mental health funding, should be the backbone of future financing, with significant State and local health and mental health involvement and appropriate contributions from such areas as Title XX of the Social Security Act also fully included.

We sought, further, to define the constituent words in the phrase "Comprehensive Community Mental Health Center."

"Comprehensive" connotes an entity which offers multiple services. These are services to multiple populations. For each of those populations, the services will involve various techniques to deal with the range of needs and problems that present themselves. Further, "comprehensive" must be seen as encompassing major variations in services and techniques from community to community depending upon local needs, and variations in the delivery system.

"Community" connotes service in a defined geographical area. We strongly support maintenance of the current catchment area concept as the definitional focal point for the organization and governance of service. We think the usage of any larger defined area with regard to delivering services would do great damage with regard to accessibility and accountability. At the same time we also support--with equal vehemence--the sharing of low-volume, specialized services across catchment area lines.

"Community" also connotes connection--to other services and to the people served. Similarly, services are not community-based in the fullest sense unless there is citizen participation in their design and implementation, through appropriate governance mechanisms and otherwise.

"Mental health" is defined more than adequately in the preliminary report of the Commission. It is surely more than the absence of mental illness. One of our members has offered a synonym: "behavioral health...a descriptive term for all health problems that are manifested through an individual's behavior." These may be exclusive of physical health or related to it in varying degrees. He says, "Interventions for behavioral health problems may include mental health, drug abuse, alcohol, or developmental disability services. They also include a wide range of related programs such as: social services, services to the aging, child health screening, criminal justice programs and other human services."

"Center" is an entity which may be under one roof or at multiple locations, but wherein the services are all linked internally and all accountable to a board or some other legally appropriate governance structure (although some of the services may be delivered on a contractual basis by another legal entity).

At the risk of repeating, there are three key definitional points which we wish to reiterate before proceeding, even though we have expressed them previously:

--Citizen input is an important element in defining what the community mental health center or service is going to do, and particularly as a primary mechanism for accountability.

--Area-based governance is a key definitional element.

--There is more to community mental health services than just community mental health centers.

COMMUNITY MENTAL HEALTH CENTERS AND COMMUNITY MENTAL HEALTH SERVICES--THE FUTURE

1. "Graduate" Centers. Perhaps the most overriding immediate issue is the future of community mental health centers now in existence but approaching or having achieved "graduate" status, the end of categorical Federal support under the CMHC program.

From the outset of the Federal community mental health centers program, it was anticipated that centers would derive their financial support from a variety of sources. Both public and private funds were seen as becoming available to the centers. Public funds were later expected to include not only the Federal grants themselves but also revenues to be derived from other Federal programs (such as Medicare, Medicaid, and grant programs for housing and community development; and it was expected also that public support for centers would be derived from State and local tax dollars that would be made available to the centers by governmental agencies in their own States and communities.

Private funds, in like manner, were also expected to come from several sources. It was expected that patient fees would become an increasingly important source of center revenue, and it was expected also that the many different types of health insurance programs would provide coverage for services rendered by the centers.

Unfortunately, many centers have not received the infusions of State and local funds originally contemplated. Moreover, they have experienced limited capacity to qualify for third-party reimbursement.

We are wary of any guarantee which would throw into imbalance the healthy theory that there must be broad-based support of centers--from State, local, patient-based, philanthropic, and other sources. At the same time, the situation is critical. We would not support any blanket, last-dollar Federal categorical funding guarantee. But action is needed. Centers can be expected to engage in a belt-tightening process, but ongoing help is still required. We therefore recommend:

> Option 1: A mechanism for ongoing funding of graduate centers that is broader than the current "distress grant" concept. This mechanism should evaluate programs based upon merit and need. It should insist on the capture of reimbursement wherever available. Especially as national health insurance develops, it should tend to offer support to services and activities where there is a strong Federal interest and/or where reimbursement is least likely: prevention, services to some of the special populations, planning, evaluation.
>
> A limitation on overall grant support would be necessary, involving perhaps both a percentage of a center's current budget and absolute ceiling. For example, if the absolute ceiling chosen were $300,000, this would average a bit under 20 percent of current CMHC operating budgets. At some time in the future (approximately 1990, given the

current rate of new starts) when all of a total of, say, 800 centers are in graduate status, this would involve a maximum, ceiling expenditure of $240 million, a figure well within current fiscal constraints.

We have considered many possible explanations as to why the community mental health centers have failed to develop adequate sources of revenue to replace their Federal grants. Especially important is the low priority State government (and particularly State legislatures) give mental health in the competition for new and additional State expenditures. While State hospitals have reduced their patient populations substantially in recent years, there has not been an automatic diversion of State-appropriated dollars from the State hospitals to the community mental health centers. In part this is because some of the apparent savings have been offset by increases in the absolute level of expenditures due to inflation; and in part, as many observers have noted also, well established State government bureaucracies have often been successful in their efforts to have the savings applied to the development of new programs or enriched staffing patterns within the State hospitals themselves. We therefore also recommend:

> Option 2: A special study of incentives and requirements that could be inserted into Federal legislation to leverage increased State and local contributions to CMHC budgets and community mental health services generally. This should not precede action on option 1.
>
> We are aware of all the complexities in conditioning Federal reimbursement in any area on any type of State compliance. Nonetheless, Medicare and Medicaid are at the heart of preserving the current unconscionable level of State hospital budgets. It is important, therefore, to determine whether any mechanism can be developed to condition Medicare and Medicaid reimbursement for State institutional care on the shifting of an appropriate portion of State resources into community mental health services.

2. <u>New Centers</u>. Below, we shall propose a new Federal initiative in the area of community mental health services. We believe the Federal commitment should be to a broad concept of service: to networks, linkages, and coordination. This, indeed, is the full meaning, as we take it, of the congressional intent of the original CMHC legislation in 1963. Nonetheless, we think new centers will also be needed. For that to occur, a careful examination of NIMH definitions of need is essential. The priority should obviously be unserved and underserved areas. Rural and poverty areas need to be examined with special care. We therefore recommend:

> Option 3: NIMH should be directed immediately to re-examine all definitions of need in specific relation to catchment area realities around the country.
>
> Option 4: New centers should be funded in areas of high need and in certain areas of moderate need, depending upon the individual circumstances.

CMHC 19

3. **The "5" vs. the "12" Services**. We believe that all 12 services mandated by the 1975 legislation are important. We have previously indicated our deep concern regarding the failure of the CMHC's to offer services to the chronically ill and the need for greater efforts to prevent inappropriate institutionalization. We have also expressed a critical concern regarding services to the special populations added by the 1975 legislation. Nonetheless, flexibility is needed. We believe a presumption is appropriate that all 12 services should be provided, but a mechanism is needed to relieve individual centers of the need to provide all 12 services where that is unnecessary. With adequate mental health representation, we see the developing network of Health Systems Agencies (HSA's) under P.L. 93-641 as the key in determining whether a particular CMHC can receive a "waiver" as to the required services.

> Option 5: The planning requirements of Public Laws 93-641 and 94-63 need to be meshed to assure integration of mental health planning with overall health planning. (We understand the Planning and Review Panel is considering this matter in detail.) Specifically, CMHC's and community mental health interests generally must be represented on HSA's (and CMHC board members must be viewed as other than providers for these purposes).

> Option 6: Sufficient funds should be made available to permit whatever expansions of existing CMHC's are necessary to reach locally determined, plan-approved levels of service within the 12-service rubric.

4. **Sharing of Services Between Catchment Areas**. As we have indicated, many services cannot practicably be delivered by each CMHC. Such specialized activities as programs for autistic children, court-related diagnostic services, and specialized community and learning disabled residences and sheltered workshops are sometimes of too low a volume and too complex a specialty to be viable for every catchment area. We note differing policy on this matter among the HEW regions currently. We therefore recommend:

> Option 7: HEW-NIMH leadership should be undertaken immediately to help identify needs and stimulate cross-catchment-area planning for services that would best be provided on a shared basis. A waiver mechanism should be developed for catchment areas that take the initiative in this regard.

5. **A New Community Mental Health Services Initiative**. Earlier we have stated our view that a new Federal initiative in the area of community mental health services is needed. We have sought to allay the concerns of many who will read this report by indicating our firm support for the CMHC program and for its place as an expanded participant in a broader initiative.

Perhaps the most important observation impelling us to recommend an added initiative is that compliance with full CMHC status may be a barrier to seeking CMHC-related funds for groups in some unserved localities. There needs to

CMHC 20

be a way of getting necessary community mental health services into underserved and unserved areas without local groups having to immediately take on the formidable responsibility of providing the full range of comprehensive and mandated service requirements. In addition, some of the specialized populations recognized in the 1975 legislation are not receiving services commensurate with their needs. Moreover, there is evidence to indicate that such special populations receive better service when there is categorical funding for specific programs focusing on their needs. Finally, as we have said, we think CMHC's themselves are now an established and visible enough delivery system that we can afford an approach of supplementation and enrichment without undermining the basic concept.

One of the options being advanced by some is a system of formula grants to States and/or localities for community mental health services. While some of us would view this with interest if it were adequately tied to citizen participation in planning and implementation, it is an unworkable approach unless sufficient funds are provided to assure assistance of meaningful scale to all participating jurisdictions. In addition, without strong Federal oversight, it can be a means of dissipating scarce resources with very little assured return.

Hence, we chose to pursue a project grant approach. We would surely not be averse to appropriate State participation in such a new program, but we also want to assure that we build upon current strengths and on the current infrastructure. We therefore recommend:

> Option 8: A Community Mental Health Initiatives Program should be proposed to Congress. It would make project grants available for the support of community mental health services to be delivered on a catchment-area basis by public or private nonprofit agencies, with provision for cross-catchment programs for low volume, highly specialized services.
>
> Services eligible for funding would include the 12 areas covered by the 1975 legislation. Project grants may cover 1 or more of the 12 service areas, and grantees need not be involved in delivering services other than those they propose to provide. Priority would be given to services targeted for underserved populations, especially children and youth and the elderly, services for previously institutionalized populations, services for patients at risk of institutionalization, and services, especially those of a clearly established preventive nature, which are unlikely to receive third-party reimbursement.
>
> An applicant entity may or may not be one which meets catchment area governance criteria as defined in P.L. 94-63. But with regard to any catchment area, priority will be given to applications submitted by entities that do meet those criteria. An applicant entity that does not meet the criteria with respect to catchment area

residents serving on its governing board must develop an advisory board from the catchment area (or catchment areas in the case of services cutting across area lines). This would be true of public agencies as well as nonprofit agencies, but the latter must also demonstrate that they have a majority of consumers on their boards.

To prevent fragmentation of services, the process of review and approval for these new initiative proposals would include considerations at the local, State, and Federal levels. At the local level, the HSA would have the responsibility to review and approve the application. This review at the local level would include an assessment of the need for the proposal and an assessment of the consistency between the proposed services and other existing and proposed services in the catchment area(s). (N.B.: This requirement is included on the assumption that the necessary statutory change will be made to require mental health representation on all HSA governing boards and adequate mental health personnel on all HSA staffs.)

Where a CMHC or new initiative service exists in the relevant catchment area, the HSA would request comment from the CMHC or service (if the applicant is not the CMHC or new initiative itself) on how the new service(s) would fit in with the system of care already in place, and the applicant entity would have to demonstrate willingness and capacity to enter into a cooperative written agreement with the CMHC or new initiative service with respect to coordination of services so as to ensure continuity of care for all patients and establish a system for regular interaction between the agency and the CMHC.

Where no CMHC or new initiative service exists in the relevant catchment area, the HSA would seek other appropriate community and local governmental comment. Again, the applicant entity would have to demonstrate willingness and capacity to enter into appropriate coordination agreements.

At the State level, review and approval authority would be vested in the State Health Coordinating Council (SHCC), but it is recommended that the SHCC delegate this authority to the State mental health authority, just as it is recommended that the SHCC delegate to the State mental health authority the responsibility for the development of the mental health portion of the State comprehensive health plan. Each application for funding under the terms of the new initiative proposal must be consistent with that State plan. Federal review and approval authority is to be vested in NIMH.

It is recommended that funding be made available to the new initiative services for a period of 5 years, and it is further recommended that the level of such funding be 80 percent in the first year, 70 percent in the second year, 60 percent in the third year, 50 percent in the fourth year, and 40 percent in the fifth year. After the fifth year, the programs funded under the new initiative proposal would be eligible for ongoing Federal support according to the same formula as is applicable to programs funded as community mental health centers.

Once established with funding under the new initiative proposal, programs may apply for additional funding for the support of other services from the list of 12 (as set forth in P.L. 94-63); and, as a further effort to promote the delivery of comprehensive and coordinated mental health services within each catchment area, programs that receive support under the new initiative proposal would be encouraged to develop additional mental health services that are consistent with catchment area needs and availability of non-Federal resources with which to match and supplement the Federal grants.

It is estimated that the average cost of each new grant made under the new initiative proposal will be $250,000 in the first year, and it is proposed that initial legislation provide authorization for 200 new grants per year for a period of 3 years. This will require a Federal investment of $50 million per year in each of the 3 years, plus the costs of continuation grants. The program should be evaluated at the end of the first 3 years to determine its appropriate scale thereafter.

In some ways, the program could be viewed as a broader reenactment of the former Part F program for children, but less narrow in focus (and concomitantly larger in size). The program could also be viewed as a "mini-center" approach, so that entities unable to cope with the barriers associated with the CMHC program in having to provide inpatient care and 24-hour emergency service could nonetheless apply for funds. Nevertheless, it is expected that this new initiative would become the catalyst for such communities to develop comprehensive and coordinated systems of care.

Option 9: As a related matter, NIMH, the National Institute of Alcohol Abuse and Alcoholism, and the National Institute of Drug Abuse should be directed to develop far greater coordination and cooperation in planning and funding of efforts in the area of substance abuse. Such an effort could well be associated in the future with the initiative we suggest above.

Option 10: All relevant plans at the State and HSA levels should be required to certify proactive measures taken to develop new community mental health services for underserved areas. This is contemplated by P.L. 93-641, but needs to be implemented in a way which is clearly articulated with P.L. 94-63.

Option 11: As we did in our preliminary report, we again wish to indicate our strong support for early steps to make Federal resources available for development of community living facilities for people who have been or otherwise would be institutionalized. Money is needed for front-end funding and for operating the facilities. This issue should be considered in relation to equally pressing needs for similar residential efforts in such human service areas as child welfare, the elderly, mental retardation, and juvenile justice. An interagency, interdisciplinary planning effort should be a matter of the highest priority.

6. <u>Manpower and Staffing Issues</u>. We recognize that there is a separate panel operating on this subject, but there are some matters of special interest to us. We are concerned that there does not appear to be a momentum of positive interest in community mental health work among any of the relevant disciplines in the CMHC's. This has been especially notable in the case of psychiatry, where there has been a striking decline in the number of psychiatrists working in CMHC's, directing CMHC's, and training there. Of special concern is the continued disengagement of psychiatric training programs in utilizing CMHC settings for training. This suggests that future psychiatrists will have even less interest in this area since they would lack exposure to community-based mental health programs. We therefore recommend that:

Option 12: NIMH should develop manpower training support programs which encourage emphasis in all relevant professional schools on community mental health services as a career option, with particular emphasis on support for onsite training experiences in community mental health settings.

Despite the commonly held assumption that minority mental health professionals have increased in substantial number, the data available indicate significant underrepresentation of specific minorities in the various professional disciplines working in CMHC's as compared to the general population. When contrasted to minority populations served by community mental health centers, the discrepancies become glaring. We therefore recommend:

Option 13: NIMH should move immediately to utilize currently available funds in ways that will have maximum impact in the direction of training more minority group people to undertake mental health careers. We note with particular enthusiasm the position taken by the Federal Government in the <u>Bakke</u> case.

Unplanned changes in the staffing patterns of the CMHC's indicate a need for a significant reexamination of the appropriate mix of professionals and paraprofessionals in the CMHC's and for clarification of their roles. We therefore recommend:

> Option 14: NIMH should undertake a study of the appropriate manpower mix for CMHC's and of their relative roles in service delivery.

Importantly, too many community mental health centers have failed to address the issue of self-renewal and have not established meaningful programs of continuing education and staff development for all patient care staff. Moreover, both professional training programs and mental health centers have insufficiently addressed the development of staff sensitive to the special needs and cultural differences of the various minority populations seeking needed mental health services. We therefore recommend:

> Option 15: "Staff colleges" for selected CMHC staff should be established and conducted on a regional basis, probably in university-related clinical settings, to assure appropriateness of response to minority patient populations and to establish a concerted thrust for the overall continuing education of CMHC staff.

7. Governance of CMHC's and Community Participation. One of the basic objectives of the CMHC program is to assure responsiveness of services to the needs of the community. As was noted above in our evaluation of this goal, the incorporation of citizen input has not been evolving as quickly as it should. In order to truly reach that goal of having representative citizens from the community actively involved in the governance of CMHC's, a meaningful community board program should be established. This program would provide board members with the tools and knowledge to perform effectively and have the desired impact on CMHC systems. Citizen boards have been treated too casually in the past. We therefore recommend:

> Option 16: NIMH should develop a broad program of training for citizen boards. Board members from around the country should participate in designing the training package, and it should be carried out regionally.

> Option 17: There should be a clearinghouse of information about the role and functioning of citizen boards, and a directory of citizen boards should be prepared, widely circulated, and regularly updated.

8. Planning, Coordination and Relationship to Other Health and Human Services. Our own experience, many studies, and a survey conducted by one of our members for our use all indicate the same thing: CMHC's are inadequately "connected" in a number of directions. They are not intermeshed with State hospital systems. They have inadequate relations in terms of both planning and referral to other human services. This program will not be alleviated overnight and much of what needs to be done is a matter for State and local initiative. Nonetheless, here are some steps we can recommend:

Option 18: Reconciliation of the planning processes contemplated by P.L. 93-641 and P.L. 94-63 is vital. This must be done in a way that makes sense for the CMHC's. Initial planning for mental health services should be done at the catchment area/CMHC level. The CMHC's should then be involved, through direct representation and otherwise, in planning at the HSA level. HSA's should be funded to have professional staff in the mental health area. There is an opportunity here from the CMHC point of view--to ensure that mental health services are properly fitted into the overall picture--but there is also a need to ensure adequate CMHC participation in the process.

Option 19: National initiative is needed through the various arms of HEW to integrate planning and develop consistent data bases and needs assessment processes. As noted in Option 3, NIMH should take steps of its own to develop more knowledge about relative catchment area needs so that we can have a national picture concerning underserved geographical areas and underserved populations, and can thereby set priorities more effectively.

9. Data Reporting and Evaluation. This is a critically important area. Prior to passage of P.L. 94-63, systematic data collection and program evaluation were not seen by NIMH or CMHC's themselves as essential or even important tasks for each CMHC. However, the increasing demand for greater accountability of Federal programs in general and the CMHC's in particular, and the growing need for data to be utilized in the planning process at all levels has brought about the enormous increase in data collecting and reporting requirements and evaluation activities specified in P.L. 94-63.

While the eventual establishment of a comprehensive data collection and evaluation system is a laudable goal, it can be stated without exaggeration that the majority of CMHC's cannot currently meet all these requirements. This is partly because they lack the necessary resources and partly because, in many cases, the requisite data and technology are not available. Moreover, scarce resources in this area are dissipated by attempting to meet the often unnecessary, duplicative, and conflicting data reporting requirements of various agencies within the Federal Government. We therefore recommend:

Option 20: The Office of Management and Budget should be directed to pursue a major effort to obtain uniformity of data categories and collection instruments. Constructive efforts have been made in the past, especially by the Division of Biometry at NIMH, but without sufficient success. Even with full attention, this effort will be complex and time-consuming, but it is important.

Option 21: We support proposals for a direct grant supplement of up to 2 percent of total program operating cost for evaluation.

Option 22: While all CMHC's must report certain basic data, it would be well to consider selecting currently a few of the CMHC's to receive as much as a 10 percent funding override and serve as "evaluation centers" in order that indepth studies of community needs, patient outcome, effectiveness of consultation and prevention activities, and similar high-cost evaluation work can be undertaken.

Option 23: If evaluation capacity is truly to improve, it would be well for NIMH to receive as much as $2 million annually over and above ongoing evaluation funding for purposes of "evaluation technology development," so that development of better, less costly, or currently unavailable evaluation techniques can occur more quickly for use at the CMHC, regional, State, and national levels.

10. Financing. We have already dealt with most of the issues associated with financing in other contexts above, especially in discussing the "graduate" centers problem at the very outset, and also in suggesting a new, supplementary community mental health services initiative. Nonetheless, we would be remiss if we did not conclude with a final recommendation:

Option 24: Those services of CMHC's which can legitimately be denominated health-related should be included under Medicare and Medicaid and, ultimately, national health insurance. Planning for such inclusion should be carefully dovetailed with planning for the expansion and elaboration of Title XX of the Social Security Act and for any new community mental health services initiative, so that all services in which there is a Federal interest can receive funding from an appropriate source.

ACKNOWLEDGMENTS

The Task Panel on Assessment of Community Mental Health Centers wishes to acknowledge the invaluable assistance of Harold Alan Pincus, M.D., Staff Liaison to the Panel.

The Panel deeply appreciates also the assistance of: Steve Epstein, Washington, D.C.; Julia Hysom, Washington, D.C.; Raymond Glasscote, Joint Information Service, American Psychiatric Association, Washington, D.C.; Beryce MacLennon, Ph.D., Government Accounting Office, Washington, D.C.; Harry Schnibbe, National Association of State Mental Health Program Directors, Washington, D.C.; John Wolfe, Ph.D., National Council of Community Mental Health Centers, Washington, D.C.; Steven Sharfstein, M.D., Harold Goldstein, Ph.D., Samuel Buker, Ph.D., and other staff of the Division of Mental Health Service Programs, National Institute of Mental Health; Rosalyn Bass, Carl Taube and other staff of the Division of Biometry and Epidemiology, National Institute of Mental Health, Rockville, Maryland; and The Mental Health Association, Arlington, Virginia.

In addition we thank the various professional groups and numerous private citizens whose interest, input and assistance was invaluable in the preparation of this report.

Report of the Task Panel

on

ACCESS AND BARRIERS
TO CARE

"Mental illness is still not
acceptable in our society.
It is not acceptable because
we keep turning our back to
the facts. We buy the myths.
We forget we are talking
about each other."
                    Rosalynn Carter

Submitted to

THE PRESIDENT'S COMMISSION ON MENTAL HEALTH

February 15, 1978

Task Panel: Access and Barriers To Care

MEMBERS

Bess Myerson, Coordinator
Syndicated Columnist and Consumer
 Affairs Consultant
New York, New York

Carolyn Attneave, Ph.D.
Professor of Psychology, Psychiatry
 and Behavioral Sciences
University of Washington
Seattle, Washington

Juan Chavira
Assistant Professor of Sociology
Department of Behavioral Sciences
Pan American University
Edinburg, Texas

John Gregory Clancy, S.T.D., S.T.M.
Vice President for Planning and
 Development
Fashion Institute of Technology
New York, New York

Chester Jones, M.P.A.
Director of Albert Einstein CMHC
Summerville Avenue and Old York Road
Philadelphia, Pennsylvania

Kelsey Kenfield
San Francisco, California

Joseph T. English, M.D.
Executive Coordinator, Service
 Delivery Task Panels
Director, Department of Psychiatry
St. Vincent Hospital and Medical
 Center
New York, New York

Annette Maxey, A.C.S.W.
Superintendent
Georgia Regional Hospital at Atlanta
Decatur, Georgia

Eric Plaut, M.D.
Commissioner
Department of Mental Health
Hartford, Connecticut

William Pollak, Ph.D.
Associate Professor
School of Social Service
 Administration
University of Chicago
Chicago, Illinois

Sanford Tom, M.D.
Director
North East Mental Health Center
San Francisco, California

Harold Visotsky, M.D.
Professor and Chairman
Department of Psychiatry
Northwestern University Medical
 School
Chicago, Illinois

A&B 2

EXECUTIVE SUMMARY

This task panel identified stigma as a primary barrier in every phase of the provision of mental health services in this country. The members unanimously concluded that only through the systematic elimination of stigma will the United States be able to give its citizens adequate and appropriate care.

The panel raised the following questions:

1. What is stigma?
2. What does it do that is so corrosive?
3. Where does it come from?
4. How do we get rid of it?

The panel identified stigmatizers:

1. The media
2. Professionals
3. Insurance companies
4. Persons who have suffered from mental illness
5. Organized religion
6. Personnel offices and employment agencies
7. Schools and educators
8. Courts and the legal system

SPECIFIC ACTIONS

A. <u>Federal Government Action in Education and Training</u>

    1. Training of mental health service providers.

    a) Phase out the emphasis on dehumanizing lables in professional education and complement it with training to evaluate coping skills as well as behaviorally oriented problem descriptions. Use of functional levels to determine need for services.

    b) Encourage the inclusion of minority personnel in all professions without requiring that they lose their unique styles and perceptions. Deploy these dual experts as consultants to primary care providers as well as in service to their own populations.

    c) Promote two-way communication between professional, paraprofessional, and paramedical personnel.

    d) Guide professional education into a consideration of the multiple causes of anxiety, time-limited nature of stress and crisis reactions, and the multiplicity of methods for reducing it to tolerable levels.

A&B 3

e) Promote training for serving the chronically ill as separate from crisis intervention.

2. Changed emphasis on mental health in general educational institutions.

  a) Support effective educational development of curricular materials at all levels, kindergarten through adult which teach human needs, life stresses, and coping skills.

  b) Develop particular courses or learning experiences for adolescents and adults which will illustrate the time limited nature of crisis stress reactions as well as the more entrenched emotional reactions of chronic illness and the problems of the neurologically impaired.

  c) Infuse a respect for appropriate competency rather than a sole emphasis on control or extrusion of emotional disturbance in school settings.

B. <u>Federal Action in Service Delivery</u>

The Department of Health, Education, and Welfare to review all federally operated, funded, and regulated service delivery programs to assure that they

  a) Promote the provision of a full spectrum of services so that alternatives to hospitalization may be utilized when appropriate.

  b) Promote the development of rehabilitation programs in the delivery of services.

  c) Promote communication between professional and paraprofessional to reduce the professional bias against minorities.

  d) Foster labeling of facilities that is appropriate to local circumstances.

C. <u>Special Federal Initiatives</u>

  1. The Secretary of Health, Education, and Welfare to explore ways to assist the development of expatient groups and foster their involvement with service delivery systems.

  2. The Secretary of Health, Education, and Welfare to promptly initiate discussions with the American

A&B 4

Psychiatric Association in cooperation with major third-party payers to assure the inclusion of a Level of Function Track in the Diagnostic and Statistical Manual III.

3. Establish a fellowship for writers and editors to improve the quality of writing about mental health.

4. The Attorney General to convene a conference of experts to study ways to clarify the current legal ambiguity regarding the insanity defense.

The Committee of One Thousand

A Committee of One Thousand prominent Americans dedicated to altering the current stigma of mental illness could, over a period of years, have a major impact. The Committee of One Thousand should be composed of members who are public figures and who can make the issue of mental illness one that they are comfortable with. The committee should:

1) Find ways to educate media on the range of mental illness and the difference between criminality and violence, and mental illness.

2) Encourage the defining of a spectrum of those subject to stress, enabling persons to identify themselves with others with similar experiences, allowing freer access to mental health service and making access acceptable without as much negative stigmatization.

3) Promote and encourage media presentations focused on the strengths of families and other support mechanisms.

4) Promote and encourage media presentations that identify the fact that problems associated with mental illness affect families, and indicate the mechanisms for recognizing and treating the problems which utilize the inherent strengths of the family system.

5) Undertake a professional poll to determine the prevasiveness of stigma associated with mental illness.

6) Develop strategies for removing the label of "expatient" from media adjectives.

7) Support special awards for positive programing in prime TV. Endorse programs like "Mr. Rogers," "Maude," and "Family" when they present accurate information on dealing with stress, providing support through family systems and educating the public about the facts of mental illness.

8) Encourage the development of a media information center which has responsibility for prompt response designed to meet media needs.

9) Develop a media handbook explaining mental illness, drawing a distinction between violent and nonviolent mental illness.

10) Make parent-teachers associations, school boards, and school administrators aware of stigmatizing effects of curriculum materials.

11) Hold publishers accountable for presenting factual information regarding mental illness.

12) Develop information for school curricula on coping, stress, the causes of mental illness, and recognizing signals.

13) Stimulate and support self-help groups. Promote the development of a patient constituency which could work toward destigmatization, education regarding the difference between mental illness and violence, and interaction with providers to insure that services are for the best interests of patients.

This task panel has identified stigma as a primary barrier in every phase of the provision of mental health services in this country. It is the unanimous conclusion of the members that only through the systematic elimination of stigma will the United States be able to give its citizens adequate and appropriate care. In an attempt to deal with the complexity of stigma, the following questions arise. What is stigma? What does it do that is so corrosive? Where does it come from? How do we get rid of it?

What It Is

Stigma is a series of myths which serve only to quarantine the mentally ill from the rest of society. It brands any person seeking professional services with a mark of shame. Bred from ignorance, fear and guilt, stigma isolates and punishes those in need of help. It creates for consumers a sense of impotency against achieving normalcy, of being acceptable within society. Stigma converts the treatment of mental illness into a horror show, complete with locked wards, bizarre and violent behavior, cruel attendants, massive medication, and shock treatment. Stigma stresses and sensationalizes illness; it disallows cure. Stigma moves mental illness to the backroom. It also unjustly characterizes mental health practitioners, depicting them as all-knowing and God-like, assigning them the sole responsibility of manipulating the consumer and his/her environment. Stigma is society's means of protecting itself against falsely conceived dangers. In doing so, it legitimatizes the ridicule, humiliation, and dehumanization of persons with emotional problems.

WHAT IT DOES

Stigma results in the following:

- <u>Lack of preventative action</u>

    Fear of mental illness and all its implications leads to denial that the problem exists. Few steps are taken by persons at preventative stages when solutions would be minimal in cost and disruption.

- <u>Escalated costs for mental health services</u>

    Because services currently stress illness rather than health, help becomes long-term and thus costly. Services emphasize dependence on expensive support systems and render natural and preexisting resources impotent. Additionally, many of the latter resources fail to give support because of the fear attached to dealing with the person requiring help, and the deep-rooted persuasion that once ill, the patient is never well.

This is not an inclusive list of the effects of stigma. But it does indicate the major areas of this panel's concerns.

WHERE IT COMES FROM

Many of the origins of stigma are universal:

- Fear of the unknowable and incomprehensible aspects of mental illness.

- Fear of what is inside oneself. There seems to be a part of ourselves which is unknown and full of dangerous or unacceptable impulses. We tend to transfer and define the actions of others in the light of our own fears.

- The belief of contagium and of hereditary inevitability.

- The need to establish what is good and right, which in times of complexity is easier by identifying what is not normal.

Some origins of stigma may be unique to our society:

- Our "success" orientation which devalues persons who are unable, for any length of time, to perform and cope adequately.

- Our focus on self-reliance which defines any dependency on others for help as moral failure.

- Our erroneous view that mental illness is untreatable and irreversible.

- Our low tolerance for nonconformity which judges any deviation from our narrow social norms as unacceptable.

A&B 7

- Our propensity for associating violence with mental illness, at a time when we are both very fearful of violence, yet still fascinated by the mirage of the simplistic solutions it affords a threatened society.

- Our lack of dealing with the problems of mental illness has caused an unrealistic denial of the seriousness of some form of such problems.

WHAT TO DO ABOUT IT

Some stigmas attached to physical diseases--tuberculosis, social diseases, etc.--have been eradicated. Those attached to mental retardation have yielded significantly in recent years due to education of the realities formerly concealed behind myths. How to accomplish the same with mental illness? How to remove the fear which paralyzes individual and community response?

The following list of possible means for destigmatization is recommended by the Access and Barriers Task Panel for two reasons: 1) as specific ways of getting rid of stigma as a barrier to services, and 2) as models for other future solutions to the causes of stigma. The objective of all recommendations is to contribute significantly to the removal of stigma as it affects the provision of appropriate mental health services in the country.

Identify the Stigmatizers

Those who contribute to the creation and extension of stigma are often unaware of their role. Persons and groups who have the power to stigmatize should be educated about the effects they have on attitudes towards the mentally ill in this country. Criteria should be established by which performance may be measured to determine who are or are not contributors in the perpetuation of stigma. The following were identified by the panel as principal offenders:

a. The media

Members of the media are the dominant opinion-shaping presence in America. Without examining the premises on which their presentations of mental illness are based, they continue to perpetuate the stereotypes reflecting the social phobias and ignorance which are the inheritance of decades past. Recent societal changes have sensitized the media and the words "Negro" and "Black" are no longer used to modify the word "criminal." The term "former patient" is still used inappropriately as a modifier to explain violent behavior, when in fact most mental patients are not violent, and this is but one instance of the panoply of abusive and inaccurate words and depictions used by the media.

b. Professionals

Professionals are as guilty of assigning unyielding and unrealistic diagnoses to the mentally ill as are nonprofessionals. Professionals consistently see each person seeking help as sick and incompetent. Professionals disallow the capability of most mentally ill persons to help themselves in varying degrees.

c. Insurance Companies

Insurers perpetuate and institutionalize stigma by classifying, quantifying, predicting, and regulating mental illness and appropriate treatment. Benefits are denied on the basis of unexamined myths about the capacities of persons to function normally who have been mentally ill. Quantification and classification of types of illness inhibit any flexible approach to the delivery of services paid through third-party financing which currently relies on the determination of where services are rendered rather than what services are needed.

d. Persons Who Have Suffered Mental Illness

The all pervasive passivity which is a condition of recovery institutionalizes an identity which prohibits positive action after recovery and mandates an acceptance of the "expatient" label. Acceptance of the expatient label confirms the myth. An intense desire for anonymity is generated putting the mentally ill in the closet forever, regardless of whether or not the person has dealt effectively with the illness. Currently there is no reward for coming out of that closet and educating the public about the realities of coping with mental illness. Thus the myths remain alive and well.

e. Organized Religion

Organized religion professes to be committed to healing the wounded human spirit. In reality, it can often create an unnecessary dichotomy between the ideal of human behavior and normal human behavior which can never be sinless. The mentally ill are thus perceived and judged as having failed in their moral duty to overcome their frailties.

f. Personnel Officers and Employment Agencies

Personnel officers and employment agencies ignore lessons learned from adaptations made in corporate hiring and work situations on behalf of other handicapped persons. Persistent efforts of the physically limited and mentally retarded have enabled corporations to utilize the strengths of those individuals. The stigmas associated with mental illness deny those organizations the benefit of the contributions of persons who have dealt with mental illness, even when no disability remains.

g. Schools and Educators

Schools and educators perpetuate the myths of mental illness by their inability to identify and cope with behavior problems of their pupils. By labeling all aberrant behavior as "emotional illness" and by confusing nonconforming behavior and mental illness, they place themselves and their pupils in a cycle of frustration which adds to the aura of hopelessness. Current knowledge and skills in coping with life's problems are not reflected in texts and curricular materials. Preparatory and inservice training in human relationships is unrealistic. While the public at large is disillusioned, the potential for reversing the impact of the stigmatizing process within the schools is great, and must not be overlooked.

h. Courts and Legal System

The courts and legal system contribute to the stigmatization process in several ways. The labels "insane," "incompetent," "alcoholic" that separate individuals from the rest of the human community are applied indiscriminantly. They tend to feed the fires of rejection by trying to excuse from responsibility and/or punishment those judged mentally ill. In protecting individual freedom they are sometimes overcautious and leave the community-at-large vulnerable or unable to cope. And by no means least, their slow accumulation of precedent means that definitions that are legally approved often represent concepts such as "insanity" no longer used by the mental health professions.

RECOMMENDATIONS

The panel recognizes the need for action directed at the removal of stigma as the primary barrier to the delivery of mental health services. Two types of action at the national level are required:

1. Activities which the Federal Government should assume;

2. Activities which could best be assumed by an independent body which would be able to develop movement from sources outside of the Government. The panel therefore recommends the establishment of a Committee of One Thousand which would be charged with sponsoring and carrying out certain activities designed to promote the dissemination of accurate information about mental illness and utilize various pressures to discourage the use of stigmatizing statements.

SPECIFIC ACTIONS

A. <u>Federal Government Action in Education and Training</u>

Removing the stigma of mental illness will require a changed attitude on the part of both professionals and the general public. This will require changes in educational policy from the earliest school years through graduate professional education. The Federal Government plays a major role in setting educational policy.

In order to guide the development of general education regarding the normalcy of emotional conflict and to promote the teaching that the mentally ill are different only in degree and not in kind, the Commission recommends that the President direct:

    1. Training of mental health service providers

       a) Phase out the emphasis on dehumanizing labels in professional education and complement it with training to evaluate coping skills as well as behaviorally oriented problem descriptions. The use of functional levels to determine need for services is a more rational basis for justifying provision of services than diagnostic labels which do not differentiate at this practical level.

       b) Encourage the inclusion of minority personnel in all professions, without requiring that they lose their unique styles and perceptions. Deploy these dual experts as consultants to primary care providers as well as in service to their own populations. This can be done by loosening the tie between numbers of minorities trained and quotas based upon percentages of the population.

c) Promote two-way communication between professional, paraprofessional, and paramedical personnel. The sanction of interdisciplinary work should include an expectation that the conventionally trained can learn from others rather than rigidifying the present hierarchy. Where possible traditional healers from other cultures should participate in this process as peers.

d) Guide professional education into a consideration of the multiple causes of anxiety, and the multiplicity of methods for reducing it to tolerable levels. Include training in the time-limited nature of stress and crisis reactions as opposed to the chronicity of more severely incapacitating mental illnesses.

e) Promote training for serving the chronically ill as separate from crisis intervention. In this connection a strengthening of rehabilitation services should recognize that there are those who recover from severe mental illness with a loss of social and economic function which may require lifelong availability of support services. If care for this population is fostered as a specialty, the indiscriminate generalization of their needs to all who use clinical services could be reduced.

2. Changed emphasis on mental health in general educational institutions

a) Support effective educational development of curricular materials at all levels, kindergarten through adult which teach human needs, life stresses, and coping skills.

b) Develop particular courses or learning experiences for adolescents and adults which will illustrate the time limited nature of crisis stress reactions as well as the more entrenched emotional reactions of chronic illness and the problems of the neurologically impaired. These differentiations are a giant first step in reducing stigma.

c) Infuse a respect for appropriate competency rather than a sole emphasis on control or extrusion of emotional disturbance in school settings.

B. Federal Action in Service Delivery

Nowhere does the stigma of mental illness cause more suffering than when it is manifest in the service delivery system. In the past 30 years the Federal Government has become an increasingly significant developer and underwriter of mental health service delivery. Accordingly, it should now take the initiative in reducing the role of stigma in the service delivery system. The panel urges the Commission to recommend that the President direct:

1. The Department of Health, Education, and Welfare to review all federally operated, funded, and regulated service delivery programs to assure that they:

   a) Promote the provision of a full spectrum of services so that alternatives to hospitalization may be utilized when appropriate, since the hospitalized are the heaviest bearers of stigma.

   b) Promote the development of rehabilitation programs in the delivery of services.

   c) Promote communication betwen professional and paraprofessional to reduce the professional bias against minorities.

   d) Foster labeling of facilities that is appropriate to local circumstances.

At the same time, the Federal Government should take the lead in acknowledging the reality of mental illness. To the extent that local circumstances permit, Federal policy should be to avoid "euphemisms" that attempt to disguise the pervasiveness of mental illness. Such deceptions only serve to further "mystify" and thereby perpetuate stigma.

C. **Special Federal Initiatives**

In addition to the above recommendations for Federal action in the general areas of education and service delivery, specific new Federal initiative is needed in a number of areas.

The utilization of expatients for education of the public, mutual support and help for the acutely ill has proven of great help in reducing stigma in other areas, most notably in alcoholism. The panel urges the Commission to recommend that the President direct:

1. The Secretary of Health, Education, and Welfare to explore ways to assist the development of expatient groups and foster their involvement with service delivery systems.

The existing psychiatric nomenclature is stigmatizing. There needs to be developed a Level of Functioning Scale for the determination of need for services. This Level of Functioning Scale could be used to justify the appropriateness of treatment for third-party reimbursement thus eliminating the need to use the current stigmatizing diagnostic categories as justification for payment. The panel urges the Commission to recommend that the President direct:

> 2. The Secretary of Health, Education, and Welfare to promptly initiate discussions with the American Psychiatric Association in cooperation with major third-party payers to assure the inclusion of a Level of Function Track in the Diagnostic and Statistical Manual III.

The need for more accurate and knowledgeable reporting about mental health is great. The panel urges the Commission to recommend that the President:

> 3. Establish a fellowship for writers and editors to improve the quality of writing about mental health.

The current confusion in the legal system regarding the use of the insanity defense in cases of violent crimes has led to increased stigmatization of the mentally ill as violent and dangerous. The panel urges the Commission to recommend that the President direct:

> 4. The Attorney General to convene a conference of experts to study ways to clarify the current legal ambiguity regarding the insanity defense.

The Committee of One Thousand

Americans are a people who look to their prominent citizens for leadership. Nothing will impact the stigma of mental illness more than a clear demonstration by our leaders that they do not share this distorted view of mental illness. Altering the pervasive stigma of mental illness in our society will require a personal commitment from our Nation's leaders.

A Committee of One Thousand prominent Americans dedicated to altering the current stigma of mental illness could, over a period of years, have a major impact. The Committee of One Thousand should be composed of members who are public figures and who can make the issue of mental illness one that they are comfortable with. Among the tasks such a committee should undertake are to:

> 1) Find ways to educate media on the range of mental illness and the difference between criminality and violence and mental illness.
>
> 2) Encourage the defining of a spectrum of those subject to stress, enabling persons to identify themselves with others with similar experiences, allowing freer access to mental health services and making access acceptable without as much negative stigmatization.

A&B 14

3) Promote and encourage media presentations focused on the strengths of families and other support mechanisms.

4) Promote and encourage media presentations that identify the fact that problems associated with mental illness affect families and indicate the mechanisms for recognizing and treating the problems which utilize the inherent strengths of the family system.

5) Undertake a professional poll to determine the pervasiveness of stigma associated with mental illness.

6) Develop strategies for removing the label of "expatient" from media adjectives.

7) Support special awards for positive programing in prime TV. Endorse programs like "Mr. Rogers," "Maude," and "Family" when they present accurate information on dealing with stress, providing support through family systems and educating the public about the facts of mental illness.

8) Encourage the development of a media information center which has responsibility for prompt response designed to meet media needs.

9) Develop a media handbook explaining mental illness, drawing a distinction between violent and nonviolent mental illness.

10) Make parent-teachers associations, school boards, and school administrators aware of stigmatizing effects of curriculum materials.

11) Hold publishers accountable for presenting factual information regarding mental illness.

12) Develop information for school curricula on coping, stress, the causes of mental illness, and recognizing signals.

13) Stimulate and support self-help groups. Promote the development of a patient constituency which could work toward destigmatization, education regarding the difference between mental illness and violence, and interaction with providers to insure that services are for the best interests of patients.

ACKNOWLEDGMENTS

The Task Panel on Access and Barriers wishes to acknowledge the highly competent and invaluable assistance of F. Dee Goldberg, M.H.A., Staff Liaison to the Panel in the preparation of this report.

We appreciate also the generous assistance of Leslie Kaplan, George Washington University; and the Citibank Corporation, New York, New York.

Report of the Task Panel

on

DEINSTITUTIONALIZATION, REHABILITATION, AND LONG-TERM CARE

Submitted to

THE PRESIDENT'S COMMISSION ON MENTAL HEALTH

February 15, 1978

PCMH/P-78/07

Task Panel: Deinstitutionalization, Rehabilitation, and Long-Term Care

MEMBERS

Stanley R. Platman, M.D.
Task Panel Coordinator
Assistant Secretary for Mental Health
  and Addictions
State of Maryland Department of
  Health and Mental Hygiene
Baltimore, Maryland

William A. Anthony, Ph.D.
Department of Rehabilitation
  Counseling
College of Allied Health Professions
Boston University
Boston, Massachusetts

Father Albert Blatz
St. Peter State Hospital
St. Peter, Minnesota

Irving Blumberg
International Committee Against
  Mental Illness
New York, New York

Don Culwell, M.A.
Texas Employment Commission
San Antonio, Texas

Steven Fields
Executive Director
Progress Foundation
San Francisco, California

Frieda Garcia
Director, Consultation and
  Education Program
Solomon Carter Fuller Mental
  Health Center
Boston, Massachusetts

Marion Javits
New York, New York

Stuart A. Kirk, D.S.W.
Associate Dean, School of Social
  Welfare
University of Wisconsin-Milwaukee
Milwaukee, Wisconsin

Joseph T. English, M.D.
Executive Coordinator
Service Delivery Task Panels
Director, Department of Psychiatry
St. Vincent's Hospital
New York, New York

Joyce Laben, R.N., M.S., J.D.
School of Nursing
Vanderbilt University
Nashville, Tennessee

Norman V. Lourie, M.A., D.H.L.
Executive Deputy Secretary for
  Federal Policy and Programs
Commonwealth of Pennsylvania
Department of Public Welfare
Harrisburg, Pennsylvania

Katherine Lower, Ph.D.
Professor Emeritus
Bryn Mawr College
Rosemont, Pennsylvania

Georgia L. McMurray, M.S.S.
Director, Department of Public
  Affairs
Community Service Society
New York, New York

Alexander S. Rogawski, M.D.
Director, Division of Socail and
  Community Psychiatry
University of Southern California
  School of Medicine
Los Angeles, California

Wymene Valand, R.N.
Raleigh, North Carolina

Arlene D. Warner, L.C.S.W.
State Ombudsman for Nursing Homes
Idaho Office on Aging
Boise, Idaho

Donald H. Williams, M.D.
Connecticut Mental Health Center
New Haven, Connecticut

DEINST 2

Joe Yamamoto, M.D.
Neuropsychiatric Institute
University of California
Los Angeles, California

EXECUTIVE SUMMARY

The Task Panel on Deinstitutionalization, Rehabilitation, and Long-Term Care recommends that:

1. Public or private agencies seeking public funds to serve the chronically mentally disabled be required to demonstrate, as a condition of receiving such funds, implementation of a plan providing for appropriate participation by these individuals and/or their family members as volunteers and employees in both service and policy capacities.

2. Federal agencies remove existing financial disincentives and provide funds for adequate respite and other supportive services when the chronically mentally disabled reside with their families.

3. Just as due process is considered important in the involuntary admission of individuals into mental health services, so must due process be ensured for those individuals who are being considered for placement in the community against their wishes.

4. The Federal Government ensure funds for the training and retraining of professionals and papaprofessionals who wish to care for the chronically mentally disabled and promote a national policy for career advancement in this special field.

5. All institutions receiving Federal mental health training funds be required to offer instruction and practica relevant to the special abilities and needs of the chronically mentally disabled.

6a. States receiving Federal funds for the care of the chronically mentally disabled must, in conjunction with local authorities, designate an agency in each geographic area to assume responsibility for ensuring that every chronically mentally disabled person's needs are adequately met.

6b. Those agencies designated to assume responsibility must provide, or assure the provision of, case management services to ensure that every chronically mentally disabled individual receives quality mental health care and supportive services, irrespective of where the individual resides.

7. The Federal Government ensure the availability of appropriate funds to train persons in case management functions for the chronically mentally disabled.

DEINST 4

8. Agencies that are recipients of Federal funds for housing and program development be required, as a condition of receiving such funds, to assist in the design and implementation of appropriate plans for establishing a range of community residences for the chronically mentally disabled; and that these plans limit funding to State, regional, or local jurisdictions that show clear evidence of nonrestrictive zoning laws for community residences for the chronically mentally disabled.

9. Agencies serving the chronically mentally disabled be required, as a condition for receiving Federal funds, to develop and implement resocialization programs and opportunities for these individuals.

10. The determination of eligibility for vocational rehabilitation services be broadened to include those chronically mentally disabled individuals who are capable of achieving goals related to daily living, avocational skills and permanent sheltered employment.

11. Federal funds, whether for health, mental health, social services, or personal income maintenance needs, be provided on a nondiscriminatory basis for the chronically mentally disabled regardless of age or whether the individual is residing in or being served by a public or private facility.

12. The Federal Government establish, as primary research priorities, the design and execution of epidemiological studies and evaluative projects specifically addressed to the needs of the chronically mentally disabled, and the development of appropriate routes for the dissemination of these and other research results in order that they may have maximum impact on service delivery policies.

DEINST 5

INTRODUCTION

The Task Panel on Deinstitutionalization, Rehabilitation, and Long-Term Care of the President's Commission on Mental Health has reviewed and studied the needs of those individuals who are chronically mentally disabled. Aware that their deliberations must represent only a beginning step in efforts needed to help this special population, the task panel submits this report to the President's Commission on Mental Health. This document represents the consensus resulting from the task panel's study and discussions. Although the recommendations contained herein refer specifically to chronically mentally disabled individuals, the task panel is in agreement that implementation of these recommendations will benefit all who suffer from mental disabilities.

The Preliminary Report of the President's Commission on Mental Health forcefully and rightfully indicates its serious concern with both deinstitutionalization and stigmatization of the mentally ill. In the 1961 report of the Joint Commission on Mental Illness and Health, Action for Mental Health, the attention of the Nation was directed to the history of neglect and rejection suffered by the mentally ill and to the dehumanization inherent in the system of care designed to serve these people. The Preliminary Report of the President's Commission on Mental Health echoes the concern of the Joint Commission by calling for more enlightened and humane mechanisms for the delivery of services to the mentally disabled.

In general, mental disability may be viewed along two continua, duration of disability and severity of disability, as shown in figure 1. The chronically mentally disabled are distinguishable as a subpopulation of the mentally ill according to both of these criteria; they represent extremes along both dimensions. Thus, the chronically mentally disabled, while heterogeneous according to capabilities as well as limitations, are generally characterized by disabilities that continue throughout their lives.

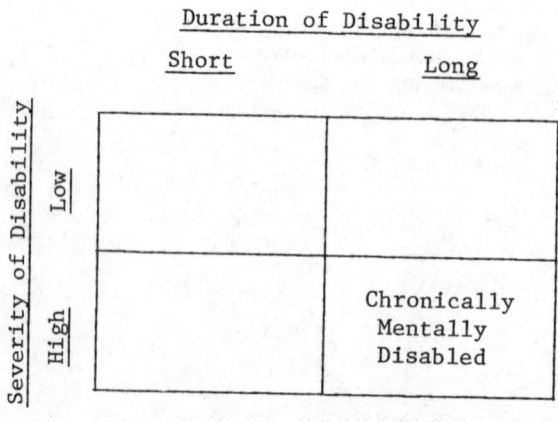

	Duration of Disability	
	Short	Long
Severity of Disability — Low		
Severity of Disability — High		Chronically Mentally Disabled

Figure 1. Delineation of the Chronically Mentally Disabled

The chronically mentally disabled are severely and persistently ill. These are the people who are, have been, or might have been in earlier times, residents of large mental institutions. They constitute that subgroup of the mentally ill for whom societal rejection has been, and is, most acute.

The chronically mentally disabled are a minority within minorities. They are the most stigmatized of the mentally ill. They are politically and economically powerless and rarely speak for themselves. Their stigma is multiplied, since disproportionate numbers among them are people who are also elderly, poor, or members of racial or ethnic minority groups. They are the totally disenfranchised among us.

These individuals must be the concern not only of the mental health professions but also of the total society. Although the problems, needs, and fate of the chronically mentally disabled should occupy us all, this clearly has not been the case. Society has failed to ensure that these individuals are given opportunities to maximize their potential and autonomy. Deinstitutionalization, ostensibly intended to assist the chronically mentally disabled by taking or keeping them out of large, understaffed, public mental hospitals and permitting them to be cared for in the community, has fallen short of its goal. Unfortunately, deinstitutionalization has too often occurred without adequate planning. It has too frequently been propelled by a desire to shift fiscal responsibility from the States to the Federal Government and has proceeded on unverified assumptions that appropriate community care for these people exists.

It is now widely acknowledged that deinstitutionalization has, in fact, often aggravated the problems of the chronically mentally disabled. All too commonly, no one reviews the requirements of disabled persons to assess whether hospitalization or community care is more appropriate to their level of functioning. Similarly, for those disabled persons who are hospitalized, there is often no one to assume the responsibility for assuring that their reentry into the community is timely and desired by them. It is not uncommon for these patients to be released, without adequate aftercare planning, to community settings that are hostile and lack the flexibility to meet their needs. Stigma does not stop when they leave the hospital; it follows them wherever they go. The community rejection that may have contributed to their hospitalization is only increased when these patients are returned to the community without the supportive services they so desperately need.

The crucial issue in serving the chronically mentally disabled is not the location, but rather the quality, of their care. As the Preliminary Report of the President's Commission on Mental Health has stated, "The focus must be people, not places," in serving the mentally ill.

Meeting the needs of the chronically mentally disabled is costly, but ignoring their needs is even more costly. Fiscally, it must be recognized that high quality care, whether provided in an institutional setting or in the community, is difficult to purchase cheaply. Even though some have lauded community care as being cheaper to afford--and have in fact used this as a rationale for emptying State hospitals--they have often failed to account for such hidden expenses as increased welfare costs, social services, and the like. Dollars, however, must not be the sole basis for decision.

DEINST 7

The social costs of withholding adequate care for the chronically mentally disabled are grave, for if these people are not treated humanely, society abandons those who are most in need. Society has much to lose if it fails to assume responsibility for the care of the chronically mentally disabled in all settings, State hospitals as well as community-based facilities.

Only with adequate care for and appreciation of the chronically mentally disabled as people can the spread of stigma for all mentally ill persons be checked; for the stigma that attaches to these people also affects the less severely disabled. Societal neglect of the chronically mentally disabled has only served to reinforce the belief that they are hopeless and to be avoided. There can be no adequate system of mental health care in the Nation if the special services required by this subpopulation of the mentally ill are not provided.

Despite expressions of deep concern for their welfare, the chronically mentally disabled have continued to reside in the margins of society and on the fringes of the human service system. Some believe that it may already be too late to reverse this situation. Others believe that if the President's Commission on Mental Health seriously addresses the needs of the chronically mentally disabled, substantial progress can still be made. But all agree that the President's Commission on Mental Health may well have the last opportunity to change this history of rejection of the chronically mentally disabled. The Task Panel on Deinstitutionalization, Rehabilitation, and Long-Term Care, in the recommendations that follow, indicates some of the steps that need to be taken to begin this process.

RECOMMENDATIONS

A number of recent studies have examined mental health service needs and shortcomings in the service delivery system. Their general conclusions indicate that comprehensive mental health services for the chronically mentally disabled are too often unavailable. Frequently, when such services are available, the agencies responsible for their delivery are not coordinated, so that the service delivery system is fragmented. Accordingly, these studies call for better coordination through improved interorganizational relationships.

The Task Panel on Deinstitutionalization, Rehabilitation, and Long-Term Care supports these studies and acknowledges the need for improvements that would reduce the fragmentation that characterizes mental health service delivery. At the same time, the task panel concludes that these efforts must be supplemented by other kinds of changes. The task panel, which is characterized by a strong consumer orientation, calls for an assessment of the human as well as organizational needs of those individuals who comprise the chronically mentally disabled population.

The recommendations that follow are directed toward improving the plight of the chronically mentally disabled by suggesting changes at three levels--the disabled individual and those who are with him daily; the programs that are designed to assist the disabled individual; and the organizations that administer these programs. The recommendations are presented in a sequence that first emphasizes the need for change at the most basic level--i.e., persons--and progresses through these levels of responsibility in a "bottom-up" approach. Ordering of the individual recommendations is thus determined by the distance of the proposed change from the individual patient, rather than on the basis of intrinsic importance; it does not reflect an assignment of priorities. Ideally, all recommendations should be implemented simultaneously.

In the development and delivery of services for the chronically mentally disabled, planners necessarily rely heavily on the judgments of professionals. Primary consumers of services are rarely asked what their needs are or how they can best be met. Just as the chronically mentally disabled are excluded from the community, they are commonly barred from filling responsible roles in the service delivery system, even when they are able to participate in the decisions that affect them. They are frequently discriminated against by the very system that was designed to help them, for this system tends to focus on their disabilities rather than on their strengths.

Despite their disabilities, disabled individuals often have much to offer. Like others who suffer from unjust exclusion, they need help of an affirmative nature to promote their responsible involvement. Measures must be taken to assure that the chronically mentally disabled and their close family members are not perceived only as passive recipients of professional services but also as persons of worth and as partners in the helping process. Therefore, the task panel recommends that:

1. Public or private agencies seeking public funds to serve the chronically mentally disabled be required to demonstrate, as a condition of receiving such funds, implementation of a plan providing for appropriate participation by these individuals and/or their family members as volunteers and employees in both service and policy capacities.

This recommendation recognizes that the chronically mentally disabled are often able to contribute to society and should be encouraged to do so. However, there are times when their ability to function autonomously is impaired. These are the times when they and their families are most in need of help. Frequently, no help or support is available to them outside of large State hospitals. And even where a few appropriate community services do exist, there may be barriers that hinder receipt of them. It has not uncommonly been necessary for the individual and his or her family to turn inappropriately to institutional care in instances when less restrictive and less intensive services might be more suitable to his level of functioning. This has led to inappropriate placement for the individual involved and to an unnecessary separation of the person from his or her family. For example, under the present system Supplemental Security Income (SSI) benefits are reduced when a disabled person resides at home.

Currently existing disincentives to the disabled individual's living with his or her family should be removed. Additionally, where care in the home is appropriate and beneficial, special services and supports should be made readily available to the family. The task panel, therefore, recommends that:

2. Federal agencies remove existing financial disincentives and provide funds for adequate respite and other supportive services when the chronically mentally disabled reside with their families.

Sometimes, even when services and a supportive family are available, the chronically mentally disabled individual will require hospitalization or other forms of 24-hour care. Over the years, because of rightful concern for the civil liberties of those involuntarily hospitalized, due process procedures have been increasingly utilized. The goal is to ensure that hospitalization is in the individual's or in society's best interests.

In contrast, the same degree of concern is much less often shown for the individual's or society's interests in returning the patient to the community. This is especially true, and particularly unfortunate, for those who have had long hospitalizations and lack a receptive family in the community. Some disabled individuals are released to living and care arrangements that are inadequate to their levels of functioning, even though patients themselves may have objected to such placements. These occurrences are popularly referred to as "dumping" and only further debilitate and stigmatize the chronically mentally disabled. Recognizing that returning the patient to the community may involve complex clinical and legal issues, the task panel recommends that:

DEINST 10

3. Just as due process is considered important in the involuntary admission of individuals into mental health services, so must due process be ensured for those individuals who are being considered for placement in the community against their wishes.

Whether the chronically mentally disabled are living in the community, in a State hospital or in some other 24-hour care facility, they need dedicated and specially trained personnel to care for them. Unfortunately, however, just as the chronically mentally disabled are themselves stigmatized, so, by extension, is stigma attached to those who work with them. This is reflected in low pay, low prestige, and limited career opportunities for both professionals and paraprofessionals who choose to work with the chronically mentally disabled. The situation has been exacerbated for some workers by the very process of deinstitutionalization in which some employees have suffered loss of jobs and other benefits. Thus, employees, as well as mentally disabled individuals, are vulnerable, and this has resulted in low employee morale.

In the mental health field, prestige and remuneration are greatest for those who work with the least disabled. States must be encouraged to protect the rights of public hospital employees by making it possible for them to use their skills in other settings without loss of employee benefits and by offering them supplementary training when needed and wanted. It must be understood that high quality services for the chronically mentally disabled can only be ensured when dedicated employees are recruited, properly trained, and equitably rewarded. Therefore, the task panel recommends that:

4. The Federal Government ensure funds for the training and retraining of professionals and paraprofessionals who wish to care for the chronically mentally disabled and promote a National policy for career advancement in this special field.

In addition, to ensure that all employees, both paraprofessional and professional, who work with the mentally disabled are sensitized to the needs of the chronically mentally disabled, the task panel recommends that:

5. All institutions receiving Federal mental health training funds be required to offer instruction and practica relevant to the special abilities and needs of the chronically mentally disabled.

Because training programs too frequently overlook the distinctive needs of disabled patients with minority cultural backgrounds, special recruitment and training efforts should be targeted toward these groups.

Even when quality care is available in the hospital and in the community, and even when dedicated and qualified staff are employed, proper coordination of the variety of services needed by the chronically mentally disabled is frequently not effected. Many recent documents, including the Government Accounting Office report (<u>Returning the Mentally Disabled to the Community</u>: <u>Government Needs to Do More</u>), the report published by the American Federation

DEINST 11

of State, County, and Municipal Employees (<u>Deinstitutionalization: Out of Their Beds and Into the Streets</u>) and other publications, have underscored the existence of a fragmented service delivery system that lacks a single locus of responsibility for coordinating services for the chronically mentally disabled. The problem goes beyond the need for high quality services; it extends to difficulties of access to care that these individuals experience.

The chronically mentally disabled are made more vulnerable and are singularly disadvantaged by a complex and fragmented service system. They not uncommonly need a range of health, mental health, and social services provided by many different agencies, but the agencies may have conflicting and incompatible goals that make coordinated care difficult. Frequently, too, these agencies prefer to serve the least disabled and may neglect the development of individualized treatment plans for the most disabled. As a consequence, there has too often been an absence of services for some chronically mentally disabled persons and a lack in continuity of care for others. Recognizing this serious problem, the task panel recommends that:

> 6a. States receiving Federal funds for the care of the chronically mentally disabled must, in conjunction with local authorities, designate an agency in each geographic area to assume responsibility for ensuring that every chronically mentally disabled person's needs are adequately met.
>
> 6b. Those agencies designated to assume responsibility must provide, or assure the provision of, case management services to ensure that every chronically mentally disabled individual receives quality mental health care and supportive services, irrespective of where the individual resides.

Case management functions require specially trained staff. Those involved in executing case management responsibilities should possess a variety of interpersonal skills, be familiar with the common difficulties of the chronically mentally disabled, and be knowledgeable about the community's resource systems. The functions to be performed by a case manager include: developing an individualized case management plan; monitoring and adapting it to the changing needs and circumstances of the chronically mentally disabled individual; and remaining in extended contact with the patient and acting as friend and advocate if required and desired by him or her. The case manager must thus serve as the link between the chronically mentally disabled person and the complicated and fragmented service system and must be responsible for ensuring that the patient receives appropriate and high quality services in a timely fashion. This is a complex task requiring special training. The task panel, therefore, recommends that:

> 7. The Federal Government ensure the availability of appropriate funds to train persons in case management functions for the chronically mentally disabled.

DEINST 12

In addition to the psychotherapeutic services needed by the majority of the mentally ill, the chronically mentally disabled require additional special services. Unfortunately, even the presence of a functioning case management capability cannot ensure the availability of adequately developed needed special services. These include provision of a range of living environments, and resocialization, vocational rehabilitation, and appropriate work opportunities.

A range of alternative community residences and residential programs with a rehabilitation component is an essential need for the chronically mentally disabled population. The spectrum of living facilities should allow for independent living for those who are able to achieve this goal. It should also provide for those who permanently require a supportive living environment. Thus, the range of residential facilities must include supportive and supervisory staff who will enhance the individual's ability to move within the continuum of residential facilities to the least restrictive, most appropriate settings.

In developing residential facilities, care must be taken that living places not be concentrated in any one area of a community. "Dumping" has frequently created ghettos by forced segregation of the disabled. The result has benefited neither disabled individuals nor the community in which they reside. Both the rights of the chronically mentally disabled to live in the community and the rights and social integrity of neighborhoods must be respected. The cultural and ethnic fabric of local neighborhoods, which is destroyed by dumping, must be kept intact. The task panel, therefore, recommends that:

>   8. Agencies that are recipients of Federal funds for housing and program development be required, as a condition of receiving such funds, to assist in the design and implementation of appropriate plans for establishing a range of community residences for the chronically mentally disabled; and that these plans limit funding to State, regional, or local jurisdictions that show clear evidence of nonrestrictive zoning laws for community residences for the chronically mentally disabled.

The assistance of the private sector and of local churches and social agencies should be encouraged in the development of these plans.

In addition, in order to maximize social opportunities for, and the social capacities of, the chronically mentally disabled, the task panel recommends that:

>   9. Agencies serving the chronically mentally disabled be required, as a condition for receiving Federal funds, to develop and implement resocialization programs and opportunities for these individuals.

Chronically mentally disabled persons have special needs for vocational rehabilitation services. Historically, the goals of vocational rehabilitation have been defined narrowly and have focused primarily on the achievement of employability in the community. An increasing portion of the caseload of vocational rehabilitation agencies is being made up of chronically mentally disabled persons for whom traditional vocational objectives are not always realistic. For this group, the objectives of vocational rehabilitation should be broadened, formally and de facto, to allow for the achievement of daily living and avocational skills without necessarily requiring employability. For other disabled individuals, sheltered work must not be regarded as transitional but rather as a permanent employment option. Productivity must not be equated with independent employability. The task panel, therefore, recommends that:

>10. The determination of eligibility for vocational rehabilitation services be broadened to include those chronically mentally disabled individuals who are capable of achieving goals related to daily living, avocational skills and permanent sheltered employment.

This task panel report has thus far given attention to the stigmatization of the chronically mentally disabled; to the need for dedicated and adequately trained personnel to work with this population; to the need for a locus of responsibility for assuring this population better access to and coordination of existing services; and to the need for further development of special services and programs. Although the task panel has deliberately stressed these issues, which have immediate and direct impact on the chronically mentally disabled, there are other issues involving Federal regulations that inhibit the delivery of appropriate services to the chronically mentally disabled.

The financing of services for the chronically mentally disabled is spread across numerous programs and laws at the Federal level. Federal monies for health services are relatively more available than are funds for other services needed by these individuals. Consequently, their problems tend to be defined primarily as health problems even when they more logically fall into the category of problems in the delivery of social services. Sometimes, fragmentation is such that vital needs fail to be addressed by any funding agency. For example, apartment living arrangements and other questions of residential care for the chronically mentally disabled in the community are not addressed adequately either through health or social welfare budgets.

Sometimes, inappropriate placements are forced upon the chronically mentally disabled by the restrictive nature of the regulations that govern distribution of Federal monies. A specific example is afforded by Medicaid funds which are not available to patients aged 21 to 65 in public or private hospitals. Thus, the level and type of care given to the chronically mentally disabled is frequently based on what services are fundable and not on what services are needed or appropriate. This not only does a disservice to disabled individuals but also distorts Federal expenditure patterns in various categorical programs. Therefore, the task panel recommends that:

>11. Federal funds, whether for health, mental health, social services, or personal income maintenance

DEINST 14

needs, be provided on a nondiscriminatory basis for
the chronically mentally disabled regardless of age
or whether the individual is residing in or being
served by a public or private facility.

Underlying all of the efforts to design, develop, and implement a
network of comprehensive services for the chronically mentally disabled
is a need for systematic and objective information pertaining to the
characteristics and needs of this population. Standardized information
regarding the types and effects of the services that they receive is
still too limited. Much mental health research has indeed had an impact
on the lives of chronically mentally disabled individuals--for example,
investigations concerning the biochemistry of mental disorder--and the
continuation of such research should be supported. However, a considerable portion of mental health research has limited or peripheral relevance
to the needs of this specific population. Much more must be known. For
example, there is a need for systematic knowledge about the characteristics of helping personnel who are most effective in working with the
chronically mentally disabled, so that recruitment and training may proceed realistically.

In addition to gaps in the knowledge base concerning the requirements
of the chronically mentally disabled, more must be done to disseminate and
utilize what is known. In order to remedy the problems associated with
conducting meaningful research and disseminating existing and new knowledge,
the task panel recommends that:

12. The Federal Government establish, as primary
research priorities, the design and execution of
epidemiological studies and evaluative projects
specifically addressed to the needs of the
chronically mentally disabled, and the development of appropriate routes for the dissemination
of these and other research results in order
that they may have maximum impact on service
delivery policies.

DEINST 15

CONCLUSIONS

The Task Panel on Deinstitutionalization, Rehabilitation, and Long-Term Care is aware of and strongly supports increased Federal and State efforts to improve care for the chronically mentally disabled. It wishes to reinforce Federal and State endeavors devoted to reviewing the organization and delivery of all human services, including mental health services, and toward improving coordination among service delivery agencies. Similarly, the task panel endorses the many efforts of the private and voluntary sector that are directed toward meeting the needs of the chronically mentally disabled. The task panel thus acknowledges the need for organizational changes in the service delivery system as well as the need for substantive changes in those programs that are directed at this target population. In addition, as the result of its strong consumer orientation, the task panel places special emphasis on the need for changes in service delivery at that level at which patients are most directly involved as persons. It is at this basic level of the individual that much can, and indeed must, be done for the chronically mentally disabled.

How, at the personal level, may the stigma and suffering of these people be reduced? The chronically mentally disabled must be allowed to have greater involvement in the design, development, and implementation of programs intended for them. They and their families must be given the financial and social supports necessary to allow them to make appropriate decisions concerning care on the basis of individual need. Their rights to prevent inappropriate hospitalization, as well as their rights to prevent inappropriate retention or placement in the community, must be safeguarded. Personnel who have devoted their lives to the care of this population must be given increased support for their efforts. Responsibility for the care of these individuals must be designated and a system of coordinating the diverse array of services for them must be designed and implemented.

At the levels of needed programmatic and systems changes, special programs and services concerned with patients' housing, resocialization and vocational rehabilitation needs must be further developed and better funded. Federal funding arrangements must be structured so that funds flow to needs, rather than services to funds. And, finally, high priority must be given to efforts to increase our knowledge about the chronically mentally disabled and how they can more effectively be helped.

The Task Panel on Deinstitutionalization, Rehabilitation, and Long-Term Care wishes to stress the particular urgency with which its recommendations concerning the chronically mentally disabled are submitted. The brevity of this report should in no way undermine the seriousness of the problems in living that these unfortunate people face nor of the responsibility that society has for relieving their distress. The chronically mentally disabled, whether residing in institutions or in the community, have too long been neglected by society. Ironically, although they are the primary reason for the existence of many mental health services, they have too frequently been excluded from the service delivery system. The President's Commission on Mental Health has at this time a unique, and extremely important, responsibility to recommend that this history of neglect be stopped.

DEINST 16

ACKNOWLEDGMENTS

The Task Panel on Deinstitutionalization, Rehabilitation, and Long-Term Care wishes to acknowledge the major contribution to our work of Leona L. Bachrach, Ph.D., Staff Liaison.

BIBLIOGRAPHY

Addlestone, Jeannette S. Communication to Stanley R. Platman, November 28, 1977.

American Psychiatric Association. "Statement on Rehabilitation." Undated.

Anonymous. Completing the mental care revolution. New York Times, November 1, 1977.

Anthony, William A. Psychological rehabilitation: A concept in need of a method. American Psychologist 32:658-662, August 1977.

Appleby, Lawrence, and Desai, Prakash M. "Chronicity Revisited". Presented at Second Annual Conference of International Association for Psycho-Social Rehabilitation. Chicago, Illinois, October 1976.

Association of Mental Health Administrators. "Statement on Deinstitutionalization." September 18, 1976.

Bachrach, Leona L. Deinstitutionalization: An Analytical Review and Sociological Perspective. Mental Health Statistics Series D, No. 4. Rockville, Md.: National Institute of Mental Health, 1976.

Blatz, Albert B. Communication to Task Panel on Deinstitutionalization, Rehabilitation, and Long-Term Care, President's Commission on Mental Health, November 23, 1977.

Brody, Laurence S. Critique of the First Report of the Carter Commission. Torrance, California, October 25, 1977.

Fields, Steve. Communication to Task Panel on Deinstitutionalization, Rehabilitation, and Long-Term Care, President's Commission on Mental Health, December 1977.

Graham, Victoria. Ship of fools: Mental patients still put "adrift." Associated Press Release, November 27, 1977.

International Committee Against Mental Illness. "Observations and Recommendations to the President's Commission on Mental Health". New York, New York, June 6, 1977.

Joint Commission on Mental Illness and Health. Action for Mental Health. New York: Basic Books, 1961.

Kelly, Joanne P. Memorandum on Welfare Reform Program (H.R. 9030). Mental Health Association of Alameda County, California, October 20, 1977.

Kirk, Stuart A. Communication to Task Panel on Deinstitutionalization, Rehabilitation, and Long-Term Care, President's Commission on Mental Health, November 23, 1977.

Kirk, Stuart A., and Therrien, Mark E. Community mental health myths and the fate of former hospitalized patients. Psychiatry 38:209-217, August 1975.

Laben, Joyce K. Communication to Task Panel on Deinstitutionalization, Rehabilitation and Long-Term Care, President's Commission on Mental Health, November 23, 1977.

Lamb, H. Richard, and Goertzel, Victor. The demise of the state hospital-- a premature obituary? Archives of General Psychiatry 26:489-495, June 1972.

Lourie, Norman V. "Case Management." Presented at American Psychiatric Association Conference on the Chronic Mental Patient, Washington, D.C., January 1978.

Lower, Katherine D. Communication to Task Panel on Deinstitutionalization, Rehabilitation, and Long-Term Care, President's Commission on Mental Health, December 6, 1977.

National Association of Social Workers. "Statement on deinstitutionalization." NASW News, July 1977.

National Council on Community Mental Health Centers. Communication to Task Panel on Deinstitutionalization, Rehabilitation, and Long-Term Care, President's Commission on Mental Health, November 1977.

Norwind, Betty L. Communication to President's Commission on Mental Health, September 12, 1977.

O'Brien, John. Designing the Balanced Service System: A Partial Review of the Literature. Atlanta, Georgia: Georgia Mental Health Institute, 1977.

Platman, Stanley R. Presentation at "Continuity-of-Care" Session, Donaldson Brown Center, Towson, Maryland, September 26, 1977.

Polak, Paul R. Communication to Senator Hubert H. Humphrey, June 2, 1977.

Rogawski, Alexander S. "Long-term patients and the psychiatrist in the community." Presented at First Regional Congress of Social Psychiatry, Santa Barbara, California, September 1977.

Santiestevan, Henry. Deinstitutionalization: Out of Their Beds and Into the Streets. Washington, D.C.: American Federation of State, County, and Municipal Employees, December 1976.

Special Technical Study Project on Overcoming Systems Barriers to Better Mental Health Service Delivery. "Providing Mental Health Services: Obstacles to Doing Better Right Now." Report to the President's Commission on Mental Health, July 1977.

Stratas, Nicholas E.; Bernhardt, David B.; and Elwell, Richard N. The future of the state mental hospital: Developing a unified system of care. Hospital and Community Psychiatry 28:598-600, August 1977.

Turner, Judith C. Comprehensive Community Support Systems for Severely Mentally Disabled Adults: Definitions, Components, and Guiding Principles. National Institute of Mental Health, Rockville, Maryland, July 29, 1977.

Uhlig, Dorothy M. Communication to Task Panel on Deinstitutionalization, Rehabilitation, and Long-Term Care, President's Commission on Mental Health, November 1977.

United States General Accounting Office. Summary of a Report: Returning the Mentally Disabled to the Community: Government Needs to Do More. Report to the Congress. Washington, D.C., January 7, 1977.

United States Senate Special Committee on Aging: Subcommittee on Long-Term Care. Nursing Home Care in the United States: Failure in Public Policy. Supporting Paper No. 7: The Role of Nursing Homes in Caring for Discharged Mental Patients (and the Birth of a For-Profit Boarding Home Industry). Washington, D.C.: U.S. Government Printing Office, 1976.

Williams, Donald H. Communication to the Task Panel on Deinstitutionalization, Rehabilitation, and Long-Term Care, President's Commission on Mental Health, November 22, 1977.

Yamamoto, Joe. Rehabilitation: "A transcultural view." Presented at American Psychiatric Association Evening Panel on "Progress in Transcultural Psychiatry," Los Angeles, California, May 10, 1973.

Yamamoto, Joe. Communication to Task Panel on Deinstitutionalization, Rehabilitation, and Long-Term Care, President's Commission on Mental Health, November 23, 1977.

Final Report

to

THE PRESIDENT'S COMMISSION ON MENTAL HEALTH

of the

SPECIAL STUDY ON ALTERNATIVE MENTAL HEALTH SERVICES

JAMES S. GORDON, M.D., DIRECTOR

February 15, 1978

SUMMARY

After an historical overview of the development of alternative mental health services and a synopsis of characteristics which are common to a wide range of them, I will present brief accounts of particular kinds of alternative services, their history and philosophy, the range of services they offer, and the numbers and kinds of people they serve. Finally, I will suggest conceptual, legislative, and programatic changes which may facilitate the work of existing services, extend our knowledge of their effectiveness, and catalyze their continued development.

BACKGROUND

Alternative services are approximately 10 years old. Most of the early ones were founded by indigenous helpers--professionals and nonprofessionals--in direct response to the physical and emotional needs of the disaffected young people who in the mid to late 1960's migrated to their communities--as alternatives to health, mental health, and social service facilities which the young found threatening, demeaning, or unresponsive.

The founders of the first alternative services resembled the earlier settlement house workers in their idealism and humanitarianism. They differed in their commitment to the kind of participatory democracy which animated the civil rights, antiwar, youth and women's movement of the 1960's. These activist workers believed that, given time and space to do it, ordinary people could help themselves and one another to deal with the vast majority of problems in living that confronted them. They questioned the appropriateness of services which labeled or stigmatized those who came for help, and in their own work blurred or obliterated boundaries between staff and clients: Psychiatrists learned to talk down "bum trippers" from street people who knew more about the effects of psychedelic drugs than they; a teenager who was panicky one night might counsel another the next. These early workers--and many of their clients--were acutely aware of the relationship between personal problems and political and social forces. They regarded advocacy for the social changes that would make individual change more possible as an inevitable complement to the direct service work they performed.

In 1967 a handful of switchboards, drop-in centers, free clinics, and runaway houses served marginal young people in the "hip" neighborhoods of a few large cities. Today there are as many as 2,000 hotlines, over 200 houses for runaways, and 400 free clinics. They have been organized by people of all ages, classes, and ideologies in small towns, suburbs, and rural areas, as well as in the large cities. In Prince George's, a suburban and rural Maryland county, for example, one of three hotlines receives 1,400 calls a month, one of two runaway houses gives shelter and intensive counseling to over 350 young people each year, and a single one of the county's nine drop-in centers provides 600 hours of individual therapy each month.

In the early years, alternative services were preoccupied with responding to the immediate needs of their young clients--for emergency medical care, a safe place during a bad drug trip, or short-term housing. More recently, they have expanded and diversified in response to their clients changing needs. Drop-in centers work with the families and teachers of the teenagers who come to them as well as the young people themselves. Houses for runaways have opened long-term residences and foster care programs for those who cannot return home or would otherwise be institutionalized; and free clinics and hotlines have helped begin specialized counseling services for other groups--women, gays, the elderly, etc.

In the 1970's, the alternative service model has been adopted by people who have identified new community needs. They have created rap rooms in schools, drug and alcohol counseling programs for suburbanites, rape crisis centers, shelters for battered women, peer counseling and street work projects, programs designed specifically for old people and particular ethnic minorities, and healing and birthing centers (a specially designed home-like center where the mother and father can both "room-in").

A number of services--alternatives to hospitalization, many hotlines, drop-in centers and crisis programs, some home birth and healing centers, and a few shelters for battered women--explicitly define themselves as part of an emerging mental health movement, one that combines psychological attention with physical care and social activism to provide effective, respectful, low cost mental health services.[1] Others are wary of being classified as a "mental health" service: Their primary concern is with the emotional well being of their clients; they use a number of techniques borrowed from mental health professionals, and indeed, include sympathetic professionals in important positions on their staffs; but they are convinced that mental health means mental illness, a field which they associate with a narrow institutional medical model based on a psychopathological view of human nature, authoritarian relationships, derogatory labeling, and political reaction. They do not speak of themselves as mental health workers or counselors but rather as friends, staff, helpers, healers, educators, members of a collective, community workers, or advocates.[2]

---

[1] Gordon, J.S. The runaway center as community mental health center. The American Journal of Psychiatry, in press.

[2] Gordon, J.S. Coming together: Consultation with young people. Social Policy. July-August 1974.

CHARACTERISTICS OF ALTERNATIVE SERVICES

Though alternative services are as diverse in their operation, staff, and structure as their communities and clients, though some do and some do not define themselves as mental health services, they share certain philosophical assumptions, attitudes, and practices which define their approach to people's "problems in living" as "alternative" and make them particularly useful and responsive to the people they serve. I have found the following to be among the most significant:

They respond to people's problems as those problems are experienced. A woman whose husband is beating her is regarded as a victim, not scrutinized as a masochist. A child who leaves his home is seen, housed, and fed as a runaway, not diagnosed as an "acting out disorder" or judged as a "status offender." A man with chronic back pain and no demonstrable organic lesion is treated as a sufferer with legitimate if not yet understood complaints.

They provide services that are immediately accessible with a minimum of waiting and bureaucratic restriction. Hotlines, shelters for battered women, rape crisis centers, houses for runaways, and many drop-in centers are open 24-hours a day, free, to anyone who calls or comes in off the street.

They tend to treat their clients' problems as signs of change and opportunities for growth rather than symptoms of an illness which must be suppressed. In drug-free alternatives to mental hospitalization like Diabasis and Soteria, even psychotic episodes are regarded as potentially transformative and illuminating experiences.

They treat those who come to them for help as members of families and social systems. This enables them to view their troubled clients' "symptoms" as reactions to and communications within their familial or social situation. It provides the underpinning for their treatment of pregnancy, childbirth, and dying primarily as shared family experiences and only secondarily, and occasionally, as medical conditions or emergencies. On a programatic level this "systems" viewpoint encourages many alternative services to advocate for and work with their clients in the arena--job, home, school, or court--in which their problems arise.

They make use of mental health professionals and the techniques they have developed but depend on nonprofessionals to deliver most of the primary care. In projects as diverse as houses for runaways and home birth programs, professionals in free clinics and alternatives to mental hospitalization serve almost exclusively as consultants, trainers, and emergency backup. They are there to share their knowledge with staff and clients and not necessarily to run the service.

They regard active participation as a cornerstone of their mental health service program and indeed of mental health. On an individual therapeutic level this means emphasizing the strength of those who seek help and their capacity for self-help: Teenage runaways are encouraged to see themselves as potential agents for a family's change rather than helpless victims of its oppression; battered wives to become strong enough to leave rather than endure

ALT 4

their husbands' brutality. In dozens of "humanistic gerontology" programs and in hundreds of free clinics and holistic healing centers, clients are encouraged to use techniques like biofeedback, progressive relaxation, acupressure, and guided imagery, and disciplines like Yoga and Tai Chi to experience, and then alter, physical and emotional states that they had always regarded as beyond their control.

Most alternative services emphasize the ability of those who have been or are being helped to use their personal experience as a basis for helping others. Clients participate in peer counseling programs and are included in the decision-making structure of the organization, in meetings of a collective governing body, or on boards of directors.

They provide both clients and staff with a supportive and enduring community which transcends the delivery or receipt of a particular service. In a time when the extended family is losing its coherence and ties to home towns and neighborhoods are fraying, alternative services are providing a continuing focus for collective allegiance and an opportunity for long-term mutual support. For many who have long ago ceased to be official clients or workers, they remain a retreat in times of trouble--a place to gather to celebrate joyous occasions.

They change and expand the work they do to meet the changing needs of their clients. Crisis oriented houses for runaways and drop-in centers have created long-term foster placement for young people who could not return home. Women's groups have evolved into rape crisis centers, counsel-collectives, and medical clinics.

They address themselves to the economic and social handicaps from which their clients suffer. It has become clear, for example, that no counseling, whether individual, family, or group, can adequately deal with the problems of a teenager who cannot read or find work. In a time of economic recession, workers in a variety of alternative services have begun to create meaningful vocational and educational programs for unskilled and previously unemployable clients.

They can provide care that is by any standards equal or superior to that offered by traditional mental health centers. Many of their reports are anecdotal (i.e., the consistent finding that large numbers of young people with psychotic or borderline diagnoses are diverted from hospitalization by a variety of alternative services), but "harder" data is also beginning to accumulate: A 2-year followup study of Soteria, a National Institute of Mental Health funded residential alternative to hospitalization, revealed that residents of the program "showed significantly better occupational levels and were more able to leave home to live independent of their families of origin" than a control group of people hospitalized on a crisis oriented general hospital ward;[3] evaluation of the SAGE (Senior Actualization and Growth Explorations) project in Berkeley has revealed significant psychological changes in

---

[3] Mosher, L. R., and Menn, A. Z. "Community Residential Treatment for Schizophrenia: Two year Follow-Up Data." Presented at the Annual Meeting of the American Psychiatric Association, May 10-14, 1976.

the older people who participated in the program of gentle physical exercise, meditation, and group discussion;[4] and a matched population study of 1,046 home births and 1,046 hospital births has revealed significantly more infections and birth injuries in the group of babies that was delivered in the hospital.[5]

They are in general more economical than the traditional services which their clients might otherwise use. Young people, many of whom come to centers for runaways to avoid being hospitalized, provide an interesting example: In 1975, an NIMH study of 15 centers for runaways around the country revealed that centers for runaways spent from $32 to $50 a day for each young person housed; in contrast, the figures for acute care hospitalization ranged from $125 to $200 a day.[6] A more recent and sophisticated analysis of one house for runaways, Someplace Else, in Tallahassee, Florida, revealed that this program was approximately three times as cost-effective as the services routinely offered by the county. Long-term residential alternatives to hospitalization for adults like Soteria and the Training in Community Living program of the Mendota Mental Health Institute tend to be as expensive as traditional programs, but here too cost-benefit analyses seem to reveal significant advantages for the alternative services.[7]

They have financial problems. The desire to work with whoever comes to them regardless of economic compensation; their attempts to provide comprehensive preventive and often unreimbursed services; their unwillingness to take funds which restrict their work with clients; the complexity of Federal, State, and local funding procedures; and the general reluctance of many agencies to fund service programs that are neither certified by a professional establishment nor proved in "scientific terms" all conspire to keep most alternative services chronically underfunded.

They use their experience in trying to meet people's direct service needs as a basis for advocacy efforts on their clients' behalf. Hotlines which have noted an increase in a particular kind of problem--battered women, child abuse, etc.--have used their statistical information and their moral authority as service providers to prod local mental health and social service agencies to create programs to meet these needs. Groups which serve old people, pregnant women, and runaways have organized on a State and national level to advocate for legislation and funding to further and protect their clients' interests.

---

[4] Personal communication from the evaluator, Morton Lieberman, University of Chicago, 1978.

[5] Mehl. L. E. Research on alternatives in child birth: What can it tell us about hospital practice. Twenty-first Century Obstetrics. NAPSAC, 1977.

[6] Gordon, J. S. "Alternative Services: A Recommendation for Public Funding." Unpublished, 1975.

[7] Weisbrod, B. A., Test, M., and Stein, L. I. "An Alternative to the Mental Hospital-Benefits and Cost." Unpublished, 1977.

HOTLINES

Hotlines were the first of the alternative services and are still the most numerous and widely used. They are vast repositories of information about medical care, housing, welfare, prescribed and illegal drugs, birth control and sex education, rides, and rock concerts. They are places you get in touch with when at 2 a.m. you feel like ending it all, or at 5 in the evening when you have to tell someone how your father molested you the night before and has threatened to do it again.

Hotlines are anonymous and instantly accessible. The people who answer the phone listed without condemnation and respond without rancor. They seem to understand. And if they do not, there are no reprisals: A caller can refuse a referral to another agency or interrupt an unwanted piece of advice by dropping the receiver in the cradle. There is no red tape to cut through to reach a sympathetic ear, no forms to follow a caller out of the conversation and into his or her family, work, or school life.

The name hotline comes from the phone connection that was instituted between the United States and the Union of Soviet Socialist Republics. The superpower hotline was meant to forestall a nuclear catastrophe. The county or citywide hotline exists to prevent personal crises from becoming disasters.

The first hotlines were inspired by Erich Lindemann and Gerald Caplan's work in crisis intervention and were concerned with suicide prevention. The National Institute of Mental Health funded the first Suicide Prevention Hotline in Los Angeles. By 1968, there were 100 such hotlines, many of them attached to Suicide Prevention Centers which provided crisis counseling in person as well as by phone.

In the late 1960's hotlines, often called switchboards, became the communications hub of the counter culture. In San Francisco's Haight-Ashbury, around DuPont Circle in Washington, D.C., in Boston, Chicago, and Boulder, the switchboard was where young people called--to find a place to sleep or a meal, to leave a message for a friend, or a parent, or to talk to someone sympathetic when the trip that seemed so good suddenly turned frighteningly bad. By 1972 there were, according to the National Directory of Hotlines and Switchboards, some 600 such services nationwide.[8]

In the early 1970's hotlines began to spring up in suburban and rural areas to meet the needs of the kids who stayed home as well as those who had gone on the run. Some were staffed by concerned adults, many by young people who wanted to find some way to be useful to friends and schoolmates who were suffering from bad drug experiences or addiction, who were confused about their sexuality or their relationship to their parents.[9]

---

[8] Baizerman, M. Toward analysis of the relations among the youth counterculture, telephone hotlines and anonymity. _Journal of Youth and Adolescence_, Vol. 3, No. 4, 1974.

[9] Gordon, J. S., Coming together, op. cit.; and Gordon, J., Youth helping youth. _Social Policy_. Sept.-Oct., 1976.

Within a few years both the hotlines and their callers began to change. They brought the needs of young people and their families to the attention of established mental health and social service agencies and frequently referred chronically troubled callers to them. Hotlines developed sophisticated training programs--in phone counseling, drug abuse, suicide prevention, and sexuality--for their own workers and in turn trained others. They taught "listening skills" to firemen, police, ministers, parents, and even mental health professionals. Meanwhile older people began to volunteer for youth-run hotlines and some adult dominated groups took in younger members.

At the same time older people began to use the hotline service--unemployed workers needing help in dealing with welfare or housing bureaucracies, women who had been beaten by their husbands, rape victims, adults with alcohol problems, and old people who were lonely and/or depressed at home.

At present there are between 1,000 and 1,500 independent hotlines providing anonymous phone counseling and information and referral. Though all stress anonymity, nonjudgmental, empathic counseling, and the provision of a range of referral options, there is enormous variety in staffing patterns, in the training offered, and in numbers of callers. A rural hotline staffed entirely by local volunteers and subsisting on $200 cash and small in-kind donations may be open only 5 or 6 hours each evening and will receive 1,000 or 1,500 calls a year. At the other end of the spectrum YES, funded by Hennepin County, Minnesota, has 5 full-time staff, 150 volunteers, and answers 84,000 calls a year. In between, the Prince George's County (Maryland) hotline receives 15,000 calls a year, with a full-time paid staff of 2, 12 part-time phone counselors, 30 volunteers, and a budget of $75,000.

There are several problems in obtaining accurate statistics on hotlines. In spite of exhortations to keep careful count, the agencies often do not record the total number of their calls (one hotline recently discovered via a telephone company check that only one-third of its 3,800 calls per month were actually logged); a guarantee of anonymity prevents hotlines from distinguishing between numbers of people calling and numbers of calls; and no definitive national survey of hotlines exists. Nevertheless, assuming low figures of some 5 to 10,000 calls per hotline per year and 1,000 hotlines, the number of calls is between 5 and 10 million each year![10] About 60 percent of these calls involve substantial "listening" and phone counseling.

Their anonymity, accessiblity, and credibility puts hotlines in the unique position of learning the problems of large numbers of people in their communities long before these problems are openly expressed. Many hotlines have used this information and their central position in a network of community services to develop or help other groups develop specific programs. A number of them, like YES, the Crisis Intervention Services of Erie County, New York, and the Prince George's County Hotline, have started mobile or walk-in crisis intervention units to followup on particularly desperate calls and to facilitate

---

[10] These figures do not include the number of calls received by some 400-500 church based and religiously oriented hotlines, by phone counseling programs attached to other alternative services described in this report, or by hotlines that industries and government agencies have set up for their workers.

service delivery to those who are unwilling or unable to use existing agencies. Some have created programs to meet specific needs of their callers--shelters for battered women, houses for runaways, free clinics--and still others have used their information as a basis for advocating for the needs of under-served groups with legislators and local government agencies.

ALTERNATIVE SERVICES FOR YOUNG PEOPLE

The earliest alternative services--hotlines, houses for runaways, free clinics, drop-in centers--were all, overwhelmingly, youth services. They were created in response to the needs of the thousands of young people who rushed to join the burgeoning counterculture of the late 1960's. Antibureaucratic, nonjudgmental, imaginative, and protean, these services were permeated by the enthusiasm and optimism of their young clients. New people were added to the staff each day; new programs blossomed each month. No problem seemed insurmountable. With enough good vibes the bad trip would turn good, a home for a homeless teenager would materialize, money would come somehow, from somewhere.

The drop-in centers and houses for runaways of the late 1960's tended to ignore, if they did not actively mistrust, mental health professionals and their techniques. Instead of offering therapy to the young people who sought them out, they responded very directly to their clients' needs for food, shelter, and a time to rap. They did not put the young down for their hair, their politics, their clothes, or their drugs; they did not call their parents or moralize about sex or tell them to take tranquilizers. Workers in these programs--professionals as well as nonprofessionals--were allies of the young in a common effort to create a new and better world, more like older brothers and sisters than parents.

During the last 10 years, workers in alternative services for young people have become keenly aware of the impossibility of creating a separate and autonomous youth culture. The declining economic situation brought the counterculture to an end, made present employment all but impossible, and future prospects doubtful for many of the young. At the same time their helpers became more aware of the complexity and depth of their problems. Though some young people could go home after a few days at a house for runaways and a brief conciliatory conference with parents, others returned over and over. Agreements were broken, old arguments resurfaced, and bewildered and angry parents brought the sanctions of the adult world to bear on bewildered and angry children: Many young people wrote their counselors to say they had been locked up in mental or penal institutions.[11]

Houses for runaways, drop-in centers, and crisis centers began to hire mental health professionals as consultants and staff to help them understand particularly disturbed and disturbing clients, to teach them to analyze and deal with their life situations. Slowly the emphasis shifted from viewing the parents as villainous and the young people as heroic, to seeing them all as participants in a mutually destructive situation; from providing crisis services to the young person to working with him or her as a member of a family. In 1978 houses for runaways employ full-time family counselors, and have begun to call themselves "youth and family crisis centers."

Virtually all of the first youth programs were started without government support. They subsisted on donations from sympathetic church and citizens groups and on benefit dances and concerts, and paid their workers when money

---

[11] Gordon, J. S. Working with runaways and their families: How the SAJA community does it. <u>Family Process</u>. June 1975.

ALT 10

was available, and barely enough to live on. By the early 1970's, Federal and State governments began to recognize the inability of established mental health and social service programs to deal with the problems of the young and to provide steady if still inadequate funding to some of these projects. They awarded contracts and grants to the alternative services that young people were already using, and provided funds for the creation of some others, in suburbs, small cities, and rural areas.

These monies sometimes tended to narrow the focus of programs, to urge them toward the kind of labeling and exclusion they had always rejected. Funds were awarded to deal with "problems" rather than people or their needs. The Law Enforcement Assistance Administration funded youth service bureaus for "status offenders" and "predelinquents," the National Institute on Drug Abuse supported crisis and drop-in centers for "drug abusers," and the Runaway Youth Division of the Office of Youth Development underwrote "houses for runaways." Still, these funds guaranteed the survival of alternative services, provided their staffs with a steady if still low ($160 per week average starting salary) income and eventually helped make these services secure enough to ask for--and sometimes receive--funding to help any young people or families who need help. By 1978 a spontaneous response to the short-lived youth culture had become a large, effective, diverse, and widely accepted mental health and social service system.

Nationwide, there are now some 900 to 1,000 drop-in and crisis centers and youth service bureaus. Some are still subsidized by precarious Federal grants, others have been put on a more secure fiscal footing through regular contracts with State or county agencies. A big city project, like Manhattan's The Door, provides comprehensive counseling, medical, vocational, educational, and legal services to hundreds of young people each night, while rural drop-in centers may serve that many people in a year. The vast majority of programs, places like Aunt Martha's in Park Forest, Illinois, the Bowie Involvement Project in Bowie, Maryland, and the Washington County Youth Service Bureau in Montpelier, Vermont, have contact with about 1,000 clients a year and provide 100 to 200 of them with a range of services including individual and family counseling, job placement, and advocacy in school and court. Using these 100 to 200 figures as an average, it would seem that these nonresidential programs have contact with a total of about 900,000 clients each year and work on an ongoing intensive basis with more than 100,000 of them.

Since Huckleberry House first opened its doors in the Haight-Ashbury in 1967, some 200 shelters for runaway youth have been created. The Youth Development Bureau (formerly the Office of Youth Development) funds 132 of them at a cost of $8 million a year. Extrapolating from their statistics, it seems likely that runaway programs in the United States given shelter to slightly more than 50,000 of the 750,000 young people who each year run from their homes and that they have brief contact by phone or in person with another 200,000. In addition, the federally funded National Runaway Switchboard receives some 40,000 calls each year from runaways and their parents.

Young people who come, by themselves or at the suggestion of a school counselor or a probation officer, to a center for runaways are housed for an average of 6 days. Usually they stay in comfortable chaos with 5 to 15 other runaways in a sprawling old house or, less often, in crisis foster homes. During this time, in individual and group meetings, their counselors try to

ALT 11

help them figure out why they left home and what they want to do next. There are usually counseling sessions with the young person and his or her family and often the counselors help the young person to straighten out complicated and frightening school and court situations.

For many young people and their families these centers for runaways are community mental health centers. They do, in fact, provide all the services mandated for CMHC's (Community Mental Health Centers) in a way that is acceptable to young people at less than one-quarter their cost--services which many of the runaways and their families sorely need: A sample taken during one quarter of 1974 at the Washington, D.C., Runaway House revealed that 10 percent of the young people had already spent time in mental hospitals, that 20 percent had been in juvenile detention facilities, and an additional 25 percent had been threatened with institutionalization by a mental health professional or probation officer just prior to running away.

In the last several years, short-term services like drop-in centers and houses for runaways have been expanding their scope and extending their commitment to young people and their families. Many, like the Neighborhood Outreach Project in San Diego and Voyage House in Philadelphia, have begun to meet teenagers on their own turf--in schoolyards and candy stores, on front stoops, and at churches--to help young people and their families to establish supportive networks in communities that are demoralized and fragmented. Some have obtained money from the Department of Labor to train and pay young people to work as counselors and administrators in the alternative services where they previously sought help, or in cooperative businesses--plant stores, groceries, craft shops--that alternative services have started.

Many programs, particularly urban ones, have also addressed themselves to the specific problems of young women, Blacks, Latinos, and Native Americans. A higher proportion of Third-World counselors has been hired in formerly white projects and established houses for runaways and crisis centers have helped Third-World people to create new programs designed to address the particular cultural identity and economic needs of their young people. Most recently, some projects--in Seattle, Minneapolis, Washington, D.C., New York, and San Francisco--have tentatively begun formal and informal shelters for prostitutes and victims of sexual abuse, consciousness raising groups for girls, workshops in sexuality, and self-defense classes.

LONG-TERM RESIDENTIAL PROGRAMS

There are at present about 200,000 teenagers in foster placement. Each year 200,000 additional young people are committed to mental and penal institutions. Few of those who are institutionalized need to be there; only a small percentage of those in foster care are placed with adults who genuinely want and can cope with adolescents, or in group homes which are truly responsive to their needs. During the last 7 years alternative services have begun to try to find more adequate living situations for young people who can not or will not live at home.

The individual placements done by programs like San Francisco's Alternative Living Program, Vermont's Spectrum, and Seattle's Youth Advocates differ from conventional foster care in a number of ways. Instead of relying on

foster parents who take adolescents only reluctantly these programs seek out--
and carefully screen and train--couples who definitely want a troubled adolescent; single people--some of them just a few years older than their foster children--who remember how much an older person had meant to them; groups of unrelated people living together who want to "have contact with the next generation." Instead of simply consigning a young person to them, these programs allow each teenager to visit a prospective foster family for a meal and then a weekend. Both the young people and the older ones have time to get to know one another, and the option of blamelessly deciding not to live together. Roles are not forced. Some 15- or 16-year-olds are looking for parental figures, others want and need only an older friend or a relaxed communal home. Once the young person is placed, the alternative foster care workers continue to hold weekly or bimonthly meetings with the entire foster family. They are always available as counselors to the young people and to continue to help them to maintain an ongoing relationship with their natural parents.

In the alternative group foster homes, five to eight young people live with two to three counselors. In these settings, cooperative living, participatory decisionmaking, and mutual respect and confrontation are far more important than behavioral controls, therapeutic imperatives, or distinctions between staff and residents. My own work suggests that even young people who bear borderline or psychotic diagnoses can--with adequate professional consultation--live successfully without pharmacologic or behavioral controls. Given responsibility in a home where they are treated as members of a household rather than patients, these young people begin, after a while, to act responsibly. Given power over their own lives and living situations they tend to use it wisely.[12]

There are currently 50 or 60 of these long-term alternative living programs serving a total of between 1,000 and 2,000 people each year. The largest, Seattle's Youth Advocates, places 125 young people in alternative foster care. Others, like the Group Live-In Experience in the Bronx and San Francisco's Alternative Living Program, have several foster homes available to them. Still others consist of a single group home or individual placements for 10 to 12 young people.

These programs were greeted by many social service departments with a great wariness. In some areas--Washington, D.C., and St. Louis, Missouri, for example--programs that were quite successful with young people never obtain local government support and eventually closed. In other locales, their willingness to work with young people on whom everyone else had given up and their

---

[12]Gordon, J. S. The alternative group foster home: A new place for young people to live. Psychiatry, Vol. 39, No. 4, 1976; Gordon, J. S. The group foster home: An alternative to mental hospitalization. Social Work, in press.

extraordinarily low cost made these long-term alternatives an obvious "last resort" for concerned public agency workers.[13]

---

[13] The group foster homes function at one-third to one-half the cost of the residential treatment centers to which these young people might otherwise be sent, and one-eighth that of a psychiatric hospital. The foster placement programs, with their extraordinarily high client-staff ratio, careful selection, training, and weekly supervision, cost less than one-half to one-third of what city social service departments spend on foster care.

WOMEN'S SERVICES

Like its 19th century ancestor, the women's movement of the 1960's was intimately connected to the struggles of Black people. The courage of one oppressed group demanding its civil rights catalyzed women, as it did youth and old people, to think, write, and then attempt to do something about their own oppression.

From its beginnings as women's caucuses and discussion groups within the civil rights and antiwar movements to its present incarnation in thousands of women's centers and in living rooms across the country, the leaderless consciousness raising group has been central to the current women's movement. It is an oasis of intimacy, an opportunity for self-discovery, an experience in collective strength, and a classroom in political education. Consciousness raising groups have helped women to understand that many of their feelings of inferiority and unhappiness are inextricably connected to the objecttive conditions of a society which considers them inferior and limits their possibilities for fulfillment.

These consciousness raising groups have helped give birth to a mass political movement focusing on the Equal Rights Amendment, child care, and reproductive self-determination, a new feminist perspective on psychotherapy which recognizes the contribution of a sexist society to the creation of individual women's problems, and a spectrum of feminist alternative services-- from the ubiquitous university, independent or church sponsored women's centers, to specific services such as counseling programs, birthing centers, health clinics, rape crisis centers, and shelters for battered women.

FEMINIST COUNSELING

Feminist counseling services are probably the most widespread of the women's alternative services. They were created because some women in consciousness raising groups felt the need for more intensive work on personal problems and because many feminists, both therapists and their clients, were dissatisfied with the condescension to women implicit in the values and ideology of conventional psychotherapy.[14]

Feminist counseling is distinguished from the consciousness raising group by the presence of a trained therapist, the exchange of payment, its focus on the personal rather than the political, and its emphasis on the client's rather than the therapist's experience.[15] Some programs, like the Somerville (Massachusetts) Women's Mental Health Collective, are run by professionals and provide individual and group therapy that is based in psychodynamic as well as feminist theory and practice. Others, like the Moon Tree in Madison, Wisconsin, are really women's centers. They offer an enormous variety of group

---

[14] Kravetz, D. Consciousness-Raising groups and group psychotherapy: Alternative mental health resources for women. <u>Psychotherapy: Theory Research and Practice</u>. Spring 1976.

[15] Leidig, M. "Feminist Therapy," University of Colorado, unpublished.

counseling experiences, as well as classes in political theory, spirituality, assertiveness training, and healing.

Though there are no reliable figures on the numbers of feminist therapists or feminist therapy centers or the kinds of problems they deal with, a few statistics are suggestive: Philadelphia's Women in Transition, an alternative service which opened in 1972 to meet the need for counseling and support of women who were newly separated, divorced, or widowed and became affiliated with a community mental health center 2 years ago, had had 500 women in its 8-week groups; in the greater Boston area there are some 20 different feminist therapy groups, each of which sees from 50 to 100 women each week; the Association for Women in Psychology numbers 250 feminist therapists and its chairperson estimates that there are another several thousand feminist psychologists, and that at least as many other therapists--professional and nonprofessional--regard themselves as feminists.[16]

BIRTH AND HEALTH

Healing and birthing centers exist because many women feel that male dominated gynecologic and obstetric practice is personally demeaning and physically and emotionally destructive. Their own health clinics and self-help groups offer women the opportunity to understand their anatomy and physiology and to participate actively in their health and medical care.[17] The alternative birth movement permits all participants--mother, child, and father--to experience fully an event that has been shrouded in mystery and fear and, to borrow Doris Haire's word, "warped" by medical technology.[18]

Protagonists of the alternative birth movement emphasize the harm that is done to low-risk infants and their mothers and fathers by the high technology births and the separation of the newborn from mother that is routine in hospitals. To prove their point they cite the by now copious literature on the deleterious effects of anesthesia, drugs, and forceps on neonates,[19] as well as the studies of Marshall Klaus and John Kennell on the "sensitive period" just after birth and on the maternal-infant bonding that can take place then.[20]

---

[16] Liff-Levenson, M. Personal communication.

[17] Marieskind, H. Helping oneself to health. <u>Social Policy</u>. September-October 1976.

[18] Haire, D. The cultural warping of childbirth. <u>International Childbirth Education News</u>. Special Report, 1972.

[19] Brazelton, T. B. Effect of maternal medication on the neonate and his behavior. <u>Pediatrics</u>. 37, 1012-1016, 1966; and Gordon, H. R. Fetal bradycardia after paracervical block. New England Journal of Medicine, 279:910-914, 1968.

[20] Klaus, M. H., and Kennell, J. H. <u>Maternal-Infant Bonding</u>. Mosby, 1976.

Klaus and Kennell's work has been of particular importance to this movement and it is particularly relevant to mental health. Their careful and thoughtful comparative studies indicate that ordinary hospital procedures may grossly interfere with the neonate's future neurologic, cognitive, and emotional development, and that the amount and quality of maternal-infant contact in the first hours of life may significantly affect the mother's future attitudes toward her offspring.

To enable the parents to enjoy and participate fully in birth and to promote close bonding between them and their child the alternative birth movement insists on the "demedicalization" of childbirth. Though its adherents rely on physicians for initial screening visits, medical backup, and for all potential high-risk deliveries, it emphasizes the active role that parents, assisted and supported by midwives, can play throughout pregnancy and childbirth. In a number of birthing programs, nurse and lay midwives spend many hours with prospective mothers and fathers consulting with them about the interpersonal strain that pregnancy creates as well as instructing them in maternal nutrition and health care.

Birth itself generally takes place at home or in a specially designed homelike birthing center where the mother and father can both "room in." The midwife comes to the mother as soon as labor begins, remains throughout its course, delivers the baby in whatever position feels good to the mother, not in the unphysiologic, uncomfortable, and potentially dangerous lithotomy position), and uses a minimum of pharmacologic and technologic interference.

In the minutes and hours after birth these midwives encourage bonding between the baby and both parents (as well as other siblings or close friends whom the parents may wish to be present). They make postnatal visits to mother and child for several months after birth and may, if necessary, serve as family counselors.

The evidence that has so far accumulated indicates that midwives--in the Frontier Nursing Service, at The Farm in Summertown, Tennessee, and elsewhere in the United States and Europe--have been extremely effective in lowering the mortality and morbidity rate in poor and rural areas and that their statistics in low-risk births among middle class women compare favorablly with those achieved by physicians in hospitals.[21] During the last few years the numbers of midwives, and children being born at home--as well as in physician- and midwife-run birthing centers--have all increased greatly. In Sonoma County, California, for example, the percentage of babies born at home has increased from less than 1 percent to 10 percent, and in Santa Cruz County from 0.5 percent during the last 5 years.[22] David Stewart, Director of the National Association of Parents and Professionals for Safe Alternatives in Childbirth, an organization of over 1,000 members, estimates that there are some 40 to 50 birthing centers in the United States as well as hundreds of nurse midwifery programs and thousands of lay midwives.

---

[21] Arms, S. <u>Immaculate Deception: A New Look at Women in Childbirth in America</u>. Bantam, 1977; Mehl, L. E., op. cit.; and Gaskin, I. M. <u>Spiritual Midwifery</u>. The Book Publishing Company, 1978.

[22] Arms, S. Personal Communication.

ALT 17

The women's health movement grows out of a feeling of outrage at the medical establishment's promiscuous use of radical mastectomies, hysterectomies, oral contraceptives, and diethylstylbesterol; a dissatisfaction with the condescension that physicians have shown women; and the conviction that women are more than capable of providing themselves with preventive care and dealing with minor complaints that are particularly female--from menstrual cramps and vaginal infection to menopausal symptoms and postpartum "blues."[23]

The National Women's Health Movement lists 97 formal health programs for women and estimates that there are another 100 unlisted. Some of these groups, like the Haight-Ashbury Women's Medical Clinic, began as part of a free clinic. Others are the outgrowth of the more than 1,200 self-help groups in which women have gathered together to examine their own and each other's breasts and pelvises; to learn about reproductive physiology, contraception, and indications for surgical and gynecologic procedures, and to discuss their sexuality.[24] Though most of the women's clinics include or employ doctors, the emphasis is on women learning how to take care of their own bodies--on education, prevention, and self-help rather than medical treatment and reliance on professionals.

RAPE CRISIS CENTERS AND SHELTERS FOR BATTERED WOMEN

Rape crisis centers and shelters for battered women are a response of the women's community to the violence which men in this society direct toward women. Both services provide an enormous amount of psychological support and counseling to the women who come to them, but they are for the most part quite adamant in resisting a therapeutic model for their services. From their point of view the only "sickness" present is in the men who abuse and rape women and the society which produces them. The women who suffer from their actions are victims, not patients.

Rape crisis centers are the older, rather better organized and more limited of the two services. They provide a 24-hour-a-day hotline to help women who have been raped to deal with their feelings about it; with the treatment they have received by police and hospital personnel; and with the reactions of their friends and families. Most centers try to help women find people who can be with them during a hospital visit or at night, after the rape has occurred, but some will also do face-to-face counseling, accompany women to physicians, and be present at trials if the rapist is apprehended. There are anywhere from 200[25] to 500[26] rape crisis centers, each one of which receives an average of approximately 200 crisis calls a year as well as 500 to 600 informational queries. This represents at least 40,000 calls from rape victims themselves and another 100,000 from those concerned with rape.

---

[23] Marieskind, H. I., and Ehrenreich, D. Towards socialist medicine: The women's health movement. <u>Social Policy</u>. Sept.-Octo. 1975.

[24] Ibid.

[25] Center for Women's Policy Studies.

[26] National Center for the Prevention and Control of Rape.

ALT 18

In addition to responding to rape victims, these groups train community groups, police, hospital workers, and other alternative service workers to deal effectively and sensitively with rape victims. Some of the older and better organized groups, like the Washington, D.C., Rape Crisis Center, publish newsletters and are also actively involved in organizing in communities with high rates of sexual abuse to prevent rapes from occurring.

Battered women's shelters are remarkable places, as filled with the excitement of self-discovery and mutual support as were the houses for runaways, free clinics, and consciousness raising groups of the late 1960's. Many of them began as gestures by one woman to another who was suffering, the offer of a couch in a living room, a safe place and some time away from a dangerous and demeaning situation. Soon, individual sisterly behavior produced collective action. Houses large enough to offer shelter to 5 or 10 women and 10 of their children were begged or rented. Within weeks twice as many people had moved in.

Though most rape crisis centers, and indeed most feminist programs, serve predominantly middle class white females, shelters for battered women have had enormous appeal to poor and working class and Third World women. This is not because, as one battered wife put it, "Money keeps you from getting your face rearranged," but because poor women who are beaten have had fewer options to continued economic dependence on the men who beat them.

Betsy Warrior and Del Martin, leaders in the movement on behalf of battered women, estimate that since Rainbow House in Phoenix opened its doors in 1973 more than 100 shelters (and another 150 to 200 hotlines for abused women) have been started, and that virtually all of them are filled to, and beyond capacity.[27] Though nationwide figures are unavailable, the statistics from La Case de Las Madres in San Francisco seem illustrative: During a 9 month period from June 1976 to February 1977, La Casa housed some 139 battered women. Extrapolating from these figures to a yearly total of 184 and allowing for the fact that Casa, though not exceptional, is larger than an average shelter, it seems likely that about 15,000 adults and 20,000 children will this year take refuge in shelters for battered women. Of these, as many as 10,000 women and their children may use the opportunity--and the concrete and extensive help in finding work and long-term housing--to leave situations which have been chronically damaging to their physical and emotional well-being.

---

[27] Personal communications; See also Warrior, B. _Working With Wife Abuse_. Personal publication and Martin, D. _Battered Wives_, Pocket, 1977.

OLDER PEOPLE'S PROGRAMS

Perhaps, the most serious problem that old people have in this country is attitude--the way the young think and feel about them, the way they think and feel about themselves. For the most part we have tried to deny the process of aging in ourselves, to shun it where the physical evidence is incontrovertible. We push the old out-of-work, segregate them in retirement colonies and nursing homes, and slide our eyes over them when we meet them on the street.[28] It is no wonder that we devote so little of our resources to the problems that beset them and the services they require.[29]

Whether they are primarily political, social service, or psychophysiologic, whether they have been started by old or young people, all alternative services for the elderly are grounded in the attempt to help them work together to change their own attitudes--from fatalistic acceptance to active enjoyment, from self-disgust to pride, from despair to optimism. None of the alternative programs calls itself a "mental health" program--joining such an enterprise would be, for most old people, one more admission of ineffectiveness, one more burdensome label to carry around--and yet most of them seem to produce remarkable changes in the participants' mental health.

Berkeley's SAGE (Senior Actualization and Growth Experience) program and Los Angeles' Institute for Creative Aging address themselves directly to the psychophysiologic well-being of the elderly. In a mutually supportive group setting old people have the opportunity to share with one another feelings of uselessness and fears of death, pride in past achievements and present successes, and intimations of some greater spiritual purpose in life. Instead of accepting limitations of motion or declining intellectual capacity as sadly inevitable, instead of relying on prescription drugs to alleviate pain and muscular stiffness of chronic disease and attrition, workers in these programs help old people to learn to use natural, nonpharmacologic self-help techniques.

These methods are drawn from a variety of cultural traditions and adapted to the needs of the elderly. Among them are Tai Chi, a moving meditation universally used by older people in China to maintain suppleness and balance; deep breathing to promote high levels of brain oxygenation; and progressive relaxation and acupressure to relieve such common functional ailments as back pain, constipation, and headache. In weekly meetings these exercises offer an experiential counterpoint to group discussions, instruction in nutrition and vocational and legal counseling.

Several hundred have already participated in these two programs and the model, which SAGE pioneered, is being considered by dozens of other groups across the country. Meanwhile some of the old people who were in these programs have become staff members. They are helping to form new groups both inside institutions for old people as well as in their communities.

---

[28] Curtin, S. R. _Nobody Ever Died of Old Age_. Atlantic: Little-Brown, 1972.

[29] Robert Butler, M.D., Director of the National Institute on Aging, notes that though people over 65 now make up 11 percent of the population and will, by the time we ourselves are old, be 25 percent of it, less than 3 percent of the National Institute of Mental Health's money is devoted to their needs.

ALT 20

At SAGE, research results are indicating significant improvement in the participants' self-esteem (versus a control group) and in the pleasure they take in their lives.[30] At the Institute for Creative Aging, studies are underway to evaluate objectively the remarkable improvements in physical and mental functioning that participants have reported.

Other programs are attempting to provide concrete and comprehensive medical, social, and legal services to old people while at the same time offering them the opportunity to participate, as volunteers or paid workers, in delivering these services. Drawing on such progressive federally funded efforts as the Foster Grandparents Program (in which 16,000 old people spend some 20 hours a week caring for formerly institutionalized younger people) and the Senior Companion Prgram (3,100 elderly participants working with older people with special problems), as well as on more conventional Federal, State, and local health and social service monies, programs in Minneapolis and San Diego have done remarkably effective work.

In San Diego, a coalition of some eight programs which are themselves part of that city's Community Congress of alternative services had helped mobilize some 10,000 older citizens to take part in nutrition programs, "problem solving" groups, cooperative buying ventures, and health clinics. In Minneapolis, the Aging and Opportunity Center, using a variety of local and Federal legislative programs in an imaginative and aggressive way, has created a comprehensive service and advocacy program--with courts, landlords, nursing homes, and hospitals, etc.--which serves some 2,800 people a month.

Though they are not strictly speaking service programs, the political organizations which old people have formed on their own behalf, in particular the several thousand member Grey Panthers--and the alliances they are making with the young have contributed significantly to their and to our mental health. A group like the Panthers--tough, humorous, and very insistent--has provided many of its members with an opportunity to express outrage and to live a "second life" as a political and social activist. They have helped some of us who are younger to experience a connection to an earlier generation and to look forward to our own aging with more hope.

---

[30] Lieberman, op. cit.

ALTERNATIVE TREATMENTS FOR PSYCHOTIC ADULTS

There is a perspective on madness that is at least as widespread and certainly as ancient as our current view that it is a disease. It considers the constellation of symptoms that we describe as schizophrenia as part of a process of self-healing. This is the tradition which animated the gentle, protective treatment given to mad people at the Greek healing temples and at monasteries throughout the ancient Orient. It is also the tradition in which the most significant, current alternative treatments for madness are grounded.

C. G. Jung is the first of this tradition in modern Western psychiatry. While his teacher Bleuler was describing and diagnosing schizophrenics ("When all is said and done," he once observed, "my patients are stranger to me than the birds in my garden.") Jung was listening to their "personal stories." He realized that "at bottom we discover nothing new in the mentally ill; rather we encounter the substratum of our own nature." Jung viewed the psychotic breakdown as the beginning of a potential breakthrough, a path to a new, more fully integrated way of being.

Most recently this perspective and the therapeutic approach it suggests has been popularized by R. D. Laing. Laing characterized schizophrenia as "a voyage into self of a potentially revolutionary nature" and in 1965 created a healing community, at Kingsley Hall in London, where such voyages could take place.[31]

According to a 1977 survey of alternative residential programs by the National Institute of Mental Health's Center for Studies of Schizophrenia, there are approximately 20 to 30 such healing communities in the United States. In them, people are "guided and guarded" during the "natural healing process" of psychosis. These programs were generally created or are supervised by psychiatrists who have a Jungian or Laingian perspective. They are staffed largely by nonprofessionals who are intuitive, imaginative, emotionally stable, and patient enough to "be with" people who are taking the arduous journey through madness.[32] Most of the programs—Soteria in San Jose, Diabasis in San Francisco—do not use tranquilizing drugs; they regard them as a hindrance to the natural healing process as well as a danger to the person's physiologic well-being. Some, like Renaissance House in Santa Barbara, have begun to use techniques like massage and natural food diets to help restore their residents' emotional and physical balance.

A controlled study done at Soteria indicates that this kind of open, drug-free communal program produces significantly better long-term psychosocial

---

[31] Berke, J., and Barnes, M. <u>Mary Barnes: Two Accounts of A Journey Through Madness</u>. Harcourt, 1973; and Gordon, J. S. Who is mad? Who is sane: The radical psychiatry of R. D. Laing. <u>The Atlantic</u>. January 1971.

[32] Hirshfeld, R. M., et. al. Being with madness: Personality characteristics of three treatment staff. <u>Hospital and Community Psychiatry</u>. Vol. 28, No. 4, April 1977.

adjustment in its "schizophrenic" residents and no greater rate of rehospitalization than for people hospitalized in a well-staffed inpatient service for the acutely ill at a community mental health center.[33]

In addition to this kind of treatment for acute psychotic episodes there are several other kinds of programs that deserve mention. Though they seem to accept a medical definition of schizophrenia and use tranquilizing drugs they do seek to help people to avoid hospitalization and the stigmatization and institutionalization that are its sequelae. Both the Mendota Mental Health Institute and the Southwest Denver Community Mental Health Center use large numbers of highly committed staff to help acutely psychotic people to remain in the community.[34] Both of these programs attempt to mobilize community resources, including either natural or carefully trained and supervised "alternative families" to help people to live and work outside the hospital. Though their effectiveness in keeping people out of the hospital system over a long period of time is in doubt, both programs seem to help participants achieve significantly higher rates of employment and social adjustment than "controls."[35]

Psychosocial rehabilitation centers, of which there are 20 to 30 in the United States, may be seen as a complement to these crisis intervention programs. They are long-term community support systems for those who have been hospitalized many times. The first of these, Fountain House, was opened in 1948. Located in New York City, it provides a comprehensive social, recreational, and vocational program to some 1,200 people a month. A 9-year study of Fountain House's work reveals a marked reduction in time spent in the hospital for those who participated in the program.[36]

There are also several embryonic efforts by former mental patients (including Project Release in New York City and Project Renaissance in Cleveland) to provide a supportive community--including a central gathering place, separate living situations, and employment in cooperative businesses--that is totally outside of the framework of psychiatric hospitalization and beyond the control or purview of mental health professionals.

And finally, there are at least several thousand people who bear schizophrenic diagnoses who have chosen to seek treatment from "orthomolecular"

---

[33] Mosher and Menn, op. cit.

[34] Stein, L. I., and Test, M. A. "An Alternative to Mental Hospital Treatment: Conceptual Model, Treatment Program, and Clinical Evaluation." Unpublished, and Community families: An alternative to psychiatric hospital intensive care. <u>Hospital and Community Psychiatry</u>, Vol. 27, No. 3, March 1976.

[35] Kirby, M. W., and Polak, P. R. "Inpatient Alternative to Psychiatric Hospitalization: A Follow-Up Study." Presented at the Annual Meeting of the American Psychological Association, San Francisco, August 1977.

[36] Malamud, T. Fountain house: A nine year follow-up study. Submitted to <u>The Schizophrenia Bulletin</u>. 1978.

psychiatrists, physicians who view their psychosis as the product of a metabolic error which may present itself as a severe, perhaps pellagra-like vitamin deficiency. Physicians who use large or "mega" doses of B vitamins to treat these people claim a high rate of success, though no well controlled studies of their work have appeared. At least one alternative residence, Earth House in New Jersey, uses megavitamins and dietary manipulation as a major part of its therapeutic approach.

FREE CLINICS AND HOLISTIC HEALTH CENTERS

During the last 10 years, increasing numbers of physicians and lay people have begun to question the premises and practices of American medicine, first the way health care was distributed, then the way it was delivered, and finally the scientific theory on which it is based.[37] These critiques and the alternative services which they have helped to shape have implications for mental health as well as health care.

FREE CLINICS

In the late 1960's while groups like the American Public Health Association and the Medical Committee for Human Rights struggled politically against the AMA's (American Medical Association) position that health care was a "privilege not a right," free clinics (i.e., free at the point of delivery of care and relaxed in style), began to provide humane and easily accessible primary medical care to the young people who crowded into the centers of the counterculture.

The first free clinics, like the one in the Haight-Ashbury district of San Francisco, were inundated by young people looking for relief from a variety of physical, emotional, and drug-related problems. Though they had a room set aside for people on bad drug trips and provided walk-in counseling services, their major contribution to their patients' mental health was the way they treated them. Clinic workers carefully explained each aspect of their care to longhaired young people who had previously feared doctors and avoided treatment. It was as important at the Free Clinic not to talk down to patients or to hurry them through procedures they feared or misunderstood or to deny them information about preventing future illnesses, as it was to prescribe the correct antibiotic.

From the beginning these clinics readily included lay people in general, and patients in particular, on their staffs. They emphasized the intensive training and participation in all aspects of medical care of paraprofessionals, collective decisionmaking in setting organizational policy, and attention to the community's changing needs.

Since the Haight-Ashbury Clinic opened in 1967 some 400 other free clinics have been created. Though some, like the Prince George's County Free Clinic and The Door in New York City still focus on the physical problems (and their emotional sequelae) that particularly concern the young--birth control and prenatal care, minor urinary and respiratory ailments, venereal disease, and abortion--many others have become the primary health care resource for people of all ages in their area.

---

[37]Health Policy Advisory Center. *The American Health Empire*. Vintage, 1971; White, K. L. Prevention as a national goal. *Preventive Medicine*, 4,247-51 (1975); Illich, I. *Medical Nemesis*. Pantheon, 1976; and Carlson, R. *The End of Medicine*. John Wiley, 1975.

Just as the first free clinics respected the values of the youth culture, so these free community clinics are particularly attuned to the needs and style of people in their areas. The Cloverfork Clinic focuses on providing the basics of preventive and primary care to the miners and hill people who live in isolated Harlan County, Kentucky. Where the Pedances Health Unit in a medically diverse but poor Manhattan neighborhood regards community education--about housing, nutrition, and landlord-tenant relationships--an advocacy with established hospitals as a primary focus, the clinics of the California Urban Indian Health Coalition try to combine attention to the immediate needs of a poverty stricken population with concern for indigenous health rituals.

Though accurate statistics on the numbers of people cared for nationally are unavailable it is possible to make some estimates based on those that are available. A small, two-evening-a-week clinic, like the one in Prince George's County, has from 1,500 to 2,000 patient visits a year whereas a sizable full-time clinic like the Haight-Ashbury or the Washington, D.C., Free Clinic may have 10,000 to 12,000 visits a year, and a rural center like Cloverfork is the only source of health care for 10,000 isolated people. It is entirely possible then that free clinics account for some 2 to 4 million primary medical care visits each year.

It is interesting to note that this care, much of which is of course based on voluntary labor, is far less expensive than that offered by the city health departments. The same primary visit care that would cost $40 at a nearby clinic run by the City of San Francisco is $10 at the Haight-Ashbury Free Clinic. And client satisfaction seems to be high: David Smith, Chairman of the National Free Clinic Council, noted in 1976 that in its 10 years of operation no one had ever sued the Haight-Ashbury Clinic for malpractice and that, so far as he knew, no free clinic had ever had a malpractice judgment made against it.[38]

HOLISTIC HEALTH CENTERS

During this same period of time, clinicians and their patients have become dissatisfied with the "best care that money can buy," specifically the care available to people--the vast majority of those who come to doctors' offices--who complain of feeling poorly but lack demonstrable organic pathology. This failure has goaded both physicians and patients to question the definitions of physical and mental health and illness under which they operate and the kinds of treatment which these definitions dictate. The focus on pathology and disease; the too rigid separation of physical and emotional problems; the iatrogenic illnesses that result from so many pharmaceutical and surgical remedies; the assumption of an asymmetrical relationship between an all powerful physician and a submissive patient; and the concomitant wrenching of the process of healing from a supportive social context have all prompted clinicians, researchers, and patients to look for therapeutic measures in other traditions and other techniques.

---

[38] Smith, D. E. The free clinic movement in the United States: A ten year perspective. <u>Journal of Drug Issues</u>. Fall 1976.

A new approach to healing--variously called "holistic," "integral," "humanistic"--is gradually emerging from this questioning. This approach conceives of and addresses itself to the "whole person in a total environment." Disease is seen as the result of an imbalance among a variety of social, personal and economic, as well as biologic, influences and healing as a method for restoring balance within the individual and between the individual and the environment. Instead of attacking the disease process with a technologic armamentarian physician and patient, healer and healee are learning techniques which permit them to make use of what Hippocrates called the "vis medicatrix naturae," the healing force of nature.

There is a growing emphasis on poor diet, lack of exercise, and stressful lifestyle as the precursors of physical and emotional dysfunction and on the relationship between social and environmental stress and physical and emotional illness.[39] Attempts to restore physical and emotional balance are making use of the centuries-old preventive medical techniques of Chinese medicine, yoga and herbalism, of homeopathy, massage, and chiropractic, and of such modern techniques as biofeedback, guided imagery, and lifestyle, and pastoral counseling. All depend on a holistic or integrated view of mind, body, and spirit, an attempt to rechannel energy and strengthen the whole person rather than to eradicate illness or erase a defect.

The editor of the most comprehensive resource guide on holistic health estimates that there are as many as 50 to 100 holistic health and "wellness" centers nationwide.[40] Most of these centers are used exclusively by middle class people--they tend to be located in wealthy areas like Mill Valley, California, or in middle class neighborhoods and the services are largely nonreimbursable as well as exotic--but some like The Wholistic Healing Centers outside of Chicago serve working class people as well. Thousands of individuals--300 in the Baltimore-Washington area, alone--have also begun to incorporate these techniques in their practice.[41] Some centers and some individual physicians, nurses, and psychologists, are using them to relieve such stress related conditions as colitis, hypertension, migraine, and chronic pain.[42] Others are helping people with anxiety, depression, and headache deal with these problems through biofeedback, meditation, yoga, acupressure, Tai Chi, and massage.

---

[39] Holmes, T. H., and Rahe, H. The social readjustment rating scale. *Journal of Psychosomatic Research*, 11:213-218, and Selye, Hans. *The Stress of Life*. McGraw Hill, 1956.

[40] Kaslof, L., ed. *Wholistic Dimensions in Healing*. Doubleday, 1978, in press.

[41] *Healing Resources of the Baltimore-Washington Area 1977*.

[42] Benson, Herbert. Systemic hypertension and the relaxation response. *New England Journal of Medicine*. May 19, 1977. pp. 1152-1155; Kroenig, R., Volen, M., Bresler, D. Acupuncture: Clinical Applications and Current Status in America. In: Gordon, J., Jaffe, D., and Bresler, D., eds. *Body, Mind and Health: Toward an Integral Medicine*. NIMH, in press; Simonton, O. C., and Simonton, S. S. Belief systems and management of the emotional aspects of malignancy. *Journal of Transpersonal Psychology*, Vol. 7, No. 1, pp. 29-48; and Polletier, J. *Mind as Healer, Mind as Slayer*. Dell, 1977.

CONCLUSIONS AND RECOMMENDATIONS

Alternative services are remarkable precisely because they are not bound or blinded by any particular professional ideology, because the people who work in them regard it as their primary responsibility to pay attention to the needs of their clients, because they respond from their heart and gut as well as their head, use techniques that work, and try to do no harm. Guided by these principles, alternative services have created situations to make it possible for people to grow and change. If their practices calcify, if a way becomes "The Way"--to operate a center for runaways or heal a sick person-- then alternatives will be just another hustle. The word will be as limiting as any label.

It has been extraordinary for me to learn as much as I have about alternative services, to see and feel the ways that people work together to create a helping and healing community. It seems vitally important for use to continue to learn from what people in alternative services are doing and to encourage their growth and development.

When I presented my preliminary report I wondered aloud if the Government should fund alternative services, and specifically if they should be funded as mental health services. The answer to the first question is inevitably "yes": "I'm here" the Black woman in the shelter for battered wives told me, "but there are too many women for the room we got. They're winding up in the hospital or in the morgue while you all think about giving us money." So, sometimes, when no one has paid attention for too long, when there is something genuinely new to do, or there are gross inequities which must be redressed, legislation and regulations and programing and the money that makes it possible are necessary.

In this first section I will recommend a general approach to legislation which affects service delivery and to the agencies which are charged with administering programs. It is particularly relevant to alternative services but is hopefully relevant to other kinds of mental health programs. In the second section I will make recommendations specifically addressed to the National Institute of Mental Health.

1. <u>Community groups which have already been providing services--whether they are shelters for battered women, centers for runaways, holistic health programs, or alternatives to mental hospitalization--should be involved in the legislative and funding process at each step</u>. They should be asked to testify and be included on agency review panels (from which, because of their lack of credentials or established connections, they are almost always excluded) and on the State or local boards which may ultimately decide where some of the monies go. When monies come directly from Federal agencies notice should be sent to the alternative services that might be interested.

2. <u>Community groups which have already been providing services should be given first priority in receiving money for those services, in providing training for workers, or in doing research</u>. The Family Violence Prevention and Treatment Act (H.R. 4948) introduced by Congresswomen Barbara Mikulski addresses some of these problems: "The most effective direct service programs for the victims of family violence have been developed in the private voluntary

sector by dedicated volunteers, and the most effective approach to the delivery of social services to such victims has involved person-to-person support systems and an emphasis on self-help." If experts--individuals, consulting firms, university professors--are necessary for a particular research or training project they should work as subcontractors for the people who are providing the services, not vice versa.

3. Legislation should always be designed for the broadest possible group of people and that group should be defined in the least pejorative, simplest way. There is an enormous temptation in formulating legislation to focus on problems. Perhaps it looks or feels good to be outraged about juvenile crime, mortified by teenage prostitution, or bellicose about cancer. As it happens, these participial attitudes are often part of the problems, not their solutions. Just as policemen cannot work without criminals so programs for runaways or juvenile delinquents or drug abusers cannot survive without people to fit these categories. They are thus induced to perpetuate what they are supposed to remedy.

It makes far more sense for people to be funded as broadly as possible to provide services to those who need them. Thus I would, on principle, prefer money to come for "services for young people and their families" from the Youth Development Bureau (an innocuous and vaguely positive, though rather cumbersome, name for an agency) than from the Law Enforcement Assistance Administration or from the National Institute on Drug Abuse: The director of one drop-in center told me that to provide her services, it defined as a drug abuser a troubled young woman who smoked two marihuana cigarettes a week on Saturday night--and that when funding switched from drug abuse to "law enforcement money" he encouraged her parents to declare her "in need of supervision" so that the agency might continue its service to her.

4. Legislation and regulations should insure the responsiveness of all services (alternative and otherwise) to their clients by insisting that all funded programs recruit clients and community people to work as volunteers and paid staff in their services, and to sit on their decisionmaking boards.

5. Agencies should assure effective and sensitive monitoring of grants and contracts by insisting that all project officers and indeed all program administrators spend some part of their time involved in direct service work in their local communities, preferably in projects similar to the ones that they are charged with administering.

6. Federal agencies should substitute a process of conscientious and informed monitoring from some of the vast amounts of paperwork normally required. Lengthy client forms and reporting requirements prevent many alternative services from applying for Federal money and tend to bureaucratize those that receive it and estrange them--or at least some workers in them--from their clients.

7. Legislation should mandate a variety of Federal agencies--Community Services Agency (CSA), Alcohol, Drug Abuse, and Mental Health Administration (ADAMHA), Office of Human Development (OHD), Law Enforcement Assistance Administration (LEAA), Housing and Urban Development (HUD), etc.--to award small amounts of money with minimal application forms and reporting requirements to community service groups. To a group of volunteers trying to rent a house for

ALT 29

a shelter, or an office for a drop-in center, $5,000 can make the difference between survival and growth and organizational collapse. A similar bill for Youth Crisis Centers was introduced by Vice President Mondale, then Senator Mondale, several years ago.

8. <u>The Executive should create an office within the Federal Government which would facilitate the exchange of information between alternative services and Congress and the Federal agencies and among alternative services</u>. This agency would also act as an "ombudsperson" for alternative services, continually raising Federal consciousness about kinds of needs the community workers were discovering and what kinds of services were being developed to meet them. This office could also provide community based alternative services with technical assistance in preparing grant applications.

9. Congress should make certain addenda to each piece of legislation regarding services that would be of small but real use to the people providing them and to their clients, among them the provision (a) that all services be on the ground floor, and therefore accessible to handicapped people, and (b) that nonprofit agencies be permitted to "write off" their telephone tax.

SERVICES AT NIMH

The heart--virtually, the whole body--of NIMH's service delivery system is the community mental health centers program. In 1963, when John F. Kennedy hailed it as a "bold new approach" to mental health, community mental health centers were remarkably progressive and exciting. Though they have brought mental health services to many people, they have never really lived up to their promise or fully come to terms with the "medical model" of mental illness, which they sometimes accept, sometimes reject. It seems to me that it is time to bring back the original spirit of the community mental health centers movement, a spirit which incidentally is remarkably close to that of alternative services--to make professional expertise available to far larger numbers of people in a way that makes sense to them, to invoke a more holistic approach to people living in communities.

Everything I have learned about alternative services over the last 10 years, and everything I have seen and heard in visiting projects and collecting information for this study leads me to believe that dedicated nonprofessionals who are in touch with the needs of the people they are serving can provide a majority of mental health services in a way that is more congenial, at least as effective, and less expensive than mental health professionals. They are already doing it in shelters for battered women, in houses for runaways, in long-term group foster care for psychotic or borderline teenagers and in alternatives to mental hospitalization. Mental health professionals are essential as consultants to these projects and the people who work in them; as trainers in such modalities as individual, family, and group therapy; occasionally as direct service workers with the most disturbed or disturbing of clients, and rarely, when organic disease is suspected, as physical and psychodiagnosticians.

I would suggest then that instead of spending the majority of their time in direct service work with patients that professionals in community mental

ALT 30

health centers devote the better part of their time to a much expanded version of the "consultation and education" that is now so often neglected; that their primary job should be to consult with people in the community about the services they have already begun, and to catalyze, but not dominate, efforts to create new residential counseling and community development programs.

One of the goals of this change in emphasis would be to provide, in any community, a place where someone who was acutely psychotic might be able to go--a crisis house or an individual family where he could be guided and protected by a specially patient and skillful staff of community residents. There, symptoms would not be suppressed by drugs. Instead the psychotic episode could become the kind of natural healing process that it is in some traditional societies and in such modern experimental communities as California's Soteria and Diabasis. Similarly, CMHC workers might consult with or help start shelters for young people who could not live at home or "women in transition" where they could gain perspective on their lives and share their problems without defining themselves as mentally ill.

Though a dangerous and uncontrollable few would continue to require institutionalization, the vast majority of those who need longer term care could be kept in their own communities--in ordinary houses easily accessible to friends and relatives. Many of these people could--if staff workers provided organization and leadership--learn to take care of one another. Already some shelters for battered women and residences for older teenagers are run by clients; certainly old people who are healthy but homeless could supervise the care of young people who are chronically ill; and students at colleges or young workers could be subsidized--well below the cost of conventional foster care--to live with runaways who lack homes to return to.

The majority of people with problems do not, of course, need crisis intervention or residential services. Instead of assuming they needed "therapy" centers would offer them the resources--professional expertise, advocacy, and education--to help them deal with their own problems. People would be helped to understand themselves as participants in and often enough sufferers from the concrete situations of their life--a part of a family, an office, a work group, or a class--and could be worked with in these settings.

At the same time some centers might begin to provide the basic health care which has been lacking in our society. Under the supervision of physician's assistants, nurse practitioners, and neighborhood people trained by them could discuss and review each person's physical and emotional well-being, could investigate the economic, occupational, familial, and intrapsychic causes of stress in their lives. Together they could formulate a regime of diet, exercise, and relaxation, or look for employment or decent housing.

Groups of people with special concerns or problems--women wanting to share with each other questions about their roles as women; parents of retarded or autistic children, old people wishing to improve their psychological and physical functioning--would be helped if needed to form groups with or without a leader in which they could discuss and deal with their common concerns.

Individual therapy would still be available but there would be a shift in emphasis toward helping people to develop the capacity to analyze their social

ALT 31

situations and physical and emotional needs and thus be able to use a network of helpers both within the center and outside. Instead of relying on drugs to elevate mood or calm anxiety, to deaden headaches, or stop gastric secretion, people would be taught to deal with those conditions through biofeedback, meditation, yoga, acupressure, Tai Chi, and massage. Learning to use these "self-help" techniques would enable people to avoid prolonged dependency on professional helpers; contribute to their sense of control over their own lives; and remove the possibility of dangerous side effects and diminshed performance which always attend the use of psychotropic drugs.

For the community as a whole, the center--which like other federally funded programs would have clients on its government board--would be the kind of gathering place that alternative services already are, a place where people could come when they just felt like being with others as well as a source of help in times of trouble.

The point of all this is not simply to produce another kind of treatment, and certainly not to insist that all centers do all things in a particular way; but to change the structure of treatment and the delivery of services; to relate to troubled people on their terms; to insist that their needs--not the preconceptions or self-interest of any professional group--shape the kind of help they receive; to give them the opportunity to use their full potential and to heal themselves; and to support--not usurp--the kinds of initiatives that alternative services have already taken. As community mental health centers change it will be important to provide support, through them or independently, to some new and innovative alternative service programs that do not easily fall into already established funding categories. Places like shelters for battered women, holistic health and birthing centers, and intentional caring communities like The Farm are remarkable natural experiments and will repay nonintrusive support with precious knowledge.

In order for a reformed community mental health center program or indeed for any large-scale attempt to fund innovative services to work, fee-for-service funding--either as it exists now or as it might under a national health insurance--might be inappropriate. The most effective kind of funding for many alternative services have been grants or contracts which pay them to provide whatever services are necessary for their particular clients and their families, for the surrounding neighborhood, and for the community at large. In a community mental health center which regarded its mission as service to the community rather than treatment of citizens, which called out to them rather than called them in for appointments, a fee-for-service model would seem counterproductive. It might be far more effective to provide funding under a National Health Service of the kind proposed by Representative Ron Dellums of Berkeley, or alternatively under some stable grant formula.

RESEARCH

The kind of service program I have described would be a real change and would demand continual evaluation and consideration. We would want to know what new community programs are most effective and why and how working in this new kind of center changes our role--and our ideas about mental health and illness.

As a complement to a program which is seeking to promote health, we will want to know more about why our working and living conditions make us so tense and so prone to psychosomatic illness, hypertension, and alcoholism, and what we can, as individuals and a community, do about these conditions. We will also want to understand other healing modalities, in their own context, before we rush to analyze what is "really happening" in our Western scientific terms; to see how effective they are in treating psychophysiological disorders. Benson's work in reducing hypertension with the meditative "relaxation response" is only one example of a variety of modalities that may help and surely will do no harm. On a still more "basic" level, there is no reason, "scientific" or otherwise, why a neurochemical level of analysis should be more likely to lead us to the biological basis or correlates of schizophrenia than say, an analysis undertaken at the level of energy balance in the acupuncture meridians. Our research should proceed in both areas.

TRAINING

Finally, any attempt to make the kinds of changes in service and attitudes that I have described will inevitably require a new kind of training, not only of the physicians, psychologists, and social workers who will help facilitate this change but of the paraprofessionals and the clients with whom they will work. Professionals need training which helps them to understand how their attitudes and convictions are formed by their own values and culture, and how they may at times prevent them from working effectively with people. They need to learn also that in addition to being bearers of knowledge and purveyors of new techniques they are the servants of those for whom they work.

There is enormous room in the projects I have described for training community people to work with particular groups and an enormous need on the part of both the young and the old to be a part of a community that has some common purpose and some larger goal. In that context even the most arduous tasks will change their character: For most attendants the experience of working with mentally ill people in a hospital setting is grim, demeaning, and uncomfortable; working with the same people in a place like Soteria, Diabasis, or Renaissance House or in one of the group foster homes that I have worked with is exciting and challenging if sometimes exhausting.

In addition to giving community people skills in counseling and group work that they may need it may make sense to train eager young people to be primary care providers and educators, the American equivalent of barefoot doctors, in their neighborhoods; if indeed midwifery is as safe in low risk deliveries as it seems, and as conducive to good family mental health then we will want to provide special training, and professional backup, for a whole new cadre of women who are particularly drawn to and skilled in that kind of work.

Within the last year, in the pages of Science and the New England Journal of Medicine, many of the most important workers in psychiatry--George Engle, Jerome Frank, and Leon Eisenberg, for example--have been calling into question the old narrow medical model of mental health and illness. They are looking for a broader understanding of the relations between body, mind, and society for a new and more "holistic" way of looking at people, their environment, and their problems. At a time when 15 percent of the population is in "need of mental help," when millions of people are addicted to drugs and alcohol, and millions of others each year consume billions of capsules of tranquilizers; when 20 million suffer from hypertension and a like number from sleep onset insomnia, it does indeed seem high time for us, together with alternative services, to rephrase the questions and to look for fresh answers to our problems.

ACKNOWLEDGMENTS

This report is the product of the years I have spent with workers in and clients of alternative services, and of more recent discussions and visits done on behalf of The President's Commission on Mental Health. Though hundreds of people have in fact contributed information and ideas, I particularly want to express my gratitude to the alternative service workers who volunteered their time to help me collect and synthesize the material contained in this report: Susan Lenz, Ann Brickson, Lori Kaplan, Ed Hendrickson, and Bobby Boyd. I would also like to thank Joy Schulterbrandt, Chief of the Center for Studies of Child and Family Mental Health, National Institute of Mental Health, who encouraged me to undertake this study, and Judy Goldstein and Gloria Goldsmith who typed it for me.

Report of the Task Panel

on

MENTAL HEALTH PERSONNEL

Submitted to

THE PRESIDENT'S COMMISSION ON MENTAL HEALTH

February 15, 1978

Task Panel: Mental Health Personnel

MEMBERS

Harold L. McPheeters, M.D., Coordinator
Director, Commission on Mental Health
    and Human Services
Southern Regional Education Board
Atlanta, Georgia

Hattie Bessent, Ed.D.
American Nurses' Association
Kansas City, Missouri

Scott Briar, D.S.W.
Professor and Dean
School of Social Work
University of Washington
Seattle, Washington

Raymond D. Fowler, Jr., Ph.D.
Professor and Chairman
Department of Psychology
The University of Alabama
University, Alabama

Alan Gartner, Ph.D.
Co-Director, New Human Services
    Institute and Professor, Center
    for Advanced Study in Education
Graduate School and University Center
City University of New York
New York, New York

Wilfred H. Higashi, Ph.D.
Director of Mental Health
Division of Mental Health
Utah Department of Social Services
Salt Lake City, Utah

Donald Langsley, M.D.
Professor and Chairman
Department of Psychiatry
University of Cincinnati College
    of Medicine
Cincinnati, Ohio

Jonathan P. A. Leopold, M.D.
Associate Professor
Department of Mental Hygiene
School of Hygiene and Public
    Health
Johns Hopkins University
Baltimore, Maryland

Patricia Locke
President, National Indian
    Education Association
Boulder, Colorado

TABLE OF CONTENTS

	Page
Introduction	4
Summary and Major Recommendations	5
Background and Review	10
Overview of Categories of Personnel	22
Overview of Mental Health Personnel Issues	36
Recommendations	54
Tables	74
Acknowledgments	80
References and Bibliography	81

INTRODUCTION

This is the report of the Task Panel on Mental Health Personnel to the President's Commission on Mental Health. The task panel was made up of nine persons representing a range of interests and perspectives in regard to personnel for the delivery of mental health services. The panel did its work through two 2-day meetings and a number of telephone calls, letters, and working papers prepared by individual members.

This report explores issues for the entire Nation--not just for the Federal Government. Many recommendations are directed to agencies of the Federal Government, but others are made to accrediting bodies, professional societies, State governments or other component actors in the national mental health personnel effort. The delivery of mental health services is a labor-intensive area, and the nature and quality of these services is dependent on the skills and availability of the people who provide them. This task panel was therefore charged with reviewing and assessing information on the current supply, distribution, education, qualifications, and utilization of mental health personnel, and of identifying possible actions to rectify any deficiencies.

It is recognized that personnel/manpower efforts must encompass a wide range of concerns and activities, including the usual matters of supply and training, i.e., development and production of mental health personnel, but also such varied functions as distribution, recruitment, utilization, policy planning, credentialing, increasing productivity, quality assurance, career systems, and evaluation of training and other personnel development activities. The mental health personnel system is a complex array of professions and occupations, educational institutions, operating mental health agencies, State and Federal governments, voluntary and official credentialing bodies, and all of the varied payment programs that decide who will be paid for what services.

The task panel early realized that there are problems in defining "mental health personnel" because many persons from the mental health professions and occupations are employed in other parts of the human services delivery system (e.g., social services, corrections, general health, child welfare, vocational rehabilitation) while at the same time many "mental health" services are provided by practitioners in those other human service programs. The report makes mention of some of the relationships and responsibilities of the formally designated mental health system to these other programs and acknowledges the interdependent role that mental health has with those programs. It has limited itself to a study of specialized mental health personnel, both professional and paraprofessional, in the service delivery area, and does not discuss those who are primarily engaged in teaching or research.

Finally, it should be stated that although the original name of the task panel was "Manpower and Personnel," the word "manpower" has been dropped because of the strong feelings of some members that it is sexist in nature. The alternate word personnel refers to a collection of individuals, and is not meant to have the connotation of a personnel system or the staff of any given organization.

SUMMARY AND MAJOR RECOMMENDATIONS

The years since the report of the Joint Commission on Mental Illness and Health have seen a dramatic growth in the utilization of mental health services, in the nature and variety of these services, the places where they are provided, and in the number and type of specialized mental health personnel. This growth is evident not only in the major professions but also in the development of diverse mid-level and paraprofessional categories of personnel. Since the etiology of mental disorders includes biological, psychological, interpersonal, environmental, and social causes, it is evident that treatment of the resulting problems must be carried out by personnel with a wide range of skills whose education or training is based on a body of scientific knowledge, technology, and experience.

In spite of the progress which has been made in enlarging the supply of these skilled service providers, many problems remain. There is a need to conceptualize new strategies for personnel development and utilization, including continuation of support for education and training, to correct these problems. The eight major recommendations of the panel to the Federal Government are listed here; the body of the report will present a more detailed analysis of the current situation and issues around mental health personnel and conclude with a further discussion of these recommendations and others brought to the panel for its attention.

UNDERSERVED POPULATIONS

Data show that many areas of the country are almost totally without specialized mental health personnel. State and county mental hospitals and other public service settings have a shortage of psychiatrists and other fully qualified professionals, and there is an extreme scarcity of personnel trained to work with children and the elderly. Of particular concern is the finding that many minority and bilingual people go without treatment or are inadequately served because facility staff do not speak their language or are insensitive to their culture and values. Minorities are grossly underrepresented in the mental health professions.

Recommendation 1

> The Federal Government should give top funding priority to train and support professional and paraprofessional personnel in programs directed at:
>
> (a) the amelioration of geographic maldistribution;
>
> (b) increasing the number of minority professionals and developing the sensitivity of nonminorities to minority culture and values;
>
> (c) training specialists in the mental health of children and the aged; and

(d) to institutions affiliated with public service agencies which teach the skills necessary for this type of career.

THE MENTAL HEALTH MANPOWER/PERSONNEL SYSTEM

The mental health manpower/personnel system is a complex set of interactions including personnel policy planning, recruitment, education and continuing education, utilization, credentialing, distribution, funding, and management of personnel to achieve the most effective delivery of mental health services to those who need them. This involves the participation of personnel planners, leaders of professional and paraprofessional associations, professional and other schools, State and local mental health agency leaders, credentialing bodies, funding agencies (Federal, State, and private), standard setting agencies, merit systems, civil service systems, and unions. This broad concept of manpower/personnel requires considerable further definition and research to enable Federal and State programs to develop and make the most effective use of all personnel.

Recommendation 2

The ADAMHA should give leadership through program activities and funding to:

(a) the formulation of a more comprehensive concept of manpower/personnel programs and

(b) State level programs of manpower/personnel development.

PROFESSIONAL EDUCATION

The panel strongly believes that the Federal Government has a role in assuring the availability of qualified mental health professionals to provide care to all its people. The National Institute of Mental Health has, over the years, helped to build the capacity of training institutions to assure an adequate supply, but recent abrupt changes in policy and decreases in funding have imperiled this capacity. Systematic program redirection is virtually impossible when there is no assurance that funds will be provided to make these new activities viable. In addition, minority students are particularly dependent on Federal support, and data show their numbers decrease when such funds for stipends are lacking.

Recommendation 3

The Federal Government should maintain the present level of mental health professionals (in proportion to the population) by increasing the funding of categorical programs for their training to the 1970 level (adjusted for inflation). In so doing, priorities should be assigned in the distribution of these funds to:

(a) training in the provision of mental health services to rural populations and rectifying geographic maldistribution problems;

(b) increasing the numbers of mental health professionals with special competence in the care of children, the aging, and minorities;

(c) increasing the numbers of minority professionals, and

(d) programs utilizing community mental health centers, public mental hospitals, and other organized care facilities as a locus for training in collaboration with established educational institutions.

PARAPROFESSIONALS

A wide array of mental health paraprofessional training and utilization programs have grown up in response to local needs and initiatives in the past 10 years. There is need for national leadership in providing better guidelines for the definition of various levels of paraprofessionals and for the utilization, credentialing, and financing of these workers so that they may be better integrated in the mental health personnel and services system.

Recommendation 4

> The ADAMHA should provide increased funding for projects to better study and define the various kinds and levels of paraprofessionals, their training and continuing education needs, their utilization in various mental health settings, their credentialing, and the financing of the services of paraprofessional workers.

RESEARCH, EVALUATION, AND STANDARDS

The technology for many areas of personnel planning, forecasting, and evaluation is weak. Little is known about programs to change personnel distribution, or about various models of team and personnel organization which can provide more effective services. Assessment of need and definition of shortage areas is hampered by a lack of agreement about standards for the optimal number, mix, and qualifications of staff categories.

Recommendation 5

> The National Institute of Mental Health should increase its funding for research and evaluation in the personnel area as a tool for program planning, technical assistance, and development of quality services. Important areas include:

(a) evaluation of which services are necessary and effective, how they can be provided, and the skills necessary to provide these;

(b) evaluation of the education and training necessary to attain these skills;

(c) the development of staffing standards for federally funded mental health facilities based on needed and effective services and which types of personnel are qualified to provide them, not merely on staff-patient ratios.

DATA

The writing of this report was severely hampered by the lack of timely, consistent, and comprehensive data on mental health personnel. Formation of policy and program planning in the areas of training, service delivery, and standard setting should rest on accurate data.

Recommendation 6

A unit should be established within NIMH to collect and analyze data on the supply, distribution, education, and activities of all mental health personnel. Such data would be used for identification of shortage areas and needs for different types of personnel, and as an aid in program planning and evaluation.

LINKAGES

Many of the mentally disordered seek help from or are served by the general health, social service, or other community service systems. The mental health system needs to give greater emphasis to improving linkages to these areas.

Recommendation 7

The Alcohol, Drug Abuse, and Mental Health Administration should provide increased funding for programs to better assist mental health professionals and agencies in training and consulting with primary health care providers, nursing homes, social service agencies and workers, the clergy, self-help groups, schools, and correctional programs. This would involve, among other things, training in psychiatry for primary care physicians, the establishment of linkages between ADAMHA and other parts of DHEW concerning program and training support, programs of prevention, and a comprehensive analysis of the interrelationships of the health, mental health, and social service systems.

CHANGES IN LAWS AND REGULATIONS

Minor changes in Public Law 94-484 (The Health Professions Educational Assistance Act) would serve to increase the availability of mental health personnel and treatment and allow for more consistent Federal health personnel planning.

Recommendation 8

> The following amendments should be made to P.L. 94-484.
>
> (a) include psychologists and social workers as health service providers, make them eligible for National Health Service Corps scholarships, and include these professionals in the designation of mental health manpower shortage areas.
>
> (b) identify psychiatry as a medical specialty in which there is a national shortage.
>
> (c) allow those medical students entering psychiatric residency training who have incurred a service obligation in return for support received during their medical training to defer such service for a period of 4 years (instead of the current 3 years) for general psychiatrists and 5 years for child psychiatrists.
>
> (d) mandate the inclusion of training in mental health/psychiatric skills in the training of all primary care physicians in programs funded by the Act.

BACKGROUND AND REVIEW

No discussion of personnel needs can take place without consideration of the vast changes that have occurred in the mental health service delivery system of the United States and the rapid expansion in recent years in the number and type of places where services are offered, of categories of personnel who provide these, in the nature of problems for which people seek help, in their expectations for solutions, and in the type of services given.

In the early years of the country, the severely mentally ill were stigmatized, sequestered at home, or kept in jails, workhouses, or almshouses. Public hospitals were often little better. During the 19th century the influence of Pinel and his "moral treatment" spread to many institutions and Dorothea Dix campaigned vigorously and successfully for the development of State operated asylums for the mentally ill.

The original mental health personnel were the medical superintendents of these asylums, physicians, and the matrons and attendants who staffed them. These medical superintendents formed an association which later evolved into the American Psychiatric Association and the physicians evolved into present day psychiatrists.

By the late 1870's it became apparent that the "moral treatment" that had been so enthusiastically endorsed by the early medical superintendents was not effective in restoring many of the severely disturbed persons who had been sent to asylums, and the institutions began to grow in population and diminish in hope and support. State legislatures, beset by economic depressions, were unable to fund these asylums as they had intended, and so economy of costs and custody for patients became the hallmarks of the late 1800's and early 1900's.

This situation largely continued until the 1940's, except that most States had established separate institutions for the mentally retarded in addition to those for the mentally ill. In the late 1930's there had been research breakthroughs in the treatment of some major mental illnesses (e.g., the dementia of pellagra, syphilitic infection of the brain, insulin treatment, and electroconvulsive therapy), but the widespread application of these new technologies was interrupted by World War II.

However, World War II provided a considerable impetus to the mental health field and its personnel system in other ways, for it was World War II that highlighted what psychiatry and behavioral therapies could do for combat neuroses and emotional disorders other than the major mental illnesses. It also provided the thrust for the expansion of the Neuropsychiatry Services of the Veterans Administration with their support of professional training.

The late 1940's and early 1950's also saw the implementation of newer therapies in the State hospitals and new enthusiasm for the support of treatment programs and the employment of more professional personnel in the State hospitals. In several States, there were major thrusts for further development of outpatient and child guidance clinics in which psychoneuroses and behavioral problems could be treated. Meanwhile the professions of clinical psychology and psychiatric social work gained prominence. At first psychologists limited themselves to designing and administering tests of intelligence, memory, personality, etc., and social workers limited themselves primarily to working with families. However, in the outpatient clinics and child guidance clinics they acquired skills in the evaluation, treatment, and prevention of mental disorders.

In 1946 Congress passed the National Mental Health Act authorizing the Public Health Service to provide funds for the support of research, training, and services in the area of mental health. The following year the National Institute of Mental Health was established and programs were begun to increase the supply and improve the quality of education of psychiatrists, clinical psychologists, psychiatric social workers, and psychiatric nurses. The programs expanded until 1969, when yearly budgetary cuts and threats of total phase-out began.

In the early 1950's the primary mode of mental health treatment was long-term, often lifetime, hospitalization for the severely ill, and opportunities for outpatient therapy were limited. As recently as 1955, there were only 1.7 million episodes of patient care in mental health facilities, and 77 percent of these were in hospitals, primarily those run by the State or county.

The introduction of the major psychoactive medications in the middle 1950's, however, made possible the deinstitutionalization of many patients suffering from chronic disorders, and the report of the Joint Commission on Mental Illness and Health in 1961 gave impetus to the "third revolution" of community-based care and the development of community mental health centers. The joint commission felt that there would never be a sufficient number of professionals to staff these facilities and provide care for the growing number of people seeking treatment, and advocated the creation of a new category of mental health worker, on the job training for subprofessionals, and greater use of physicians, nurses, public welfare workers, scoutmasters, and others who were in positions to offer counseling to those with emotional problems.

American Society in the 1960's and 1970's

The years beginning with the Kennedy Administration and continuing to the present have brought vast changes in our American society that have had far-reaching implications for all of the human services including mental health and its personnel system.

The Congress with the encouragement of the Presidents affirmed the responsibility of the Federal Government to provide funds for the direct support of health services of several kinds. Basic health care was declared to be a right of the American people together with income security and housing. This concept was embodied in the legislation establishing the community mental health centers program in 1963. This mandate that mental health care is an entitlement of every citizen clearly called for a great expansion of both public and private services that would require corresponding increases in the personnel to deliver these services.

At the same time the Great Society programs of President Johnson called for increases of many other human service programs--family services, childrens' services, aging programs, vocational rehabilitation programs, community action programs, etc. These programs also demanded more personnel--often persons from the same professions that served mental health--especially social workers and psychologists. Despite increases in Federal funding from many different agencies and increases in State support for professional schools, the professional schools were unable to keep up with the demand. Vacant professional positions were often filled with persons who had only a baccalaureate degree in the social sciences, but no specialized training for human service work.

Meanwhile the War on Poverty was seeking ways to find jobs and career opportunities for poor people whose poverty or minority status or other living situations had denied them earlier opportunities to receive advanced education and then jobs. The Office of Economic Opportunity, Model Cities Programs, and the Department of Labor's New Careers Program, among others, developed projects to recruit persons from these circumstances and employ them in a wide range of human service agencies where they would be trained on the job either by the agency itself or in collaboration with a technical school or community college. Many of these new careers programs were in mental health agencies. Emphasis was placed on career systems with several levels and opportunities for advancement for these workers.

The so-called paraprofessional worker concept was further aided by the extensive development of community colleges in the higher education systems of the States and local communities. Many of these community colleges established associate degree education programs for nurses and a variety of other human service workers. Some of these programs were oriented to preparing workers related to the established professions of nursing and social work, but many more were targeted to preparing workers for an overall program area (e.g., Mental Health Technicians, Child Care Workers, Aging Program Workers, Corrections Workers).

Individual Rights

Perhaps the greatest change in American society that has had an impact on the human services and on mental health personnel during the past 15 years has been the increasing affirmation of the rights of individuals in our society. This has grown from the Civil Rights Movement of the early 1960's, but it is presently manifested in such far-reaching aspects as consumer rights, minority rights, students' rights, employee rights, rights of the handicapped, the women's movement, and patient rights.

The affirmation of the right of all Americans to mental health care which is available, accessible, acceptable, and affordable has already been noted. This has been the basis for the expansion of both private and public services, but especially it is the basis for assuring that there are mental health personnel to deliver services to persons who are now lacking care (those in rural areas, the poor, minorities, children, the aged, the chronically mentally ill, the retarded, alcoholics, and drug abusers).

However, there are other implications for mental health personnel that are being articulated in recent judicial decrees related to patient rights. Among them are:

--The right to treatment. No longer can a patient be held in a mental hospital without an active treatment program.

--The right to treatment in the least restrictive alternative. These two rights together have led the State hospitals to discharge large numbers of chronic patients. Courts are now insisting that treatment services be provided to them in the communities. This will require personnel for community based services.

--The right of informed consent to treatment procedures and the right to refuse treatment. The affirmation of these rights has made it appropriate to give sufficient information to patients for them to make their own decisions on the basis of facts. This has sometimes created another problem when needed treatment has not been strongly recommended and thus not given, a situation which can harm both patients and their families.

The minorities rights issues have led to affirmative action programs in both schools and agencies to recruit and retain minority persons as students and as employees.

Human Services Trends

As already noted, the past 15 years have seen a great increase in the numbers of and kinds of programs to serve people in all of the human service field. The human service field is the entire field of endeavor that is devoted to improving the bio-psycho-social functioning of the people, preventing disorders in any of these areas of functioning, remedying disorders that occur, and providing support services for those with chronic conditions.

It includes mental health together with general personal health, public health, social services, child welfare, youth services, vocational rehabilitation, aging, and corrections. As services in all these areas expand, the relationship among them becomes more evident, particularly since the stresses that produce disabilities in one are likely to cause problems requiring services from the other areas as well. The fragmentation of the present multiple delivery systems then creates new problems in terms of financing and overall responsibility for the well-being of the individual being served. This is especially visible in the mental health field. As a consequence of deinstitutionalization and the move to community care it is now being realized that to be maintained outside the hospitals, patients need a great many services that the mental health system itself is not equipped to give. There is increasing emphasis on the need for generic workers or case managers who can perform this integrating function. This may be a social worker or psychiatric nurse, since these activities are central to the role of these disciplines; or it may be one of the allied generic human service workers now being trained.

The human services represent a different field from health, and include the community support systems and the social services which must clearly relate to health. Mental health has been and must remain a part of health. However, rehabilitation and community support of the long-term mentally ill is a social service activity which cannot be abandoned by mental health. It is important to distinguish the separate systems while at the same time acknowledging that mental health requires support and linkages to both systems. It has already been noted that certain mental health personnel (especially social workers) carry on many of their activities within other human service systems, thus providing linkage with these systems.

The following are some trends affecting the overall human services as well as the mental health field:

--The trend to deinstitutionalization and the development of community based services. This is posing problems of retraining and relocating personnel and is particularly a problem for the large mental hospitals and schools for the mentally retarded.

--The trend to the development of self-help groups and renewed interest in natural systems of support in neighborhoods and communities (churches, friends, lodges, etc.). In the mental health field are Recovery, Inc., patient clubs, Alcoholics Anonymous, etc. Mental health personnel must know how to work with and assist these groups.

--The trend to greater interdependence of these systems as they all work with multiproblem persons and families in the communities. Mental health personnel must be prepared to offer timely and practical consultation and assistance to the workers of these other programs both in regard to the management of their mentally disabled clients and in regard to the mental or emotional aspects of whatever other problems their clients may have.

--The trend to the sharing not only of the same kinds of personnel, but even of the same persons over a period of time. Many social workers, psychologists, and nurses make their careers by moving from positions in one part of the human service system to positions in another program. In this sense they too are human service generalists.

--The trend to innovative service delivery programs. All the human services are experimenting with new service forms such as hot lines, halfway houses, social retraining programs for their clients, sheltered employment, drop-in centers, satellite operations, etc. These require personnel with the skills to organize, operate, and evaluate such innovative and small scale projects which are often not-for-profit contract agencies rather than large public bureaucracies.

--The trend to preventive activities and the promotion of well-being in addition to remedial and supportive services. It is essential to develop a knowledge base in these areas and to have personnel who are qualified to conduct prevention programs.

--Trends to comprehensive State and local planning programs including planning for personnel. In almost every human service program area there is a Federal mandate for State and local planning for the service area. We are developing a multitude of separate planning systems in the health, mental health, and social service fields, often based on different geographic areas and philosophies, and responsible to different units of government, and there is no mechanism for coordinating them. There is usually a requirement that there be a personnel component in such a plan, but most planning in this area so far has been very minor.

--<u>Trends to demand accountability in terms of cost control, productivity, and quality assurance</u>. With the large amounts of public monies, both Federal and State, have come increasing requirements for various program controls. The two that particularly affect personnel are the concerns for effectiveness and for assuring that the quality of services remains adequate. Also required are peer review mechanisms, evidence of continuing competence, and credentialing mechanisms to assure the quality of the services that the personnel deliver.

<u>The Mental Health Personnel System</u>

In addition to the trends already described for personnel in all of the human service programs, which also are affecting mental health, there have been some specific trends in the mental health field itself that affect personnel needs:

--<u>New techniques of intervention</u>. Since 1960 there have been developed a range of interpersonal therapeutic techniques--behavioral therapy, family therapy, transactional analysis, reality therapy, and others. These techniques have been adopted by many of the professions and disciplines for their work with clients. This is one of the reasons there is frequent mention of the "blurring of roles" of the individual professions, although others prefer to view it as role expansion.

--<u>The movement of all mental health professionals into positions of top administrative leadership in mental health programs</u>. At present the largest number of directors of community mental health centers from a single profession are social workers. There is also a recent trend to turn the overall administration of mental health programs over to persons trained primarily and/or solely in administration. Generally such persons are placed at the second level in the organization where they provide direction to fiscal management, support services, and facility maintenance. These persons are not often thought of as mental health personnel, but they are critically important to the efficient operation of the mental health system. In addition, there is increasing recognition of the need to provide training for administration in both the basic and continuing education curricula of all mental health professions.

--<u>The trend to provide for the rehabilitation and restoration of patients to community settings</u> rather than only diagnosis and treatment. At one time it was the custom to treat a patient until his mental status was clear and then to discharge him. Many patients were soon readmitted because they were unprepared to meet the demands of independent social and vocational functioning. Mental health programs are now more likely to provide for reeducation, and social and vocational training for patients, although many rely on the social service system to meet these needs. As a result, a variety of vocational, educational, and activities specialists are now coming into the mental health personnel system.

--<u>The trend for persons suffering from a wider variety of mental and emotional problems to seek treatment from mental health programs</u>. At one time only patients with major mental illness came to the mental health system. In the past 20 years much of the stigma once associated with mental health care has diminished--especially among younger and better educated persons. As a result many persons are seeking help for other problems--psychoneuroses, psychosomatic problems, personality disorders, behavior disorders of children, family and marital conflicts, acute crises, and situational problems. Many persons are looking to mental health programs to guide them in such endeavors as raising their children, preparing for retirement, living with elderly or handicapped family members, and coping with the emotional stresses of serious illness or death in the family. These are services that can be provided by a variety of mental health personnel.

--<u>The trend of society to define problems as mental health problems that were formerly criminal justice problems</u>. This has been especially true of alcoholism and drug abuse, but it has recently been happening also in regard to child abuse and wife beating. At the same time, however, there has been a trend away from excusing much criminal behavior on the basis of mental illness or mental instability.

<u>The Mental Health Personnel System, 1955-77</u>

In addition to these overall trends in mental health services and personnel, it may be well to examine some of the figures that show how extensively the mental health system has changed since 1955 when the major tranquilizing medications were introduced and the patient populations of the large State mental hospitals began to decline.

In 1955, the State mental hospitals were the mainstay of the mental health system. The patient census of those hospitals was over 750,000 in 1955; this population of resident patients in the State hospitals had declined by 1975 to just under 220,000. It has declined even further since that time.

The data being kept by the Office of Biometry of the National Institute of Mental Health in 1955 were primarily that for the mental hospitals, because those institutions made up the most identifiable part of the mental health system. There were also outpatient clinics, child guidance clinics, psychiatric units in general hospitals and private practitioners, but the reporting from these was incomplete. Today there are much better data on the activities and workloads of community based programs.

Location of Treatment

Recent data from NIMH (Regier, Goldberg, and Taube, in press) estimate that 6.7 million people were seen in the specialized mental health sector, both public and private, in 1975. Many were seen in more than one location. Approximately one-quarter of the treatment episodes in specialized facilities were in the inpatient units of hospitals, but only 9 percent were in State and county hospitals. An increasing number and proportion of people requiring inpatient services are receiving them in general and VA hospitals, or in units affiliated with CMHCs. Both inpatient and outpatient CMHC facilities accounted for 29 percent of the patient care episodes in 1975 and over 1.6 million people were seen there. Freestanding outpatient clinics saw 1.8 million people and 47 percent of the treatment episodes were in these facilities and in clinics affiliated with hospitals.

In addition to the persons seen in facilities, NIMH estimates that 1.3 million people were seen in the private offices of psychiatrists and psychologists, and perhaps 131,000 college students sought help in campus clinics. Even this total of 6.7 million accounts for only 21 percent of the estimated 32 million Americans with some emotional disorder.

The bulk of such individuals were seen in the health sector. Almost 1 million were treated in hospitals without separate psychiatric units and at least 207,000 were cared for in nursing homes. Over 19 million, or 60 percent of the total, were seen in the outpatient medical sector, the majority in the offices of nonpsychiatric physicians and the rest in clinics or emergency rooms. Finally an estimated 6.9 million people were either not seen or sought advice from the social services sector or community support systems. There are no data to describe the effectiveness of these services or of the skills of general health care or social service practitioners in diagnosing and treating mental disorder. There is some evidence that the most seriously disturbed people are seen in specialized facilities or by mental health professionals in private practice.

In summary, the years since 1955 have seen a tremendous rise in outpatient services, and there were 12 times as many outpatient care episodes in specialized mental health facilities in 1975 as in 1955. The number and rate of inpatient treatment episodes has continued to grow but there are far fewer in State hospitals and more in general hospitals, many without psychiatric wards. The private practice sector has increased rapidly in recent years, largely because of the addition of psychologists and social workers.

Facilities and Programs

The specialized mental health system now includes a much wider range of facilities than it did in 1955, largely as a result of the community mental health centers movement. Today there are at least the following kinds of facilities:

Inpatient

--State mental hospitals

--private mental hospitals

--psychiatric units of general hospitals

--psychiatric admissions to medical wards of general hospitals

--nursing homes

Outpatient

--community mental health centers

--outpatient clinics

--private offices of psychiatrists, psychologists, social workers, nurses, and general physicians

--emergency services

Transitional

--day care programs

--halfway houses

--social rehabilitation programs

--hot lines

--sheltered workshops

--board and care homes

Indirect Services

--consultation

--education

--community planning

Since 1955 there has been a considerable shift away from long-term hospitalization and even away from hospitalization at all if persons can be maintained in the community while receiving outpatient care or participating in some transitional service. Also under the community mental health movement there has been an increase in the amount and kinds of indirect services. The community mental health centers are mandated to provide consultation and education services, and 5 percent of the time of professional staff of the centers is reported to be devoted to these services.

The types of services provided by mental health personnel in these mental health facilities and programs have also broadened considerably since 1955. Among the major types of services provided are:

1. Client assessment

    --mental status studies

    --physical and neurologic studies

    --laboratory and X-ray studies

    --psychological tests

    --social living studies

    --vocational assessments

2. Therapies

    a. Physical therapies--Medications, including major and minor tranquilizers, antidepressants, psychic energizers, and a range of general health medications, and electroconvulsive therapy.

    b. Psychological therapies--

        --psychoanalysis and long-term psychotherapy

        --short-term psychotherapy

        --counseling

        --group therapy

        --behavioral therapy

        --family therapy

        --transactional analysis

    There are many other variations and forms of psychological therapies than are described (hypnotherapy, rational emotive therapy, insight therapy, biofeedback therapy, etc.).

3. Education and Rehabilitation Services

    --special education

    --vocational testing and instruction

    --vocational counseling

    --occupational therapy

--*social group work*

--*sheltered employment (transitional)*

4. *Social and Supportive Services*

--*casework services with clients and families*

--*referral services to other agencies*

--*advocacy services*

--*socialization services*

--*domiciliary services*

--*sheltered employment (terminal)*

--*recreational services*

--*pastoral care*

--*physical care*

5. *Indirect Community Services*

--*consultation*, both case consultation and agency consultation;

--*educational services* for the general public and special risk groups or to groups of community caregivers;

--*community planning* to develop new resources or obtain better services.

6. *Administrative and Managerial Services*--(These are services directed to maintaining and improving the mental health system rather than to clients or communities but they are important activities of mental health service personnel.)

--*planning and program development*

--*supervision*

--*program management*

--*program evaluation and research*

--*staff development*

There are other administrative functions such as obtaining resources, financial management, and public information, which belong to top level administrators rather than to the rank and file of professional personnel in the mental health delivery system, but the previously mentioned functions are likely to be found in the duties of any mental health professional in an organized care system in addition to his or her clinical service responsibilities.

Staffing of Facilities

As already noted, psychiatrists, clinical psychologists, social workers, and psychiatric/mental health nurses provided most of the services labeled "mental health" in 1955. There have been some substantial changes in these professions over the years as well as several additions to the types of providers in the mental health system.

The staff of inpatient facilities, formerly untrained aides and attendants, has been upgraded through inservice training and the employment of numbers of mental health workers trained at the associate of arts level. Other paraprofessionals have been employed in outpatient facilities in a variety of roles. There has also been a growth in the category of bachelors' level and above "other mental health professionals." These include counselors, vocational, recreational, and educational specialists as well as pastoral counselors and other mental health workers. In table 1, the increase is shown in staff of mental health facilities over the last 4-6 years, indicating a growth of 20 percent in the number of patient care staff from 1972-76. The categories showing the greatest proportional growth are psychologists, social workers, and other mental professionals. Those with less than a bachelor's degree have increased only slightly. On tables 2 and 3, the differences are shown in staffing patterns between State hospitals (with predominantly inpatient services) and community mental health centers (with predominantly outpatient services). CMHCs are staffed primarily by professionals, and the proportion of paraprofessionals has been dropping. Slightly more than half of the full-time equivalent patient care staff is from the four major professional disciplines, but the proportion of psychologists and social workers has been rising while that of psychiatrists and nurses has been falling. State mental hospitals, on the other hand, are primarily staffed by paraprofessionals, principally aides and attendants. Here too the percentage of patient care staff which is professional has been rising.

If the data are analyzed another way (table 4), it is evident that the large majority (78 percent) of all mental health staff work in inpatient facilities and almost half of them in State and county mental hospitals. Psychologists and social workers are most likely to be found in outpatient facilities, with about half of the staff in each discipline in either CMHCs or free-standing outpatient clinics. Mental health workers with less than a B.A., licensed practical nurses, and registered nurses are predominantly found on the staff of inpatient facilities.

The following sections will report in more detail the supply, distribution, training, and activities of the various categories of specialized mental health personnel (professional and paraprofessional), identify and discuss problems in the personnel area, and finally make recommendations for the solution of these problems directed toward the Federal Government, State governments, service agencies and training programs.

OVERVIEW OF CATEGORIES OF PERSONNEL

A. **Psychiatry**

Psychiatry is the medical specialty which deals with the diagnosis and treatment of mental disorder. As a physician, the psychiatrist possesses special skills in comprehensive evaluation, including the organic causes of mental illness and the psychiatric complications of organic disease, the management of psychiatric emergencies, the competent use of psychoactive medications, and the use of other physical treatments for mental illness. His role includes that of consultant to primary health care practitioners and to other medical specialists, as well as that of diagnostician, therapist, administrator, researcher, supervisor, and member of the mental health care team.

The supply of psychiatrists in the United States has grown from approximately 7,100 in 1950 to over 27,000 today, a ratio of 12.4 psychiatrists per 100,000 population. However, this number includes many retired persons, or persons primarily in administration. It also includes a large number of foreign medical graduates, most of whom have received their psychiatric training in the United States. These foreign medical graduates (FMG's) now constitute over 50 percent of the staffs of State and county hospitals. Many of them have considerable difficulty in relating to their American patients because of differences in language and culture. The new Health Professions Educational Assistance Act of 1976 (P.L. 94-484) is likely to reduce drastically the number of FMGs coming to the United States. The full impact of this law is difficult to predict, but it is sure to result in a reduction in the number of residents in training and ultimately in the staff of the State hospitals of those States which rely heavily on FMGs.

Meanwhile the supply of American medical graduates who have entered psychiatry has increased by only 1 percent since 1965. The number of American medical graduates in psychiatric residency training has dropped in each year since 1971-72 when there were 3,381 American medical graduates in training. In 1975-76 the number was 2,928, rising slightly to 3,006 in 1976-77. This shift is taking place despite a near doubling of the number of M.D.'s graduating from American medical schools in the past 12 years.

The distribution of psychiatrists is heavily weighted in favor of the urban centers and the wealthier and more urbanized States. Alabama, Idaho, Mississippi, North Dakota, South Dakota, and West Virginia have ratios of more than 25,000 population per psychiatrist while New York, Maryland, Massachusetts, and the District of Columbia have ratios of less than 5,000 persons per psychiatrist. Overall 68 percent of all counties in the United States have no psychiatrist at all. Most of these are small rural counties that are often located within driving distance of a city where there is a psychiatrist, but this travel poses special problems for poor people, children, and the aged. Altogether 82 percent of psychiatrists practice in cities of 100,000 or greater.

Psychiatrists report that approximately half of their work is in public service and half in private practice. Several studies show that slightly less than half of all psychiatrists not in training are primarily in private practice, and the other half primarily located in public mental hospitals, community mental health centers, medical schools, etc. The picture is not a clear one, because most psychiatrists work in more than one location. There were, for example, over 15,000 full-time equivalent psychiatrists working in mental health facilities in 1976. Recent data indicate that there may be an accelerating move toward public service. Approximately 10,000 psychiatrists report that they do primarily private practice, but there is some evidence to show that many of the kinds of patients seen and services delivered are similar in private practice and in public service.

Psychiatry, like the other professions, has dismayingly few minority practitioners. This is the result of the small number of minority persons who have graduated from medical schools plus the inclination, until very recently, for those few minority physicians to choose general practice. There will be special problems for psychiatry in recruiting more minority members since psychiatric residents must first be medical graduates.

Another supply issue in psychiatry lies in the relatively small numbers of psychiatrists who specialize in child psychiatry and in geropsychiatry. There are only about 2,800 child psychiatrists in the United States. Yet children make up 40 percent of the population. The Nation would need 11,000 child psychiatrists to provide the same proportion of child psychiatrists as children in the population. Only about 200 child psychiatrists complete training each year, barely enough to maintain the supply. There would seem to be some need for a special stimulus to increase the number of psychiatrists to meet this special need area.

At the other end of the age spectrum there are only a handful of psychiatrists who specialize in psychiatric problems of the aged, but there are no figures available. By the year 2000 it is estimated that 25 percent of the population will be over age 65; however, it seems unlikely that psychiatry could achieve that proportion of geriatric subspecialists.

A special problem is posed by the State mental hospitals which are often located in remote areas and which are often poorly funded and staffed. Psychiatrists are reluctant to take such positions when they have so many more attractive options. The State hospitals are reducing their populations so the need for psychiatrists there will slacken a bit. Studies have shown that special recruitment and training links to university training and consultation programs can help. Some States are experimenting with physician assistants and nurse practitioners to help with routine physical examinations and lesser medical problems which consume much of the time of State hospital physicians. Improved salaries, professional consultation, and sabbatical arrangements all offer promises of some assistance to the State hospitals.

Psychiatrists comprise a diminishing proportion of the staffing of community mental health centers. Between 1970 and 1976 the number of psychiatric staff positions per center has dropped from 6.8 full-time equivalents to 4.3 per center. The average number of psychologists has nearly doubled and that of social workers has increased by 35 percent. There has also been a drop from 29 percent to 14 percent in the proportion of trainees of community mental health centers who are psychiatric residents. Whether this is the result of an antimedical bias in the centers or difficulties in recruitment of psychiatrists or other causes is not clear. It does appear desirable to increase the amount of psychiatric training that is carried out in community mental health centers to acquaint more young psychiatrists with work in organized community mental health settings.

Competent psychiatric services must be accessible in any mental health program. The knowledge of psychiatrists regarding the major mental illnesses, the uses of medication and physical therapies, the influence of other medical conditions on mental functioning, and their depth of knowledge about psychiatric emergencies and mental disorders makes this essential. They are most intimately involved in the diagnosis and treatment of the major mental illnesses and the psychoneuroses and psychosomatic disorders but they serve as consultants in the treatment of all mental conditions. In many organized care systems, psychiatrists play a major role in the diagnostic process and in setting the treatment plan, but then they play primarily supervisory and consulting roles to other personnel who carry out the day-to-day work with patients. Psychiatrists also, of course, continue to carry medical responsibility for the patient. This kind of role is especially likely for the long-term mentally ill and for patients with more acute mental disorders.

From the earlier data showing that 54 percent of the mentally disordered receive mental health services primarily from the general health care system it is apparent that psychiatrists have a major consulting responsibility to the primary health care system. In many places psychiatrists do, in fact, provide frequent consultation and assistance to family physicians, general hospitals, and nursing homes regarding the recognition and treatment of mentally disordered persons in those systems, but much more needs to be done to prepare psychiatrists for this role and to encourage them to do more of it.

Aside from their special expertise as physicians, psychiatrists use many of the same psychological techniques of intervention in the treatment of psychological problems of their patients as the other mental health professionals. This leads to some of the talk of "role blurring" of the mental health professions.

All psychiatrists must be licensed as physicians. The national certification program for psychiatrists is the American Board of Psychiatry and Neurology, Inc. About 52 percent of psychiatrists are certified. Increasing numbers of psychiatrists are receiving certification, and a recertification program is in the planning stages.

Psychiatrists are trained in residency training programs which require 4 years for general psychiatry and 5 years for specialties such as child psychiatry. Most residency programs are affiliated with university medical schools (196), but there are still 60 unaffiliated resident training programs which are located in State mental hospitals, private mental hospitals, children's treatment centers, or CMHCs. State hospital based residency programs have drawn their candidates heavily from among foreign medical graduates, and some are completely dependent on these physicians. However, university affiliated psychiatric residency programs have also accepted increasing numbers of foreign medical graduates as the number of candidates from American medical graduates has declined. At present 38 percent of all psychiatric residents are FMGs. Thus both university affiliated programs and the State hospital programs will be hurt when the flow of foreign medical graduates is shut off by the requirements of the Health Professions Educational Assistance Act.

It is difficult to know why there has been a recent decline in American medical graduates seeking to specialize in psychiatry. Perhaps it represents success of the national thrust to encourage new physicians to enter primary care specialties such as family medicine. Or it may be the result of the cut in Federal support for psychiatric residency training which began in 1970 and has continued in each succeeding year. These dollar cuts combined with the effects of inflation have reduced the real dollar value of Federal support to about 50 percent of what it was in 1970. Unless restorations are made, it appears that there will be reductions of up to 40 percent in the numbers of new psychiatrists produced each year.

One possible source of a few more psychiatric residents would be to allow psychiatric residents who received support during medical school under P.L. 94-484 to defer their service pay back obligations for 4 or 5 years rather than 3 as at present. This would permit completion of residency training in psychiatry.

In regard to the training itself, there is a concentration on the diagnosis and treatment of individual patients. It is suggested that psychiatry residency programs include experience in such settings as rural community mental health centers. In such programs, residents could also learn about multidisciplinary practice, administration and management, and consultation and education, all of which are skills needed for practice in organized delivery systems. This would require cooperation between academic centers and service delivery systems.

There also must be more systematic training for all the mental health professions about the social structures, beliefs, value systems, and patterns of subcultures and how to work with persons from these cultures in therapy. Psychiatrists also need more insights in their preparation regarding the broad human service delivery system and the resources it has to serve the mentally ill. Too often psychiatrists are familiar with only the formal health care system and overlook the others.

B. Psychology

Most professional psychologists are trained in clinical psychology, which stresses the assessment of psychological functions and the application of psychological principles to the resolution of mental disorder, but also includes an emphasis on research knowledge and skills. The practicing professional psychologist usually has a Ph.D., but several newer training programs in professional schools of psychology grant the Psy.D. (Doctor of Psychology) degree. Masters level psychologists generally function under the supervision of Ph.D.'s. The subspecialties of educational, developmental, counseling, school, and community psychology also contribute greatly to health and mental health service delivery.

There has been a great expansion in the number of psychologists in recent years, and membership in the American Psychological Association has risen from 7,300 in 1950 to over 42,000 in 1976. In all there may be as many as 70,000 masters and doctoral level psychologists in the country. According to the 1977 National Register of Health Service Providers in Psychology there are currently 25,510 licensed/certified psychologists, that is, psychologists qualified for the independent practice of applied psychology. About 19,000 of these are providing health services and an additional 3,700 are qualified to do so. Of the 19,000, about one-quarter are in full-time private practice, 57 percent do some private practice, and the rest do none. Similar data from a survey of members of the American Psychological Association show that 40 percent of the doctoral level health service providers are primarily employed in educational institutions, 34 percent in hospitals, clinics, etc., 23 percent in independent or group practice, and the rest in a variety of other settings. Most private practice is done on a part-time basis, but it is the primary setting for delivery of service for over 40 percent of the doctoral level health service providers.

The geographic distribution of psychologists very closely follows that of psychiatrists, and other professionals, in that they are most heavily concentrated in the large urban States and in the cities. Psychologists are found on the staff of nonmetropolitan CMHCs, however, in proportions about equal to those in metropolitan centers.

Health service provider psychologists are predominantly white (95 percent) and Blacks, Asian-Americans, American Indians and other minorities make up less than 1 percent each of the total. Active recruitment efforts are changing this picture, however, and over 10 percent of graduate students in psychology are now from minority groups. Seventy-six percent of the doctoral level and 55 percent of the masters level providers are male, but in 1976, 33 percent of psychology Ph.Ds were awarded to women, and 40 percent of first-year psychology graduate students are women.

Psychologists have been moving into mental health service programs in large numbers over the past 20 years, where they are active not only in therapy but in administration, community consultation, and research. In therapy, psychologists use a wide range of psychological approaches, but there is a trend to favor behavioral therapies or therapies that have measurable aspects, possibly because of their training in measurement and research technology. They are also frequently found in positions concerned with program planning and evaluation. Many community mental health center directors or unit directors are psychologists. However, like most other mental health professionals, there is little in the training of psychologists to prepare graduates for work in administration.

Psychologists are licensed or certified in all States and the District of Columbia. In most of the States, it is the practice of psychology which is licensed and restricted to qualified persons, but in a few States the process is one of certification which simply restricts the use of the term "psychologist" to qualified persons. In almost all of the States the basic training required for licensure is the doctoral degree (Ph.D. or Doctor of Psychology). However, in a few States there is some kind of limited licensure of persons holding only masters' degrees in psychology, but these provisions usually prohibit independent private practice. For the most part, licensure laws exempt psychologists who practice in organized care settings, so that most unlicensed psychologists are employed in schools or mental health facilities, even though the majority of psychologists in these settings may be licensed. A small number (about seven) of States require a minimum number of hours of continuing education for renewal of a psychologist's license. All but one of the States require an initial examination for licensure, but examination is usually waived for applicants who have already received diplomate status by the American Board of Professional Psychology. This is the national organization for the certification of psychologists.

Identification of psychologists qualified to provide health care services was facilitated by the development, in 1974, of the National Register of Health Service Providers in Psychology. All registrants are licensed/certified at the independent practice levels by a State examining board, have a doctorate in psychology, and have 2 years of supervised experience in health services in psychology, including an internship. All are eligible for third-party health care reimbursement.

Federal funding for the education of psychologists has played a significant role as evidenced by the 36 percent of all recent doctoral graduates who have received Federal support for their education.

C. Social Work

Social work is the profession that provides a variety of social and human services for the purpose of encouraging and sustaining optimal social functioning in individuals, families, groups, and communities. The National Association of Social Workers lists about 70,000 members (a rise from 20,000 in 1955), but there may be as many as 300,000 social service workers in the Nation overall. Many of these have had no specific training, or have been educated to the associate of arts or bachelor's rather than the masters level. They are employed in a variety of human service agencies. The figures from NIMH (1976) show 31,212 social work positions in mental health facilities, a tenfold increase over the level of 1950 and a 50 percent increase over 1972. Of these 22,780 (73 percent) were at the masters degree (MSW) level, and 74 percent were full-time. In addition to these social workers in mental health facilities another 12,000 social workers were in full-time or part-time private practice, a trend which is increasing in the profession.

There are little data on the geographic distribution of social workers who work in mental health. Social work has a much higher percentage of minority practitioners than either psychiatry or psychology. For example, 9.0 percent of master's level social workers in community mental health centers are Black, 2.79 percent are Spanish-American, 1.52 percent are Asian-American, and .22 percent are American Indians. In 1976, 23 percent of the bachelors' degrees and 17 percent of the masters' degrees in social work were awarded to minority students. The profession is presently approximately 60 percent women. Men have come into this previously women's field in large numbers in the past 25 years.

Social work has its primary area of expertise in working with families and the social problems that clients face, but they often become involved in essentially therapeutic work, especially in much of the family counseling, marriage counseling, and interpersonal counseling which they do. Social work's strength lies in the integrating work it does for clients, families, and communities rather than in a specific technology. It uses some of the same basic skills of intervention as the other professions, but there is greater emphasis on group work and community process skills. Social work has often had to defend itself against the allegation that it has no unique skills of its own, but the overall functions of integrating the client with his family and community, social assessment and social integration are most significant roles which are gaining in importance as the mental health delivery system moves to deinstitutionalization and more community based services.

Social workers have also moved into middle and top level administrative positions so that at present social workers constitute the largest professional group among directors of community mental health centers, and social workers are one of the two largest professional groups on the staffs of health planning agencies.

Social workers are licensed in 23 of the States, but efforts are underway to pass licensing laws in all of the remaining States. In 14 of the 23 States the law licenses the practice of social work rather than just the title.

The notion that social workers are independent providers of services has only recently been recognized by third-party payment programs. However, this concept is gaining rapid acceptance.

The training of service oriented social workers takes place at many levels: the associate of arts (often called social service technicians, community or human service workers, etc.) as well as the baccalaureate (BSW), the masters (MSW), and the doctoral levels in programs accredited by the Council on Social Work Education. Formal recognition of the BSW as a beginning professional practice degree is a relatively new development (1972). Previously the MSW, obtained in a graduate school of social work, was the beginning professional level. There is still some debate over the relative emphasis of the curriculum between these two academic levels. The MSW generally provides several elective options beyond the basic knowledge and skills of the field, including specialized preparation in mental health. Twenty graduate schools of social work provide specialized programs in administration of human service agencies for those students who intend to pursue careers in management.

Social work has given more attention to training for cross-cultural values than any of the other professions. This was long ago recognized as important because of the large numbers of clients of the broad human service fields who come from disadvantaged and minority groups. The Council on Social Work Education, the accrediting body in social work, requires such training as one of the accreditation requirements for schools of social work.

D. Psychiatric/Mental Health Nursing

Psychiatric/mental health nursing is the specialized area of nursing which employs theories of human behavior as well as traditional nursing concepts in the prevention and correction of mental disorders. Nurses who work in mental health settings are often counted as psychiatric nurses, but actually this title should be reserved for those nurses who have special training at the masters degree level in psychiatric or mental health (community oriented) nursing. There is some training for psychiatric work in the basic training of all nurses, but only the masters level specializes in work with the mentally disabled. Traditionally psychiatric nurses have worked in mental hospitals and psychiatric units of general hospitals where many of them still work in leadership positions. A smaller number work in community mental health settings, and a considerable number of trained psychiatric nurses are employed in educational programs where they teach mental health principles to nursing students at all levels.

The American Nurses' Association has recently (1975) established a Division on Psychiatric and Mental Health Nursing which certifies qualified nurses through examination and demonstrated expertise in clinical practice. These highly qualified psychiatric nurses make up only a small proportion of all the nurses who work in mental health settings. In fact, most of these specialists are in academic or administrative leadership positions in which they perform valuable functions, but the large bulk of direct nursing care in mental health facilities is provided by general nurses.

Of an approximate total of 1 million nurses roughly 177,000 belong to the American Nurses Association, which is the national organization for professional nurses. Of this membership, 14 percent or 29,000 are categorized as psychiatric nurses, largely by virtue of working in mental health settings.

Of these 29,000 members of the Division of Psychiatric and Mental Health Nursing, 97 percent were female, 4 persent were Blacks and 3 percent of other races. Of these 46 percent had a baccalaureate degree or higher.

Of the Psychiatric and Mental Health Nursing Division members nearly 14 percent were instructors and 10 percent were administrators. In the 1972 survey 36 percent of the respondents who were employed in mental health settings were in State or county hospitals; 13 percent were in psychiatric units of general hospitals.

The profession of nursing has had a tremendous range of educational levels ranging from the associate degree nurse to the doctoral level nurse. There is some psychiatric training in all levels, but there is need for more widespread understanding of the differences in these levels. Nurses with less than a baccalaureate degree do much of the general service delivery while those trained at the bachelors' level and above provide the leadership, supervision, and some services. They are also the instructors and researchers. Nursing has traditionally been weak in the area of research, and the need for more research is a compelling reason to continue the support of advanced psychiatric training for nurses.

Nursing education also has need for more cross-cultural training to help nurses to understand and better serve their patients from other cultures. This is a particular need for those who work in psychiatric nursing where understanding of the language and culture of the patients is of special importance to obtaining good clinical results. Nursing also needs to intensify its efforts to recruit more minority group persons.

The NIMH has supported the training of psychiatric nurses for many years. The number of nurses receiving stipends for their masters degree training reached a peak of 1,065 in 1970-71. With the fund cuts this declined to 882 by 1976-77. Thus in nursing there is a direct relationship between the Federal funds and the number of trainees, as there are few trainees without stipends.

E. Other Allied Mental Health Professions

The past 20 years have seen the addition of a range of additional professionals in the mental health personnel system, so that they now make up 12 percent of the full-time equivalent patient care staff in mental health facilities. Among them are:

Pastoral Counselors and Chaplains--Pastoral counselors and chaplains are clergymen who work in mental health settings or do special work in counseling of mentally disordered persons. There are special training programs in several seminaries for training in pastoral counseling, and there are special programs for clinical chaplain training. Some are employed as chaplains in mental hospitals, but an increasing number of pastoral counselors are employed in community mental health centers or by churches and pastoral counseling centers in the larger cities where they do counseling work much like that of the other professions.

Counseling and Guidance Personnel--These are persons trained in masters or doctoral level programs in counseling and guidance. Many of these persons work in public school or college counseling programs or in industrial counseling positions, but an increasing number are being employed in community mental health centers and in outpatient clinics.

Occupational Therapists--Occupational therapists evaluate and treat individuals with functional disabilities, using activity experience to assist in the learning or relearning of self-care work and leisure skills, promoting the rehabilitation of the mentally and physically disabled. The area of psychiatric occupational therapy employs about one-quarter of the profession. Occupational therapists are trained in baccalaureate and graduate programs in schools of allied health. There has been a considerable expansion in both the numbers of occupational therapy training programs and in the numbers of graduates, and there are now over 23,000 active members of the American Occupational Therapy Association.

Vocational Counselors--Vocational counseling is the specialty that is concerned with the vocational assessment, counseling, and placement of mentally and physically disabled persons. Vocational counselors are trained in masters degree programs in colleges of education or allied health. Increasingly vocational counselors are being employed in community mental health settings and in institutions, but most of them work for vocational rehabilitation agencies.

Special Education Teachers--Special education teachers/instructors are teachers with additional special training to work with disabled persons. The whole area of work with the emotionally disturbed and learning disabled is a major subspecialty of the field as is the area of mental retardation. While many of these special education teachers are employed in public school programs, an increasing number is employed in children's mental health programs in both hospital settings and in community mental health settings. Many are employed in mental retardation institutions and community programs. The whole field of special education has expanded many times over since 1955.

Recreational Therapists--Recreational therapy is the subspecialty of the field of Physical Education and Recreation that works in the rehabilitation and restoration of disabled persons through general recreational programs. This is usually masters level training for the specialized area of therapeutic recreation. Most graduates work in institutional programs, but a number are employed in community mental health programs, especially those devoted to the social rehabilitation of the mentally disordered.

Marriage Counselors--Marriage counseling is the specialty that works with couples in times of marital stress. This is often the point at which separation and divorce are imminent, a very critical period for the mental health of the pair. Marriage counselors are trained in masters degree programs and have a system of professional certification. While most marriage counselors work in private practice, a number are employed in community mental health centers or by churches and family counseling programs. There are over 5,000 members of the American Association of Marriage and Family Counselors, many of them either psychologists or social workers.

Arts Therapists--Art, music, and dance therapists have been employed increasingly in mental health settings. They utilize their skills in a nonverbal therapeutic approach to reach the mentally ill and retarded which is especially effective with persons who cannot express their emotions or thoughts verbally, or who have great difficulty doing so. There are over 1,000 members each of the American Art Therapy Association and the American Dance Therapy Association, and over 1,200 registered music therapists. Degrees are awarded at both the bachelors and masters levels.

Other Physical Health Professions--There are several other professionals from the general health professions who work in mental health settings to provide their usual technical services. These include general physicians, dentists, dietitians, physical therapists, laboratory and X-ray technicians, licensed practical nurses, etc. They are mentioned here only to note that they comprise an additional 3.3 percent of the patient care staff of mental health facilities.

F. Paraprofessionals

In many ways the category of paraprofessionals is a catchall. Until the past 10 years there were few middle level workers in the mental health delivery system. Psychiatric aides were persons who had no training for their largely custodial jobs in institutions and no status in the system. They were given brief inservice training to provide basic nursing care, surveillance of wards, and housekeeping and escort services.

However, under the impetus of the civil rights movement and the new careers movement there began to be established a number of programs to train and employ mental health workers at middle levels. Many of these workers were hired as part of the new careers movement and trained in agency based programs of relatively short duration (3-6 months). Others were trained in technical institutes or community colleges where they received associate degrees. Altogether over 500 such programs have trained over 30,000 such workers. A few are trained in baccalaureate programs to prepare mental health/human service workers. The development of training programs has been largely a local initiative that has been responsive to local needs rather than to any coordinated national initiative, although the new careers program of the Federal Government provided impetus for the "hire now-train later" movement for all of the human services. The NIMH provided grant assistance to a variety of experimental training programs in the early 1960's, and in the late 1960's there were several time-limited developmental grants to a number of 2-year training programs in community colleges or in 4-year colleges. Then in 1970, NIMH created the New Careers Branch which became the Paraprofessional Manpower Development Branch in 1975. This program has concentrated on developing curriculum guidelines, studies of employment patterns, issues in credentialing, etc., more than on the ongoing funding of training.

The Southern Regional Education Board recently conducted a national survey that detected 354 paraprofessional training programs--over 200 in community colleges or 4-year colleges. The graduates of these associate degree programs have increased from 4,000 in the year 1970 to 10,000 per year in 1977 and are projected to be 12,500 per year in 1980.

The statistics regarding the staffing of mental health facilities show that 45 percent of all the full-time-equivalent patient care staff had less than a BA degree, and this total comprises 130,000 mental health workers. This includes psychiatric aides, mental health technicians, and a number of other job titles; indeed, one of the difficulties in classifying these workers is that they tend to be titled by functional job titles rather than by any overall occupational title. Over 90 percent of these paraprofessionals working in mental health facilities are employed in inpatient settings (table 4).

Surveys of the work of paraprofessionals, however, show that they work in virtually every kind of mental health setting from mental hospital to community outreach and aftercare. They work with clients of all ages, and with all kinds of disorders, and studies show that they are effective in their therapeutic work with many clients.

This is a relatively new personnel development which is still being formed. There is no national credentialing program, but efforts are underway to develop such a program based on measurement of competence, but such measures are difficult to devise. This movement has drawn heavily from among women and minorities and these new occupations are heavily represented in many of the institutional and community mental health programs in rural areas, poverty areas, and in ghetto areas. Among the occupational groups that are emerging in the mental health field are:

<u>Mental Health Technician/Associate</u>--These are generally persons with an associate degree in Mental Health Technology from a 2-year program in a community college or other college. They work in a variety of intake, outreach, aftercare, and active treatment programs.

Alcohol Counselors--These are workers trained to work with alcoholic clients in clinics and inpatient units. They are often selected because they have had some personal experience with alcohol abuse prior to their training and employment.

Drug Abuse Counselors--These are workers with similar backgrounds and employment except that their experience and work is in drug abuse.

Ombudsmen/Patient Advocates--These are persons who work with patients to assure that their rights are respected and to help them obtain the services they require when the system might otherwise ignore or reject them. These persons may be employed by the mental health agency or by a citizen group such as a mental health association. Some States are setting up separate patient advocate services in which these people work.

Foster Parents for the Emotionally Disturbed--These are persons who take emotionally disturbed children into their homes and provide parenting and carry out therapeutic regimes outlined by professionals in the mental health agencies. There is usually a period of intensive training and continuing education for these special foster parents.

Board and Care Home Providers--These are persons who operate group homes in which chronic mentally ill persons are placed for domiciliary care and supportive living arrangements. Since the large mental hospitals have been "deinstitutionalized" (especially since 1970) there has been a great expansion of these board and care homes to receive those long-term hospital residents who had no family or place to go in the community. They are a very important part of the community support program of the mental health system.

Day Care Program Workers--These are the staff persons for day care programs of crafts, recreation, and social activities which are increasingly being provided for chronic and elderly patients who live in board and care programs or even in their own homes.

Other Social-Vocational Program Workers--These are the persons who staff a variety of social rehabilitation programs, halfway houses, sheltered work programs, etc., which have grown up to serve the mentally ill in the communities. They work mainly in small contract agencies.

There are no good figures on the numbers of these workers since there are no data systems concerned with them. In addition, their disbursement into small contract agencies makes it difficult to count them. The job titles and the training programs are all so variable that it is impossible to categorize them as has been done with the professions.

There are several issues concerning paraprofessionals that remain unresolved. One of these is the role of such workers in mental health organizations. There are at least five possible structural roles:

(1) As aides to single professions (e.g., social work aides, psychology assistants). This is the historic role favored by the professions. The new job is composed by factoring of the professional's job.

(2) Around specific tasks (e.g., administering psychological tests, taking social histories).

(3) Around major functions (e.g., intake worker, rehabilitation worker).

(4) Around agency administrative needs (e.g., day ward supervisor, night supervisor).

(5) Around the total needs of a small group of clients (e.g., the so-called generalist model).

In various agencies jobs have been structured in all of these ways, but there are enormous implications for training for clients and for other workers depending on which structural role is selected. The failure to make clear which model has been selected in any particular setting has sometimes led to staff conflict and rejection of the paraprofessionals.

Sometimes job positions with appropriate salaries have not been created by the Civil Service after the mental health agency had indicated the workers were needed. Sometimes the trained associate degree level mental health paraprofessionals have been passed over in hiring in favor of persons holding bachelors degrees in subjects with no specific relevance to human service work. Often there have been no career ladders so that the paraprofessionals found themselves in dead end jobs. These are only some of the problems.

Several studies show that when problems such as these have been resolved, harmonious relationships develop so that 54 percent of mental health administrators state that they prefer the use of paraprofessionals to full professionals because they fill new roles based on patient needs that were not previously being filled by any staff and because of the lively and vital relationships the paraprofessionals were able to develop with clients. This turned out to be an effective way of extending the expertise of the professionals to more clients.

Much more needs to be done to gather more extensive data on employment patterns, team relationships, the supervision provided, etc. The paraprofessional movement has provided an entreé into the mental health personnel system for large numbers of minority persons (at least 20 percent) and for deprived persons who otherwise would have had no chance. It has also attracted a number of middle life persons, mostly women, who have already had a career as parents and are looking for human service work. Many paraprofessionals go on to professional training and this group should be viewed as an excellent source of minority candidates.

Most of the candidates for the paraprofessional training programs are already familiar with the culture of the clients they will serve. They also tend to be people with high levels of the interpersonal skills of empathy, warmth, and genuineness which make for effective helpers. The training programs tend to be heavily competency based and they provide a large portion of experiential learning, most of it in field settings. However, much more study and development is needed before the system of paraprofessional training and utilization is complete.

G. **Other Related Personnel Groups**

There are at least three other categories of personnel who are clearly important in maintaining the mental health of the people although they are not usually considered a part of the mental health personnel system. They are:

<u>Indigenous Healers</u>--In many minority cultures there are eminent and prestigious healers who are sought out by their people in times of illness and stress. These include the Indian medicine men, the curanderos of Mexican American cultures and the "granny ladies" of many rural Black cultures. These persons should not be incorporated into the mental health system but they should be sought out as consultants and collegial workers in providing mental health services to persons of those cultures. It is a mistake to disdain or bypass them. Training for American Indian indigenous mental health practitioners often takes as long as 5 to 20 years. There are serious implications here for the funding and recognizing of these alternative mental health systems. Indian tribal governments are always the primary entity for the Federal Government to deal with in developing training programs for indigenous Indian practitioners.

<u>Self Help Group Workers</u>--These are persons who work with community groups of persons who establish and operate self-help groups such as expatients' clubs, Alcoholics Anonymous, Recovery, Inc. The move to develop more of these programs grew out of the patient rights era. The participants in these self-help groups should also be recognized for their role in the maintenance of mental health.

<u>Volunteers</u>--There are many thousands of persons who offer regular volunteer services to mental health programs. Many serve as part of an organized group while others serve as individuals. The range of their activities runs the gamut from such custodial skills as paring patients' fingernails to full professional services.

There is presently no way to count these persons or to incorporate them into the official mental health system, but it is important to recognize the significance of the work they do and to encourage and support their efforts.

OVERVIEW OF MENTAL HEALTH PERSONNEL ISSUES

Policy planning for mental health personnel should be based upon the policy planning for mental health services. Obviously there are points at which the services system and the personnel systems will not precisely coincide since there are relatively short-term fluctuations in the delivery system based on the condition of the economy, changes in social expectations, changes in technology, and even on the political climate of the times, while mental health personnel require several years preparation and then have a working career of 30 to 40 years. Yet much might be done to achieve greater correspondence between the needs of the service system and personnel policies.

It has been characteristic for the mental health system to think of personnel only in terms of "supply" and primarily in terms of the professions, probably because they require the most training and provide leadership functions. At the Federal level, the training program of the National Institute of Mental Health was established to assure an adequate supply of well qualified professionals and has largely continued this emphasis. Over the years programs for research training, continuing education, paraprofessional manpower development, and experimental training have been added, but these have usually been smaller in funding than any of the four professional branches.

Definition of the Manpower/Personnel System

The personnel system may be defined as the full range of activities to develop and use human power to deliver effective and efficient mental health services to all of the people. The personnel system is described as having four major but interrelated components:

A. Personnel Policy Planning and Evaluation
   A Coordinated Personnel Data System
   Personnel Policy Planning
   Evaluation of Personnel Activities

B. Personnel Recruitment and Production
   Early Recruitment to Mental Health Careers
   Professional and Occupational Education
   Continuing Education

C. Personnel Administration
   Distribution (geographic, specialty, public service)
   Deployment of Staff (teams, organization)
   Development of Career Systems
   Maximizing Productivity of Personnel
   Assuring Quality of Performance

D. Regulation of Personnel
   Credentialing Bodies (licensure, certification, accreditation)
   Standards (laws, court orders, regulations)
   Professional Societies and Unions

M&P 36

Administrative Agencies (merit systems, budget offices)
Payment Programs
Planning and Review Programs

At this time, there are no points in either the Federal Government or in the States where all of these personnel issues are considered as a system. The major groups involved in all of these pieces (planners, educators, service program administrators, professional leaders, regulators and program funders) almost never come together. The result is a nonsystem with many constraints and inefficiencies.

Some suggest that this kind of personnel planning and coordination must be implemented at the State level with a secondary focus at the Federal level, and that the basic level for the planning and coordination of the mental health delivery system is the State. Mental health has been a State responsibility since Dorothea Dix urged the States to establish the original mental hospitals, and it remains the basic responsibility under existing Federal laws--in mental health, alcohol, drug abuse, and developmental disabilities--which mandate each State to develop a plan for these respective services. In addition, the States provide the primary site for licensing of personnel and facilities, and States provide the major funding for mental health services in State institutions, for higher education programs that train personnel and for a good part of the support of community mental health services through community services matching programs.

Though States have had the responsibility for providing direct services, the Federal role has become increasingly important, especially in the past quarter century. The Federal Government has assumed considerable responsibility for manpower development, for research, and for direct services. Since mental health professionals are highly trained and extremely mobile, they have been viewed as a national resource. Federal policy has clearly indicated the responsibility of the Federal Government in developing and funding the education of mental health professionals. It has also been responsible for creating the new careers programs and for funding experiments in new personnel development and activities. In terms of research, the Federal responsibility clearly relates to the fact that new knowledge will affect all citizens. The services funded by Federal Government have included insurance and third party payment schemes as well as the development of new service systems, demonstration projects and the funding of mental health prevention and consultation programs. A cogent concern in regard to the Federal (as compared with the State) role is that States and local government are pressed by immediate needs for services, whereas the Federal Government, by virtue of some distance and a long-term perspective, may view the development of mental health personnel as it relates to the future needs of the total Nation.

While several States are moving toward mechanisms that bring together several of the major groups who would be involved in a comprehensive mental health personnel development program, none yet has such a full-scale mechanism in operation. One problem lies in the fact that the technology for dealing with many of these problems is very weak or nonexistent. There simply is not much known about personnel policy planning or about personnel utilization or about the effects of the various personnel regulators. This broad conceptualization of personnel development is simply too new to have received much implementation as yet.

However, this need for a better technology points to a significant role for the Federal Government--first in helping develop and refine these technologies, and second in helping the States in the development of entities that might initiate planning and action strategies to implement more effective mental health personnel development in the States. Some feel that the Federal Government has served the States best when it has provided technical assistance and overall facilitation of State efforts, while others hold that the development of national criteria and standards is essential for the provision of quality services to all of the Nation's people, regardless of where they live. A further role of the Federal Government is in relation to the American Indian tribal governments, because tribal governments are political entities that are an integral party of the Federal system and that relate to the Federal Government as a whole and not through State governments. The Federal Government should assist tribal governments in training and action strategies to implement improved mental health personnel development.

The kind of personnel policy planning and coordination that is needed in the States should not be limited to planning and personnel development for only the State mental health agencies, but rather for the full range of personnel required for community programs and the private sector as well as for the State agency. Obviously special concern must be paid to the problem areas and special need areas that so often fall to the public sector, but the concern should be for a personnel program to deliver effective and efficient mental health services to all the States' citizens. Thus a State mental health personnel planning and development program must involve public and private mental health agencies, public and private colleges and universities, the mental health professions, licensure boards, health and mental health planners, the major related agencies of State government (the merit system, the budget division, the higher education coordinating body) and major third party payers.

Conceptual Bases for Service Delivery

One of the basic needs is to articulate policies about the mental health delivery system and its personnel component. Too often policies have not been articulated and so conflicting philosophies come into being. One of the basic philosophies to be made explicit concerns the nature of mental disorder and its treatment. Following are the major models often used. They are not mutually exclusive and often refer to different kinds of disorder.

Medical-psychiatric model--This is the traditional model that assumes that mental disorder is an illness like any other illness. Some individuals would go so far as to claim that the etiology and therapy of the mental disorders are all physical and neurologic (i.e., "there is no twisted thought without a twisted molecule"). Even when this model assumes that the causes of mental disorders are basically psychological and that the appropriate treatments are psychotherapeutic, it postulates a medical-psychiatric model of personnel utilization. This model presumes that a psychiatrist (a physician) will be involved in diagnostic and treatment efforts, and it requires that all of the members of the team work with a physician.

This is the model that seems most appropriate for the treatment of the acute psychiatric disorders classified as psychoses and psychoneuroses. It is the pattern usually reimbursed by health insurance or other third party health payment plans. However, this model usually limits the roles of other professionals, and it provides little opportunity for the use of middle level workers. There have been many criticisms of the use of this model in situations in which it is not appropriate (Albee, 1969; Arnhoff, 1969; and Carroll, 1975).

Psychological-behavioral model--This model assumes that the pathology of mental disorders lies in psychological and behavioral reaction patterns and that therapy must help the individual to psychological insights into his behavior and/or the adoption of new behavioral patterns. In its pure form, this philosophy of mental disorder makes no use of medications.

While various forms of psychotherapy and behavior therapy are used by psychiatrists, they are equally as likely to be the therapeutic modalities of psychologists and social workers and other kinds of counselors and middle level workers.

The psychological-behavioral model lends itself to the therapy of neurotic, personality and character problems, habit disturbances, and acute situational crises. Together these conditions comprise a large portion of the disorders seen in mental health programs. This model expands the kinds of mental health workers who may serve the clients in more or less independent service relationships and allows several different models of team organizations (Bower, 1970).

Social-learning model--This model assumes that the basic difficulty in mental disorder lies in the interpersonal and social relationships between people, and that the remedy lies in helping persons to learn new patterns of interpersonal and social interactions. The interventions are social or educational and make most significant use of social workers and educators, but rehabilitation workers, recreation workers, and pastoral counselors also use these approaches. Middle level workers are also widely used in both individual and group approaches under this model. This model is especially appropriate for many marital and family problems, for many adjustment problems, and for many aspects of work with the mentally retarded and the chronically disabled mentally ill. This model provides for the utilization of a wide range of workers in the support and rehabilitation of the mentally ill and retarded, but it is often the policy of "health" payment programs not to offer reimbursement for these modes of intervention.

Social engineering model--This model assumes that the basic causes of mental disorders lie in the broad fabric of society--such social problems as poverty, racism, unemployment, overcrowding, etc. The remedy is to make adjustment in the laws, regulations, policies, and procedures of the larger society to relieve the stresses on persons at risk. This is a broad community action or political approach. Persons holding this view of mental disorder may come from any discipline, but, in fact, most come from the fields of law, social work, and political science. This model does not think of either "patients" or "clients," but sees the society and its institutions as the problem. The practitioners see themselves as social activists or social engineers rather than as direct client workers. They have had a considerable impact on mental health services through State and Federal legislation, court action and intervention in the regulation writing process. These persons are often not conceptualized as mental health workers, but actually most community mental health centers have some staff dedicated to this kind of activity through their community consultation and education mission.

Each of these models has its valid indications and uses, but problems result in personnel utilization when only one model is espoused and allowed to exist or to receive compensation through payment programs. These models need to be studied more closely for their implications for the most effective use of available mental health personnel, especially in view of present trends to deinstitutionalize long-term patients and place them in the community for continued care.

There are other philosophical views to be considered concerning the nature of mental disorder and appropriate treatments. Views intrinsic to the variant cultural world views of the American Indian Nations are different from those of the predominant society. Non-Judeo-Christian cultures may perceive mental disorder to be a disharmony with the values and social behavior expectations of their particular cultures. Appropriate treatments may include various healing ceremonies of certain kinds of medicine men, curandero-administered therapy, and contemplative activities.

Another area of philosophic conflict that often troubles the mental health personnel system is the dilemma between the goal of providing the highest possible level of care for a few clients for whom one has a contractual obligation and the idea of providing some basically adequate level of care to as many clients as possible. This is a typical philosophic dilemma between the private sector and the public sector. This same dilemma exists in areas such as housing and transportation, but it has seldom been acknowledged in mental health. Policy planners must be clear about which philosophy is to apply to which sectors of their planning.

Another philosophic dilemma concerns the basic objectives of the mental health delivery system. The rehabilitation and restoration of individuals to social functioning in the community will require different kinds of services and more personnel than objectives limited to diagnosis and treatment. Policy planners must articulate these and other philosophies which have clear implications for the kinds of services and personnel that will be needed.

Patient/Client Inputs

An issue which has traditionally been overlooked is the role of the patient/client. In mental health and human service work it is almost essential that the patient/client understand and participate in the treatment process for a favorable outcome to result. Much more attention is now being mandated to the issue of patient rights—the right to effective treatment, the right to refuse treatment, the right to the least restrictive environment, the right to informed consent to procedures, etc. There must be procedures to assure that the client is involved in the decisionmaking process about what happens to him. Several mental health programs are currently establishing patient advocate workers whose job is to assure that patients/clients are made aware of their rights and that these rights are respected in the professionals' procedures.

Natural Support Systems

Closely related to client needs is the issue of the use of natural support systems in the client's environment. Most persons with mental disorders probably never come to the mental health system at all, but receive the support and assistance they need from natural systems such as families, friends, churches, lodges, clubs, neighborhood groups, and other agents of the community (e.g., family doctors, clergymen, public health nurses, school teachers, family assistance workers, recreation program workers, etc.). Many potential clients prefer to work with these natural support systems rather than to risk the cost of treatment and the potential liabilities of being labeled as "mentally" disabled. Other groups that do not utilize or are not served by the prevailing mental health system are the American Indian Tribal Governments and many Asian-American and Mexican-American communities, among others. Differing linguistically and culturally, they prefer their own natural support systems of mental health.

Special efforts must be made to acquaint professionals in both the basic training and in continuing education programs regarding these natural support systems and how the mental health system can assist and improve them in their work with mentally disordered persons.

Definition of the Professions

The professions, and the members thereof, have a unique status in society, as a result of which they assume certain responsibilities and are accorded certain privileges. Characteristics of professions may be briefly summarized as follows:

(1) the profession and its members are sanctioned by society, i.e., they are recognized and licensed (and are delegated and accept specific responsibilities), on the basis of,

(2) a unique body of knowledge, which is,

(3) passed on by members of the profession to new or apprentice members, and

(4) the profession is self-regulating, i.e., it sets its own standards of ethics, practice, entry, and discipline for members, and these characteristics then,

(5) allow the members to be individual and upon their own choice, independent practitioners of the profession.

The universally recognized professions in American society are law, medicine, (higher) education, and the ministry.

The core professions in mental health are (1) psychiatry; a recognized specialty of the profession of medicine; its members are physicians who have had 4 or more years of postgraduate training in the diagnosis and treatment of mental disorders. (2) Psychiatric/mental health nursing; a specialty of the profession of nursing characterized by specific graduate training in the care and treatment of mentally disordered persons. (3) Clinical and counseling psychology, specialties of the profession of psychology. (4) Psychiatric/mental health social work, a specialty of the profession of social work.

The core professions each have specific roles and responsibilities in the provision of mental health services; these roles and responsibilities are delineated and defined by:

(1) State licensing laws which define the scope of practice of the various professions and fix responsibility for the actions of the individuals so licensed.

(2) The professions themselves, which speak to these roles and responsibilities through their professional organizations or societies.

(3) Traditions which have been established during the period of evolution of the professions.

(4) The body of scientific knowledge and technology which the members of the professions utilize in the provision of mental health services.

(5) The organization of staff and services within the agencies or institutions, some examples of each are briefly described:

   A. Staff organization by professional disciplines--This traditional pattern is most commonly used in large programs but some people feel that it tends to reinforce the turf battles and jurisdictional disputes among the professions.

   Staff organization by functional units--In this case staff are assigned to a unit (children's unit, geographic unit, alcohol treatment unit). This tends to reinforce the mission of that unit. The leadership may come from any profession and allegiance is to the unit and its mission rather than to one's profession.

   Staff organization by specific clients--Here each client is assigned to a specific staff person who becomes his or her case manager and principal therapist regardless of which service (e.g., inpatient, outpatient, day hospital) the client is assigned to. This provides for a kind of personal continuity of care and provides for greater sensitivity to the client's wishes and feelings.

   Staff organization to specific teams--Because virtually every mental health program claims to use teams, there is wide variation in what is meant by the word "team." Teams may be made up according to medical, behavioral, social, or rehabilitative models, or some blend of these. The leadership, personnel makeup and functions will vary considerably according to which team model is chosen.

B. <u>Service organization units organized by characteristics of patients</u>--age, sex.

<u>Service organization units organized by disorder</u>--mental illness, alcohol, drugs.

<u>Service organization units organized by geographic catchment areas</u>.

<u>Units organized by treatment</u>--admission, active treatment, continuing treatment, custodial care.

Relationship of Core Professions to Other Service Provider Personnel

A number of factors, with wide individual variability in each, will determine the working relationship of the core profession members to other personnel within the service delivery system. These factors include:

(a) The extent and nature of the utilization, as well as the number, of professional extenders, or persons with a lesser amount of education than the members of professions. They are educated/trained to provide some of the skills and techniques used by core profession members in the care of patients/clients and thus, with adequate supervision by core professions members, extend the abilities of such workers, hence the term. They are usually called paraprofessionals.

(b) The conceptual model on which extender personnel (paraprofessionals) are used. Many of the extender type personnel are based on the medical model or adaptations thereof: others are based on social learning models, psychologic behavioral models, social engineering models.

Examples of the previously mentioned relationships are physician assistants based on the medical model, nurse practitioners based on the medical model, psychiatric aides based on the nursing model, social work aides based on a social work profession model, and psychologic assistants based on a psychology profession model.

In each of these examples, the individual paraprofessional is delegated a reduced (i.e., less than the parent profession) authority for decisionmaking and a reduced level of responsibility for patient care, although the amount of time spent with the individual patient/client or groups of patients/clients may markedly exceed the amount of time spent by the professionals with the patients/clients.

Within this context, then, the following aspects of working relationships between professionals and paraprofessionals can be stated. Major decisionmaking rests with the core professions; that is, the diagnostic assessment and the formulation of the treatment plan. The exceptions to these are in areas of special expertise by allied health professionals; for example, occupational therapists, recreation therapists, rehabilitation counselors. Minor decisions in regard to diagnosis or treatment plan may be made by or participated in by members of allied health professions and the paraprofessionals. Daily implementation of the treatment plan may rest with paraprofessionals, with responsibility for supervision vested in the same professionals charged with overall responsibility for diagnosis and treatment.

Thus it can be seen that the core professions retain responsibility for:

(1) Appropriate decisionmaking involving diagnosis, treatment and care of patients/clients, including ultimate responsibility (and liability) for patient care.

(2) Specific aspects of information gathering and treatment implementation which require special expertise and/or experience, not usually associated with paraprofessionals.

(3) Supervision including education and training of paraprofessionals and unskilled workers, including guidance and counseling for their career development for all such persons working in mental health services.

Roles and responsibilities for core professions also include:

(1) Skills, competence, and assumption of responsibility for program administration including management, planning, and program evaluation.

(2) Extramural functions of mental health service agencies including relationships with advisory and policy making boards.

(3) Liaison activities with executive and legislative branches of government at all levels; State, Federal, and local.

(4) Development and maintenance of effective communication and working relationships with other human services organizations within the area of responsibility.

(5) Public education and maintenance of effective public relations.

General functions unique to the core professions and members therof include:

(1) Decisionmaking including that which is determined by mandate; for example, licensing of physicians includes assumption of medical responsibility as defined by the licensing statute and as further defined by various financing and payment systems, as well as other administrative law, e.g., comprehensive Community Mental Health Centers Act, and nursing care responsibility as defined by the Nurse Practice Act of the licensing State, as well as administrative law as described above.

(2) Supervision of paraprofessionals, subprofessionals, and unskilled workers in the service delivery system.

(3) Education and training of these groups.

(4) Consultation, both program consultation and case consultation, on an intramural basis within the mental health service agency and extramural to other human services agencies within the community.

(5) Creative thinking based on professional expertise and experience. Examples of this would include research design and implementation, new developments in care and programing, as well as strategies for change.

Problems of Supply

The previous sections of this report have shown how the supply of trained mental health personnel has grown over the years (see tables 1 and 5). The question of the adequacy of the supply is, however, dependent on the models of service delivery used. If the scope of the mental health system is to include many activities now done in the social services system (such as help in housing, employment, income maintenance, vocational training, etc.) and if services are to be given to all who might seek them, then the implication is clear that more personnel are needed. Similarly, the quality of the service to be given and the qualifications of the provider will influence the supply needed. Many facilities now have less than fully trained staff, and they may continue to hire these individuals simply because they command lower salaries. An upgrading of staff, perhaps through the imposition of staffing standards, would expand the need for qualified personnel.

There is special need to recognize the geographic maldistribution of professionals, the shortages of qualified specialists in the mental health of children and the elderly, and the need for more minority professionals. While the present production of some types of personnel may be sufficient, existing personnel cannot be geographically redistributed, and so increases are needed in many areas. The existing supply of qualified service providers must be at least maintained with special programs to encourage newly trained professionals to settle in underserved geographic areas. Over and above this the supply of professionals from minority groups and subspecialists to work with children and the aged must be greatly increased.

Academic departments are continuing to train psychologists and social workers in increasing numbers (table 6), but there is cause for concern in the disciplines of psychiatry and psychiatric nursing. Psychiatry has for years attracted a diminishing proportion of American medical school graduates into its residency training programs, but has in part compensated by recruiting foreign medical graduates who presently constitute almost 40 percent of all psychiatric residents. Since the supply of incoming foreign physicians will soon be drastically reduced as a result of recent legislation, and since an adequate supply of psychiatrists is vital to the provision of mental health services, several steps are required to increase the attractiveness of psychiatry as a profession to American medical graduates. These range from changes in P.L. 94-484 to expanded training and recruiting of medical students.

The continued supply of psychiatric nurses is also in jeopardy. There are relatively few masters level nurses, and almost all have received stipends from NIMH to help support them while in training. Cessation of this support could result in a diminished pool of these specialists.

Finally, any discussion of supply must consider not only sheer numbers but also the type of individual and the quality of the training received. Support from NIMH has made it possible for poor and minority students to receive graduate education and for academic departments to provide innovative programs to meet emerging needs. With diminishing support social work, for example, has already shown a reduction in the number of minority students in training. If the diversity of the student body and the quality of education suffer, then the supply becomes less adequate, regardless of numbers.

Distribution Problems

The distribution of mental health personnel, especially of qualified professionals, is a major problem. There is a tendency to congregate in the cities and in the wealthier States, so that New York, for example, has 26 psychiatrists, 19.1 licensed psychologists, and 10.2 registered social workers per 100,000 population, while Mississippi has only 3.0 psychiatrists, 4.4 licensed psychologists, and 0.5 registered social workers for each 100,000 residents. Even within individual States the rural areas show a scarcity of professionals, and those who do work there are often less highly trained than those who work in urban areas.

Another form of maldistribution is that between the public and private sectors. Many public facilities, such as State mental hospitals and community mental health centers are unable to attract qualified professional staff. Slightly over 50 percent of the physicians and psychiatrists staffing State and county mental hospitals are graduates of foreign medical schools, and even such States as New York and Connecticut, which otherwise have a comparatively ample supply of psychiatrists, depend on foreign medical graduates for approximately 70 percent of their State hospital physician staff. The average number of full-time equivalent psychiatrists in community mental health centers has dropped from 6.8 to 4.3 between 1970 and 1976, and in 1976 50 percent of the centers reported having less than 2.3 FTE psychiatrists on the staff. In part, this is a function of the supply not being able to keep pace with the demand, in part a result of unattractive jobs, and in part, it is a manifestation of the maldistribution problem.

The causes of this maldistribution are many. Professional people are highly mobile and can select the place in which they wish to work. Several studies have shown that they value urban areas with a high income, cultural amenities, good education for their children, pleasant climate, the opportunity for professional stimulation and academic connections, and the freedom to work in the area of their own interest. Rural areas are usually unable to provide these attractions; many, in fact, have no mental health facilities in which to work, and the population is unable to support professionals in private practice. Where there are jobs, professionals may not fit into the rural culture, they may not be adequately trained for the multiple functions they must perform, they may feel isolated from their peers, and the pressure of the work may result in exhaustion and "burn out," so that those who do come soon leave.

Just as the causes of maldistribution are multiple, so must be the solutions. One approach is to require a period of service in shortage areas in return for financial support given during training. This mechanism, under the Health Professions Educational Assistance Act of 1976, is expected to provide a number of psychiatrists and other physicians to work in areas of need in the National Health Service Corps. Similar support, with payback provisions, should be given to psychologists, social workers, and psychiatric nurses. Since no single strategy is likely to suffice by itself, multiple incentives should be provided to work in shortage areas. People raised in a locality are more likely to stay in practice there and to have more understanding of the community, so that special consideration should be given to the funding of programs located in rural areas which draw their students from that area.

Many of the States which have the most severe personnel shortages do not have medical schools or professional programs, however, and for those interstate agreements for the training of students and the AHEC (Area Health Education Center) concept is a possible mechanism. AHECs can also provide continuing education and professional stimulation for those already employed. Agencies should also arrange for sabbaticals or staff exchange programs for professional stimulation and to combat the feelings of isolation which lead to rapid turnover. Such exchanges would also be a mechanism for introducing fresh ideas into the agency. The States, in drawing up their mental health service plans, should be required to show how new and existing facilities can be staffed, that the pay scales are commensurate with other positions in similar areas, and, where possible, how the facility might be used as a training site. Any training should occur in close affiliation with a university and include faculty exchange with the agency to provide a high quality of education. If this is not done, mere on-the-job training may result, and this will discourage the student, and he or she will not remain in this type of work.

More sophisticated analysis must be done about what types of personnel are needed in rural areas and on the definition of shortage areas. To some extent a supply of specialists, and particularly of subspecialists, is and should be an urban phenomenon. The more sparsely settled parts of the country should, however, have access to mental health personnel who can treat the less complicated problems, refer the most difficult, and obtain consultation on the others. This may require some combination of general practitioners with mental health skills and nonmedical mental health professionals and paraprofessionals. Research must be done on which combinations or models are most feasible and effective.

Minorities

It has been stated repeatedly throughout this report that minorities are greatly underrepresented in the mental health disciplines. This is particularly true for the most highly trained specialties, psychiatry and psychology. Fewer than 2 percent of all psychiatrists are Black, and data on other minorities are difficult to interpret due to the large number of foreign medical graduates of Asian or South American origin. A recent survey by the American Psychological Association estimates that of all doctoral level health service providers in psychology, 0.9 percent are Black, 0.7 percent Asian, 0.4 percent Hispanic, and 0.1 percent Native American origin. Social work and nursing are more representative of the population, with an estimated 15 percent of NASW (National Association of Social Workers) members and 7 percent of nurses belonging to the division of psychiatric and mental health nursing coming from minority groups.

The professions have been making attempts to increase these proportions. The number of Black psychiatry residents has been climbing yearly, and they now comprise 3.4 percent of the total. Slightly over 6 percent of the Ph.Ds awarded in 1976 in psychology were to minority students, and over 12 percent of first year graduate students were from these groups. In social work, 23 percent of the BSWs and 17 percent of the MSWs awarded in 1976 were to minority students, as were 18 percent of the degrees to nurses graduating from basic RN programs in 1975.

These efforts must continue and accelerate for a sufficient supply of minority professionals to be built up, not only for the provision of services but also for teaching, research, and administrative positions. Training in the skills and knowledge necessary for successfully communicating with and treating minorities must be built into the curriculum of all programs for all students, and this cannot be done without a sufficient number of minority faculty and students. There is a danger that the momentum built up, largely with the aid of Federal training money, will slow down or be reversed. There is still a limited pool of highly qualified and motivated minority candidates for the professions, especially those requiring long training.

Recruitment, remedial education, special preparation, and student support all require money, and it cannot be stressed enough that a phaseout of Federal training programs will have its greatest effect on poor and minority students.

In addition to support for minorities in graduate training programs, the panel felt that there was a need to fund midlevel and college preparation for minorities, and even extend this support to the high school level. Some of this is now being done within NIMH, and NIH has established its MARC (Minority Access to Research Careers) program as a prototype. Minority paraprofessionals should be recognized as an excellent source of motivated candidates and scholarships could be provided for their graduate education.

Increasing the sensitivity of all service providers to the special needs, values and culture of the different minority groups is another need. If the staff cannot understand the language or the meaning and context of the distress, treatment will be ineffective. This may be one reason minorities either do not come for services, or leave after one or two visits. There are many ways of attacking this problem. Certainly there should be minority content in all training programs, taught either by minority faculty or resource persons in the community, who need not be mental health professionals. Area centers for this training could be established for continuing education programs. Actual work with minority patients, and collaboration with minority professionals and paraprofessionals is essential. In this regard, learning from and working with native healers respected by their culture, such as Curanderos, Indian medicine men, etc., can be a vital factor.

The previously mentioned programs will not come into being and continue through good wishes and exhortations. They will require planning, work, and funding.

Problems of Utilization

Previous sections have discussed the training and skills of the various categories of personnel and outlined the special role of the professions. There is, however, a considerable degree of overlap of function both among the professionals and between professionals and paraprofessionals. Members of all groups perform individual and group therapy, consultation, management, and administration. This has led to problems of role blurring, rivalries, and turf battles. In some ways this has been a healthy development, inasmuch as it expands opportunity and increases the numbers of service providers. In other ways it promotes bitterness if one discipline has higher pay, privileges, or status than another and is perceived to be doing essentially the same thing. Unfortunately the data are extremely weak on what staff actually does, the way it is done, the effectiveness, and for which functions and responsibilities various categories of personnel are qualified. Greater prestige and reimbursement are attached to doing therapy, so this is a sought-after function.

Some would solve this dilemma by doing away with differences in compensation rates, abolishing professional departments, removing professional perquisites and designations, and moving to the concept of a generic mental health worker. Others feel that some overlap of function is natural and normal, but that each profession possesses its own unique skills, in addition to common ones, and that the present trend is toward greater role differentiation. Professional identity permits a person to move easily from one type of job to another, not simply remain in a State personnel system. It also permits expansion of function, creation of new roles and responsibilities, and the utilization of training in the solution of unique problems. This is the essence of professionalism. Mutual respect for the unique qualities of each profession and the individual's pride in his/her own role can do much to eliminate turf battles. This can also be fostered by having multidisciplinary training in facilities, preferably after identities are formed. There are many skills, such as consultation, supervision of paraprofessionals, administration, and collaboration with the health, social service, and community support systems that are best taught in an interdisciplinary setting, either in basic or continuing education.

The mechanisms of financing services, particularly through insurance payments, often act as constraints on the utilization of personnel. When only physicians are reimbursed for services that can be provided by other categories of personnel then either these other categories are badly utilized or the physician may be reduced to an "on paper" supervisor to satisfy regulations.

Payment for services rendered by qualified providers, regardless of discipline, with review of quality of service, would do much to solve utilization problems.

An allied need is for further study of the functions to be performed in agencies and of the type of personnel qualified to perform them. This can lead to general staffing standards or alternative models both by function and discipline (with room for overlap) which will assist in clarifying roles and planning for hiring and utilization. Such standards should also include administrative, supervisory, consultation, and evaluation functions, and will differ by type of facility and urban/rural area.

Other problems in personnel utilization relate to productivity, constraints imposed by unions, the rigidities of a civil service system, and the lack of career systems related to education and continuing education. While these matters are primarily State concerns, Federal studies and models can be of great use in helping devise a more rational and realistic system.

The question of organizational linkages to the health and human services systems is another area deserving study. The same functions may be attempted in all three areas, and done less well than possible, because of lack of coordination and of personnel trained to interact effectively with other modes of service delivery.

Credentialing procedures and their relation to quality of care and optimal utilization also require study. The professions all have developed their own certification procedures at a National level, and all are licensed by the States. The need for uniformity of State licensing and certification to promote mobility and wider recognition of skills has long been recognized. While licensure is a State function, Federal regulations can aid in the development of National standards. Mental health paraprofessionals have as yet no National credentialing procedures, although efforts toward development of these are being made for alcohol and drug abuse counselors and mental health workers. It is an appropriate Federal role to look into the feasibility of such a system, and possibly assist in its development.

Criteria for licensure and certification for the professions generally require passing an examination as well as the possession of educational credentials. Much has been written about competency-based certification, but measures of competency are extremely difficult to devise, even though theoretically attractive. Educational requirements at least assure that the individual has been given certain knowledge and experience. Until there is an accepted way of measuring an individual's effectiveness, educational criteria should be retained. Studies should, however, be done on ways of demonstrating competency and attainment of skills.

Training and the Financing of Training

The quality of and access to both basic and continuing education are central issues in a discussion of personnel. Professional training is both long and expensive. It is generally provided in university settings, and the cost is borne by the student (through tuition) and by the university, either through endowment income or State funds for education.

When the National Institute for Mental Health was established, one of its major purposes was to increase the numbers of trained mental health personnel and improve the quality of their education. Funds were given, on the basis of peer review, to academic departments to enlarge and improve their faculty and to provide stipends for their students. The training budget of NIMH increased from an initial $1 million in 1948 to $4.8 million in 1955, $24.8 million in 1960, and reached a high of $120 million in 1969. Although funds were allocated to research training, experimental and special projects, continuing education and, later, paraprofessional manpower development, the major emphasis was on basic education for the four major mental health professions. It is estimated that in 1972, 44 percent of the psychiatric residents, 28 percent of the clinical psychology graduate students, 38 percent of the master's level psychiatric social work students, and 90 percent of the master's degree candidates in psychiatric nursing were receiving NIMH stipends. The vast majority of academic based professional training programs received departmental support.

Since that time NIMH appropriations for training have become progressively lower, the number of stipends has been reduced, particularly in psychiatry where comparatively few residents receive them now, and faculty support for other professional departments has been slashed. These differences occur because residents are often able to be paid out of income received for services, but this is seldom true for the other disciplines. The last decade has also seen inflation, rising tuition costs, and a tightening of State budgets. While many training institutions have relied to some extent on funds from other Federal agencies, such as the Veterans Administration, and other parts of the Department of Health, Education, and Welfare (Social and Rehabilitation Service, Health Resources Administration, Vocational Rehabilitation), indications are that these too are dropping or disappearing.

The impact of decreasing Federal support will not necessarily be in a reduced number of professional graduates, although this may occur. It will be more evident in the quality of education and the type of student admitted. New faculty may not be hired, new programs started, multidisciplinary training undertaken, or new (and expensive) relationships with community agencies and support systems formed. Already the changing priorities and uncertainties about funding have caused many departments to cutback on innovations and be skeptical about NIMH mandates. The loss of stipends will make it much harder to recruit and support poor and minority students, and graduate and professional schools may become the preserve of the upper middle classes, oriented toward private practice.

For these reasons, there must be continuation of categorical grants at an increased level for the training of mental health professionals. These funds will in no way cover the full costs of education, but they will maintain the viability of academic centers of excellence which have become National resources and at the same time permit the Federal Government to exercise leverage in seeing that training institutions stress the priorities identified elsewhere in this paper so that all persons with emotional problems will have access to care from qualified and sensitive providers.

The funding for the training of paraprofessionals has never been a major NIMH responsibility. The brief period of support for community colleges was for developmental purposes only and has long since expired. In addition it reached only about a third of all of the programs at its peak. Primary sources for the Federal funding of paraprofessional training have been from the social welfare agencies in DHEW, from the Department of Labor's Comprehensive Employment and Training Act (CETA), and from other agencies such as Housing and Urban Development. NIMH has primarily supported research and demonstration regarding the training and utilization of paraprofessionals, and this should be continued and expanded. Consideration should also be given to increasing NIMH support for paraprofessional training.

Funding for the category of American Indian and minority indigenous mental health practitioners has always been infinitesimal. Only two programs to train medicine men (Rosebud and Navajo) have been funded out of over 200 possible tribal mental health systems.

The issue of continuing education remains to be faced. The program support from Continuing Education Branch of NIMH is only a token amount of the total. Continuing education for the major professions is usually financed through fees charged to the participants. However, these high fees are not realistic for paraprofessionals or even for the poorer paid professionals. Mental health agencies support much of the continuing education which they conduct or for which they make contracts. These costs are passed on to those who pay for service, and thus raise the costs of mental health care.

This raises serious questions about the use of funds which are intended for service delivery being spent on education. In fact, this is an issue for all kinds of mental health professional and occupational education, much of which takes place in service delivery agencies where it is supervised by agency staff persons. In recent years, there has been a strong trend to separate mental health training budgets from service budgets and to place training funds in the budgets of the educational programs. However, the reductions in training program budgets are forcing reexamination of this policy.

Data Needs

Rational planning in the mental health area is severely hampered by the lack of satisfactory data on the supply, education, distribution, and utilization of personnel. Instead of a coordinated system, there is disjointed information from several sources which lacks uniformity, overlaps, and is seldom complementary. For example, staffing data for health and mental health facilities is obtained from surveys conducted by NIMH and the National Center for Health Statistics, licensure data exists for some professions, the American Medical Association monitors the supply of physicians, and professional associations maintain a roster of their membership and may conduct surveys of their activities, place of work, and salaries. Unfortunately, the staffing data are weak on differentiating the various categories of paraprofessionals and cannot provide information on professionals in private practice or employed in places other than the traditional mental health facilities, licensure data often provide little more than a head count and are incomplete for those professions, notably psychology and social work, where licensure is not universally mendatory for practice, and surveys by professional associations usually include only members.

Data on geographic distribution are gross and insufficient for planning purposes, and we know little of the pattern of multiple employment that exists for many professionals. These data are necessary for a meaningful assessment of mental health personnel needs and supply. Information should be obtained not only on the number of persons in the various disciplines or performing mental health related services, but also on their training and credentials, where they are employed both geographically and by type of employer, the number and kind of patients being seen, the nature of the problems being dealt with, and the type of services provided. Measures of outcome or quality of care, while desirable, are far more difficult to obtain.

While States and localities can assist in the collection of these data, Federal support and direction are essential for consistency and comprehensiveness and as a vital part of National identification of needs and program planning. NIMH should devote more attention and resources to the development of a data system, and use it as an integral part of its policymaking and program evaluation.

RECOMMENDATIONS

The recommendations being made in this report are partly to the mental health field in general and partly to specific agencies of the Federal Government or State governments. Still other recommendations are being made to the professional schools or to specific National organizations such as accrediting bodies. For this reason they cannot be organized in the same way as the recommendations presented in the front of this report. Rather they present the ways different entities can help solve particular problems.

The personnel component of the mental health delivery system makes up the largest part of the operating budget (ranging from 70-80 percent). Yet the personnel component is in many ways the most inelastic element of all. In many ways this is the result of the traditions and mind-sets that were established 30-40 years ago when the mental health system was essentially confined to the treatment of the mentally ill in the State mental hospitals. Since that time there has been a great expansion of the scope of mental health to include a wider range of mental disorders and the treatment of alcoholism and drug abuse. There have been changes in the technologies of treatment and there has been the development of the entire community mental health movement. Civil rights changes in our society have brought about the movement of chronic patients to the communities, and mental health services have been declared to be the right of all our people including the disadvantaged and persons in hard-to-reach rural areas. These recommendations, therefore, relate to the total range of personnel, and the ways in which they are educated, utilized, and financed.

Training Priorities

Supply has been the traditional concern of the mental health personnel system. From all indications the Nation is finally reaching the point at which the training capacity is keeping pace with the need in many areas. It is difficult to predict future needs since so much depends on the system of delivery and the decisions made about the quality of care to be provided and the quality and training of personnel. While there does not appear to be a need to prime the pump to increase the production of new workers, it would be a serious mistake to cut back on the present overall training capacity of the Nation's professional and occupational mental health training programs.

Recommendation 1

> The Federal Government and State governments should maintain support for education of mental health professionals at the level of FY1970 and this support should be associated with the establishment of strategies to meet special need areas of mental health personnel.

Support has been given to both professional training programs and to student stipends. The panel feels it would be destructive to cut the present training capacity of these programs, but that the greater problems of mental health personnel for the future will be those of distribution. The support for both training programs and students should be associated with the development of strategies designed to meet the distribution problems.

Distribution problems fall into four major areas: (a) geographic, (b) to subspecialty areas of mental health of children and the aging, (c) to minority providers, and (d) to organized public service programs rather than to private practice.

Geographic Distribution

All the data indicate that rural areas have disproportionately few mental health professionals. Individual studies have shown that the ghetto areas of cities need more personnel. In addition, State mental hospitals, especially those in rural areas, are inadequately staffed in proportion to other mental health facilities. Special efforts must be made to implement strategies to facilitate the distribution of mental health professionals to these special need geographic areas.

Recommendation 2

> A series of related strategies should be implemented to facilitate the distribution of mental health professional personnel to rural areas, ghetto areas, and to State mental hospitals. Studies have shown that simplistic strategies used separately are unlikely to be successful, but sophisticated combinations of strategies can be at least partially successful. The specific actions recommended are:
>
> (1) Priority for Federal support for training of mental health personnel should be given to training programs that can document that they are implementing strategies to improve the staffing of these special need areas, and stipends be given to students who agree to work in a special need area upon completion of training.

Geographic need areas would be only one of the special need areas; others are the subspecialties of child and geropsychiatry and public service. Minority candidates would also be included in such a program of support.

> (2) Professional training programs should plan and implement special activities in the recruitment, selection, training, and counseling of candidates to enhance their likelihood of staffing special need areas. Minority candidates are also to be included.

Selected training programs have already experimented with a series of strategies which now need further refinement and expansion. Among the possibilities are:

(a) Selective recruitment of candidates from rural areas, ghetto areas, minority groups, etc., who are more likely to return to such areas for practice.

(b) Programs of special counseling and orientation of candidates to rural practice, ghetto practice, public service, and special attention to the special training to maintain their skills and competence.

(c) Conducting the training of candidates in public agencies located in special need areas (e.g., rural community mental health centers, area health education centers, inner-city mental health centers, State mental hospitals). It is essential to provide faculty to these agencies to assure the quality of training and to provide appropriate faculty role models. The training in these centers should include an orientation to the entire service delivery system--not just the diagnosis and treatment of individual clients.

(d) Recruitment of candidates from mental health paraprofessionals, especially those working in rural areas or who are members of minority groups.

> (3) Accrediting bodies for professional training programs should encourage these variations in training programs and develop guidelines for helping in their implementation.

Some training programs may fear to undertake innovations of these kinds if it would threaten their accreditation. Not only should this not happen, but the accrediting bodies should help programs become more innovative to meet special needs.

> (4) State and local mental health agencies should develop economic incentives, special programs, and arrangements to facilitate professional practice in rural areas.

These special programs might include such arrangements as:

(a) Sabbatical leaves for rural practitioners or those in other need areas.

(b) Prominent visiting consultant/teachers.

(c) Higher salary schedules for professionals who work in special need areas, such as rural areas, ghetto areas, and Indian reservations.

(d) Higher fee schedules under reimbursement plans for these practitioners.

> (5) State mental hospitals should implement innovative approaches to relieving the crisis in recruitment of physicians and psychiatrists.

With the cutbacks in the number of foreign medical graduates coming to this country, the State mental hospitals will be severely hurt unless they undertake new strategies for physician recruitment including some of those listed previously and others such as:

    (a) Use of physician extenders for management of medical problems and routine physical examinations.

    (b) Use of contract physicians and psychiatrists from local areas.

    (c) Use of contracts for care of public patients in private psychiatric hospitals or in general hospital psychiatric units.

        (6) The Public Health Service should declare the State hospitals as shortage areas so that they may receive Health Service Corps personnel. The regulations for the Health Service Corps should be modified to include psychologists and social workers in addition to physicians and nurses.

Subspecialty Training

The data indicate that the mental health professionals trained for work with children fall considerably short of the need for qualified subspecialists in this area. There are virtually no good data regarding specialized workers for the elderly in any of the professions, and there are very few training programs that are known to specialize in the mental health problems of the aged. Yet the data show that elderly patients are poorly served in community mental health centers and in all other mental health facilities. Some of the specific strategies proposed are:

Recommendation 3

        The Federal programs through NIMH should provide special incentives for establishing specialized training programs in child and aged mental health and extra stipend assistance to students who agree to work in these need areas.

These programs should be oriented to patterns of managing the clinical problems of children and the aged by the agencies that already serve them (e.g., schools, nursing homes, senior citizen programs) as well as the specialized treatment of these clients in mental health facilities. It is likely that a major part of the work of a mental health child specialist or a mental health specialist for the aging will be consultation to these agencies. There are additional aspects to this recommendation.

    (1) The NIMH should consider funding exemplary treatment programs for the aged in which these specialists would receive their training.

    (2) The paraprofessional program should also feature the development of training programs for work with children and the aged.

(3) The Federal Government and the specialized training
centers should concentrate on the development of
training materials and guidelines regarding child
mental health and aging mental health for incorporation in all professional, paraprofessional, and
continuing education training programs so that all
workers are better prepared in these subspecialty
areas.

Minorities

All of the data show that the minorities make up a much smaller portion of the professional mental health personnel than their portion of the population. Because of the importance of cultural and values issues in mental health work, it is essential that more minority persons be brought into the mental health professions and that the existing professions learn more about the problems of delivering services to persons from minority cultures.

Recommendation 4

The Federal Government, State governments and training
programs should make special efforts to recruit, counsel,
and support minority group candidates in entering the
mental health professions and develop training materials
and programs regarding working with minority clients for
inclusion in the training of all professionals.

There are several subrecommendations to this item:

(1) Special efforts must be made at secondary school and
general college levels to recruit competent minority
persons into human service training programs.

(2) The mental health system (Federal, State, and academic)
must recognize that the paraprofessional movement represents a potential route for developing minority
candidates for the professions. This may involve
acceptance of competency assessment procedures and
transfer of credits on a wider basis than is presently
done.

(3) Federal and State governments must provide financial
assistance for predoctoral minority candidates, most
of whom have very limited financial resources.

(4) Professional training programs must establish special
recruitment and counseling programs for minority
candidates. Unless there is a special welcome and
specific arrangements for regular review and assistance, minority persons are unlikely to enroll or remain
in a program that is overwhelmingly oriented to majority values and procedures.

(5) The Federal programs through NIMH should assist in the
development of training materials regarding minority
cultures and serving minority clients to be integrated
in the basic and continuing education training programs
of all mental health professions and paraprofessions.
NIMH has supported programs such as the Chicano Training Center in Houston to do some of this. More is
needed.

    (a) Demonstrations are needed for how this content
material can be integrated in all of the curriculum and not just provided as isolated lectures.

    (b) Minority persons and minority programs should
be employed to do this kind of training whenever
possible.

(6) Accrediting bodies for mental health professional
training programs should require evidence that there
is a program for recruiting and retaining minority
persons and that minority content material is included
in the curriculum for all students.

These accrediting bodies should also develop and disseminate guidelines and standards for how these requirements might be fulfilled. This has already been
done in social work.

Public Service and Organized Care Systems

There is a trend for mental health professionals of all kinds to enter private practice as well as service in organized care systems. This leaves the public services relatively unstaffed and yet obligated to provide services to the disadvantaged and those suffering from chronic mental illness. Public service must be made more attractive to compete with the attractions of private practice.

Recommendation 5

The Federal Government, State governments, payment plans,
and training programs should implement strategies to
attract and prepare practitioners to work in public
service and organized care settings.

There are several component suggestions here:

(1) Federal and third party reimbursement programs should
provide differential reimbursement schedules for services as follows:

    (a) Highest levels for services in organized care
settings.

(b) Intermediate levels for services in private sector where no comparable public service program exists.

(c) Lowest levels for private services in areas where comparable public services exist.

(2) State and local agencies must review and adjust their salary schedules and working conditions to provide incentives to professionals.

(a) Salary schedules are often unrealistically low and need upgrading.

(b) Staffing standards and working conditions must be reviewed so that bureaucratic procedures, routine activities and unrealistic models of treatment and personnel utilization are minimized.

(3) Training programs should ensure that significant parts of the field training of students is conducted in public, organized care systems in which the candidate learns about the delivery system as well as individual client therapy. Funds must be granted to the agencies for this training responsibility.

This training should concentrate on working and learning with other disciplines and paraprofessionals and not be limited to the confines of one's own profession. Some training of mental health personnel should be done in Area Health Education Centers. It should also include opportunities for the student to participate in supervision and some middle level program management as well as in clinical work with clients. The emphasis should be on the challenges of leadership in organized and public service work, but still recognizing the realities of these environments.

(4) Professional training programs should incorporate basic content materials in supervision and public program management in the curriculum for all students.

Statistics show that virtually all professionals in organized care systems serve both supervisory/managerial roles and clinical roles within a few years of employment. They are generally totally unprepared for these middle management roles in their professional education. Because this is so much a part of the professional role in organized care systems, it should be incorporated in the basic training of all professionals. This is not the same content that is taught in most training programs for top level administrators. There is need for more careful analysis and the development of guidelines for teaching this supervisory/middle management level of administration. This should also include content material related to the uses of paraprofessionals and the uses of teams in the delivery of services.

Recommendation 6

> The concept of the mental health personnel system must be expanded to include all aspects of developing, deploying, utilizing, and managing all personnel to deliver the most effective and efficient mental health services to all Americans. This includes all of the components of:
>
> --Policy Planning and Evaluation for all Mental Health Personnel
>
> --Education and Continuing Education for all Mental Health Personnel
>
> --Administration/Management of all Mental Health Personnel in Mental Health Service Delivery Systems
>
> --Modifications of the Regulatory Mechanisms in Mental Health Personnel to aid in the Achievement of Problem Resolution.

This more comprehensive concept of a dynamic system of interacting forces was described in the previous sections. Such a conceptualization requires the participation of many actors in the personnel system--mental health agency administrators, professional associations, professional schools, licensing boards, higher education commissions, State merit system and civil service administrators, State budget directors, third party payers, credentialing bodies and the Federal Government--especially the officials of the Alcohol, Drug Abuse, and Mental Health Administration and its three Institutes.

This overall recommendation is thus directed to all of these leaders wherever they are in the Nation. However, it provides the framework for several specific recommendations:

> (1) The National Institute of Mental Health should emphasize this broader conceptualization for personnel development and utilization.
>
> > (a) The establishment in NIMH of a program of support for research and development activities in broad personnel/manpower areas in addition to training.

The technology for many areas of personnel planning, forecasting, and evaluation is weak. Little is known about programs to change personnel distribution or to improve productivity or about various models of teams and personnel (credentialing, payment patterns, etc.) The NIMH through a program of grants or contracts could significantly assist the entire mental health field to develop the technology and guidelines for manpower/personnel development in all of these areas.

The task panel recommends several possible topical areas for such research and development efforts:

--Evaluation of the effectiveness of various strategies of early intervention with students from disadvantaged backgrounds or minority groups on their subsequent career patterns in public service in underserved areas.

--Studies of the effects of labor unions, merit systems, payment programs, licensing restrictions, and other regulators on personnel utilization and development of strategies to modify these when they are hinderances.

--Studies of the effects of various patterns of personnel deployment in teams, staff organizations, etc., and development of recommendations for more rational deployment.

--Projects to develop appropriate roles for mental health personnel in regard to the broad human services--especially the social services system and the primary health care system. Perhaps more mental disorders are cared for by these sectors of the human services than by the mental health system, but we know little about how these problems present themselves out there or how mental health personnel can best help those systems to recognize and work with these mentally disordered clients.

> (b) The establishment in NIMH of a support program for State level manpower/personnel development entities that could (a) develop personnel/manpower planning, and (b) bring together all of the key personnel actors in a State to set and implement statewide personnel development plans.

As noted in the previous section, one basic level at which comprehensive personnel planning and development must be done is the State. States will need assistance of two kinds to move into such statewide mental health personnel planning and development programs:

--Technical assistance regarding the technology and procedures.

--Financial assistance to staff these personnel planning and development entities.

> (2) The States should take action to implement statewide personnel planning and development entities.

While the State mental health authority may be the proper agency to initiate such efforts and even to provide the administrative support services for it, the entity itself should be made up of leading mental health personnel actors from all of the State's major components of the mental health system and the planning should be for all of the personnel needed for private and public mental health programs. It should not limit its concern to only personnel for the State mental health agency's operations.

Such a program also recognizes the mental health personnel needs of programs such as Veterans Administration hospitals, academic institutions, and private nonprofit agencies located in the State. Such State personnel entities must also include planning for certain kinds of professional personnel across State lines since very few States are totally self-sufficient in respect to all kinds of professional personnel. These programs in the States would, of course, be related to regional and national programs in personnel development. Both of these--the manpower/personnel research and development program and the State mental health manpower development program--are very new and have only minimal funding. These need to be expanded through both grant and contract mechanisms.

Equal attention must be given to tribal government entities which are outside of State jurisdiction. The Indian Health Service mental health division should provide support to implement tribal government mental health personnel development plans.

Paraprofessional Personnel

The entire area of the development of middle level workers (paraprofessionals) is very new and requires stronger Federal and national definition and leadership. Much of the present system has grown in response to local needs and issues rather than from any national leadership. There is more need for definition and integration of these workers into the personnel system than support for training programs themselves.

Recommendation 7

> The NIMH and other Federal manpower programs should strengthen efforts to define and integrate the paraprofessional movement in the mental health delivery system. There are several specific subitems:
>
> (1) The funding of the Paraprofessional Manpower Development Branch of NIMH should be increased to better recognize the size of the paraprofessional personnel component of the mental health delivery system.

These workers comprise almost half of the personnel component. The funding authority should be for both grants and contracts to a variety of educational institutions, mental health agencies, and other organizations primarily for research and development of the various aspects of the credentialing, education, utilization, and evaluation of paraprofessionals and indigenous mental health professionals.

> (2) The ADAMHA and other Federal agencies should initiate efforts in-house and with contracts and grants to develop a coordinated conceptualization of the role and functions of paraprofessional workers and their relationships to the professionals and their clients.

Because the paraprofessional movement has grown from many different local initiatives, there is presently a somewhat confusing welter of levels, roles, titles, training programs, and career systems.

Some specific issues to address are:

(a) The development of a set of definitions of terms that can be generally accepted in the field.

(b) Further exploration and definition of the role of a generic Human Services Worker.

(c) Definition of the various levels in a career system for paraprofessional in mental health delivery programs.

(d) Further exploration and definition of the appropriate roles and functions for various models of paraprofessionals.

(e) The development of guidelines for the utilization of paraprofessionals vis-a-vis the existing professions in various team models, staff structures, and supervisory relationships. This kind of information needs to be included in the continuing education and the preprofessional training of the professionals as well.

   (3) Paraprofessional Manpower Development Branch and other components of ADAMHA should pursue efforts to define an appropriate credentialing program for paraprofessionals. The possession of credentials promotes recognition of skills and facilities both geographic and interagency mobility.

   (4) NIMH, NIDA, and NIAAA should encourage further studies and guidelines for competency based approaches to training and credentialing of paraprofessionals.

The paraprofessional programs have already done considerable work in this area which promises to develop more efficient approaches to training and worker assessment for actual service delivery.

   (5) NIMH should encourage the development of guidelines and training materials for the training of paraprofessionals in specialty areas such as:

   (a) child mental health;

   (b) mental health of the aging; including the training of older paraprofessionals;

   (c) prevention;

   (d) work with self-help groups and community support programs; and

   (e) relocation of institutional workers for community service work as institutional jobs are phased out.

(6) NIMH should support the development of linkages between the training programs for paraprofessionals and those for the professionals to assure that persons who wish to move up in academic careers can do so with a minimum of lost time, lost academic credits, and money.

This requires credit transfer arrangements, methods for assessing competence developed from experience, and curriculum linkages. The professional schools should recognize the paraprofessionals as a rich potential resource for the recruitment of motivated and experienced candidates, many of whom are minority persons.

(7) The ADAMHA and NIMH should include representation of the paraprofessionals and indigenous mental health practitioners on any advisory committees related to personnel, services, or data for which the inputs of the professions is deemed important.

There has been a tendency to recognize the professions only in the various advisory councils and committees. The paraprofessionals and indigenous mental health practitioners, although very diverse in function and training, should also be represented as they have substantial inputs to make into deliberations.

Credentialing

In the past few years, there has been accelerated interest in credentialing mental health personnel in various ways (licensure, certification, registration) or in credentialing training programs and service programs in various ways (licensing, accreditation). Legislators, agency administrators, and educators are harried by the confusion of the many proposals and requirements. There needs to be some order to all of this:

Recommendation 8

The Federal Government should work with professional accrediting bodies and the States to promote national standards for the credentialing of mental health personnel, training programs, and service programs when the standards include personnel.

The Public Health Service has already done a great deal of work in this area, and ADAMHA/NIMH should carry it further for mental health personnel. Specific possibilities include:

(1) <u>Guidelines for which professions are most appropriately licensed, certified, or registered.</u>

(2) <u>Guidelines for interstate compacting for State licensure and State certification.</u>

(3) <u>Guidelines for renewals of licenses, certificates, etc., and the criteria and procedures for requiring reexamination or continuing education as a condition for renewal.</u>

(4) <u>Guidelines for credentialing of continuing education which is rapidly expanding but with little quality control procedures.</u>

Data and Special Studies

The field of mental health personnel has serious deficiencies in the data available. The NIMH has assembled routine data on numbers of the various professions and numbers of other major groups of employees in mental health facilities, but there is a lack of data on utilization or many other aspects of the personnel system that should be present for personnel policy planning and evaluation.

Recommendation 9

The NIMH should implement the collection of a wider range of personnel data and facilitate the conduct of special evaluation studies of several aspects of personnel development and utilization.

This has several aspects:

(1) A national advisory committee should be formed to advise NIMH of data needs. It should be made up of representatives from agencies, academia and the various professions and paraprofessionals and indigenous mental health practitioners.

(2) NIMH should establish routine data collection systems on several areas not presently collected.

   (a) Formal training programs with data on enrollments, costs, etc.

   (b) The utilization of mental health personnel including paraprofessionals. There is need to know the activities as well as the geographic location and type of employment of personnel.

(3) NIMH should encourage and support special studies in various aspects of personnel. Several of these have already been mentioned, but others are:

   (a) Effects of unions, merit systems, and payment plans on personnel.

   (b) Evaluation of personnel and training activities.

(c) Studies on productivity of personnel, especially related to outcome measures of clients.

(4) NIMH should develop guidelines for the development of personnel data systems to be used by State manpower personnel development entities. Much of this State level data is presently in fragmentary pieces in the hands of professional associations, licensure boards, agency personnel systems, training institutions, etc. The States need help in pulling it all together and relating to it in useful ways.

(5) The Federal Government should make greater use of these data in program planning and evaluation.

Standards for Mental Health Personnel

Another area in which work is needed is in the development of standards for mental health personnel. There are several court orders or sets of standards that have been somewhat arbitrarily developed or are out-of-date.

Recommendation 10

NIMH and the other institutes of ADAMHA should initiate activities to develop guidelines for standards for mental health personnel of all kinds in various settings.

These should not be just staff-patient ratios but should be related to the services to be provided and the range of various personnel qualified to perform them. These should include supervisory and managerial functions as well as programmatic functions for various kinds of services and clients. Reimbursement programs could be based on these standards.

Continuing Education for Mental Health Personnel

Continuing education is becoming a major industry in our society. For mental health personnel it is necessary to provide continuing education to help workers: (1) keep up-to-date on new developments in clinical knowledge and skills, (2) improve their service delivery skills in a variety of programmatic activities (consultation, education, prevention, etc.) and, (3) learn the skills of management and administration. Programs of continuing education are now provided by professional schools, professional societies, mental health agencies, and a variety of private and voluntary groups.

Recommendation 11

The NIMH should give leadership to the development of guidelines for further continuing education programs for mental health personnel.

(1) NIMH should provide assistance to the development of coordinated quality standards for continuing education and accreditation of continuing education programs in mental health.

There are presently several systems of credentialing continuing education in the various professions, but they are not in harmony with each other and most have no accreditation system for quality assurance.

(2) NIMH should give leadership to the development of mechanisms for the financing of continuing education for the full range of mental health personnel.

At this time continuing education is primarily financed through private fees. Serious efforts must be made to develop new sources of funding. Area Health Education Centers and Continuing Education Centers such as those in North Carolina are promising prototypes.

(3) The NIMH should provide leadership in developing staff exchange programs between service institutions and universities as well as among other public and private agencies delivering mental health services (within as well as out of the State) to provide continuing education opportunities similar to the sabbatical leave concept.

Such a staff exchange program would provide new professional stimulation and be very beneficial to the individual's professional growth as well as to the agency. The intent is to allow the mental health staff to get work experience in a different setting for a period of 6 months to 1 year.

(4) The NIMH should exercise leadership in developing the curriculum for programs in mental health administration and assist in the implementation of such programs.

The Staff College of NIMH has already taken leadership in this area but more needs to be done in program development at two levels:

(a) The development of full scale programs in mental health administration for persons in top administration. This would include training in budgeting and financing, program planning and evaluation, mental health law, personnel administration, public information, etc. It will also include short-term continuing education programs in various sections of this.

(b) The development of materials regarding middle level management and supervision which can be used in continuing education and staff development programs for personnel who have had only clinical training but find themselves in positions that require both managerial and clinical activities.

Broader Relationships of Mental Health

The panel was impressed with the limitations of conceptualizing the mental health personnel system as being limited only to those persons who work in the specialty mental health facilities. As the statistics make clear, far more of the mentally disordered are served by the other health and human service programs than by the mental health system. For example, 60 percent of the mentally disordered are believed to be receiving services from the general health care system; half of the persons in youth and adult correctional institutions have been judged to have emotional and mental disorders; the largest single group of persons receiving support under the Federal-State assistance program for the totally and permanently disabled are the mentally disabled.

In addition, large portions of the mentally disabled are being served by the other health and human service agencies and the personnel who serve them are often the same kinds of workers who are employed in the specialty mental health system--social workers, psychologists, nurses, physicians, special teachers, rehabilitation counselors, etc. The training programs for these individual professions are often supported by funds from several different Federal and State agencies (e.g., NIMH, NIDA, NIAAA, Vocational Rehabilitation Administration, Administration on Aging, Office of Child Development, Department of Education, Department of Labor, Veterans Administration).

The limitations of the organizational structure of mental health services seem to shut off the mental health system's view of the rest of the human services. The mental health system must consider how it might better relate to and use the broader health and human service system and natural community support systems for more effective care of the mentally disordered and especially for preventive work which is probably best done by those personnel who are more likely to be in touch with people on a day-by-day basis than are the personnel in mental health facilities.

Recommendation 12

> The ADAMHA and the entire Department of HEW should explore broader linkages and implications for ways in which mental health can better relate to the other health and human service systems. There are several aspects:
>
> (1) Within the U.S. Government there should be a liaison group to explore such program linkages for mental health purposes across the Federal agencies. Most of the health and human service programs that mental health should be related to are in the Department of Health, Education, and Welfare, but there are others in the Department of Labor, the Department of Justice, the Veterans Administration, and others. This relationship should be reinforced by liaison persons in various specific areas (e.g., in social work education or in psychology).

(2) The NIMH should support special studies to develop guidelines for the linkages between mental health and the other health and human service programs and their personnel to better serve the mental health needs of their clients. Such guidelines would be oriented to State and local level program linkages rather than exclusively Federal programs.

(3) Federal and State mental health programs should recognize the importance of the family and of natural support systems and encourage and assist mental health programs and personnel to make use of these systems. Among them are:

(a) Eminent and prestigious indigenous healers such as medicine men and curanderos.

(b) Self-help groups.

(c) Churches, lodges, voluntary community agencies, such as the Salvation Army, and Family Service Associations, etc.

Special Needs of Individual Professions

There are several regulatory or legislative recommendations that will facilitate the recruitment, training, and subsequent distribution of members of these professions.

Recommendation 13

The Federal Government should make the following changes in laws or regulations to facilitate the training of mental health professionals.

(1) P.L. 94-484, the Health Professions Educational Assistance Act, should be amended to permit medical students entering psychiatry to "pay back" scholarship aid after 4 or 5 years of residency training rather than 3 years. This present restriction dissuades students from entering psychiatry.

(2) Amend P.L. 94-484 to identify psychiatry as a specialty in which there is a national shortage. This would highlight the impending shortage of psychiatrists as foreign medical graduates are withdrawn and encourage more American medical graduates to choose psychiatry.

(3) The Health Professions Education Assistance Act (P.L. 94-484) should be amended to specifically include psychologists and social workers among the

"health professions." Data show that more than 20,000 members of each of these professions are primarily engaged in providing mental health or other health services.

(4) The regulation restricting predoctoral support for the first 2 years of graduate study in psychology should be eliminated. This is especially necessary for minority candidates and women.

(5) Predoctoral support should be continued in psychology. This is perhaps more important to psychology than other professions--especially to assure the influx of minority candidates and women. This relates to a recommendation of the National Academy of Sciences that there be a gradual shift of Federal support to postdoctoral training in scientific disciplines.

(6) Title 1 of the National Research Act (P.L. 93-348) and Section 303 of the Public Health Services Act should be amended to acknowledge the dual nature of psychology and social work by specifically allowing funding for clinical programs with a research component and research training programs with some clinical portions. Psychologists and social workers have been excluded because of the dual nature of their training. The fear that research funds would be spent on clinical training has not proved to be true.

Recommendation 14

The professional training programs and their accrediting organizations should promote the following specific additions in their curricula:

(1) In psychiatric residency training there should be required training for consultation and support to the general health sector regarding the recognition and management of mental disorder. This should include work with physicians, general hospitals, nursing homes, etc. Data show that probably half of the mentally disordered are seen by the general health sector rather than by the specialty mental health system. Psychiatrists and other mental health professionals must be prepared to assist through consultation, continuing education, etc.

(2) The other side of this coin will require that family practice residencies include some training in psychiatry to be able to recognize and more effectively manage mentally disordered patients and their families, and to appropriately refer them to mental health care facilities.

M&P 71

Personnel for Prevention

The mental health programs are charged by law with carrying out prevention programs in alcoholism, drug abuse, and mental health, but little is actually done because there are few mental health personnel skilled in the development of prevention techniques and programs.

Recommendation 15

> The ADAMHA should initiate program support for the development of personnel qualified to do primary prevention.

This has three aspects.

(1) Federal support for graduate and postgraduate education of mental health professionals in schools of public health should be reinstituted. This earlier program was eliminated in the recent funding cuts. Such programs should prepare specialists in programming for consultation and education for primary prevention.

(2) Recommend Federal support of programs in schools of public health for career development of mental health/public health career scientist/educators, especially from the core mental health professions to provide an expanded supply of such persons for scientist/educator careers in settings other than schools of public health, and to provide the public health and population prevention orientation for education/training programs in educational institutions for the core professions. The capability for producing such career educators in mental health/public health is far too small to provide the necessary expansion of education/training opportunities to meet currently mandated needs.

(3) Guideline materials should be developed under Federal support for training of all professionals and paraprofessionals in the area of primary prevention. Many professional education programs presently offer virtually nothing about the theories and skills of primary prevention. A basic orientation module could be developed for all professional education programs.

Financing of Mental Health Services

The financing of mental health services is a complex area that requires study and action.

Recommendation 16

> The NIMH should take leadership in conducting studies and developing guidelines for various funding programs to use in financing or reimbursing mental health service personnel.

Several of the payment programs are set by other agencies of the Federal Government or by other third-party payers outside of government, but the NIMH should lead in doing the studies and making recommendations for making the payment systems more favorable to maximum personnel utilization.

> (1) NIMH should develop guidelines for payment of the various services of professionals and paraprofessionals based on the staffing standards already listed.
>
> (2) NIMH should initiate studies of the funding mechanism for primary care workers who carry out mental health services in the general health care system.
>
> (3) Studies are needed of the effects of various funding patterns on personnel distribution, the type of services rendered, and the utilization of personnel.
>
> (4) Reimbursement for services by agencies of the government or by other third party payers should be based upon the services performed and the qualifications and certification of the provider within his/her own discipline. Regulations should not favor one discipline over another when both are qualified by training and experience.

Recommendation 17

> State and local government salaries for mental health workers in public service should be pegged to defined labor markets in the State or region to be eligible for reimbursement from Federal funding sources.

Often public salary schedules for mental health and other personnel are badly out of phase with private local salaries or with each other, thus making it difficult to attract qualified staff. Federal funding leverage could be exerted to remedy this.

Full-Time Equivalent Positions, by Discipline, All Mental Health Facilities, United States, 1968-1976

	1968	1972	1974	1976
Psychiatrists	9,891	12,938	14,947	15,339
Other Physicians	2,736	3,991	3,548	3,356
Psychologists	5,212	9,443	12,597	15,251
Social Workers	9,755	17,687	22,147	25,887
Registered Nurses	24,256	31,110	34,089	39,392
Other Mental Health Professionals (BA + or =)	12,136	17,514	29,325	34,249
Physical Health		8,203	10,507	9,631
Total Professional Patient Care Staff	63,986	100,886	127,160	143,105
LPN, LVN		19,616	17,193	15,337
MH Worker (BA minus)		120,753	128,529	130,021
Total Patient Care Staff		241,255	272,882	288,463
Admin, Clerical, Maint.		134,719	130,142	134,795
TOTAL		375,974	403,024	423,258

Disciplines as a Percent of Total Patient Care Staff

	1972	1974	1976
Psychiatrists	5.4	5.5	5.3
Other MD	1.7	1.3	1.2
Psychologists	3.9	4.6	5.3
Social Workers	7.3	8.1	9.0
Registered Nurses	12.9	12.5	13.7
Other MH Professionals (greater or equal to BA)	7.3	10.7	11.9
Physical Health	3.4	3.9	3.3
Total Professional Patient Care	41.8	46.6	49.6
LPN, LVN	8.1	6.3	5.3
MH Worker (less than BA)	50.1	47.1	45.1
TOTAL PATIENT CARE	100.0	100.0	100.0

Source: NIMH

M&P 74

Full Time Equivalent Positions, By Discipline, Community Mental Health Centers, U.S., 1970-1976

	1970	1972	1974	1976
Psychiatrists	1,394	1,583	1,848	2,292
Other Physicians	103	241	270	274
Psychologists	1,005	1,807	2,994	4,543
Social Workers	1,989	3,044	4,418	6,752
Registered Nurses	1,989	2,722	3,459	4,588
Other Mental Health Professionals (BA + or =)		2,441	4,306	6,336
Physical Health		158	252	305
Total Professional Patient Care Staff		11,996	17,546	25,090
LPN, LVN		1,244	1,367	1,288
MH Worker (BA minus)		5,574	7,605	9,273
Total Patient Care Staff	13,123	18,814	26,518	35,651
Admin, Clerical, Maint.		5,841	8,791	12,816
TOTAL		24,655	35,309	48,467

Disciplines as a Percent of Total Patient Care Staff

	1970	1972	1974	1976
Psychiatrists	10.6	8.4	7.0	6.4
Other Physicians	0.8	1.3	1.0	0.8
Psychologists	7.7	9.6	11.3	12.7
Social Workers	15.2	16.2	16.7	18.9
Registered Nurses	15.2	14.5	13.0	12.9
Other MH Professionals (greater or equal to BA)		13.0	16.2	17.8
Physical Health		0.8	0.9	0.9
Total Professional Patient Care		63.8	66.2	70.4
LPN, LVN		6.6	5.2	3.6
MH Worker (less than BA)		29.6	28.7	26.0
TOTAL PATIENT CARE	100.0	100.0	100.0	100.0

Source: NIMH

M&P 75

Full Time Equivalent Positions, by Discipline, State and County Mental Hospitals, United States, 1968-1976

	1968	1972	1974	1976
Psychiatrists	3,815	4,389	4,714	4,333
Other Physicians	1,795	2,440	2,286	2,047
Psychologists	1,516	2,484	3,045	3,039
Social Workers	3,471	5,324	5,934	5,948
Registered Nurses	13,537	13,353	14,398	15,098
Other Mental Health Professionals (BA + or =)	(6,545)	5,890	10,317	10,551
Physical Health	( )	4,636	5,890	5,580
Total Professional Patient Care Staff	30,679	38,518	46,584	46,596
LPN, LVN		12,277	8,971	7,458
MH Worker (BA minus)		87,514	91,383	87,073
Total Patient Care Staff		138,307	146,938	141,127
Admin, Clerical, Maint.		85,579	80,344	77,879
TOTAL		223,886	227,282	219,006

Disciplines as a Percent of Total Patient Care Staff

	1972	1974	1976
Psychiatrists	3.2	3.2	3.1
Other Physicians	1.8	1.6	1.5
Psychologists	1.8	2.1	2.2
Social Workers	3.8	4.0	4.2
Registered Nurses	9.7	9.8	10.7
Other MH Professionals (greater or equal to BA)	4.3	7.0	7.5
Physical Health	3.4	4.0	4.0
Total Professional Patient Care	27.8	31.7	33.0
LPN, LVN	8.9	6.1	5.3
MH Worker (less than BA)	63.3	62.2	61.7
TOTAL PATIENT CARE	100.0	100.0	100.0

Source: NIMH

Distribution of Hours Worked in Mental Health Facilities,
By Category of Staff and Type of Facility - 1976 (in percentages)

	Total	Profess- ionals	Non Pro- fessionals	Psychia- trists	Psychol- ogists	Social Workers	R.N.'s	Other MH Profs.	LPN LVN	Mental Health Workers
TOTAL-All Facilities	100.0	100.0	100.0	100.0	100.0	100.0	100.0	100.0	100.0	100.0
All Psych. Hospitals	54.9	39.4	70.0	37.3	23.6	26.0	47.0	39.0	56.2	71.8
State & County	48.9	32.5	65.0	28.4	19.9	23.0	38.4	30.8	48.5	67.1
Private	6.0	6.9	5.0	8.9	3.7	3.0	8.6	8.2	7.7	4.7
All V.A	9.1	9.8	8.5	9.6	8.2	6.3	13.5	5.1	10.2	8.3
N.P. Hospital	5.3	5.0	5.6	2.1	2.5	2.6	7.5	2.7	5.8	5.6
General Hospital Inpatient	3.3	3.8	2.8	5.7	3.8	2.1	5.6	2.0	4.3	2.6
General Hospital Outpatient*	0.5	1.0	0.1	1.8	1.9	1.6	0.4	0.4	0.1	0.1
All Non-Fed Hospitals	11.8	14.8	8.8	25.6	8.9	9.7	24.0	9.9	21.9	7.2
Inpatient	9.9	11.2	8.5	12.6	3.5	4.2	23.1	8.6	21.7	6.9
Outpatient*	1.9	3.6	0.3	13.0	5.4	5.5	0.9	1.3	0.2	0.3
Children's Residential Treatment Centers	4.8	6.3	3.3	1.0	2.8	6.9	0.8	17.7	0.8	3.6
Free Standing Outpatient Clinics*	5.8	10.2	1.5	9.4	24.3	22.2	2.1	7.3	1.2	1.5
CMHC*	12.3	17.5	7.3	14.9	29.8	26.1	11.6	18.5	8.4	7.1
Other*	1.3	2.0	0.6	2.2	2.4	2.8	1.0	2.5	1.3	0.5
Free Standing Day/ Night Facilities	0.3	0.4	0.1	0.2	0.3	0.4	0.0	1.2	0.0	0.1
Other-Multi-Service	1.0	1.6	0.5	2.0	2.1	2.4	1.0	1.3	1.3	0.4
Estimated Outpatient Total*	21.8	34.3	9.8	41.3	63.8	58.2	16.0	30.0	11.2	9.5

*NOTE: Outpatient-Inpatient breaks are estimates. There are, for example, outpatient units in psychiatric hospitals and inpatient units in CMHCs.

Source: NIMH, Staffing of Mental Health Facilities, US, 1976.

SUPPLY OF PROFESSIONAL MENTAL HEALTH PERSONNEL, BY DISCIPLINE

Year	Psychiatrists [1]	Psychologists [2]	Social Workers [3]	Registered Nurses [4]
1950	7,100	7,300	N.A.	N.A.
1955	10,600	13,500	20,000	N.A.
1960	14,100	18,200	26,200	504,000
1965	18,500	23,600	41,600	600,000
1970	23,200	30,800	49,600	722,000
1975	25,700	39,400	64,500	906,000
1976	26,500	42,000	69,600	961,000

[1] Data through 1960 include American Psychiatric Association membership plus filled psychiatric residencies; thereafter, data also include non-members of APA who report a psychiatric specialization to the American Medical Association.

[2] Membership, American Psychological Association. Approximately 37% of all psychologists are in clinical or counseling and guidance psychology. Many others are in mental health related areas.

[3] Membership, National Association of Social Workers. Approximately 20-25% of all social workers are estimated to be in psychiatric or mental health areas.

[4] Source: American Nurses' Association. It is estimated that 5% of all nurses are in mental health areas.

DEGREES AWARDED IN MENTAL HEALTH SPECIALTIES, AND RESIDENTS IN TRAINING, BY DISCIPLINE

Year	Psychology Ph.D. [1]	Masters Social Work [2]	Masters-Psychiatric Nursing [3]	Residents Psychiatry [4]
1960	773	2078	193	3400
1965	955	3206	235	3899
1970	1883	5638	405	4295
1975	2749	8824	551	4765
1976	2878	9080	N.A.	4864

[1] Source: National Academy of Sciences

[2] Source: Council on Social Work Education

[3] Source: American Nurses Association

[4] Figures through 1970 are from the American Medical Association; later figures from the American Psychiatric Association. Somewhat less than one quarter of these residents will complete training each year.

ACKNOWLEDGMENTS

The Task Panel on Manpower and Personnel wishes to acknowledge the highly competent professional assistance of Joan W. Jenkins, Ph.D., Staff Liaison to the panel. Her contribution to our work was invaluable.

We appreciate also the special assistance of Ann Reinert, Pennsylvania State University.

This report would not have been possible without the generous cooperation of the following organizations:

American Association of Marriage and Family Counselors

American Association of Psychiatric Services for Children

American Federation of State, County and Municipal Employees

American Nurses Association

American Psychiatric Association

American Psychological Association

Council on Social Work Education

National Association of Social Workers

National Association of State Mental Health Program Directors

National Institute of Mental Health

National Research Council, National Academy of Sciences

REFERENCES AND BIBLIOGRAPHY

Albee, George W. Mental Health Manpower Trends. Monograph Series No. 3, Joint Commission on Mental Illness and Health. New York: Basic Books, 1959.

Albee, George W. The relation of conceptual models of disturbed behavior to institutional and manpower requirements. In: Arnhoff, F; Rubenstein, E; Speisman, J., eds. Manpower for Mental Health. Chicago: Aldine Publishing Co., 1969, pp. 93-112.

American Association of Chairmen of Departments of Psychiatry. The Crisis in Psychiatric Manpower: Toward a National Psychiatric Manpower Policy. Washington, D.C.: American Psychiatric Association, 1977.

American Medical Association. Directory of Accredited Residencies. Chicago: AMA. Annual (all years).

American Medical Association. Physician Distribution and Medical Licensure in the United States. Chicago: AMA. Annual (all years).

American Nurses' Association. Facts About Nursing. Kansas City: ANA. Annual (all years).

American Nurses' Association. The Nation's Nurses: 1972 Inventory of Registered Nurses. Kansas City: ANA, 1974.

American Psychiatric Association. "Distribution Data on APA Member Psychiatrists: 1977." Washington, D.C., 1977. (Xerox)

Arnhoff, Franklyn N., Rubenstein, E., and Speisman, Joseph C. eds. Manpower for Mental Health. Chicago: Aldine Publishing Co., 1969.

Bachrach, L. L. "Utilization of Services in Organized Mental Health Settings in the United States." Draft report prepared for the President's Commission on Mental Health. Washington, D.C., 1978. (Xerox)

Bachrach, L. L. Deinstitutionalization of mental health services in rural areas. Hospital and Community Psychiatry, September 1977, p. 669.

Bass, R. D. and Ozarin, L. D. "Community Mental Health Center Program: What is Past is Prologue." Paper prepared for the annual meeting of the American Psychiatric Association, Toronto, Canada, May 1977.

Bessent, H. "Psychiatric and Mental Health Nursing Manpower." Report to the Task Panel on Manpower and Personnel, President's Commission on Mental Health. (Xerox)

Bloom, B. L. Interdisciplinary training and interdisciplinary functioning: A survey of attitudes and practices in community mental health. *American Journal of Orthopsychiatry*, 46(4):669-677, October 1976.

Bloom, G. L. and Parad, H. J. Professional activities and training needs of community mental center staff. In: Iscoe, I.; Bloom, B. L.; and Spielberger, C. D., eds. *Community Psychology in Transition*. Washington, D.C.: Hemisphere Publishing Co., 1977, pp. 229-240.

Bower, Willis H. Recent developments in mental health manpower. *Hospital and Community Psychiatry*, Vol. 21H, 1970, pp. 11-17.

Briar, S. "Social Workers in Mental Health." Report to the Task Panel on Manpower and Personnel, President's Commission on Mental Health. (Xerox)

Caplan, G., and Killilea, M., eds. *Support Systems and Mutual Help*. New York: Grune and Stratton, 1976.

Carkhuff, R. R. *Helping and Human Relations*. Vol. 1 and 2. New York: Holt, Rinehart, and Winston, 1969.

Carkhuff, R. R. and Truax, C. B. Lay mental health counselling: The effects of lay group counselling. *Journal of Counselling Psychology*, 1965, 29, pp. 426-431.

Carroll, Jerome F. X. Mental illness and disease: Outmoded concepts in alcohol and drug rehabilitation. *Community Mental Health Journal*, Vol. 11, No. 4, 1975, pp. 418-429.

Council on Social Work Education. *Statistics on Social Work Education in the United States*. New York: CSWE. Annual (all years).

Cowen, E. L. Social and community interventions. In: Mussen, P. H. and Rosenzweig, M. R., eds. *Annual Review of Psychology*, Vol. 24. Palo Alto, Calif.: Annual Reviews, Inc., 1973, pp. 423-472.

Department of Health, Education, and Welfare, National Center for Educational Statistics. *Earned Degrees Conferred*. Washington, D.C.: U.S. Government Printing Office. Annual (all years).

D'Augelli, A. R. and Danish, S. J. Evaluating training programs for paraprofessionals and nonprofessionals. *Journal of Consulting Psychology* (In Press).

Dyer, S. *Early Labor Market Experiences of 1975 Doctoral Recipients in Psychology*. Washington, D.C.: American Psychological Association, 1977.

Ellsworth, R. B. *Nonprofessionals in Psychiatric Rehabilitation*. New York: Appleton-Century-Crofts, 1968.

Executive Committees of the American Association of Chairmen of Departments of Psychiatry and the American Association of Directors of Psychiatric Residency Training. "Toward a National Policy for Psychiatric Manpower: Problems, Assets and Recommendations." Unpublished paper prepared for submission to the President's Commission on Mental Health, 1977.

Fowler, R. D., Jr. "Psychology." Report to the Task Panel on Manpower and Personnel, President's Commission on Mental Health. (Xerox).

Gartner, A. *Paraprofessionals and Their Performance.* New York: Praeger Publishers, 1971.

Gartner, A. "The effectiveness of Paraprofessionals in Service Delivery." Report to the Task Panel on Manpower and Personnel, President's Commission on Mental Health. (Xerox)

Gartner, A., Jackson, V. C., and Riessman, F. *Paraprofessionals Today, Vol. 1. Education.* New York: Human Sciences Press, 1977.

Gartner, A., and Riessman, F. The performance of paraprofessionals in the mental health field. In: Gerald Caplan, ed. *The American Handbook of Psychiatry.* New York: Basic Books, 1971.

Gartner, A., and Riessman, F. *Self-Help in the Human Services.* San Francisco: Jossey-Bass, 1977.

Gensberg, Stewart T., Manolio, Anthony P., and Salerno, Joseph. SCOPE: A venture in hospital-community collaboration. *Hospital and Community Psychiatry,* Vol. 21, January 1970.

Ginzberg, E. "Manpower for Mental Health." Paper submitted to the President's Commission on Mental Health, Washington, D.C., 1977. (Xerox)

Gottfredson, G. D. and Dyer, S. E. *Health Service Providers in Psychology: 1976.* Washington, D.C., American Psychological Association, 1977.

Jenkins, J. and Witkin, M. J. *Foreign Medical Graduates Employed in State and County Mental Hospitals.* DHEW Publication No. (ADM) 76-158. Rockville, Md., National Institute of Mental Health, 1976.

Joint Commission on Mental Illness and Health. *Action for Mental Health.* New York: Basic Books, 1961.

Karlsruher, A. E. The nonprofessional as a psychotherapeutic agent: A review of the empirical evidence pertaining to his effectiveness. *American Journal of Community Psychology,* 1974, 2, pp. 61-77.

Kimmel, W. A. "Mental Health Manpower Development at the State Level: Five Pilot Projects." Contract No. 278-76-0071 with the National Institute of Mental Health. Washington, D.C., 1977. (Xerox)

Langsley, D. G. "Psychiatry and Mental Health Manpower." Report to the Task Panel on Manpower and Personnel, President's Commission on Mental Health. (Xerox)

Leopold, J. P. A. "The Civil Service System: Processes and Problems." Report to the Task Panel on Manpower and Personnel, President's Commission on Mental Health. (Xerox)

Locke, P. "Special Concerns of American Indians." Report to the Task Panel on Manpower and Personnel, President's Commission on Mental Health. (Xerox)

Longest, J., Konan, M., and Tweed, D. "A Study of Differentials in the Distribution of Mental Health Manpower in Facilities." Research Team in Applied and Social Sciences, University of Maryland. Contract No. 278-75-0028 with the National Institute of Mental Health. College Park, Md., 1977. (Xerox)

McPheeters, H. L. "Issues in Mental Health Personnel Utilization." Report to the Task Panel on Manpower and Personnel, President's Commission on Mental Health. (Xerox)

National Association of Social Workers. "Annual Report of Membership Statistics." Washington, D.C.: NASW. Annual (all years).

National Institute of Mental Health. Community Mental Health Centers: the Federal Investment. Draft Report. Rockville, Md. NIMH, 1977.

National Institute of Mental Health. "Professional Characteristics and Work Patterns of Mental Health Personnel Supported under NIMH Training Grants, 1948-1968." Rockville, Md. 1977. (Xerox)

National Institute of Mental Health. Staffing Patterns in Mental Health Facilities - 1968. Public Health Service Publication No. 5034, Superintendent of Documents, U.S. Government Printing Office, Washington, D.C., 1970.

National Institute of Mental Health. Staffing of Mental Health Facilities, United States, 1972. DHEW Publication No. (ADM) 74-28. Washington, D.C.: Superintendent of Documents, U.S. Government Printing Office, 1974.

National Institute of Mental Health. Staffing of Mental Health Facilities, United States, 1974. DHEW Publication No. (ADM) 76-308. Washington, D.C.: Superintendent of Documents, U.S. Government Printing Office, 1976.

National Institute of Mental Health. Staffing of Mental Health Facilities, United States, 1976. Rockville, Md., NIMH, 1977.

National League for Nursing. Education Preparation for Nursing. Nursing Outlook. New York: NLN. September Issue, all years.

National League for Nursing. Some Statistics on Baccalaureate and Higher Degree Programs in Nursing. New York. Annual (all years).

National Research Council, National Academy of Sciences. "Summary Report, Doctoral Recipients from United States Universities." (Various years). Washington, D.C.: National Academy of Sciences.

Olmedo, E. L. and Lopez, S., eds. Hispanic Mental Health Professionals. Monograph No. 5 of the Spanish Speaking Mental Health Research Center, University of California, Los Angeles, 1977.

Pearl, A., and Riessman, F. New Careers for the Poor. New York: Free Press, 1965.

Poser, E. G. The effect of therapist training on group therapeutic outcome. Journal of Counsulting Psychology, 1966, 30, pp. 283-289.

Regier, D. L., Chairman. "Report of the NIMH Work Group on Mental Health Training of Primary Care Providers." National Institute of Mental Health, Rockville, Md., 1976. (Xerox)

Regier, D. A., Goldberg, I. D., and Taube, C. A. The defacto mental health services system: A public health perspective. American Journal of Psychiatry, in press.

Reiff, R., and Riessman, F. The Indigenous Nonprofessional: A Strategy of Change in Community Action and Community Mental Health Programs. New York: National Institute of Labor Education, 1964.

St. Clair, Catherine H., Silver, Joseph M., and Spivack, George. An instrument to assess staff time utilization in a community mental health center. Community Mental Health Journal, Vol. 11, No. 4, 1975, pp. 371-380.

Schneider, S. "Psychology." Paper prepared for the Task Panel on Manpower and Personnel, President's Commission on Mental Health. Rockville, Md.: National Institute of Mental Health. (Xerox)

Seitz, P. F. D., Jacob, E., Koenig, H., Koenig, R., McPherson, W. G., Miller, A. A., Stewart, R. L., and Whitaker, D. S. The Manpower Problem in Mental Hospitals. New York: International Universities Press, 1976.

Siegel, S. Social Service Manpower Needs: An overview to 1980. New York: Council on Social Work Education, 1975.

Smith, E. R., Chairperson. "Report of the NIMH Workgroup on the Role of the National Institute of Mental Health in Relation to State Mental Health Services Manpower." National Institute of Mental Health, Rockville, Md., 1976. (Xerox)

Sobey, F. The Nonprofessional Revolution in Mental Health. New York: Columbia University Press, 1970.

Solomon, Kenneth, and Harris, Michael. A study of client acceptance of various professionals in psychiatric home visits. Hospitals and Community Psychiatry, September 1977, pp. 661-662.

Steinberg, S. S., Freeman, K. A., Steele, C. A., Balodis, I., Batista, A. L. "Information on Manpower Utilization, Functions, and Credentialing in Community Mental Health Centers." University Research Corporation Contract No. ADM 45-74-158 with the National Institute of Mental Health. Washington, D.C., 1976. (Xerox)

Straus A., Schatzman, L., Bucher, R., Ehrlich, D., and Sabshin, M. Psychiatric Ideologies and Institutions. New York: Free Press of Glencoe, 1964.

Sue, S. Community mental health services to minority groups: Some optimism, some pessimism. American Psychologist, 32:616-624, August 1977.

Teague, Dutton, and Buck, Dorothy. Utilization of Manpower in Mental Health and Related Areas. Boulder, Colorado: Western Interstate Commission on Higher Education, 1969.

Truax, C. B. and Carkhuff, R. R. Toward Effective Counselling and Psychotherapy: Training and Practice. Chicago: Aldine, 1967.

Truax, C. B., and Lister, J. L. Effectiveness of counsellors and counsellor aides. Journal of Consulting Psychology, 1970, 17, pp. 331-334.

Turner, A. Jack, and Lee, W. E., Jr. Motivation through behavior modification: Part I: The job contract. Health Services Manager, Vol. 9, 1976, pp. 1-9.

Turner, A. Jack, and Lee, W. E., Jr. Motivation through behavior modification: Part II: Evaluation. Health Services Manager, Vol. 9, 1976, pp. 1-9.

U.S. Department of Health, Education, and Welfare, Public Health Service. Credentialing Health Manpower. DHEW Publication No. (OS) 77-50057. Washington, D.C.: Superintendent of Documents, U.S. Government Printing Office, 1977.

Wellner, A. M. and Mills, D. H. "Register Research Reports." Washington, D.C.: Council for the National Register on Health Service Providers in Psychology, 1977. (Xerox series).

Zeverling, I. Part time and shared staff. Hospital and Community Psychiatry, Vol. 21, No. 2, February 1970, p. 59.

Zunker, V. G., and Brown, W. F. Comparative effectiveness of student and professional counsellors. The Personnel and Guidance Journal, 1966, 44, pp. 738-743.

Report of the Task Panel

on

COST AND FINANCING

Submitted to

THE PRESIDENT'S COMMISSION ON MENTAL HEALTH

February 15, 1978

Task Panel: Cost and Financing of Mental Health

MEMBERS

Howard N. Newman, Coordinator
President
Dartmouth-Hitchcock Medical Center
Hanover, New Hampshire

Nicholas Cummings, Ph.D.
Department of Psychiatry
Kaiser-Permanente Medical Group
San Francisco, California

Rashi Fein, Ph.D.
Harvard Center for Community Health
 and Medical Center
Boston, Massachusetts

Robert W. Gibson, M.D.
Sheppard and Enoch Pratt Hospital
Towson, Maryland

Mitchell I. Ginsberg, Ph.D.
Dean
Columbia University School of
 Social Work
New York, New York

Melvin A. Glasser
Director
Social Security Department
United Auto Workers International
 Union
Detroit, Michigan

Stanley B. Jones
Program Development Officer
Institute of Medicine
National Academy of Science
Washington, D.C.

Morton D. Miller
Vice-Chairman of the Board
Equitable Life Assurance Society of
 the United States
New York, New York

Selma J. Mushkin, Ph.D.
Director
Public Services Laboratory
Washington, D.C.

Joseph Noshpitz, M.D.
Director of Education and Training
Children's Hospital
Washington, D.C.

Daniel W. Pettengill
Vice-President
Group Division
Aetna Life and Casualty
Hartford, Connecticut

Hilda Robbins
Mental Health Association
Fort Washington, Pennsylvania

Howard Rome, M.D.
Professor of Psychiatry Emeritus
Mayo Graduate School of Medicine
Rochester, Minnesota

Bert Seidman
AFL-CIO
Washington, D.C.

TABLE OF CONTENTS

	Page
Executive Summary	4
List of Options	7
Medicare	7
Medicaid	7
Cost and Financing of Mental Health	9
Gaps in Financing of Mental Health Services	9
Gaps from the Perspective of the Individual	10
Gaps from the Perspective of Services Needed	10
Gaps from the Perspective of the Provider	11
Quality of Care Perspective	13
Benefits From Mental Health Services	13
Humane	13
General Economy	14
Health Economy	16
Agreements and Disagreements	18
Medicare and Mental Health Services	20
Medicaid and Mental Health Services	22
Data Requirements and Research	31
Appendix - The Cost of Mental Illness	34
Acknowledgments	41
References	42
Bibliography	45

EXECUTIVE SUMMARY

The Panel on Cost and Financing of Mental Health was selected from experts from the many diverse aspects of the financing of mental health services. Among the members of the panel are mental health professionals, health economists and administrators, executives of universities, insurance companies, and labor unions, as well as representatives of consumers of mental health services.

Their divergent backgrounds and opinions provoked stimulating discussions, but limited the possibility that the panel's report would present agreements on the causes and cures for the problems of mental health financing. Nevertheless, considerable consensus was achieved. The panel's report reflects these agreements as well as the inevitable differences.

The panel realistically limited the scope of its report to identifying the areas where public policy on mental health financing warranted immediate attention, and where the panel's expertise would be most beneficial.

The panel believes that there are considerable gaps in the financing of mental health services and that these financing gaps are creating barriers to access to needed services. The panel believes further that the benefit structure of many health care plans acts as a disincentive to obtaining the most appropriate mode of mental health care.

Insofar as mental health services are needed and are not being provided, or not being provided well, the deficits in financing are detracting from the quality of life of the potential recipients and their families, friends, and communities. Changes in the policies of financing mental health services are justified on humanitarian grounds alone.

Changes in mental health financing appear to be justified on economic grounds as well. Successful mental health services have resulted in improvements in work performance, reductions in morbidity, fewer absences from work duties, and reductions in staff turnover. In some instances, the improvements in production efficiencies have offset the costs of these mental health services.

In other instances, the use of more appropriate mental health services has reduced the need for other health services and so reduced cost. In instances where care in outpatient settings is preferable to resident care, there are savings in health care costs. Preventive services and other means of detection and early intervention reduce the need for more expensive crisis care or longer term care as inpatients in resident institutions. Good economic policy demands that the financing mechanisms encourage the use of less expensive modes of treatment when these are more therapeutic.

The panel also believes that when a financing program covers somatic health services, but not mental health services, somatic health services are sought and provided for certain conditions that would more appropriately, and perhaps even less expensively, be treated with mental health services.

The panel urged that the highest public priority involved overcoming the barriers to access to mental health services for the poor--particularly children and the elderly. These people seldom have and cannot afford to purchase adequate mental health coverage. For persons with limited mental health coverage the kind of coverage provided may also be creating difficulty.

Financing was frequently too limited to provide incentives for the development and support of ambulatory care, preventive care, early detection, early treatment, outreach, case management, health education, and certain social support services. Financing was frequently restricted, so that there was little encouragement to care by mental health professionals who were not physicians or to care provided by clinics and health maintenance organizations. Financing was frequently focused on inpatient services, causing disincentive to less costly alternatives, such as ambulatory care, home care, or community-based care for those who have recently left resident institutions.

The panel urged that the financing of mental health services should become more consistent with the need for mental health services and with the current preferred modes of treatment. To this end, the panel urged that national health insurance should benefit from the experiences of current financing programs and should correct their deficiencies.

The panel did not prepare a national health insurance proposal which could overcome the present problems of financing mental health services. This omission stemmed in no small part from the composition of the panel and the unlikelihood that it would agree on a single solution to complex and controversial issues. But the omission stemmed largely from the conviction that the development of a national health insurance package by any one panel would be inappropriate and premature. This panel looks to the Commission to recommend solid national policy with regard to mental health services. A national health insurance package should then be developed to be consistent with the parameters of this new national policy.

The panel considered that its purview definitely involved suggesting some of the principles on which national health insurance should be based. The panel also believed that its greatest contribution could be made through suggesting how these principles could be applied to improving current financing programs, particularly the federally financed programs, Medicare and Medicaid.

First of all, the panel stressed that the financing of medical care should be less dependent upon whether the diagnosis had been for a mental or a physical disorder, but should be appropriate to the needs of the recipient. The financing of care should permit patients a choice of modes of obtaining needed care. The financing of care should facilitate the most efficient use of health resources:

- discouraging unnecessary utilization of inpatient care

- encouraging ambulatory, preventive care, and early diagnosis and treatment

- encouraging optimal use of manpower, particularly in underserved areas

- encouraging planning and development of mental health resources

The panel urged that measures to control the rapid rise in health care costs should be an integral part of programs for financing mental health services. In this regard, the panel urged the review by peers and by others of the quality of care provided, evaluating the effectiveness, the safety, the outcome, and the patients' satisfaction with their treatment. A most effective cost containment measure is the assurance that only the most appropriate care is provided.

The panel expressed concern that some cost containment measures tended to be counterproductive. Some panelists cited the use of copayments and deductibles, and the establishment of limitations on eligibility and benefits in public programs as serving to discourage even further the use of mental health services by those who needed them most, but were least likely to seek them.

The panel suggested that there were at least three major options regarding current national policies which were consistent with these principles: (1) reform of Medicare programs for mental health services; (2) reform of Medicaid programs for mental health services; and (3) development of a stronger data and research base on which to found the Nation's policies with regard to the financing of mental health services.

The changes in Medicare relate to legislative proposals for the improvements in the ceilings on mental health benefits, and the amounts of copayments required for these services. The changes in Medicaid relate not only to improvements in Federal enforcement of existing statutes and regulations, but to legislative proposals to reduce some of the inequities in benefits and eligibility which characterize this major health program for the low-income population.

LIST OF OPTIONS

MEDICARE

The discriminatory treatment of mental health services under the provisions of Medicare must be eliminated in order to reduce the financial barrier to mental health services. Without losing sight of the ultimate goal of removing all reimbursement discrimination with regard to mental health care in the Medicare law, the panel recognizes that an acceptable short-range alternative is reduction of the beneficiary coinsurance from 50 percent to 20 percent--in line with standard Medicare coverage--and increase of the maximum allowable reimbursement for mental conditions to $750 in any calendar year.

MEDICAID

1. Stronger Federal leadership is needed with regard to the Medicaid mental health programs. This includes:

    a. Providing States with technical assistance in developing comprehensive mental health plans and in providing ambulatory services, outreach services, certain support services, and health education services;

    b. demonstrating Federal commitments to improving the quality of care provided through mental health programs, presenting to the States the benefits which would be derived from additional efforts;

    c. enforcing Federal requirements with regard to: systems of certification of institutions, utilization review, plans of care, and review and evaluation of such care; assuring that Medicaid State plans offer a reasonable amount of ambulatory mental health services; assuring that State reimbursement policies do not impede the availability of reasonable amounts of mental health services; assuring that States have effective systems to prevent discrimination on the basis of diagnosis; the availability of mental health servcies within the Medicaid child health programs (Early and Periodic Screening, Diagnosis and Treatment of detected problems, for eligibles under 22 years of age).

2. Develop legislative proposals, and introduce legislation to amend Title XIX, to:

a. establish national minimum mental health benefits to be included in every Medicaid State plan;

b. establish national minimum eligibility standards for income and assets (for example, every Medicaid State would have to provide medical assistance for all those who satisfied the categorical requirements, and whose income, after deducting medical expenses, was below the poverty line);

c. remove the categorical requirements for eligibility for Medicaid. This proposal might be patterned on the proposals for "welfare reform," which would provide that everyone who satisfied the definitions of financial need would be given assistance.

3. Introduce proposals including mental health benefits for a national health program, absorbing Medicaid, and possibly other insurance programs.

REPORT OF THE PANEL ON COST AND FINANCING OF MENTAL HEALTH

The Panel on the Cost and Financing of Mental Health has focused its attention on the gaps in financing of mental health services and the public and private measures which are needed to fill these gaps, primarily those for the poor and near poor.

In this regard, our operating assumptions were:

(1) Possibly more than any health service, the outcome of mental health services depends upon economic and social issues--such as unemployment; poverty; income support programs; war; race, age, and sex discrimination; and social stress--which are generally beyond the province of health providers and health policy makers. Without belittling the significance of these issues in determining mental health (or of mental health in determining the outcome of these issues), this panel believes that it must limit its discussions to the costs and financing of mental health services.

(2) The current system of financing mental health services presents barriers for many in obtaining adequate and appropriate help that they need to lead fully productive lives. Changes are needed and are possible. The potential benefits to the recipient, family, employer, and community warrant such changes. The panel has considered ways in which the financing system may be improved. It has focused its attention on ways in which the current financing system may be improved with regard to the low-income populations and the disabled. The changes it recommends are specific to Medicare and Medicaid, but should be extended to the broader programs of national health insurance.

GAPS IN FINANCING OF MENTAL HEALTH SERVICES

Gaps in access to mental health services have been identified by most authorities in this field and, in particular, by task panels of this Commission. This panel has concentrated its attention on those deficiencies in the receipt of mental health services which have been created or exacerbated by the ways in which mental health services are financed.

The gaps in mental health financing may be viewed from four perspectives:

- the individual
- the services needed
- the provider
- the quality of services.

These four perspectives are closely linked. It is difficult to describe the problems of one without recognizing this interrelation. For example, the elderly poor have difficulty getting any mental health services, and despite Medicare and Medicaid are unlikely to obtain care in ambulatory settings from psychiatrists.

Gaps From the Perspective of the Individual

The individuals who have been identified as the Nation's highest priority for improvements in the financing of medical services are also those most in need of improvements in the financing of mental health services. These include low-income individuals, and particularly the elderly, children, minorities, the unemployed, and those not expected to work. These individuals are most likely to be unable to finance their own mental health services or to be able to maintain private insurance which includes mental health coverage; they must rely on public categorical programs or public health financing programs. The panel recognized that problems exist for workers as well, especially those who have minimal insurance coverage or difficulty getting time away from their jobs.

The two major Federal programs, Medicare and Medicaid, have severe deficiencies with regard to treatment of mental, emotional, or nervous disorders. (Discussion of the special problems of these programs appear in separate sections of this report.) Because of the limited benefit package, and the large deductibles, premiums, and copayments, Medicare fails to provide adequate coverage for many of the aged and disabled.

Medicaid assists the poor in obtaining medical services, but many of the poor who need help are ineligible for Medicaid. Single adults, childless couples, and intact families are unlikely to receive Medicaid help, regardless of how poor they may be. Even poor who are aged, blind, disabled, or members of single-parent families may be ineligible for help. The problems of Medicaid relate as much to limited benefits as they do to eligibility. Many of the poor who are located in "poor" States with "poor" Medicaid packages receive no mental health coverage at all.

Gaps From the Perspective of Services Needed

The existing means of financing mental health services focus on the provision of care in institutions. This focus is true for charity support, support through public programs, and support through private insurance plans. The high cost of inpatient care is largely responsible for this concentration. For some patients, inpatient care is the most appropriate treatment. It is expensive and may always require the majority of funding. But it does not warrant a concentration of funding that causes inadequate funding of other services which may be more appropriate and beneficial in many cases. Balance in funding is _critical_. Funding mechanisms and funding authorizations must support treatment modalities which are alternatives to institutionalization, including halfway facilities and day hospitals, and which are oriented toward early detection, treatment, and prevention.

About 92 percent of employee benefit plans have _some_ coverage of physician outpatient care for mental conditions (Reed 1975 p. 24); all the State Medicaid plans are _supposed_ to include such outpatient care. However, support for outpatient mental health services tends to involve large copayments, limits on the numbers of services supported, and limits on the dollars available for insurance support of these services. These limitations on outpatient services discourage their use, particularly by the poor and near poor, who have very little disposable income.

C/F 10

Private health insurance plans, Medicare, and all but a very few State Medicaid plans provide little or no funding for home care services which are nonmedical in character. The absence of home support services, essential to maintaining the individual within the family, home, or community, sends many of the aged and chronically ill to institutions and to less appropriate services. Reports from the Department of Health, Education, and Welfare (DHEW) state that as many as 100,000 of the 700,000 people in acute care hospitals do not need to be there and could be better cared for at home (Califano 1977). At least a similar proportion of the million residents of nursing homes could have been better served at home but that alternative was not financially feasible.

The panel applauded deinstitutionalization, where appropriate, on humane grounds as well as economic ones. "Savings" are often attributed to comprehensive programs in this area.

The panel was concerned, however, that some of these "savings" have been at a significant human cost. The panel was very concerned that deinstitutionalization must be conducted with safeguards, lest the pressure for short-term savings would cause some individuals to be thrust into more unstable, threatening situations than even an institution might provide. The panel cautioned that adequate community programs are also expensive. The panel urged that any savings in expenditures which might be realized from deinstitutionalization should be redirected to social and other community-based services to meet the needs of individuals following institutionalization.

Despite the limits on funding, there have been dramatic shifts over the past 20 years in the relative proportion of episodes of mental health care which take place in outpatient settings. In 1973, almost two out of every three episodes of mental health care were in outpatient settings; in contrast, in 1955, less than one out of four episodes had been in outpatient settings (DHEW/NIMH Draft Report 1976, p.21).

It is urgent that the funding mechanisms' policies become consistent with the current preferred modes of treatment. Most insurance programs, including Medicare, provide funding only for a diagnosed illness. Preventive services, services to identify high risks, health educational services to advise about warning signs and treatment programs, outreach programs, and other support services are frequently not reimbursable under existing financing mechanisms. The absence of such funding discourages their use, particularly by the low-income population.

Gaps From the Perspective of the Provider

Gaps in reimbursement to providers of mental health services stem from two interrelated areas:

(1) Nonphysician providers whose fees are not reimbursable except when they work under the direct supervision of a physician; and

(2) Providers of services not currently recognized by third-party reimbursement.

In the first area are clinical psychologists,[1] psychiatric nurses, and clinical social workers who provide services which are reimbursable when they are provided by a psychiatrist. Psychologists, nurses, and social workers are not universally eligible for reimbursement on an individual fee-for-service basis under Medicare, Medicaid,[2] and private insurance unless the care is provided under the direct supervision of a physician. This has frequently been interpreted to mean that the physician must be physically present in the facility when care is given. These difficulties are not limited to mental health services but are increasingly present in discussions of the delivery of all health services. Insurers frequently accept the mental health services of nonphysician mental health practitioners only when performed in an organized setting under the supervision of a psychiatrist. According to insurers this limitation was introduced as both a cost and quality control measure. Accordingly, some control measures would have to be established before such insurers would accept removal of this restriction.

These three professions provide a large percentage of mental health care, especially to the poor, to those in rural areas, and to those in community mental health centers (Mechanic 1977). The issue of direct provider status is, therefore, particularly important to community-based mental health programs, rural communities, and populations reliant upon these providers when seeking reimbursement on a fee-for-service basis. Community mental health centers (CMHC's) rely heavily on nonphysician manpower to provide mental health services and they are dependent upon Government funding to remain operational. Most CMHC's and other ambulatory care facilities can only qualify as providers of ambulatory care on a fee-for-service basis under Medicare if they are affiliated with a hospital (the National Council of CMHC's estimates that only 12 percent are so affiliated) (Morris Associates 1975, p. 5) and have medical supervision and case management by a physician. Ambulatory care centers may qualify as "clinic" providers under Medicaid if the State offers this optional service in its Medicaid package--which more than 10 States do not (DHEW/Health Care Financing Administration/Medicaid Bureau 1978). Even when they are recognized as "clinic" providers, reimbursement is usually severely limited.

With all of these difficulties in reimbursement, CMHC's rely on categorical funding by State and Federal Governments. In 1973, 69.3 percent of CMHC funds were from categorical government funds (about half Federal and half State monies), according to the CMHC Task Panel), 1.7 percent from Medicare, 8.6 percent from Medicaid, 7.9 percent from commercial insurance, and 4.5 percent from patient fees (Morris Associates 1975, p. 10).

---

[1]The services of clinical psychologists are somewhat more widely recognized for third-party reimbursement than other nonphysician manpower; 31 States require insurance policies to reimburse for the direct unsupervised services by clinical psychologists to the same extent as if the service had been rendered directly by a physician (M.D.).

[2]Federal Medicaid statute does not impose these restrictions; however, some State Medicaid programs do follow the Medicare pattern.

The issues regarding status of nonphysician manpower and CMHC's are the crux of discussion of other President's Commission on Mental Health panels; the Cost and Financing Panel did not pursue these issues at great length.

The second gap in reimbursing providers of services is where the services, rather than the provider per se, are not recognized within the package of available services. As outlined in the preceding section, this limitation is most severe for ambulatory services, preventive services, health education, and certain supportive services. With respect to these categories of service, it is important that they become recognized as essential components of comprehensive care delivery--in the general health delivery system as well as the mental health delivery system specifically.

Quality of Care Perspective

The panel expressed concern that the pressure to control costs of mental health care might result in reduction below acceptable standards in the quality of care provided. It insisted, therefore, that along with measures to contain costs and improve efficiency, there should be ongoing measures of the quality of the care delivered. The panel also emphasized that such measures to control quality, particularly those which prevented unnecessary or inappropriate care, could themselves serve as cost control measures.

The panel cited the Federal efforts to develop PSRO's (Professional Standards Review Organizations) and described the potentials of these peer review organizations to contain costs through eliminating unnecessary utilization. In addition to peer review, the PSRO programs contain many features to maintain and improve the quality of care, such as the use of medical care evaluation studies, retrospective reviews according to established standards and criteria, as well as analysis of profiles of provider performance.

The panel also noted the efforts at cost containment and quality assurance in mental health services which were made through several SCOPCE (Select Committee on Psychiatric Care and Evaluation) projects conducted for the Department of Defense CHAMPUS Program (Civilian Health and Medical Program for the Uniformed Services). SCOPCE reviews not only identified and eliminated improper treatment programs, but led to significant savings as well. It is estimated that the SCOPCE I Project, which cost $100,000, led to a savings of $5 million (DHEW/NIMH Draft Report 1976, p. 62), or a return of $50 for every dollar spent.

The panel believed that further support should be given to research on review systems for mental health services, both inpatient and outpatient, using nonphysician reviewers as well as psychiatrists.

BENEFITS FROM MENTAL HEALTH SERVICES

Humane

The panel was unanimous in its feeling that mental health care should be available and financially accessible to all who are in need of such care. Where

C/F 13

cost of treatment is a barrier to receipt of treatment, a method of financing should exist so that mental health care is available to those who need it--not only to those who can afford services. This report deals with mental health care within the financing structure. In this context, phrases such as "cost," "cost/benefit," and "cost containment" will frequently be used. The concentration on costs is not because the panel feels cost is the determinant for providing treatment, but because it is often a major deterrent in receiving treatment.

Mental health care can be expensive--it can also be relatively inexpensive; and it may also result in savings. Mental illness is not a single illness and, therefore, treatment can be effective in a myriad of ways, over a range of time, in a variety of settings, by a variety of providers, for a wide range of costs. In personal terms, mental illness or emotional disorders can be devastating, debilitating, upsetting, or merely disconcerting. Emotional factors play significant roles in the "quality of individual lives, the strength of personal relationships, and the opportunities that exist for all people . . ." (President's Commission on Mental Health Interim Report). Mental illness can prevent individuals from taking part in such programs as education and employment training that are so important not only to them but to the total society. Emotional factors are known to impact on somatic conditions, morbidity, and mortality (Markush et al. 1977; Cummings 1978). Some data suggest a 9-year loss in life expectancy for schizophrenics and a 7-year loss for depressives. These findings are not accounted for by suicide rates alone.

The cost of human suffering to the individual, the family, and friends--although not included in estimates of the cost of mental illness--remains the most important argument for better mental health care, and for its improved public financing.

Benefits in the General Economy

The cost of mental illness and emotional or nervous disorder to the general economy has never been fully calculated. "Clearly, mental illness is a major and exceedingly costly national health problem that seriously affects not only the afflicted individual but his family and, in the aggregate, the general welfare and economy as well" (Cohen, W. 1968). In 1974, the National Institute of Mental Health (NIMH) estimated the indirect cost of mental illness at nearly $20 billion (Levine and Willner 1976). "Indirect costs are the income or income-equivalent losses which result from deaths due to mental illness, total disability due to mental illness and the loss of productive time to those individuals who are institutionalized or who utilize outpatient therapy for mental illness" (Levine and Willner 1976, p. 1). NIMH admits a conservative bias and goes on to state:

> In the area of indirect costs all losses associated with partial disabilities, with pain and suffering not fully reflected by lost earnings, with homicides in the population not treated for mental illness, and with the excess death incidence among those who have a history of mental illness but received no care in 1974 are excluded from the estimated costs of mental illness. Inclusion of

these costs might double the total shown here (Levine and Willner 1976, p. 2).

Even under a conservative bias, indirect costs make up more than half of the total cost of mental illness.

A number of limited studies are underway in the business community regarding the cost of, and the relationship between, emotional and mental distress and productivity. Factors being considered are performance on the job; absenteeism; employee relations; labor relations; hospital, medical, and surgical cost; workman's compensation; and turnover rates. The trend toward expansion of mental health coverage, coupled with an increasing number of "troubled employee" or "broad brush" counseling services, indicates increasing business and union awareness of the impact or interference of employees' mental distress on their daily lives. While these early results may not have the validity of clinical trials, they are nonetheless indicative of the efficacy of mental health intervention and of the cost to the general economy when emotional problems are not treated.

The Equitable Life Assurance Society's Emotional Health Program includes conventional insight-oriented and behavioral modification psychotherapy and Stress Management Training. The Stress Management Training program treats employees with stress-related disorders such as general anxiety, tension, and migraine headaches. Before treatment the "average hourly interference effect" of stress was estimated by the employees at 25 percent. After treatment this measure dramatically decreased to 3 percent. Based on early findings, Equitable estimates that for every $1.00 of treatment cost there was a $3 return in recovered productivity (Manuso 1978).

The INSIGHT Program at Kennecott Copper Company is a 24-hour-a-day, 7-day-a-week counseling and referral program available to the 32,000 employees and dependents. The comparative results of the INSIGHT Program of 150 participants and 150 nonparticipants for a 1-year period are impressive. Hospital, medical, and surgical costs for participants decreased 55.4 percent compared with a 1.5 percent increase for nonparticipants; participant absenteeism decreased 52 percent compared with a 6.3 percent increase for nonparticipants; and nonoccupational Accident and Sickness Insurance costs decreased 74.6 percent compared with a 38.5 percent decrease for nonparticipants (PA International Management Consultants 1973, p. 17; Jones 1978). Estimated savings per participant based on "before" and "after" figures amounted to $905 per man annually (Hospital, Medical, and Surgical savings, $620; Absenteeism, $51; and Nonoccupational Accident and Sickness Insurance savings, $233). Conservative projections by Kennecott based on 6.25 percent of the work force participating in the counseling program would amount to savings in excess of $1 million for a work force of 20,000 employees (PA International Management Consultants 1973, pp. 18-19). Other companies contacted concurred that the employee assistance programs were valuable to the company, the employees, and to productivity. These companies, which had either not costed out savings or could not release their data, included International Paper Company, CNA Insurance, Polaroid, and U.S. Steel.

Experts in this area, including Dr. Shelly Akabas of the School of Social Work of Columbia University, Carvel Taylor of CNA Insurance and the University of Chicago School of Social Work, James Manuso of the Equitable Life Assurance

Society, and Otto Jones of Human Affairs, Inc., agreed with members of the panel that the availability of care to most workers and their families and their ability to finance such care are generally overstated. By and large, workers and their families do not have access to adequate mental health care and the imposition of significant cost-sharing requirements creates serious barriers against their obtaining such care. This is not to ignore the greater stress that accompanies unemployment, or the legitimate concerns about negative potential of such programs. Nonetheless:

> In hundreds of workplaces throughout the country, mental health service delivery systems have been put in place. Some are sponsored by trade unions, others by corporate management and others by a joint effort of labor and industry. There are many advantages to such services, perhaps foremost is their preventive character. It is relatively easy to identify a person at the workplace who is in need of some kind of assistance, to reach him early and to connect him with care (Akabas 1977).

These are highly innovative service delivery programs. They have exciting potential for delivering effective, efficient, quality care without government funding. At the very least, the programs mentioned above are indicative of what the costs can be when mental health services are not provided.

Benefits to the Health Economy

Two aspects of the relationship between mental health costs and the health economy were discussed:

1. The prevalence of mental health problems in the general health care system and

2. The effect of mental health care on the utilization of general medical services.

In the first instance, a significant number of mental or emotional problems are currently cared for in the general health system, and to some degree are financed through general health reimbursement. Studies indicate as many as 15 percent of the patients seen in general medical settings may be diagnosed as having a psychiatric or emotional disorder (DHEW/NIMH Draft Report 1976, p. 27). Significantly higher rates of psychiatric disorders have been found for specialized medical settings such as hospital-based clinics and emergency rooms (DHEW/NIMH Draft Report 1976, p. 27). Cummings estimates that "60% or more of the physician visits are made by patients who demonstrate an emotional, rather than an organic etiology for their physical symptoms" (American Psychologist Sept. 1977, p. 711). The classification of these conditions as a somatic problem results in part from the stigma attached to mental health conditions and the limitations on reimbursement for mental health services, and in part from the difficulties in detecting and treating the mental conditions underlying physical symptoms.

Available evidence supports the view that funding of somatic medical care currently pays for a significant amount of care for emotional or mental problems, even though they are not defined or reported as such. In such situations where the provider is not specifically trained to provide mental health services, the quality of care may be questioned and expenditures for such care may be misdirected and of questionable benefit.

The second area deals with the substitution effect on general medical utilization when mental health services are provided. Several widely quoted papers have reported results of longitudinal, controlled studies of nonpsychiatric services before and after psychiatric intervention. They are briefly described here.

The Kaiser Foundation Plan in Northern California studied a randomly selected group of psychiatric patients who received either a single session, a moderate series of sessions, or long-term therapy (Follette and Cummings 1967; Cummings and Follette 1968). Utilization of all plan services for the year prior to psychiatric intervention was compared to the utilization for the next 5 years. In each subgroup hospital utilization immediately decreased by over 50 percent. Outpatient visits, including psychiatric visits, decreased sharply for those receiving either a single or moderate number of sessions; by the end of 5 years, their utilization was less than half of what it had been prior to intervention (Jones 1977). There was a significant decline (from 11.4 to 4.4 visits) over 6 years in medical utilization for the group receiving psychotherapy compared with a slight increase (from 11.4 to 12.9 visits) in medical utilization by the control group. This decline was apparent whether the measure used was the number of outpatient visits, days of hospitalization, or a combination of these with psychiatric services (Lewin and Associates 1978).

In a similar study, Group Health Association of Washington, D.C., found that in the year following psychiatric referral, the number of visits for physician services and X-ray and laboratory procedures both decreased by approximately 30 percent (Goldberg, Krantz, Locke 1970).

Blue Cross of Western Pennsylvania compared the medical/surgical utilization of 169 subscribers who used an outpatient psychotherapy benefit in community mental health centers with that of a control group (Jameson, Shuman, Young 1976). Medical/surgical utilization was significantly reduced for the group who used the psychiatric benefits. Medical/surgical inpatient days and outpatient visits per month decreased by more than 54 percent. The monthly cost per patient in the study group for medical services dropped by $9.41 (from $16.47 to $7.06)--well below the average per-patient cost for the control group. The reduced medical/surgical utilization following outpatient psychotherapy benefits was found to be independent of age, sex, or employment level (Lewin and Associates 1978).

These reports of positive indications of health economic benefits achieved through mental health intervention are provocative. Each study individually must be interpreted conservatively. But, as a group, this research is striking. Research from health maintenance organizations (HMO's), from industrial programs, and from regular health insurance plans suggests that providing outpatient mental health services can reduce overall health services utilization and overall health costs.

The evidence strongly suggests that the cost of including or expanding mental health coverage would be partially or wholly offset by decreasing use of general medical services. Current data do not allow a firm estimate of the <u>net</u> effect of including mental health care, but "these studies suggest that mental health treatment may reduce other health service utilization and lead to more appropriate utilization and improved quality of care" (DHEW/NIMH Draft Report 1976, p. 67).

AGREEMENTS AND DISAGREEMENTS

The panel called for changes in policies in the financing of mental health services in order to reduce the barriers to needed services. The panel proposed that some changes should be introduced and implemented quickly, while others may involve a longer time for preparation and development. The panel urged that productive use be made of the lead time before national health insurance becomes effective; it recommended steps which could be undertaken immediately to improve the financing mechanisms needed to assure access to essential mental health services.

The panel identified the poor, the near poor, and within these the child and the elderly populations, as those most in need of additional help in financing mental health services. In this regard, the panel recommended changes in the Medicare and Medicaid programs to make appropriate mental health services more accessible to their target populations. Details of these options are contained in the following sections on Medicare and Medicaid.

The panel believes that specific mental health services are underserved by the current financing mechanisms and that at least the following services should be reimbursable through public and private insurance: mental health care in ambulatory settings; support services and educational services with specific mental health focus; and services provided by mental health care professionals, including certain nonphysician personnel.

The panel did not agree on a single set of circumstances in which nonphysician personnel should be reimbursable. Options discussed included: limiting such coverage to "organized settings," adding only Ph.D. level psychologists, permitting their reimbursement only where there was physician supervision, and extending their reimbursement to instances where care was provided without restrictions on supervision, but only when licensed by the State and/or only in a designated manpower shortage area.

The panel considered various ways of enlarging the financing of mental health services in non-Federal programs. These included technical assistance, persuasion, and other forms of encouragement to States, insurance companies, employers, unions, groups, and individuals for more inclusive mental health care coverage. They also discussed urging or requiring States to mandate enlarged mental health coverage. The panel did not agree on preferences among these options.

The issue of organized care settings as distinct from fee-for-service was discussed several times during the course of the panel meetings. The organized care setting was mentioned as a possible qualification for reimbursement of nonphysician manpower. Proponents of this approach felt that organized settings offered controls that would prevent the proliferation of manpower and new professions which fee-for-service reimbursement might encourage. Several panelists felt organized settings afforded greater opportunity for peer review and ease of licensing standards.

Several panelists also felt that organized settings offered greater opportunity for outreach, which would enhance the accessibility of populations who might otherwise be unaware of available services. It was believed that active outreach and case management would provide a safeguard against having people who did not use services, because they were not aware of them, support services for others, especially those with higher incomes.

Further discussion centered on the possibility of limiting mental health benefits when provided on a fee-for-service basis, but providing more extensive, or even unlimited, benefits in an organized setting.

There was no consensus by the panel on the above issues, particularly since the panel could not agree on a single workable definition of what constitutes an organized care setting. Recommended research may resolve some of the issues raised.

The panel acknowledged that neither fiscal resources nor mental health resources are unlimited. Effective measures to control the costs of health services must be an integral component of a plan to broaden mental health coverage.

On the other hand, the panel was apprehensive about some of the cost-control mechanisms within existing financing programs and their impact on the use of mental health services by the poor. They pointed to the fact that limitations and exclusions of benefits, limitations on eligibility of beneficiaries, and deductibles and copayments had served to reduce the availability and utilization of financing for those with low incomes and for those with small health insurance packages. It is these groups, particularly, whose ability to self-finance their mental health benefits is most constrained and who have the smallest propensity to use needed mental health services. It is clear that cost-sharing measures deter obtaining services where there is high income elasticity or price elasticity; both conditions are particularly true for low-income populations with regard to outpatient mental health services. Such methods of cost control of mental health services, when applied to the low-income populations, may be counterproductive and exacerbate the problems already identified as gaps in mental health financing.

The panel believed that increases in mental health coverage would be more attractive politically if that expansion were well defined, predictable, and controllable. To that end, the panel agreed that the expansion in mental health benefits should be planned, and geared to the availability of mental health resources. The panel was concerned that unplanned expansion might have more negative effects on the access of the poor and the near poor to mental health services. To counteract adverse possibilities, categorical programs may be required to increase the availability of mental health professionals and mental health centers in particular underserved areas.

The panel noted that some individuals have small health insurance coverage, and feared that any expansion of mental health coverage might result in the loss of some of their somatic care coverage, or it might price insurance out of the reach of the poorest purchasers.

The panel acknowledged that the financing of mental health services was far from parity with the financing of other medical services, and that this discrimination against mental health services was serving as a barrier to access to care. The panel concurred in the appropriateness and importance of parity of funding. The panel agreed that, in the long run, the funding of services should be independent of whether the diagnosis had been for a mental or physical condition. The panel discussed, but without complete resolution, the question of how quickly such parity could be achieved.

The panel was concerned that parity of financing would not necessarily imply parity of services. Without direct measures to change the existing patterns of utilization, and within the fee-for-service system, it is likely that increases in mental health benefits would result in more services to the more affluent and would not assure adequate services to the poor and those less educated to mental health service benefits. The panel recognized that mental health treatment often requires special services not essential to somatic medical care, possibly through different organization and delivery systems.

MEDICARE AND MENTAL HEALTH SERVICES

One-third of the elderly are below or hover at the poverty line (U.S. Senate Special Committee on Aging 1977). The average single older person has approximately $75.00 a week on which to live (Butler and Lewis 1977). For these reasons, expansion of ambulatory mental health benefits must include a financing mechanism which enables the elderly to afford available services. Passage of the Medicare Program in 1965 was intended to alleviate much of the financial burden of the elderly seeking health care. However, Medicare legislation also established an unfortunate precedent for discriminatory treatment of mental health care.

Title XVIII of the Social Security Act--Health Insurance for the Aged--became effective on July 1, 1966, and was expanded in 1972 to Health Insurance for the Aged and Disabled. Title XVIII, the Medicare Program, consists of two separate but coordinated programs: Part A Hospital Insurance (HI) and Part B Supplemental Medical Insurance (SMI) (DHEW/Social Security Administration 1974, p. 12). Part A is available to all those over age 65 as well as some eligible disabled persons under age 65. In 1975, 25 million aged and disabled persons were covered by Part A Hospital Insurance (DHEW/Social Security Administration/Office of Program Policy and Planning 1977). Coverage of inpatient psychiatric hospital services under HI is limited to 190 days during a person's lifetime in addition to restrictions applicable to all hospital care under the Medicare Program.

All persons entitled to coverage under Part A (HI) are eligible to enroll in the SMI program on a voluntary basis by paying a monthly premium, currently $7.70. Part B coverage includes a variety of medical services and supplies furnished in connection with physicians' services, outpatient hospital services, and home health services after a deductible of $60.00 has been met. In general Part B reimbursement is 80 percent of reasonable charges; however, reimbursement for medical care of a patient with mental illness on an outpatient basis cannot exceed 50 percent of the charges or $250 in each calendar year, whichever is less. The arbitrary 50-percent coinsurance rate and $250 maximum reimbursement ignore the fact that mental illness is often acute and that the patient benefits from prompt treatment. If intervention for mental illness is not prompt, it, like physical disease, can become chronic and more difficult (and expensive) to treat.

The reimbursement limitation does not apply when the physician renders medical or psychiatric care to a mentally ill beneficiary who is an inpatient of a hospital (DHEW/Social Security Administration 1971). The discriminatory financing for ambulatory mental health services provides incentive to seek hospitalization and to use general physician services not designed for treatment of mental disorders. Current Medicare restrictions often reward inappropriate service for mental and emotional distress. The limitation "not only affords inadequate coverage but promotes hospitalization rather than care in the community, often contrary to sound psychiatric practice" (Committee on Aging 1970).

NIMH's Center for Studies of the Mental Health of the Aging recently stated that "whereas the elderly are underserved at outpatient clinics, a staggering 30 percent of public mental hospital patients are over 65. This is in part due to skewed Medicare coverage, where outpatient reimbursement for mental health care is severely restricted, thereby forcing a number of otherwise unncessary hospitalizations" (Cohen, G. 1977). As restrictive as the original Medicare legislation was with regard to financing ambulatory mental health treatment, the current situation is even worse. Since its enactment in 1965, the portion of the Medicare Act restricting outpatient mental health coverage has never been rerevised. Soaring inflation within the health care system has, in effect, further reduced the limited coverage originally endorsed by Congress. Since 1965, charges for psychiatric office visits have increased by 68 percent (DHEW/Health Care Financing Administration/Office of Policy, Planning, and Research 1977). With no corresponding increase in the $250 maximum, today's elderly are reimbursed for less than half of the services they would have been able to receive a decade ago. It is noteworthy that in the same time span, the monthly premium for Supplemental Medical Insurance (Part B) has been revised eight times and more than doubled (from $36.00 to $92.40 per year) and is scheduled to be increased again in July 1978.

At present utilization rates, in 1979 an estimated 285,000 beneficiaries will use some mental health service under Part B. In 1975, Medicare reimbursement for all mental health treatment (both Parts A and B) was $241 million. Part B reimbursement for mental conditions was less than 1 percent of the total SMI reimbursement; Part A was approximately 2 percent of the HI total (DHEW/Health Care Financing Administration/Office of Policy, Planning, and Research 1977).

> The discriminatory treatment of mental health services under the provisions of Medicare must be eliminated in order to reduce the financial barrier to mental health services. Without losing sight of the ultimate goal of removing all reimbursement discrimination with regard to mental health care in the Medicare law, the panel recognizes that an acceptable short-range alternative is reduction of the beneficiary coinsurance from 50 percent to 20 percent--in line with standard Medicare coverage-- and increase of the maximum allowable reimbursement for mental conditions to $750 in any calendar year.

Official DHEW cost estimates for 1979 for mental health services show anticipated expenditures of $19 million under present Part B restrictions and an additional $18 million cost if the coinsurance were reduced and the maximum tripled (DHEW/Social Security Administration/Office of the Actuary 1977). However, these estimates do not include estimates for anticipated offsetting reduced hospital expenditures commensurate with a more realistic and more liberal ambulatory mental health benefit. Nor do the estimates take into account substitutions of mental health services for existing physician services.

A 5-year cost projection for implementing this option follows (DHEW/Social Secutity Administration/Office of the Actuary 1977). The panel feels that discriminatory language in the law must be removed within the next 5 years, as it is unlikely that a $750 maximum reimbursement in 1983 will be any more realistic than $250 is today.

	Under Present Law	Additional to reduce coinsurance to 20 percent and increase maximum to $750
1979	$ 19 million	$ 18 million
1980	22 million	22 million
1981	26 million	26 million
1982	31 million	32 million
1983	38 million	38 million

The panel again cautions that the additional cost to cover the short-term option is not discounted by the savings to be realized from anticipated lower hospitalization expenditures or the subtitution for existing Part B expenditures.

Other considerations regarding Medicare deserving further consideration are:

1. Enact legislation to permit the participation of community mental health centers in Medicare.

2. Enact legislation to eliminate all discriminatory limitations under Parts A and B on mental health services and reimbursement.

3. Provide for the substitution by a Medicare patient of 2 days of partial hospitalization for each inpatient hospital day under Part A.

4. Enact legislation to remove the 100-visit limit from home health care and expand the definition to include home care support services.

MEDICAID AND MENTAL HEALTH SERVICES

Title XIX, Medicaid, was established by the Social Security Amendments of 1965 to supply Federal financial resources to the States in their programs of medical assistance for certain low-income populations. The Medicaid Program has made tremendous financial contributions toward the support of mental health services for the low-income population.

It is estimated that $4.1 billion was spent under Medicaid for mental health services for the mentally ill. (See Medicaid Expenditures Table.) (This total does not include the amounts spent as physical health services which were really treatments of mental or emotional problems.) <u>Thus Medicaid is the largest single mental health program in the country</u>.

The figure for Medicaid was estimated on the same basis as the figure for the total U.S. expenditures for mental health care. But there is some question about their validity, since as much as 40 percent of the costs of nursing home care has been estimated as mental health services (Levine and Levine 1975, pp. 8-9, 23).

With this limitation in mind, it would appear that Medicaid constituted about 25 cents out of every dollar spent for mental health care for everyone in the United States (DHEW/Health Care Financing Administration/Medicaid Bureau 1978). The Medicaid funding clearly provided, along with certain other State programs, the most significant sources of funding for mental health services for the low-income population.

It is also clear that given the relative magnitude of Medicaid expenditures, most of the problems of the mental health delivery system apply to Medicaid, and many of Medicaid's problems are reflected in the mental health delivery system.

Information about the mental health services under Medicaid is extremely limited.[3] It is difficult to determine how many people received each of these services, or more significantly, the benefits which have been derived from these services. Most analyses of Medicaid have ignored the accomplishments of the program and have focused on its difficulties and deficiencies. This report will not be an exception.

Medicaid is structured so that at least one out of every three persons below the poverty line is not eligible for any help in paying for medical bills (DHEW/Health Care Financing Administration/Medicaid Bureau 1978). The proportions who get help and the amount of that help vary from State to State.

Many mental health services are not reimbursed under Medicaid, including many outreach and support services. The program focuses on institutional services, and the proportion of Medicaid patients receiving ambulatory services is far less than among wealthier patients.

---

[3] Improved data, properly categorized, are needed concerning these services and financial support. In addition, institutional funding needs to be further subdivided into residential living/custodial cost, rehabilitation costs, and treatment costs.

MEDICAID EXPENDITURES FOR MENTAL HEALTH SERVICES[a]

FY 1977

Type of Care or Service	Estimated Expenditures[4] (millions of dollars)
State, County and Private Mental Institutions and Psychiatric Hospitals[b]	$ 558
General Hospital, Inpatient, Outpatient and Emergency Care, Related to Mental Health[c]	$ 185
Community Mental Health Centers[d]	$ 100
Private Free-Standing Clinics	$ 25
Physicians and other Practitioners[e]	$ 82
Nursing Homes[f]	$2,189
ICF/MRs[g]	$ 702
Residential Treatment Facilities, Rehabilitation and Children's Programs	$ 110
Drugs	$ 110
TOTAL	$4,091

---

[a] Estimates include direct costs to Medicaid for mental illness and retardation.

[b] FY 1977 Budget Estimates, MMB/DOB

[c] General hospital expenditures are estimated at four percent of Medicaid's projected inpatient general hospital expenditures in FY 1977.

[d] Estimate based on the Medicaid reimbursement to CMHCs as reported by NIMH for FY 1975.

[e] Mental health related expenditures for physicians and other practitioners were estimated at four percent and one percent, respectively, of total projected expenditures to those providers under Title XIX in FY 1977 (DOB).

[f] Nursing Home expenditures (SNF, ICF) related to mental health services, are estimated at forty percent of the projected nursing home expenditures for FY 1977.

[g] Drug expenditures related to mental health under Medicaid are estimated at eleven percent of projected drug expenditures for FY 1977.

[4] Technique based on methods used by Levine and Levine 1971.

SOURCE: DHEW/HCFA/MMB/DAE/Kugelman, November 3, 1977

MEDICAID SERVICES STATE BY STATE, JUNE 1, 1977

BASIC REQUIRED MEDICAID SERVICES: Every Medicaid program must cover at least these services for at least everyone receiving federally supported financial assistance: inpatient hospital care; outpatient hospital services; other laboratory and X-ray services; skilled nursing facility services and home health services for individuals 21 and older; early and periodic screening, diagnosis, and treatment for individuals under 21; family planning; and physician services. Federal financial participation is also available to States electing to expand their Medicaid programs by covering additional services and/or by including people eligible for medical but not for financial assistance. For the latter group States may offer the services required for financial assistance recipients or may substitute a combination of seven services.

Services provided only under the Medicare buy-in or the screening and treatment program for individuals under 21 are not shown on this chart.

Definitions and limitations on eligibility and services vary from State to State. Details are available from local welfare offices and State Medicaid agencies.

● offered for people receiving federally supported financial assistance

+ offered also for people in public assistance[2] and SSI[3] categories who are financially eligible for medical but not for financial assistance

Additional services for which Federal financial participation is available to States under Medicaid

FMAP[4]	BASIC* REQUIRED MEDICAID SERVICES SEE ABOVE	State	Clinic services	Prescribed drugs	Dental services	Prosthetic devices	Eyeglasses	Private duty nursing	Physical therapy and related services	Other diagnostic, screening, preventive and rehabilitative services	Emergency hospital services	Skilled nursing facility services for patients under 21	Optometrists services	Podiatrists services	Chiropractors services	Care for patients 65 or older in institutions for mental diseases	Care for patients 65 or older in institutions for tuberculosis	Care for patients under 21 in psychiatric hospitals	Institutional services in intermediate care facilities	
74	●	Alabama		●						●		●			●			●[5]	AL
50	●	Alaska	●			●				●		●			●			●[5]	AK
60	●	Arizona																	AZ
75	+	Arkansas	+	+	+	+				+	●			+	+	+		●[5]	AR
50	+	California	+	+	+	+	+		+	+	+	+	+	+	+	+	+	+[5]	CA
55	●	Colorado		●		●			●			●	●			●		●[5]	CO
50	+	Connecticut	+	+	+	+	+	+	+		+	+	+	+	+			+[5]	CT
50	●	Delaware	●	●								●			●		●		DE
50	+	D.C.	+	+		+	+		+		+	+	+		+	+		+[5]	DC
57	●	Florida		●						●					●	●		●[5]	FL
66	●	Georgia	●	●	+	●				●		●			●			●[5]	GA
50	+	Guam	+	+	+	+	+		+		+	+	+						GU
50	+	Hawaii	+	+	+	+	+		+	+	+		+					+	HI
68	●	Idaho	●	●						●		●	●		●			●[5]	ID
50	+	Illinois	●	+	+	+	+	+	+	+	+	+	+	+	+	+		+[5]	IL
57	●	Indiana	●	●	●	●	●	●	●	●		●	●		●		●	●[5]	IN
57	●	Iowa		●	●					●		●	●		●			●[5]	IA
54	+	Kansas	+	+	+	+		+	+		+	+	+		+		+	+[5]	KS
71	+	Kentucky	+	+	+	+			+		+	+			+	+	+		KY
72	●	Louisiana	●	●						●		●			●		●	●[5]	LA
71	●	Maine	●	+		+			●	+		●	+		●			●[5]	ME
50	+	Maryland	+	+		+	+					+			+	+			MD
50	+	Massachusetts	+	+	+	+	+	+	+	+	+	+	+	+	+			+[5]	MA
50	+	Michigan	+	+	+	+	+		+		+	+	+		+		+	+[5]	MI
57	+	Minnesota	+	+	+	+	+	+	+	+		+	+		+	+	+	+[5]	MN
78	●	Mississippi		●	●					●					●			●[5]	MS
59	●	Missouri		●	●						●		●		●			●[5]	MO
63	+	Montana	+	+	+	+	+	+	+	+		+	+		+		+	+[5]	MT
56	+	Nebraska	+	+	+	+	+	+	+		+	+	+	+	+			+[5]	NB
50	●	Nevada	●	●	●	●	●			●		●	●					●	NV
60	+	New Hampshire		+		+	+	+	+		+	+	+		+				NH
50	●	New Jersey	●	●	●	●	●		●	●		●	●	●	●			●	NJ
73	●	New Mexico	●	●		●					●		●					●[5]	NM
50	+	New York	+	+	+	+	+	+	+	+	+	+	+	+	+	+	+	+[5]	NY
68	+	North Carolina	+	+							+				+	+		+[5]	NC
58	+	North Dakota		+	+	+	+	+	+	+	+		+		+		+	+[5]	ND
54	●	Ohio	●	●	●							●			●			●	OH
67	●	Oklahoma		●	+	●						●			●			●[5]	OK
59	●	Oregon	●	●	●	●			●		●	●	●		●			●[5]	OR
55	+	Pennsylvania		+	+	+				+		+	+		+	+		+[5]	PA
50	+	Puerto Rico	+	+	+				+	+		+			+				PR
57	+	Rhode Island		+	+	+	+				+		+		+			●[5]	RI
74	●	South Carolina	●	●	●	●				●		●			●		●	●[5]	SC
67	●	South Dakota	●	●	+		●		●			●			+	+		●[5]	SD
70	+	Tennessee	+		●		+				+							●[5]	TN
64	●	Texas		●		●	●			●		●	●		●			●[5]	TX
70	+	Utah	+	+	+	+	+	+		+		+	+		+		+	+[5]	UT
70	+	Vermont	+	+	+					+		+		+			+	+[5]	VT
50	+	Virgin Islands	+	+		+	+												VI
58	+*	Virginia	+	+				+	+						+				VA
54	+	Washington	+	+	+	+	+	+	+	+	+	+	+	+	+	+	+	+[5]	WA
72	+	West Virginia	+	+		+	+	+			+	+	+		+	+		+	WV
60	+	Wisconsin	+	+	+	+	+	+	+	+		+	+	+	+	+	+	+	WI
61	●	Wyoming								●								●	WY
	21 ● / 32 + / 53 Total		14/28/42	21/30/51	12/23/35	15/28/43	10/25/35	5/14/19	9/23/32	4/16/20	18/25/43	18/26/44	13/24/37	13/24/37	10/18/28	13/28/41	9/17/26	10/21/31	25/25/50	

Intermediate Care Facilities (ICF); P.L. 92-223 transferred the ICF program to Medicaid (Title XIX) as an optional service, effective 1-1-72. States may at their option include institutions for the mentally retarded, both public and private. See footnote five.

1/ Data from Regional Office reports of characteristics to State programs and State plan amendments.
2/ People qualifying as members of families with dependent children (usually families with at least one parent absent or incapacitated).
3/ People qualifying as aged, blind, or disabled under the Supplemental Security Income program.
4/ FMAP - Federal Medicaid Assistance Percentage: Rate of Federal financial participation in a State's medical vendor payment expenditures on behalf of individuals and families eligible under Title XIX of the Social Security Act. Percentages, effective from July 1, 1975, through June 30, 1977, are rounded.
5/ Including ICF services in institutions for the mentally retarded.

UNITED STATES DEPARTMENT OF HEALTH, EDUCATION, AND WELFARE — Health Care Financing Administration — Medicaid Bureau

Division of State Management

(HCFA)-76-24201*

TABLE 1

TABLE 2

MEDICAID: Selected Mental Health Services, State by State, November 1977

	BASIC SERVICES	Care of patients, 65 or older in hospitals for mental diseases	Care of patients, 65 or older in SNFs for mental diseases	Care of patients, 22 or younger in psychiatric hospitals	Care in ICFs for mentally retarded	Clinic Services (Including CMHCs)
TOTALS						
Alabama	0			0	0	
Alaska	0	0		0	0	0
Arizona						
Arkansas	+	+	+	+	+	+
California	+	+	+	+	+	+
Colorado	0	0	0	0	0	.
Connecticut	+	+	+	+	+	+
Delaware	0	0	0	0		0
Dist. of Columbia	+	+	+	+	+	+
Florida	0	0	0		0	
Georgia	0	0	0		0	0
Guam	+					+
Hawaii	+					+
Idaho	0				0	0
Illinois	+	+	+	+	+	+
Indiana	0	0	0	0	0	0
Iowa	0				0	
Kansas	+	+	+	+	+	+
Kentucky	+	+	+	+	+	+
Louisiana	0	0	0	0	0	0
Maine	+	+	+	+	+	+
Maryland	+	+	+		+	+
Massachusetts	+	+	+		+	+
Michigan	+	+	+	+	+	+
Minnesota	+	+	+	+	+	+
Mississippi	0	0	0		0	
Missouri	0	0	0		0	
Montana	+	+	+	+	+	+
Nebraska	+	+	+		+	+
Nevada	0					0
New Hampshire	+	+	+		+	+
New Jersey	0	0	0	0		0
New Mexico	0				0	0
New York	+	+	+	+	+	+
North Carolina	+	+	+	+	+	+
North Dakota	+	+	+	+		
Ohio	0	0	0	0	0	0
Oklahoma	+	+	+	+	+	
Oregon	0	0	0	0	0	0
Pennsylvania	+	+	+	+	+	+
Puerto Rico	+					+
Rhode Island	+	+	+		+	
South Carolina	0	0	0	0	0	0
South Dakota	0				0	0
Tennessee	+	+	+	+	+	+
Texas	0				0	
Utah	+	+	+	+	+	+
Vermont	+	+	+	+	+	+
Virgin Islands	+					+
Virginia	+	+	+		+	+
Washington	+	+	+	+	+	+
West Virginia	+	+	+			+
Wisconsin	+	+	+	+	+	+
Wyoming	0					
	0-21 +-22	0-13 +-23	0-12 +-19	0-10 +-21	0-17 +26	0-14 +-29
	53	41	40	31	43	43

Before addressing the ways to improve the financing of mental health services for the poor, this report examines some underlying principles of the Medicaid Program which result in the current limitations and problems which present barriers to access to mental health services.

1. <u>Medicaid is intended to be responsive to State initiatives</u>. Within fairly broad Federal guidelines, States may choose who gets medical assistance, what medical assistance they may get, who may provide the medical services, and how much they may be reimbursed for providing such services. The result of this flexibility and responsiveness to local needs, capabilities, and pressures is that Medicaid is essentially 53 different programs with significantly different characteristics.

In poorer States, less than 20 percent of the poverty population receive help in paying their medical bills. In other States, particularly in the industrialized North, the number of those receiving medical assistance is equal to more than 125 percent of their "poverty population" (DHEW/Health Care Financing Administration/Medicaid Bureau 1977, pp. 58-59).

The amount of medical assistance which eligibles may receive varies from State to State. To illustrate, the average Medicaid recipient in Missouri, during 1974, received $215 in medical assistance; his counterpart in Minnesota received over $900 (DHEW/Health Care Financing Administration/Medicaid Bureau 1977, p. 77).

These State-to-State differences apply equally to mental health services. Eligibility and services range from severe eligibility requirements and few separately identifiable mental health services (e.g., Nevada, Wyoming) to inclusive eligibility and all Federal Medicaid mental health options (e.g., New York, Illinois, and Wisconsin).

2. <u>Medicaid is a welfare program</u>. To be eligible for Medicaid, an individual or family must be on cash assistance or must be eligible to be on cash assistance if they could deduct their medical expenses from their income. A Medicaid recipient must not only be poor, but must be "categorically" poor; he must be either aged, blind, disabled, or a member of a family with dependent children and only one parent capable of providing support. Intact families, the working poor, singles, childless couples, and in fact, most poor people between the ages of 21 and 65 may not receive Medicaid assistance, and accordingly, may not receive Medicaid help in obtaining mental health services. More than one out of every three poor persons do not fulfill the categorical definition.

3. <u>Federal Medicaid money is intended to supplement State money, but not to replace it</u>. Title XIX provides no Federal matching funds for many services which States are expected to provide. Many institutional mental health services are not covered under federally matched Medicaid. These include inpatient psychiatric hospital services for individuals between 22 and 65; skilled nursing facility services in an institution for mental diseases; and intermediate care facility services in an institution for mental diseases for patients who are under age 65. Exclusion of Federal dollars may be desirable as a policy of deinstitutionalization, but a clear policy is necessary to ensure appropriate financing of alternative care.

C/F 27

4. **States, under Medicaid, are afforded opportunities to control their costs, and consequently, Federal costs**. States are permitted to determine reimbursement rates for most classes of providers. Medicaid reimbursement rates for physicians, clinical centers, and other health professionals are sometimes below the costs of providing such services, and frequently below the rates paid by other third-party payers. As a result, many health care providers refuse to participate in Medicaid, and many poor eligibles are denied access to needed services. It is no benefit to Medicaid eligibles if the State plan officially includes health and mental health benefits but the reimbursement rate is so low that the services are not provided.

States may not deny services to a beneficiary simply on the basis of the patient's diagnosis. Theoretically, an individual who has mental or emotional problems is entitled to appropriate treatment under Medicaid to the same extent he would be entitled to appropriate treatment for a physical problem. With the exception of the services specifically excluded from Medicaid (see 3 above), States theoretically maintain "parity" between mental health and physical health services.

The ability of the States to determine rates of compensation may result in no service being offered. In some States, for example, community mental health centers are reimbursed as little as 25 percent of their costs. In Maryland, a psychiatrist is reimbursed $6 per hour-long psychiatric visit, a rate equivalent to that paid other physicians for a shorter, routine office visit (DHEW/Health Care Financing Administration/Medicaid Bureau 1978).

5. **Medicaid programs focus attention and funds on institutional services**. This concentration derives in part from the fact that the costs of institutional services are catastrophic and financial help is almost always needed. It also is related to the fact that institutional services are organized and therefore easier to regulate. Some two-thirds of Medicaid expenditures are for hospitals, nursing homes, and other residential treatment facilities (DHEW/Health Care Financing Administration/Medicaid Bureau 1977, pp. 42-43).

Almost 70 percent of the mental health care reimbursed under Medicaid in fiscal year 1977 were for inpatient services, including State, county, and private mental institutions and psychiatric hospitals, nursing homes, and residential treatment facilities. At most, 30 percent of the estimated direct costs for mental health under Medicaid were for physicians and other practitioners, hospital outpatient services, community mental health centers, private free-standing clinics, and drugs (DHEW/Health Care Financing Administration/Medicaid Bureau 1978).

There have been a number of attempts in the Medicaid program to improve the quality of mental health services financed through Medicaid. Requirements have been written into the statute for certification and accreditation of mental institutions, the conduct of utilization review, medical review and independent professional review, the medical review of the patient's need for care in a mental hospital, a written plan for care for these patients, periodic inspection of the facilities and the care provided, for adequacy and appropriateness, along with periodic review and evaluation by physicians of the need for care and the appropriateness of that care.

Compliance by the States with these Federal requirements has been uneven, and Federal enforcement of these requirements has generally been weak or at best erratic. Improvements in the Medicaid mental health programs, and more generally corrections of the deficiencies in the financing of mental health services for the low-income population, may be approached from a number of directions. These include: improving the existing structure, making significant changes in the statute to establish higher national floors on eligibility and benefits for the low-income population, replacing Medicaid with a program of universal health insurance. Elaboration of these options involves:

1. Stronger Federal leadership with regard to the Medicaid mental health programs. This includes:

    a. Providing States with technical assistance in developing comprehensive mental health plans and in providing ambulatory services, outreach services, certain support services, and health education services;

    b. Demonstrating Federal commitments to improving the quality of care provided through mental health programs, presenting to the States the benefits which would be derived from additional efforts;

    c. Enforcing Federal requirements with regard to: systems of certification of institutions, utilization review, plans of care, and review and evaluation of such care; assuring that Medicaid State plans offer a reasonable amount of ambulatory mental health services; assuring that State reimbursement policies do not impede the availability of reasonable amounts of mental health services; assuring that States have effective systems to prevent discrimination on the basis of diagnosis; the availability of mental health services within the Medicaid child health programs (Early and Periodic Screening, Diagnosis and Treatment of detected problems, for eligibles under 22 years of age).

2. Develop legislative proposals, and introduce legislation to amend Title XIX, to:

    a. Establish national minimum mental health benefits to be included in every Medicaid State plan;

    b. Establish national minimum eligibility standards for income and assets (for example, every Medicaid State would have to provide medical assistance for all those who satisfied the categorical requirements, and whose income, after deducting medical expenses, was below the poverty line);

c. Remove the categorical requirements for eligibility for Medicaid. This proposal might be patterned on the proposals for "welfare reform," which would provide that everyone who satisfied the definitions of financial need would be given assistance.

3. Introduce proposals including mental health benefits for a national health program, absorbing Medicaid and possibly other insurance programs.

These three options offer major opportunities for improving the mental health services for the low-income population. They are not mutually exclusive. It is possible to increase efforts for national health insurance while reforming Medicaid within its existing statute. Given the time needed to introduce and enact legislation and to plan for the effective implementation, action on all three options is appropriate.

The out-of-pocket financial costs of undertaking these reforms may be the major factor in determining the pace at which these reforms are undertaken. Unfortunately, there is very little reliable information about the use of mental health services by the low-income population, the costs of providing mental health services under Medicaid and, accordingly, the probable costs of filling the gaps in mental health services for the low-income population.

The panel strongly recommends that measures be undertaken quickly to repair these deficiencies in information. Reliable data are needed if policymakers are to be able to make reasonable decisions concerning options on improving the financing of mental health services. Specific data requirements are introduced in the next section.

Estimates are presented below for the costs of some of the reform measures described. Given the severe limitations of available data, these values must be considered general estimates intended to provide only an indication of the relative magnitudes of the costs of these options.

Cost of Reforms of Financing of Mental Health for the Low-Income Population

1. _Stronger Federal leadership within existing Medicaid statute_: The costs of these measures will depend on the magnitude of the deficiencies in the kind and quality of care currently being provided through Medicaid. The marginal costs of improving Medicaid would be zero if the institutions providing mental health services to Medicaid eligibles were currently fulfilling all of the certification, utilization review, and medical review requirements of Medicaid. Furthermore, the marginal costs would be close to zero if the concentration on extending outpatient and clinic mental health services made it possible to substitute ambulatory services for acute care of inpatients in hospitals.

One cautionary note is appropriate. Over two-thirds of psychiatric beds are in State and county mental hospitals; undoubtedly, a larger proportion of Medicaid hospitalized psychiatric patients are in such public institutions (DHEW/NIMH Draft Report 1976, p. 92). Accordingly, a program to upgrade the

Medicaid care given in mental hospitals might create the need for increases in public capital costs. Given the existing pressure by States and localities for fiscal relief in their Medicaid programs, a program to improve mental institutions would probably be accompanied by pressure to increase the Federal share of the Medicaid costs, as would any proposal to expand Medicaid benefits.

2. <u>Legislative changes in Medicaid to enlarge benefits or eligibility</u>: Proposals to enlarge Medicaid eligibility for medical assistance would involve making physical as well as mental health care services available to those who were made eligible. The entire costs of these extensions would not, therefore, be chargeable to improvements in mental health financing (although much of the benefits might occur there). The costs of additional Medicaid eligibility, assuming the current Medicaid packages in the various States, would be: about one billion dollars to raise the national floor on income to the poverty level while retaining all of the categorical differences from State to State; $2 to $4 billion to raise the income floor to the poverty level and to permit every "categorical" eligible to disregard medical expenses in computing income (in other words, a universal medically needy program); $12 to $20 billion to establish a medical assistance program for everyone whose income, after deducting medical expenses, would fall below a national poverty level (there would be no categorical requirements, and everyone who was considered poor would be eligible regardless of family characteristics) (DHEW/Health Care Financing Administration/Medicaid Bureau 1978). Each of these cost estimates would be increased if, instead of accepting the variation from State to State the benefits offered, the proposal involved a minimum set of benefits for each person eligible. Each of these cost estimates would be reduced if individuals not currently covered by Medicaid but made eligible by the proposal had insurance coverage through other programs.

3. <u>National health insurance</u>: The costs of providing additional coverage for mental health services would depend upon the richness of the benefit package, the amount of costsharing involved, and the numbers of people made newly eligible for coverage.

Without knowing the degree of comprehensiveness of coverage or even broad parameters (i.e., catastrophic or comprehensive coverage) any estimate of cost would be merely speculation. It would be irresponsible to discuss total potential program costs without more detailed deliberation than was possible for the panel. The panel's inability to address specific mental health benefits under a national health proposal is not indicative of lack of interest. On the contrary, the panel felt this issue to be of critical importance and emphasized the urgency of providing continuing forums for planners, providers, consumers, and the government to deal with specific benefit options, data requirements, and cost estimates.

DATA REQUIREMENTS AND RESEARCH

The panel's discussions and report have reflected the inadequacies of existing data on the prevalence of mental illness and the costs of mental health services.

C/F 31

Individual need for mental health services, the cost of providing services, and the costs accrued by not providing mental health care to those in need will continue with or without a valid data base. But the ability to base major policy decisions on sound projections, the ability to use finite resources to the best advantage of the largest number in need, and the ability to contain costs without risking quality depend on the commitment to fill existing data gaps.

The panel firmly believes that we must improve mental health activity reporting and expand the mental health data base in order to evaluate effective mixes of services, resources, and need. The following list of data requirements represents the major shortcomings identified during the panel's discussions.

1. <u>Replication of the National Institute of Mental Health's study "The Cost of Mental Illness - 1971"</u> (Daniel S. Levine and Dianne R. Levine, Report Series on Mental Health Statistics, Series B, No. 7): Current data on direct and indirect costs attributable to mental illness and distribution of expenditures for direct care by type and locale of care are essential to future discussions and policy decisions regarding the cost and financing of mental health services. The Cost of Mental Illness study should be maintained and updated on an annual basis.

2. <u>Studies and demonstration of effectiveness/efficiency of various mental health treatment modes and providers</u>: Included should be comparisons of various treatment modes (e.g., inpatient, outpatient, short-term therapy, long-term therapy); comparisons of services by various mental health providers (e.g., psychiatrists, psychologists, clinical social workers, psychiatric nurses). Findings should include total costs, unit costs, and length of treatment, both by diagnosis and by patient characteristics.

3. <u>Studies comparing treatment in organized care settings (especially CMHC's) with similar treatment in other care settings (e.g., private practice)</u>: Findings should include total costs, unit costs, and length of treatment, both by diagnosis and by patient characteristics.

4. <u>Studies of the incidence and prevalence of mental illness by socio-economic characteristics of patients.</u>

5. <u>Development of standardized mechanisms for collection and display of mental health data</u>: Including standard reporting format for all Medicaid, Medicare, and Federal Employees Benefits programs including number of inpatient and outpatient episodes, length of stay, number of outpatient visits, by type of provider, age and sex of patient, amount charged, and amount reimbursed.

6. <u>Detailed examination of institutional, especially nursing home, costs currently attributed to mental illness</u>: Nursing homes are the single largest source of mental health costs, estimated to be 40 percent of all nursing home costs (Levine and Willner 1976, p. 7). Institutional costs should be subdivided into residential living/custodial costs, rehabilitation costs, and treatment costs. Accuracy of diagnosis (somatic and/or mental illness) should be verified. Attempts should be made to determine the extent to which mental health funding in institutions and nursing homes is actually for somatic care and how much is actually for mental health <u>treatment</u>.

7. __Additional studies regarding the "substitution effect" of mental health services on the utilization of medical services__: Studies similar to the ones at Kaiser and Group Health Association should be replicated, especially in non-prepaid settings.

8. __Development of better and more rigorous data on which to base major policy decisions regarding national health insurance__: This research should address a number of issues (some of which are incorporated in the studies above): comparison of the impact of various funding mechanisms; evaluation of a range of service delivery alternatives, particularly on the availability of services and on the quality of services provided; innovative organizations for service delivery, particularly models of case management within organized settings; and evaluation of different mixes of prevention, outreach, rehabilitation, and treatment services. These studies must examine the clinical outcome, the behavioral/life functioning outcome, _and_ the cost. Real benefit/cost determination depends on assessments of outcome as well as costs. The studies should provide opportunities for input from administrators, providers, consumers, and economic perspectives.

APPENDIX

THE COST OF MENTAL ILLNESS

In 1977 this Nation spent an estimated $17 billion for mental health care and treatment (DHEW/NIMH/Division of Biometry and Epidemiology 1977). This expenditure is approximately 11 percent of the total $161 billion spent for all health care (DHEW/Health Care Financing Administration/Office of Policy, Planning, and Research 1977). These direct care costs represent only 40 percent of the total cost attributed to mental illness. Indirect costs have been estimated at nearly $20 billion, bringing the total cost of mental illness close to $40 billion (see Figure 2) (Levine and Willner 1976).

The largest share of direct care spending for mental health is in institutions. Over half is for care in nursing homes and public mental hospitals, 12 percent for general hospital psychiatric services, and 9 percent for private practice psychiatrists. All other components represent 5 percent or less of direct care expenditures (Levine and Willner 1976, p. 7). The following chart (see Figure 1) shows the distribution of mental health expenditures by the type of care provided.

It is important to note that all the above data include only individuals with a primary diagnosis of mental illness and only in the settings indicated. Costs attributed to care in which mental illness may be a contributory but not the primary cause are not included; nor are costs included which arise from lay therapy care by family and friends or other supportive services.

UTILIZATION OF MENTAL HEALTH SERVICES

Cost of care is important not only in terms of the dollars spent, but also in terms of what services these dollars bought. The mix of inpatient and outpatient services is an especially important cost issue because of the greater individual cost of providing institutional care compared with outpatient treatment. According to 1973 estimates, 30 percent of all persons receiving mental care were treated in inpatient facilities, 68 percent were seen in outpatient facilities excluding private practice, 13 percent received outpatient treatment by psychiatrists and psychologists in private practice, and 4 percent received day treatment services (the total exceeds 100 percent because some patients were treated in more than one setting) (DHEW/NIMH Draft Report 1976, p. 15).

These utilization figures represent several significant shifts in utilization of mental health services, the type of services, average length of service, and the locale in which the services are delivered. In the past decade utilization, measured by patient care episodes, increased threefold. In 1955 there were 1.7 million episodes, by 1973 that figure increased to 5.5 million (DHEW/NIMH Draft Report 1976, p. 12). There is a significant trend in the shift from inpatient to ambulatory services, including the addition of day treatment services. In 1955, 77 percent of the episodes were treated on an inpatient basis; in 1973, 32 percent of the episodes were inpatient (DHEW/NIMH 1976). Also significant is the increased utilization of nursing homes rather than psychiatric hospitals for the elderly. Finally, a dramatic decrease in average length of stay for psychiatric inpatient treatment has taken place. The 1970-71 figures show that median length of stay ranged from 7-24 days for public, non-Federal

PERCENT DISTRIBUTION OF EXPENDITURES FOR DIRECT CARE
OF THE MENTALLY ILL, BY TYPE OF CARE: (1974)

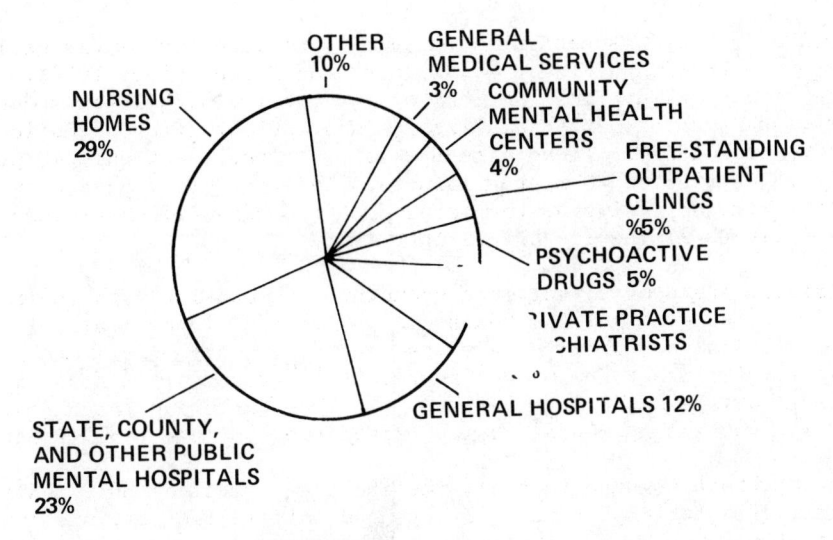

FIGURE 1

- NURSING HOMES 29%
- OTHER 10%
- GENERAL MEDICAL SERVICES 3%
- COMMUNITY MENTAL HEALTH CENTERS 4%
- FREE-STANDING OUTPATIENT CLINICS %5%
- PSYCHOACTIVE DRUGS 5%
- PRIVATE PRACTICE PSYCHIATRISTS
- GENERAL HOSPITALS 12%
- STATE, COUNTY, AND OTHER PUBLIC MENTAL HOSPITALS 23%

THE COST OF MENTAL ILLNESS -- 1974

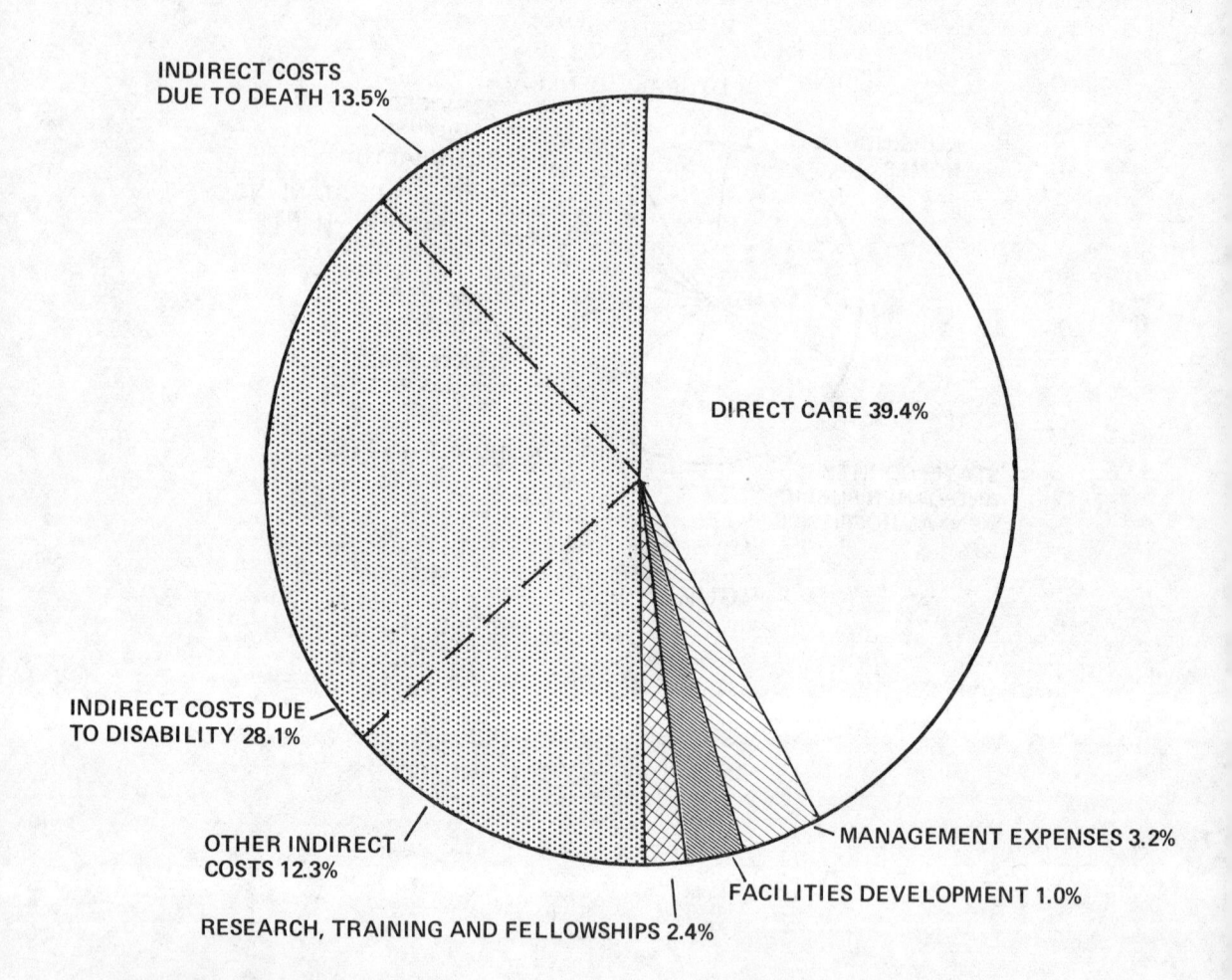

- INDIRECT COSTS DUE TO DEATH 13.5%
- DIRECT CARE 39.4%
- INDIRECT COSTS DUE TO DISABILITY 28.1%
- OTHER INDIRECT COSTS 12.3%
- RESEARCH, TRAINING AND FELLOWSHIPS 2.4%
- FACILITIES DEVELOPMENT 1.0%
- MANAGEMENT EXPENSES 3.2%

TOTAL COST IN (000'S)	$36,785,827
DIRECT CARE*	14,506,028
RESEARCH'	607,003
TRAINING AND FELLOWSHIPS	284,842
FACILITIES DEVELOPMENT	385,230
MANAGEMENT EXPENSES	1,167,298
INDIRECT COSTS	19,812,768
DUE TO DEATH	4,942,320
DUE TO DISABILITY	10,345,951
DUE TO PATIENT CARE ACTIVITIES	4,524,497

* ESTIMATED AT 17 BILLION FOR 1977

SOURCE: STATISTICAL NOTE NO. 125, DIVISION OF BIOMETRY AND EPIDEMIOLOGY, NATIONAL INSTITUTE OF MENTAL HEALTH

FIGURE 2

general hospitals, private and voluntary general hospitals, private mental hospitals, and Veterans Administration general hospitals. State and county hospitals had a median length of stay of 44 days; 75 percent of the patients stayed less than 3 months and 85 percent less than 6 months (DHEW/NIMH Draft Report 1976, p. 9). Unfortunately, summary data on actual length of stay trends are not readily available.

WHO PAYS THE MENTAL HEALTH CARE BILL?

The issue of funding is especially important because the payment mechanism is a significant factor in the provision of treatment. Limitations and exclusion of coverage serve as barriers to care.

There are four major sources of funds for personal health services: Federal Government, State and local government, private insurance, and out-of-pocket. The latest data for mental health care (1971) indicate that 35 percent of all expenditures are out-of-pocket; about 31 percent are State and local government money; 21 percent, Federal Government; 11 percent private insurance; and 2 percent, from other sources (NIMH data based on Levine and Levine 1975). The distribution of source of funds for mental health services is quite different from that for total health care costs. (See Figure 4.) In 1976, when this Nation spent $139 billion for health services, 33 percent was private out-of-pocket expenditures, 14 percent was from State and local government, 28 percent was Federal money, and private insurance reimbursed 25 percent (DHEW/Health Care Financing Administration/Office of Policy, Planning, and Research 1977).

State and local governments pay a significantly larger share of mental health costs, and private insurance carriers a significantly smaller share, compared with total health care spending. Private health insurance policies generally contain exclusions and limitations which restrict benefits for treatment of nervous and mental disorders. Mental health coverage, where it does exist, is generally more limited, of shorter duration, and requires higher cost-sharing than corresponding coverage for general medical care.

FEDERAL ROLE IN MENTAL HEALTH

Approximately 21 percent of all expenditures for mental health services are made by the Federal Government (NIMH data based on Levine and Levine 1975). Medicare and Medicaid are the major Federal programs financing health care services, yet coverage and reimbursement for mental disorders are painfully inadequate. Medicare, Title XVIII of the Social Security Act of 1965, provides health insurance for the aged and disabled. However, coverage for mental disorders is limited to a lifetime maximum of 190 days of inpatient psychiatric hospitalization and a $250 annual maximum for ambulatory services. Total Medicare payments for psychiatric services are minimal ($241 million in 1975). Less than 1 percent of all Medicare reimbursement was for mental health treatment (DHEW/Health Care Financing Administration).

Medicaid, Title XIX of the Social Security Act, provides for Federal financing assistance to the States for medical expenses incurred by the categorically needy and the medically indigent. States may limit the amount of services provided and may establish eligibility criteria for benefits. Medicaid

PERCENT DISTRIBUTIONS OF INPATIENT AND OUTPATIENT CARE EPISODES IN MENTAL HEALTH FACILITIES, BY TYPE OF FACILITY: UNITED STATES, 1955 AND 1973

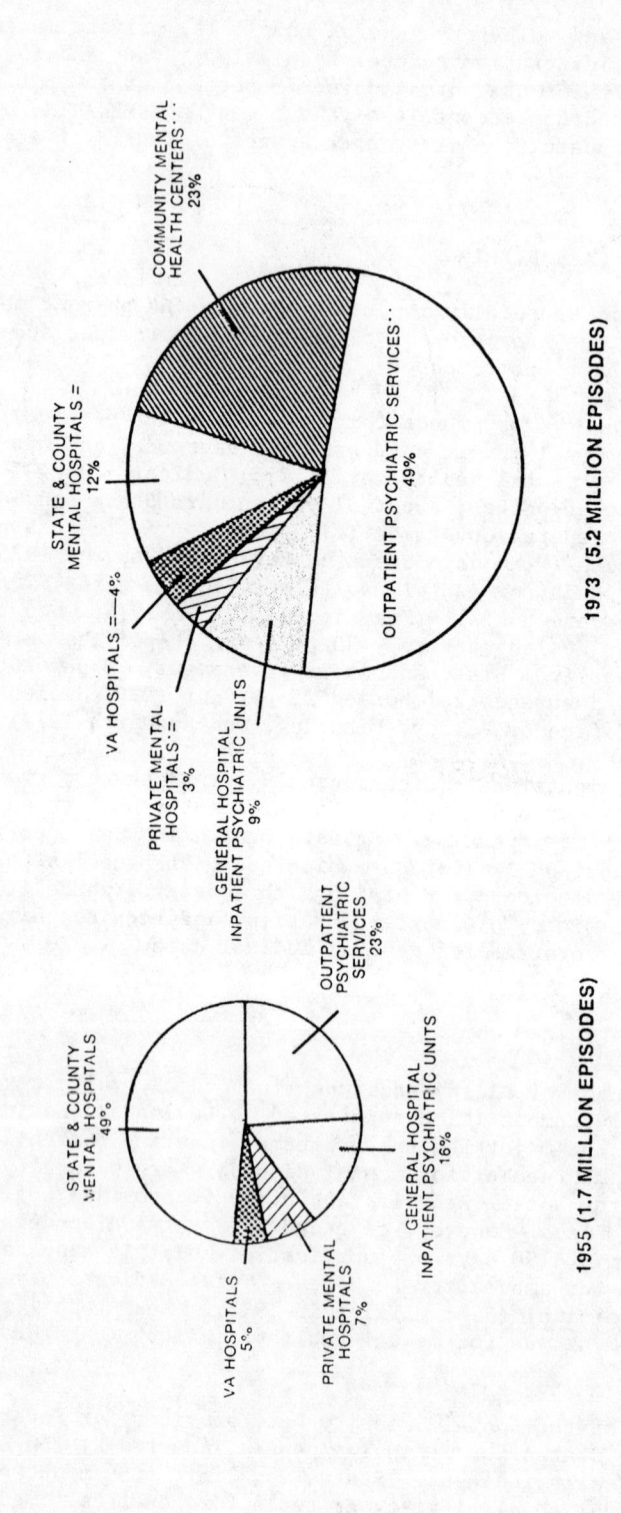

1955 (1.7 MILLION EPISODES)

- STATE & COUNTY MENTAL HOSPITALS = 49%
- VA HOSPITALS = 5%
- PRIVATE MENTAL HOSPITALS = 7%
- GENERAL HOSPITAL INPATIENT PSYCHIATRIC UNITS = 16%
- OUTPATIENT PSYCHIATRIC SERVICES = 23%

1973 (5.2 MILLION EPISODES)

- STATE & COUNTY MENTAL HOSPITALS = 12%
- VA HOSPITALS = 4%
- PRIVATE MENTAL HOSPITALS* = 3%
- GENERAL HOSPITAL INPATIENT PSYCHIATRIC UNITS = 9%
- OUTPATIENT PSYCHIATRIC SERVICES** = 49%
- COMMUNITY MENTAL HEALTH CENTERS*** = 23%

Source: Taube, C.A. and Redick, R.W. Provisional Data on Patient Care Episodes in Mental Health Facilities, 1973. Statistical Note 124, November 1975. Rockville, Md., Division of Biometry & Epidemiology, National Institute of Mental Health.

*INCLUDES RESIDENTIAL TREATMENT CENTERS FOR EMOTIONALLY DISTURBED CHILDREN. SOURCE: DIVISION OF BIOMETRY, NATIONAL INSTITUTE OF MENTAL HEALTH =INPATIENT SERVICES, ONLY
**INCLUDES FREE-STANDING OUTPATIENT SERVICES AS WELL AS THOSE AFFILIATED WITH PSYCHIATRIC AND GENERAL HOSPITALS.
***INCLUDES INPATIENT AND OUTPATIENT SERVICES OF FEDERALLY FUNDED CMHCs

FIGURE 3

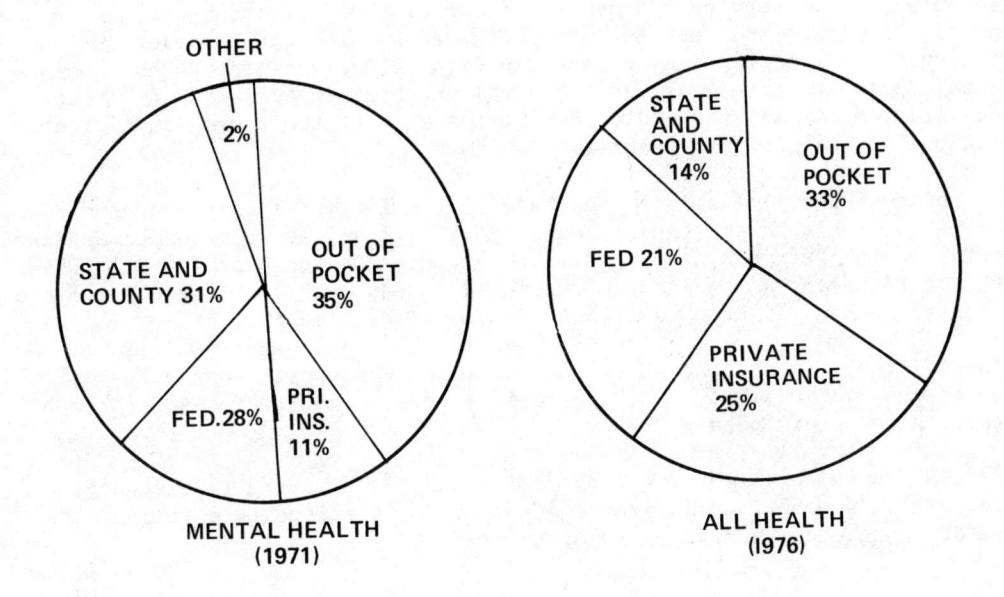

FIGURE 4

MENTAL HEALTH (1971): OTHER 2%, OUT OF POCKET 35%, PRI. INS. 11%, FED. 28%, STATE AND COUNTY 31%

ALL HEALTH (1976): STATE AND COUNTY 14%, OUT OF POCKET 33%, FED 21%, PRIVATE INSURANCE 25%

States are not supposed to differentiate or exclude services on the basis of diagnosis. Federal Medicaid matching is available for inpatient hospital services in psychiatric wards of general hospitals; treatment in mental hygiene outpatient clinics; diagnosis, evaluation, and treatment by psychiatrists; skilled nursing home services; and care of certain aged and young people in psychiatric hospitals and institutions. States may also opt to cover psychotropic drugs, and treatment in freestanding mental hygiene centers and community mental health centers. Although Federal matching is available for these services under Medicaid, the individual States may set their own administrative restrictions and eligibility requirements.

In spite of the limitations, Medicaid is the largest single source of funding for mental health care. An estimated $4.1 billion was spent under Medicaid for mental health services and for direct services for the mentally ill (DHEW/Health Care Financing Administration/Medicaid Bureau 1978). Almost 25 cents of every mental health dollar came from Medicaid reimbursement.

In addition, under Title XX the Social Service Support Program, a good portion of the $2.7 billion and the matching funds in 1977 were used for mental health services (Ginsberg 1978).

Federal spending for health programs in 1979 is expected to exceed $63 billion. This is more than 5 times the _total_ health expenditure in 1950 (Office of Management and Budget 1978).

ACKNOWLEDGMENTS

The Task Panel on Cost and Financing wishes to acknowledge the invaluable assistance and professional competence and support of Connie Hirschman, Staff Liaison to the Panel. It also wishes to express special appreciation to Lucille Reifman, Health Care Financing Administration, for her assistance and energies in the preparation of this report.

In addition the Panel wishes to thank the following persons and associations for the information and help they provided: Shelly Akabas, Columbia University School of Social Work, New York, New York; Dennis Andrulis, Office of Technology Assessment, U.S. Congress, Washington, D.C.; Mildred Arrill, Division of HMOs, Health Services Administration, Rockville, Maryland; Barbara Cooper, Health Care Financing Administration, Washington, D.C.; Charles Fisher, Health Care Financing Administration, Baltimore, Maryland; Robert Gibson, Health Care Financing Administration, Washington, D.C.; Richard Hessler, International Paper Company, New York, New York; Otto Jones, Human Affairs, Inc., Murray, Utah; Ida Kloze, Washington, D.C.; John Krizay, American Psychiatric Association, Washington, D.C.; Leo Miller, Polaroid, Inc., Cambridge, Massachusetts; Evelyn Meyers, American Psychiatric Association, Washington, D.C.; James Manuso, The Equitable Life Assurance Society of the U.S., New York, New York; William Pollack, School of Social Service Administration, University of Chicago, Chicago, Illinois; Daniel Patterson, Group Health Association, Washington, D.C.; Richard Redick, Division of Biometry and Epidemiology, National Institute of Mental Health, Rockville, Maryland; Steven S. Sharfstein, Division of Mental Health Service Programs, National Institute of Mental Health, Rockville, Maryland; Carvel Taylor, CNA Insurance, Chicago, Illinois; Gary R. VandenBos, American Psychological Association, Washington, D.C.; Frances Wales, Dartmouth-Hitchcock Medical Center, Hanover, New Hampshire; Sten Wallack, Lewin and Associates, Washington, D.C.; Andrew Weissman, U.S. Steel Corporation, Chicago, Illinois; Daniel Zwick, Health Resources Administration, Rockville, Maryland.

REFERENCES

Akabas, Sheila, Ph.D. "Social Functioning: The Role of Services at the Workplace". National Conference on Social Welfare, Chicago, Illinois. May 16, 1977, p. 9.

Babigian, H. M. and Odoroff, C. L. The mortality experience of a population with psychiatric illness. American Journal of Psychiatry, Vol. 126, 1969, pp. 470-480.

Butler, Robert N. and Lewis, Myrna I. Aging and Mental Health. C. V. Mosby Co., St. Louis, 1977, p. 11.

Califano, Joseph, Secretary, Department of Health, Education, and Welfare. Congressional Record, Vol. 123, No. 134, Part II. August 4, 1977, p. 2.

Cohen, Gene D., M.D. "Mental Health and the Elderly: Problems and Approaches". Draft report. DHEW/NIMH/Center for Studies of the Mental Health of the Aging. February 28, 1977, p. 3.

Cohen, Wilbur J., Secretary, Department of Health, Education, and Welfare. "Financing Care of Mentally Ill Under Medicare and Medicaid: A Report to the House Committee on Ways and Means and the Senate Committee on Finance". December, 1968, p. 3.

Committee on Aging, Group for the Advancement of Psychiatry. "Toward a Public Policy on Mental Health Care of the Elderly". Report No. 79, November, 1970, p. 682.

Cummings, Nicholas. The anatomy of psychotherapy under NHI. American Psychologist, Vol. 32, No. 9, September 1977, pp. 711-718.

Cummings, Nicholas, 1978 based on: Babigian H. M. and Odoroff, C. L. The mortality experience of a population with psychiatric illness. American Journal of Psychiatry, Vol. 126, 1969, pp. 470-480.

Cummings, Nicholas and Follette, William. Psychiatric services and medical utilization in a prepaid health plan setting: Part II. Medical Care, Vol. 6, 1968, pp. 31-41.

DHEW/HCFA/Medicaid Bureau. "Data on the Medicaid Program. Eligibility Services, Expenditures - Fiscal Years 1966-77". Washington, D.C., 1977.

DHEW/Health Care Financing Administration/Medicaid Bureau. Conversations 1978.

DHEW/Health Care Financing Administration/Office of Policy, Planning, and Research. Conversations 1977, 1978.

DHEW/Health Care Financing Administration/Office of Policy, Planning, and Research. Conversation April 21, 1977.

DHEW/NIMH/Division of Biometry and Epidemiology. Conversations 1977.

DHEW/NIMH. Draft Report: "The Financing, Utilization, and Quality of Mental Health Care in the United States". April, 1976.

DHEW/Social Security Administration. Medicare - health insurance benefits for the aged and disabled. <u>Social Security Bulletin, Statistical Supplement</u>. 1974.

DHEW/Social Security Administration/Office of Program Policy and Planning/Office of Research and Statistics. Health Insurance Statistics HI Note 78, September 29, 1977, p. 1.

DHEW/Social Security Administration/Office of Research and Statistics. "Financing Mental Health Care Under Medicare and Medicaid". <u>Research Report No. 37</u>, U.S. Government Printing Office, Washington, D.C., 1971, p. 23.

DHEW, Social Security Administration, Office of the Actuary. Conversations 1977.

Follette, William and Cummings, Nicholas A. Psychiatric services and medical utilization in a prepaid health plan setting. <u>Medical Care</u>, Vol. 5, January-February 1967, pp. 25-35.

Ginsberg, Mitchell. Dean, Columbia School of Social Work. Conversation February 13, 1978.

Goldberg, Irving D.; Goldie Krantz; and Ben Z. Locke. Effect of a short-term outpatient psychiatric therapy benefit on the utilization of medical services in a prepaid group practice medical program. <u>Medical Care</u>, Vol. 8, September-October 1970, pp. 419-428.

Jameson, John; Shuman, Larry J., and Young, Wanda, W. <u>The Effects of Outpatient Psychiatric Utilization on the Costs of Providing Third-Party Coverage</u>. Research Series 18, December 1976.

James, Kenneth. "Cost Containment and Alcohol, Drug Abuse, and Mental Health Services". Draft. U. S. Department of Health, Education, and Welfare/PHS/ADAMHA/OPPE, April 28, 1977.

Jones, Otto. President, Human Affairs, Inc. Murray, Utah. Conversation February 1, 1978.

Levine, Daniel S., Ph.D. and Levine, Dianne R. "The Cost of Mental Illness - 1971". DHEW/Public Health Service/Alcohol, Drug Abuse and Mental Health Administration/NIMH. DHEW Publication No. (ADM 76-265). Superintendent of Documents, Government Printing Office, 1975.

Levine, Daniel S. and Willner, Shirley G. The cost of mental illness, 1974. Mental Health Statistical Note No. 125. DHEW/Public Health Service/Alcohol, Drug Abuse and Mental Health Administration, NIMH, Division of Biometry and Epidemiology, Survey and Reports Branch, February 1976.

Lewin and Associates, Inc. "The Cost and Financing of Mental Illness". Prepared for the President's Commission on Mental Health, January 1978.

Manuso, James S. J. Clinical Psychologist, The Equitable Life Assurance Society of the U.S., Employee Health Services Department. New York, New York, Conversation January 1978.

Markush, Robert, M.D.; Schwab, John, M.D.; Larris, Patricia, M.A., Present, Paula, M.A.; Holzer, Charles, III, Ph.D. Mortality and community mental health. Archives of General Psychiatry, Vol. 23, December 1977, pp. 1393-1401.

Mechanic, David. Considerations in the Design of Mental Health Benefits under National Health Insurance. Center for Medicine, Sociology, and Health Services Research; Health Economics Research Center; University of Wisconsin, Madison, 1977.

Morris Associates, Inc. "A Summary of the Problems Facing Community Mental Health Centers Seeking Federal Reimbursements Through Insurance and Public Assistance Programs". Paper prepared for the National Council of Community Mental Health Centers, August 1975.

Office of Management and Budget. Special Analyses: Budget of the United States Government 1979. Health Special Analysis (L). January 1978.

PA International Management Consultants. Insight Program Study, Kennecott Copper Company, 1973.

Reed, Louis S., Ph.D. Coverage and Utilization of Care for Mental Conditions under Health Insurance. Various Studies, 1973-1974. American Psychiatric Association, 1975, p. 24.

U.S. Department of Commerce. Bureau of the Census, Economic Surveys Division. Status: A monthly chartbook of social and economic trends. Washington, D.C.: The Department. September 1976.

U.S. Senate Special Committee on Aging. Developments in Aging. Report 95-88, April 17, 1977, p. 5.

BIBLIOGRAPHY

Akabas, Shelia, Ph.D. "Mental Health Program Models: Their Role in Reducing Occupational Stress". Conference on Reducing Occupational Stress, New York, May 10-12, 1977.

Akabas, Shelia, Ph.D. and Bellinger, Susan, MSW. Programming mental health care for the world of work. Mental Health, Vol. 61, No. 1, Spring 1977, pp. 4-8.

Albee, George. Does including psychotherapy in health insurance represent a subsidy to the rich from the poor? American Psychologist, Vol. 32, No. 9, September 1977, pp. 719-721.

American Academy of Child Psychiatry. "Position Statement on National Health Insurance". Washington, D.C., January 19, 1977.

American Hospital Association. "Recommendations for Financing Mental Health Care in the U.S." Chicago, Illinois, 1973.

American Occupational Therapy Association, Inc. "Policy Statements on Mental Health". The Government and Legal Affairs Division, Rockville, Maryland, May 1977.

American Psychiatric Association. "Delivering Mental Health Services: Needs, Priorities, and Strategies". Washington, D.C., 1975.

American Psychiatric Association. "Discussion Guide on National Health Insurance". Washington, D.C., 1974.

American Psychiatric Association. "What About the Mentally Ill?" Washington, D.C., February 1977.

American Psychological Association. "Report to the National Advisory Mental Health Council". Washington, D.C., August 1977.

Association of Mental Health Administrators. "Report of the National Health Insurance Task Panel of the Mental Health Liaison Group". Washington, D.C., October 1, 1976.

Berk, Aviva; Paringer, Lynn; and Mushkin, Selma. "The Economic Cost of Illness, Fiscal 1975". Washington, D.C., April 1977.

The Blue Sheet. Stanford business professor's national health insurance plan looms big in administration. Vol. 20, No. 43, October 26, 1977, pp. 10-11.

Brosin, Henry; Lugilson, Eugene; Michels, Robert; Morrison, Andrew; Panzarino, Peter; Reichsmann, Franz; Robbins, Lewis; Rosenblatt, Allan; Simon, Justin; Tupin, Joe and Offenkrantz, William. Psychotherapy and its financing within the national health care system. Committee on Therapy, Department of Psychiatry, University of Chicago, Chicago, Illinois, June 1977.

California Psychological Health Plan. <u>Statistics</u>. Los Angeles, California. (undated)

Cline, Sibyl. "Alcohol and Drugs at Work". Drug Abuse Council, Inc., Washington, D.C., October 1975, 54 pages.

Coalition of Voluntary Mental Health, Mental Retardation, and Alcoholism Agencies, Inc. Collection of papers. New York, New York, June 3, 1977.

Cooper, Barbara S. and Rice, Dorothy P. The economic cost of illness revisited. <u>Social Security Bulletin</u>, February 1976, DHEW Publication No. (SSA) 76-11703.

DeLeon, Patrick H. Psychology and the Carter Administration. <u>American Psychologist</u>, Vol. 32, No. 9, September 1977, pp. 750-751.

DHEW/Health Care Financing Administration. <u>Research in Health Care Financing</u>. Washington, D.C., Spring/Summer 1977.

DHEW/National Health Insurance Advisory Committee. "Discussion Paper on Benefits." Benefits and Eligibility Team, October 28, 1977.

DHEW/National Institute of Mental Health. <u>Forward Plan FY 1979-83</u>. Public Health Service, Alcohol, Drug Abuse, and Mental Health Administration. In press.

DHEW/Office of the Assistant Secretary for Planning and Evaluation. "Coverage of Mental Illness under NHI - Information Memorandum". Washington, D.C., July 28, 1972.

DHEW/Public Health Service/ADAMHA/Office of Policy, Planning, and Evaluation. "Review of an ADM Cost Containment Paper". Rockville, Maryland, May 4, 1977.

DHEW/Public Health Service/Health Services Administration. <u>Inclusion of Mental Health Services in Health Maintenance Organizations</u>. DHEW Publication No. (HSA) 75-13019, Rockville, Maryland, 1974.

DHEW/Social Security Administration, Office of Research and Statistics. "Evaluation of the Colorado Clinical Psychology/Expanded Mental Health Benefits Experiment: Process Evaluation Report". Health Insurance Studies. Contract Research Series, DHEW Publication No. (SSA) 77-11722, July 1977.

DHEW/SSA/Office of Research and Statistics. <u>Medicare and Care of Mental Illness</u>.

Eisenberg, Leon, M.D. and Gruenberg, Ernest, M.D. "The current status of secondary prevention in child psychiatry". <u>American Journal of Orthopsychiatry</u>, Vol. XXXI, No. 2, April 1967, pp. 355-367.

Equitable Life Assurance Society of the United States. The Emotional Health Program for Employees of the Equitable Life Assurance Society of the U.S. (undated)

Gibson, Robert M. and Mueller, Marjorie Smith. <u>National Health Expenditures, Fiscal Year 1976</u>. DHEW/Social Security Administration. Social Security Bulletin, HEW Publication No. (SSA) 77-11700, April 1977.

Goldberg, F. Dee. State laws mandating mental health insurance coverage. Hospital and Community Psychiatry, October 1977, pp. 759-763.

Goldstein, Marcus S. and Schwartz, Peggy J. Medicare and Care of Mental Illness. Health Insurance Statistics, USDHEW/Social Security Administration, Office of Research and Statistics, March 7, 1968.

Gordon, James S., M.D. "Special Study on Alternative Mental Health Services". Preliminary Report for the President's Commission on Mental Health, Washington, D.C., 1977.

Health Insurance Association of America. Survey of various health care coverages. Statistical Information Bulletin No. 10-74, New York, New York, September 23, 1974.

Health Insurance Institute. Source Book of Health Insurance Data 1976-77. New York, New York.

Herman, Edith. Employee mental health becomes good for business. Chicago Tribune, December 8, 1977, Chicago, Illinois, pp. 8-9.

Kiesler, Charles. American Psychological Association Correspondence. Washington, D.C., January 12, 1978.

Kreps, Juanita. Social Security in the Coming Decade: Questions for a Mature System. DHEW Publication No. (SSA) 76-11703. Social Security Administration, Social Security Bulletin, March 1976.

Levin, Arnold M., President, Illinois Society for Clinical Social Work. Statement before the House Ways and Means Committee, Subcommittee on Health. Homewood, Illinois. February 27, 1976.

Manuso, James S. J., M.A. Coping with job abolishment. Journal of Occupational Medicine, Vol. 19, No. 9, September 1977, pp. 598-602.

McNerney, Walter J. "Financing Psychiatric Benefits in the Private Sector". American Psychiatric Association, Toronto, Ontario, Canada, May 5, 1977.

Mental Health Association. A Plan of Coverage for the Mentally Ill in National Health Insurance. Virginia, March 1977.

Mental Health Association. "Summary of Findings Concerning the California Psychological Health Plan". Arlington, Virginia, September 1977.

Muller, Charlotte, Ph.D. and Schoenberg, Mark, M.D. Insurance for mental health. Archives of General Psychiatry, Vol. 31, December 1974, pp. 871-878.

Myers, Evelyn. NHI: Prospects and problems. Psychiatric Annals, Vol. 4, No. 1, January 1974, pp. 6-21.

Pennsylvania Society for Clinical Social Work, Inc. Third Party Reimbursement for Mental Health Care Delivered by Clinical Social Workers--The Case for its Expansion. Philadelphia, Pennsylvania, January 1976.

Pollack, William. *A Perspective on Parity*. School of Social Service Administration, University of Chicago, Chicago, Illinois, November 1977.

Psychiatric Annals. Psychiatry and the third revolution. Milton Greenblatt, M.D., Guest Editor, Vol. 7, No. 10, October 1977.

Redlich, Fritz, M.D. and Kellert, Stephen R., Ph.D. "Trends in American Mental Health: A Preliminary Report." Yale University School of Medicine, New Haven, Connecticut. (undated)

Rice, Dorothy. Estimating the Cost of Illness. (Health Economics Series, No. 6), U.S. Public Health Service, Washington, D.C., 1966.

Richman, Alex, M.D., MPH. "Cost Containment and Quality Assurance Requirements for Third Party Coverage for Ambulatory Psychiatric Care". Draft, Joint Session of Mental Health and Medical Care Sections, 105th Annual Meeting of American Public Health Association, October 30 - November 3, 1977.

Sharfstein, Steven S., M.D. *Benefits of Mental Health Care for Health Service Utilization*. DHEW/NIMH, Rockville, Maryland. (undated)

Sharfstein, Steven, M.D. "Third-Party Payors: To Pay or Not to Pay". American Psychiatric Association Annual Meeting, Toronto, Canada, May 5, 1977.

Smith, Robert N., M.D., Assistant Secretary of Defense - Health Affairs. Correspondence. Washington, D.C., August 15, 1977.

Trapnell, Gordon R. Associates. *A Comparison of the Costs of Major National Health Proposals, Executive Summary*. DHEW/Office of the Assistant Secretary for Planning and Evaluation. Contract No. HEW-OS-74-138, September 1976.

Washington Business Group on Health. Goldbeck, William. "Corporate Mental Health Benefits". Boston University Health Policy Institute Conference on Industry Sponsored Health Programs, June 1, 1977.

Willens, Joan G. Colorado medicare study: A history". *American Psychologist*, Vol. 32, No. 9, September 1977, pp. 746-749.

Williams, Stephen J.; Diehr, Paula; Drucker, William L; and Richardson, William C. *Mental Health Service: Utilization by Low Income Enrollers in a Prepaid Group Practice Plan and in an Independent Practice Plan*. DHEW/Health Resources Administration, National Center for Health Services Research Grants No. R18 HS 00694. No. HS 01978. In press.

Report to the President

from

The President's Commission on Mental Health

<u>Volume I</u>

The Commission report is for sale by the Superintendent of Documents, U.S. Government Printing Office, Washington, D.C. 20402. Use Stock Number 040-000-00390-8 when inquiring about purchase and price.

<u>Volumes II, III, IV</u> - Appendices

These Appendices to Volume I contain the reports to the Commission of task panels which assisted in the study. This documentation is also for sale by the Superintendent of Documents, U.S. Government Printing Office. When inquiring, use the following Stock Numbers: Volume II 040-000-00391-6; Volume III 040-000-00392-4; Volume IV 040-000-00393-2.

- Volume II -- Nature and Scope of the Problems - Community Support Systems - Mental Health Service Delivery: Planning and Review; Organization and Structure; Community Mental Health Centers Assessment; Access and Barriers to Care; Deinstitutionalization, Rehabilitation and Long-Term Care - Alternative Services - Mental Health Personnel - Cost and Financing.

- Volume III -- Mental Health of American Families: General Issues and Adult Years; Infants, Children, and Adolescents - Learning Failure and Unused Learning Potential - Special Populations: Mental Health of Minorities, Women, Physically Handicapped - Mental Health of the Elderly - Rural Mental Health - Migrant and Seasonal Farmworkers - Mental Health Problems of Vietnam Era Veterans.

- Volume IV - Legal and Ethical Issues - Research - Prevention - Public Attitudes and Use of Media for Promotion of Mental Health - Arts in Therapy and Environment - State Mental Health Issues - Liaison Task Panels: Mental Retardation; Alcohol-Related Problems; Psychoactive Drug Use/Misuse.

<u>Individual Task Panel Reports</u>

Individual reports submitted to the Commission by the task panels may be purchased from the National Technical Information Service, U.S. Department of Commerce, 5285 Port Royal Road, Springfield, Virginia 22161. When inquiring, identify the individual report by name and code number PCMH/P-78/--, which appears in the lower left-hand corner of the title page of each report in Volumes II, III, IV. These order numbers are as follows:

Volume II Appendix

TASK PANEL REPORTS   ORDER NUMBER

    Mental Health -- Nature and Scope of the Problems   PCMH/P-78/01
    Community Support Systems   PCMH/P-78/02
    Mental Health Service Delivery
      Planning and Review   PCMH/P-78/03
      Organization and Structure   PCMH/P-78/04
      Community Mental Health Centers Assessment   PCMH/P-78/05
      Access and Barriers to Care   PCMH/P-78/06
      Deinstitutionalization, Rehabilitation, and
        Long-Term Care   PCMH/P-78/07
    Alternative Services -- A Special Study   PCMH/P-78/08
    Mental Health Personnel   PCMH/P-78/09
    Cost and Financing   PCMH/P-78/10

Volume III Appendix

    Mental Health of American Families
      General Issues and Adult Years   PCMH/P-78/11
      Infants, Children, Adolescents   PCMH/P-78/12
    Learning Failure and Unused Learning Potential   PCMH/P-78/13
    Special Populations: Mental Health of Minorities,
      Physically Handicapped, Women   PCMH/P-78/14
    Mental Health of the Elderly   PCMH/P-78/15
    Rural Mental Health   PCMH/P-78/16
    Migrant and Seasonal Farmworkers   PCMH/P-78/17
    Mental Health Problems of Vietnam Veterans   PCMH/P-78/18

Volume IV Appendix

    Legal and Ethical Issues   PCMH/P-78/19
    Research   PCMH/P-78/20
    Prevention   PCMH/P-78/21
    Public Attitudes and Use of Media for
      Promotion of Mental Health   PCMH/P-78/22
    Arts in Therapy and Environment   PCMH/P-78/23
    State Mental Health Issues   PCMH/P-78/24
    Liaison Task Panels:
      Mental Retardation   PCMH/P-78/25
      Alcohol-Related Problems   PCMH/P-78/26
      Psychoactive Drug Use/Misuse   PCMH/P-78/27